HOTELS & GUEST HOUSES

The Official
Where to Stay Guide
2001

Scotland is split into eight tourist areas.
You will find accommodation listed
alphabetically by location
within each of these areas.
There is an index at the back of this book
which may also help you.

INTRODUCTION

ACCOMMODATION

APPENDIX

FROM WORLD-FAMOUS HOTELS TO FRIENDLY GUEST HOUSES, YOU'LL FIND ALL THE VARIETY OF SCOTLAND REFLECTED IN THE WIDE CHOICE AVAILABLE IN THIS GUIDE. HUNDREDS OF HOTELS IN ALL KINDS OF LOCATIONS, ARE LISTED EACH WITH THEIR OWN SPECIAL CHARACTER AND ATMOSPHERE.

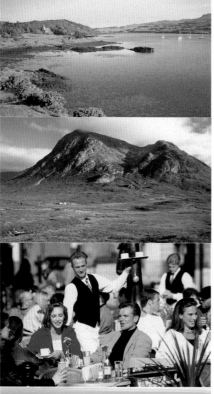

THERE ARE CITY HOTELS, located within walking distance of all the main attractions, which also offer the high-tech and sophisticated facilities for the business traveller, as well as some of the best conference and function facilities in Europe. Outwith the city, there is an exciting range of country retreats, where you can relax in luxurious and peaceful surroundings, which are ideal for a spot of golf, fishing or stress-relieving spa treatments.

SCOTLAND ALSO PROVIDES numerous friendly and welcoming family hotels, with sports, activities and entertainment for all ages, and excellent value for weekend breaks. Many of these large hotels have modern leisure complexes, for a work-out, swim or sun-tan, whatever the weather.

STAYING IN ONE OF Scotland's hotels or guest houses give you the ideal opportunity to tempt your taste-buds with the distinctive quality of Scottish produce. In addition, these guest houses are friendly and economical, and almost all are family-run to provide great value and comfort in a homely atmosphere.

FROM THE FURTHEST-FLUNG islands to the busy hub of Scotland's capital, there is something to suit everyone's taste – so go out and experience the very best of Scotland's traditional welcome and hospitality!

WHERE TO STAY...?

Over 1400 answers to the age-old question!

REVISED ANNUALLY, this is the most comprehensive guide to hotels and guest houses in Scotland.

EVERY PROPERTY in the guide has been graded and classified by Scottish Tourist Board inspectors. See page vi for details

HOW TO FIND ACCOMMODATION

This book split into eight areas of Scotland:

ACCOMMODATION

THE MAP on page xix shows these areas. Within each area section you will find accommodation listed alphabetically by location.

ALTERNATIVELY THERE IS an index at the back of this book listing alphabetically all accommodation locations in Scotland.

LEARN TO USE THE SYMBOLS IN EACH ENTRY – They contain a mine of information!

THERE IS A KEY TO SYMBOLS ON THE BACK FLAP.

NATURALLY, IT IS always advisable to confirm with the establishment that a particular facility is still available.

PRICES IN THE GUIDE are quoted per person and represent the minimum and maximum charges expected to apply to most rooms in the establishment. They include VAT at the appropriate rate and service charges where applicable.

THE PRICES OF accommodation, services and facilities are supplied to us by the operators and were, to the best of our knowledge, correct at the time of going to press. However, prices can change at any time during the lifetime of the publication, and you should check again when you book.

BOOKINGS CAN BE made direct to the establishment, through a travel agent, or through a local Tourist Information Centre.

REMEMBER, WHEN you accept accommodation by telephone or in writing, you are entering a legally binding contract which must be fulfilled on both sides. Should you fail to take up accommodation, you may not only forfeit any deposit already paid, but may also have to compensate the establishment if the accommodation cannot be re-let.

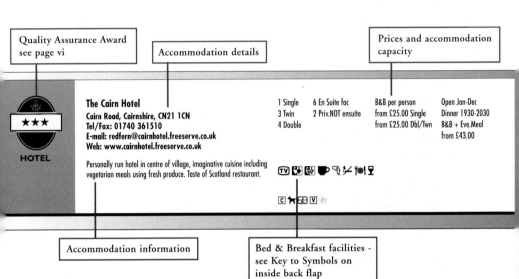

Quality Assurance Award
see page vi

Accommodation details

Prices and accommodation
capacity

The Cairn Hotel
Cairn Road, Cairnshire, CN21 1CN
Tel/Fax: 01740 361510
E-mail: redfern@cairnhotel.freeserve.co.uk
Web: www.cairnhotel.freeserve.co.uk

Personally run hotel in centre of village, imaginative cuisine including
vegetarian meals using fresh produce. Taste of Scotland restaurant.

★★★

HOTEL

1 Single   6 En Suite fac
3 Twin   2 Priv.NOT ensuite
4 Double

B&B per person   Open Jan-Dec
from £25.00 Single   Dinner 1930-2030
from £25.00 Dbl/Twn   B&B + Eve.Meal
                      from £43.00

Accommodation information

Bed & Breakfast facilities -
see Key to Symbols on
inside back flap

FOLLOW THE STARS AND YOU WON'T
BE DISAPPOINTED WHEN YOU GET TO
THE INN.

THE SCOTTISH TOURIST BOARD STAR SYSTEM is a
world-first. Quality is what determines our
star awards, not a checklist of facilities.
We've made your priorities our priorities.

QUALITY MAKES or breaks a visit. This is why
the most important aspects of your stay;
the warmth of welcome, efficiency and
friendliness of service, the quality of the food
and the cleanliness and condition of the
furnishings, fittings and decor earn Scottish
Tourist Board Stars, not the size of the
accommodation or the range of available
facilities.

LOOK OUT FOR THIS DISTINCTIVE SIGN
OF QUALITY ASSURED ACCOMMODATION

THIS EASY to understand system tells you at a
glance the quality standard of all types and
sizes of accommodation from the smallest
B&B and self-catering cottage to the largest
countryside and city centre hotels.

Quality Assurance awards correct at end
September 2000

HOTELS &
GUEST HOUSES

SIGNS YOU NEED TO KNOW
QUALITY GRADING

VII

THE OFFICIAL WHERE TO STAY G

THE STANDARDS YOU CAN EXPECT.

MORE DETAILS AVAILABLE FROM:

★ ★ ★ ★ ★   **Exceptional**

★ ★ ★ ★   **Excellent**

★ ★ ★   **Very good**

★ ★   **Good**

★   **Fair and Acceptable**

A TRAINED SCOTTISH TOURIST BOARD QUALITY
ADVISOR grades each property every year to
give you the reassurance that you can choose
accommodation of the quality standard
you want.

TO HELP YOU further in your choice the
Scottish Tourist Board System also tells you
the type of accommodation and the range of
facilities and services available.

PLEASE TURN OVER FOR DETAILS.

FOR FURTHER INFORMATION call into any Tourist
Information Centre, or contact the Scottish
Tourist Board.

Quality Assurance Department
Scottish Tourist Board
Thistle House
Beechwood Park North
INVERNESS
IV2 3ED
TEL: **01463 723040**
FAX: **01463 717244**
EMAIL: **qa@stb.gov.uk**

ACCOMMODATION TYPES

SELF CATERING

A HOUSE, cottage, apartment, chalet or similar accommodation which is let normally on a weekly basis to individuals where facilities are provided to cater for yourselves.

SERVICED APARTMENTS

SERVICED APARTMENTS are essentially self catering apartments where services such as a cleaning service is available and meals and drinks may be available. Meals and drinks would normally be provided to each apartment or in a restaurant and/or bar which is on site.

GUEST HOUSE

A GUEST HOUSE is usually a commercial business and will normally have a minimum of 4 letting bedrooms, of which some will have ensuite or private facilities. Breakfast will be available and evening meals may be provided.

B&B

ACCOMMODATION OFFERING bed and breakfast, usually in a private house. B&B's will normally accommodate no more than 6 guests, and may or may not serve an evening meal.

HOTEL

A HOTEL WILL NORMALLY HAVE a minimum of twenty letting bedrooms, of which at least half must have ensuite or private bathroom facilities. A hotel will normally have a drinks license (may be a restricted licence) and will serve breakfast, dinner and normally lunch.

SMALL HOTEL

A SMALL HOTEL WILL normally have a maximum of twenty letting bedrooms and a minimum of six. At least 50% of the bedrooms will have ensuite or private facilities. A small hotel will be licenced (may be a restricted license) and will serve breakfast, dinner and normally lunch. It will normally be run by owner(s) and reflect their style and personal input.

INTERNATIONAL RESORT HOTEL

A HOTEL ACHIEVING a 5 Star quality award which owns and offers a range of leisure and sporting facilities including an 18 hole golf course, swimming and leisure centre and country pursuits.

LODGE

PRIMARILY PURPOSE-BUILT overnight accommodation, often situated close to a major road or in a city centre. Reception hours may be restricted and payment may be required on check in. There may be associated restaurant facilities.

INN

BED AND BREAKFAST accommodation provided within a traditional inn or pub environment. A restaurant and bar will be open to non-residents and will provide restaurant or bar food at lunchtime and in the evening.

RESTAURANT WITH ROOMS

IN A RESTAURANT WITH ROOMS, the restaurant is the most significant part of the business. It is usually open to non-residents. Accommodation is available, and breakfast is usually provided.

CAMPUS ACCOMMODATION

CAMPUS ACCOMMODATION is provided by colleges and universities for their students and is made available-with meals-for individuals, families or groups at certain times of the year. These typically include the main Summer holiday period as well as Easter and Christmas.

SERVICED ACCOMMODATION
FACILITY AND SERVICE SYMBOLS

TV TV in bedrooms

Satellite/cable TV

Tea/coffee making facilities in bedrooms

Telephone in bedrooms

Hairdryer in bedrooms

Evening meal available

Room service

Restaurant

Leisure facilities

Indoor swimming pool

Laundry service

Porterage

Lounge

TV Lounge

Full alcohol drinks license

Restricted alcohol drinks license

Non-smoking establishment

Smoking restricted

Payphone provided

Washbasin in bedrooms

Ensuite bath and/or shower for all bedrooms

Ensuite bath and/or shower for some bedrooms

Private bath and/or shower for all bedrooms

Private bath and/or shower for some bedrooms

P Private parking

P Limited parking

No TV

YOU NOT ONLY WANT TO BE SURE OF THE STANDARD OF ACCOMMODATION YOU CHOOSE TO STAY IN, which ever type it may be, you want to be sure you make the most of your time.

THE SCOTTISH TOURIST BOARD not only inspects every type of accommodation every year, but also a wide range of visitor attractions every second year to grade the standard of customer care provided for visitors.

THE INSPECTION SCHEME for visitor attractions provides you with the assurance that an attraction has been assessed for the condition and standard of the facilities and services provided – the warmth of welcome, efficiency of service, level of cleanliness, standard of visitor interpretation and of the toilets, restaurant and shop, if provided.

A LARGE WORLD FAMOUS CASTLE, or small local museum can attain high grades if their services for the visitor are of a high standard.

THE STANDARDS YOU CAN EXPECT.

★ ★ ★ ★ ★   Exceptional
★ ★ ★ ★   Excellent
★ ★ ★   Very good
★ ★   Good
★   Fair and Acceptable

IN ADDITION TO THE STAR GRADES, every attraction is categorised under one of the following types to help give the visitor an indication of the type of experience on offer:

Visitor Attraction

Castle

Historic Attraction

Museum

Tour

Garden

Activity Centre

Tourist Shop

Leisure Centre

Arts Venue

Historic House

LOOK FOR THE SCOTTISH TOURIST BOARD SIGN OF QUALITY:

VISITORS WITH PARTICULAR MOBILITY NEEDS MUST BE ABLE TO BE SECURE IN THE KNOWLEDGE THAT SUITABLE ACCOMMODATION IS AVAILABLE TO MATCH THESE REQUIREMENTS. Advance knowledge of accessible entrances, bedrooms and facilities is important to enable visitors to enjoy their stay.

ALONG WITH THE QUALITY awards which apply to all the establishments in this, and every Scottish Tourist Board guide, we operate a national accessibility scheme. By inspecting establishments to set criteria, we can identify and promote places that meet the requirements of visitors with mobility needs.

THE THREE CATEGORIES of accessibility – drawn up in close consultation with specialist organisations are:

Unassisted wheelchair access for residents

Assisted wheelchair access for residents

Access for residents with mobility difficulties

LOOK OUT FOR these symbols in establishments, in advertising and brochures. They assure you that entrances, ramps, passageways, doors, restaurant facilities, bathrooms and toilets, as well as kitchens in self catering properties, have been inspected with reference to the needs of wheelchair users, and those with mobility difficulties. Write or telephone for details of the standards in each category – address on page vii.

FOR MORE INFORMATION about travel, specialist organisations who can provide information and a list of all the Scottish accommodation which has had the access inspection write (or ask at a Tourist Information Centre) for the Scottish Tourist Board booklet "Accommodation for Visitors with Mobility Difficulties".

Holiday Care
2nd Floor
Imperial Buildings
Victoria Road
Horley
Surrey RH6 7PZ
TEL: **01293 774535**
FAX: **01293 784647**
EMAIL: **holiday.care@virgin.net**
WEB: **www.holidaycare.org.uk**

IN ADDITION, a referral service to put enquirers in touch with local disability advice centres is:

UPDATE
27 Beaverhall Road
Edinburgh
EH7 4JE
TEL: **0131 558 5200**
EMAIL: **info@update.org.uk**
WEB: **www.update.org.uk**

OVER 900 QUALITY ASSURED ACCOMMODATION PROVIDERS ARE OFFERING AN EXTRA WARM WELCOME FOR VISITORS who are cycling or walking for all, or part, of their holiday in Scotland.

AS WELL AS having had the quality of the welcome, service, food and comfort assessed by the Scottish Tourist Board, they will be able to offer the following:-

★   hot drink on arrival
★   packed lunch/flask filling option
★   late evening meal option
★   early breakfast option
★   drying facilities for wet clothes
★   local walking and/or cycling information
★   daily weather forecast
★   local public transport information
★   secure, lockable, covered area
     for bike storage
★   details of local cycle specialists

Walkers Welcome Scheme

Cyclists Welcome Scheme

LOOK OUT FOR the logos in this guide and other accommodation listings.

GREEN TOURISM

IN RESPONSE TO the increasing need for businesses throughout the world to operate in an environmentally friendly way, the Scottish Tourist Board has developed the Green Tourism Business Scheme.

WHERE OWNERS OF accommodation are taking steps to reduce waste and pollution, to recycle and to be efficient with resources they are credited in this Scheme with a "Green Award". In our assessment of the degree of environmental good practice the business is demonstrating they are awarded one of the following;

BRONZE AWARD   BRONZE
for achieving a satisfactory level

SILVER AWARD   SILVER
for achieving a good level

GOLD AWARD   GOLD
for achieving a very good level

HOTELS &
GUEST HOUSES

SIGNS YOU NEED TO KNOW
TASTE OF SCOTLAND
THE SCOTCH BEEF CLUB

XIII

THE OFFICIAL WHERE TO STAY G

FROM SCOTLAND'S NATURAL LARDER COMES A WEALTH OF FINE FLAVOURS.

THE SEA YIELDS crab and lobster, mussels and oysters, haddock and herring to be eaten fresh or smoked. From the lochs and rivers come salmon and trout.

SCOTCH BEEF AND LAMB, venison and game are of prime quality, often adventurously combined with local vegetables or with wild fruits such as redcurrants and brambles. Raspberries and strawberries are cultivated to add their sweetness to trifles and shortcakes, and to the home-made jams that are an essential part of Scottish afternoon tea.

THE SCOTS HAVE a sweet tooth, and love all kinds of baking – rich, crisp shortbread, scones, fruit cakes and gingerbreads. Crumbly oatcakes make the ideal partner for Scottish cheeses, which continue to develop from their ancient farming origins into new – and very successful – styles.

AND IN OVER a hundred distilleries, barley, yeast and pure spring water come together miraculously to create malt whisky – the water of life.

MANY SCOTTISH HOTELS and restaurants pride themselves on the use they make of these superb natural ingredients – around 400 are members of the Taste of Scotland Scheme which encourages the highest culinary standards, use of Scottish produce and a warm welcome to visitors. Look for the Stockpot symbol at establishments, or write to Taste of Scotland for a copy of their guide.

In Shops		£8.99
By Post:	UK	£9.50
	Europe	£10.50
	US	£12.00

TASTE OF SCOTLAND SCHEME

33 Melville Street
Edinburgh, EH3 7JF
TEL: **0131 220 1900**
FAX: **0131 220 6102**
E-MAIL: **tastescotland@sol.co.uk**
WEB: **www.taste-of-scotland.com**

THE SCOTCH BEEF CLUB is an international association of restaurants of considerable repute.

THE MEMBERSHIP PROFILE is wide and varied – ranging from intimate establishments, through beautiful country houses, to city centre hotels. The membership includes 5 Star golf resorts, former vicarages, cottages, a bakehouse and even a station. Their styles are individual but what they all have in common is a recognised excellence and a commitment to using only the finest quality produce in their award winning kitchens. This commitment is demonstrated by their choice of beef – Scotch Beef.

GIVE YOURSELF a treat and try one of the Scotch Beef dishes on the menu at a Scotch Beef Club member.

SCOTLAND HAS SOME OF THE FINEST FOOD PRODUCTS IN THE WORLD. Our seafood, beef, lamb, venison, vegetables and soft fruit are renowned for their high quality. These fine indigenous raw materials and a wide assortment of international food products are skillfully combined by cooks and chefs into the vast range of cuisine available in Scotland.

AS YOU TRAVEL throughout the country you will find an excellent standard of cooking in all sorts of establishments from restaurants with imaginative menus to tea rooms with simple wholesome home-baking.

YOU WILL FIND some of these culinary gems by reading of their reputation in newspapers and magazines, from advice given by Tourist Information Centre staff, by looking for the Taste of Scotland logo, or by using your own instinct to discover them yourself.

THE SCOTTISH TOURIST BOARD has recognised that it would be helpful to you, the visitor, to have some assurance of the standards of food available in every different type of eating establishment; and indeed to be able to find a consistent standard of food in every place you choose to eat.

WE LAUNCHED THE NATURAL COOKING of Scotland as a long-term initiative to encourage eating places to follow the lead of those who are best in their field in providing a consistently high standard of catering.

WE HAVE HARNESSED the skills of chefs, the experience of restaurateurs and the expertise of catering trainers to introduce a series of cooking skills courses which will encourage the use of fresh, local produce, cooked in a simple and satisfying way. We are providing advice and guidance to eating places throughout Scotland on high quality catering and the skills involved in efficient food service and customer care. Many more initiatives are being planned to support this enhancement of Scottish cooking standards and a high dependency on the food available on our own doorsteps.

WHILST YOU WILL appreciate the food experiences you will find in eating your way around Scotland this year, the Natural Cooking of Scotland will ensure that the profile of fine Scottish cooking is even greater in future years.

THE OFFICIAL WHERE TO STAY G

SCOTLAND IS A SMALL COUNTRY AND TRAVEL IS EASY. There are direct air links with UK cities, with Europe and North America. There is also an internal air network bringing the islands of the North and West within easy reach.

SCOTLAND'S RAIL NETWORK not only includes excellent cross-border InterCity services but also a good internal network. All major towns are linked by rail and there are also links to the western seaboard at Mallaig and Kyle of Lochalsh (for ferry connections to Skye and the Western Isles) and to Inverness, Thurso and Wick for ferries to Orkney and Shetland.

ALL THE USUAL DISCOUNT CARDS are valid but there are also ScotRail Rovers (multi journey tickets allowing you to save on rail fares) and the Freedom of Scotland Travelpass, a combined rail and ferry pass allowing unlimited travel on ferry services to the islands and all of the rail network. In addition Travelpass also offers discounts on bus services and some air services.

INTERCITY SERVICES are available from all major centres, for example: Birmingham, Carlisle, Crewe, Manchester, Newcastle, Penzance, Peterborough, Preston, Plymouth, York and many others.

THERE ARE FREQUENT InterCity departures from Kings Cross and Euston stations to Edinburgh and Glasgow. The journey time from Kings Cross to Edinburgh is around 4 hours and from Euston to Glasgow around 5 hours.

COACH CONNECTIONS include express services to Scotland from all over the UK; local bus companies in Scotland offer explorer tickets and discount cards. Postbuses (normally minibuses) take passengers on over 130 rural routes throughout Scotland.

FERRIES TO AND AROUND the islands are regular and reliable, most ferries carry vehicles, although some travelling to smaller islands convey only passengers.

CONTACT the Information Department, Scottish Tourist Board, 23 Ravelston Terrace, Edinburgh EH4 3TP, or any Tourist Information Centre, for details of travel and transport.

MANY VISITORS CHOOSE to see Scotland by road – distances are short and driving on the quiet roads of the Highlands is a new and different experience. In remoter areas, some roads are still single track,and passing places must be used. When vehicles approach from different directions, the car nearest to a passing place must stop in or opposite it. Please do not use passing places to park in!

SPEED LIMITS ON Scottish roads:
Dual carriageways 70mph/112kph;
single carriageways 60mph/96kph;
built-up areas 30mph/48kph.

THE DRIVER AND front-seat passenger in a car must wear seatbelts; rear seatbelts, if fitted, must be used. Small children and babies must at all times be restrained in a child seat or carrier.

OPENING TIMES

PUBLIC HOLIDAYS: Christmas and New Year's Day are holidays in Scotland, taken by almost everyone. Scottish banks, and many offices, may close in 2001 on 1 and 2 January, 13 and 16th April, 7 and 20th May, 27 August, 25 and 26 December. Scottish towns also take Spring and Autumn holidays which may vary from place to place, but are usually on a Monday.

BANKING HOURS: In general, banks open Monday to Friday, 0930 to 1600, with some closing later on a Thursday. Banks in cities, particularly in or near the main shopping centres, may be open at weekends. Cash machines in hundreds of branches allow you to withdraw cash outside banking hours, using the appropriate cards.

PUBS AND RESTAURANTS: Pubs and restaurants are allowed to serve alcoholic drinks between 1100 hours and 2300 hours Monday through to Saturday; Sundays 1230 hours until 1430 hours then again from 1830 hours until 2300 hours.

RESIDENTS IN HOTELS may have drinks served at any time, subject to the proprietors discretion.

EXTENDED LICENSING HOURS are subject to local council applications.

TELEPHONE CODES

IF YOU ARE CALLING from abroad, first dial your own country's international access code (usually 00, but do please check). Next, dial the UK code, 44, then the area code except for the first 0, then the remainder of the number as normal.

QUARANTINE REGULATIONS

IF YOU ARE COMING to Scotland from overseas, please do not attempt to bring your pet on holiday with you. British quarantine regulations are stringently enforced, and anyone attempting to contravene them will incur severe penalties as well as the loss of the animal.

SCOTLAND ON THE NET

VISIT OUR WEB SITE AT:

www.visitscotland.com

"THE SCOTTISH TOURIST BOARD IS COMMITTED TO ENSURING THAT OUR NATURAL ENVIRONMENT, UPON WHICH OUR TOURISM IS SO DEPENDANT, IS SAFEGUARDED FOR FUTURE GENERATIONS TO ENJOY."

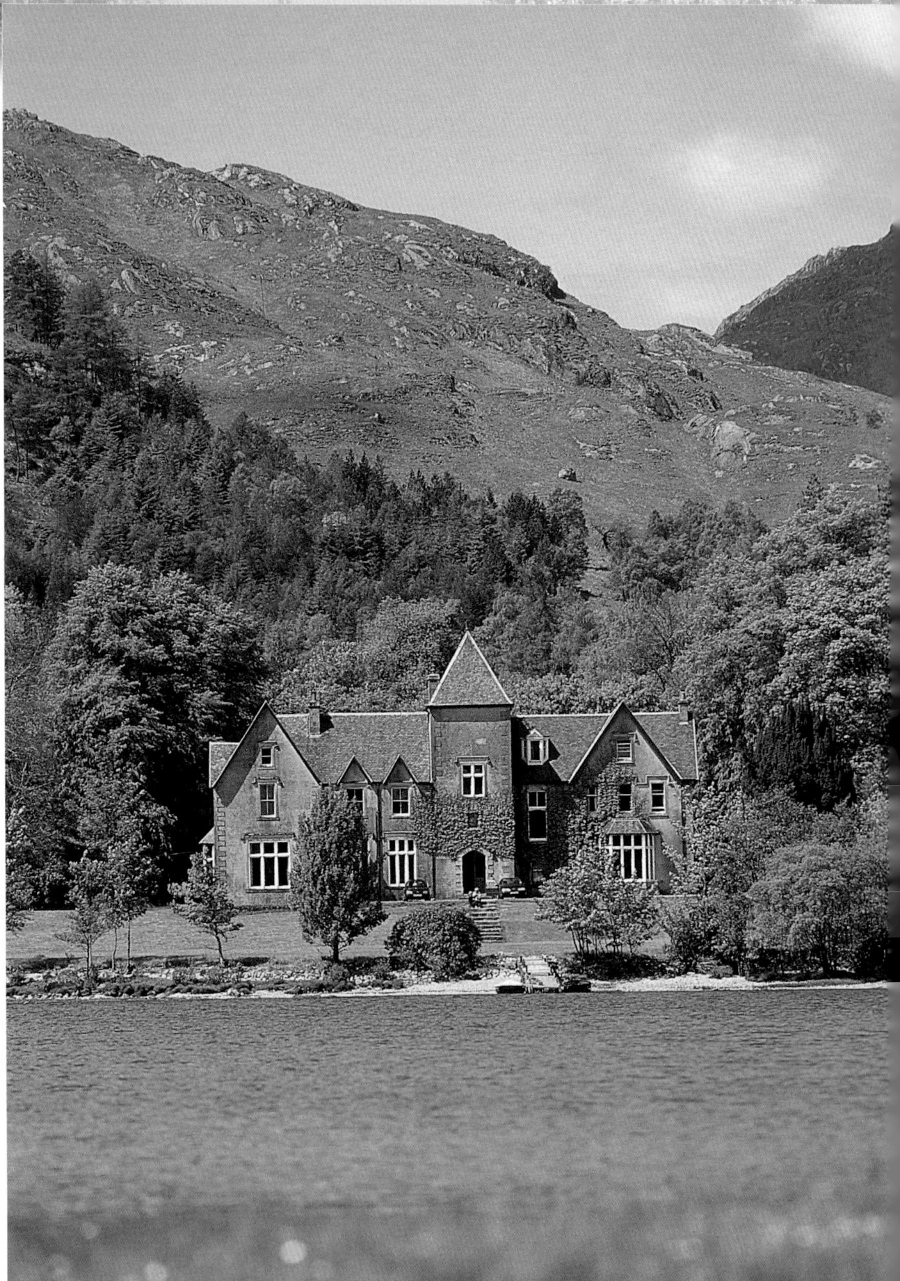

ACCOMMODATION

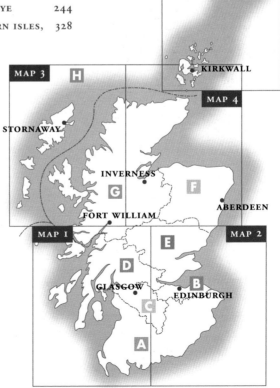

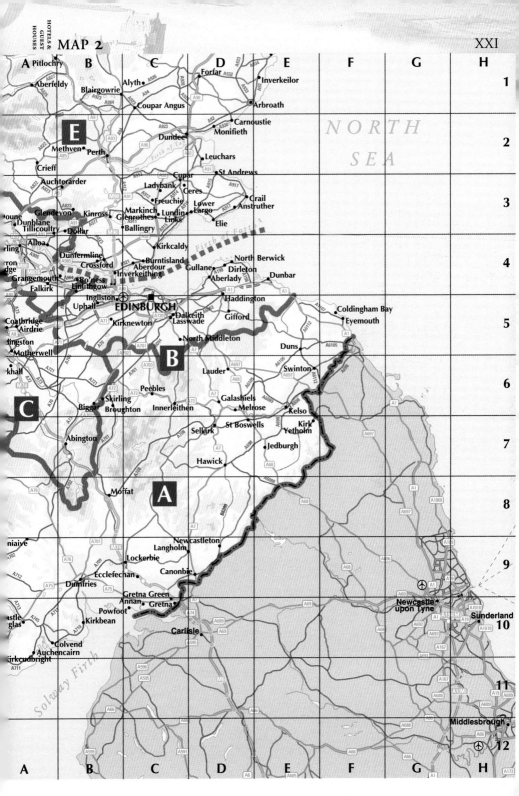

These maps are for "Hotels & Guest Houses" locations only.
For route planning and touring please use a current
road atlas.

MAP 4 XXIII

HOTELS & GUEST HOUSES

ORKNEY

A B C D E F G H

1

H

Scapa Flow

Stromness

HOY

Longhope

SOUTH RONALDSAY

Pentland Firth

2

Mey

John o'
Groats

Scrabster

A836

Thurso

A9

A882

3

Tongue

A838

A836

A9

A9

4

Lybster

A99

Dunbeath

5

Helmsdale

Car ferries
and terminals:

Brodick ● ● Rothesay

6

Lairg

Golspie

Brora

Dornoch Firth

A9

A949

Dornoch

A836

Scale 1:1 300 000

0   10   20 miles

© Bartholomew Ltd 2000

7

Tain

Portmahomack

Moray Firth

Fraserburgh

Cullen

Buckie

Portsoy

Alness

Garmouth

Macduff

Banff

Evanton

Invergordon

8

Rosemarkie

Nairn

Forres

Elgin

A96

Peterhead

Strathpeffer

Auldearn

A96

A940

A96

A95

A98

A952

A950

ir of Ord

Beauly

Inverness

A82

A9

Ballindalloch

Dufftown

Huntly

Rothienorman

Methlick

9

Grantown
-on-Spey

A95

Carrbridge

A938

Dulnain Bridge

Nethy Bridge

Kildrummy

Oldmeldrum

Newburgh

Drumnadrochit

Loch Ness

Inverurie

Foyers

Boat of
Garten

Invermoriston

Aviemore

A95

A96

10

Whitebridge

Tarland

Aberdeen

ort Augustus

Feshie Bridge

A9

A93

Newtonmore

Kingussie

A86

A889

Ballater

Banchory

A90

A957

Stonehaven

11

Braemar

A93

A9

F

A944

A980

A93

12

E

Laurencekirk

B966

B967

Blair
Atholl

Glenshee

Edzell

A90

A937

A93

Killiecrankie

A924

A935

Montrose

A B C D E F G H

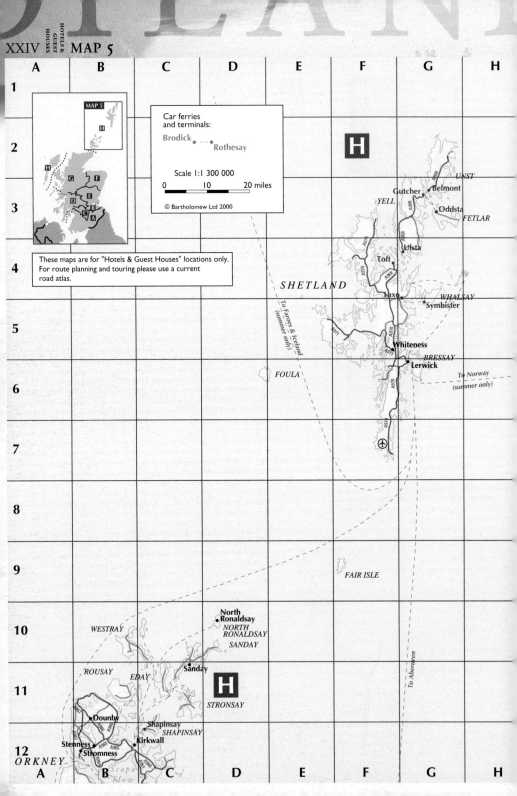

MAP 5

Car ferries
and terminals:

Brodick • • Rothesay

Scale 1:1 300 000

0   10   20 miles

© Bartholomew Ltd 2000

These maps are for "Hotels & Guest Houses" locations only.
For route planning and touring please use a current
road atlas.

SHETLAND

UNST
Gutcher • • Belmont
YELL
Oddsta
FETLAR
Ulsta
Toft
Voe
WHALSAY
• Symbister
Whiteness
BRESSAY
Lerwick
To Norway
(summer only)

To Faroes & Iceland
(summer only)

FOULA

FAIR ISLE

North
• Ronaldsay
NORTH
RONALDSAY
SANDAY

WESTRAY

ROUSAY
EDAY
Sanday

STRONSAY

Shapinsay
SHAPINSAY

Dounby

Stenness
Stromness
Kirkwall

ORKNEY

Scapa
Flow

To Aberdeen

SCOTLAND

HOTELS & GUEST HOUSES

The Official
Where to stay guide
2001

S COTLAND'S SOUTH WEST OFFERS A BEAUTIFUL AND UNCROWDED LANDSCAPE WHERE YOU CAN ENJOY A REAL FEELING OF SPACE.

River Tweed near Peebles

HERE YOU WILL find over 400 miles of the National Cycle network plus superb golf courses. There is also great walking country to be found, including the 212 mile coast-to-coast Southern Upland Way. This long-distance footpath begins in Portpatrick, goes through the Galloway Forest Park – the largest in Britain – then it crosses the Moffat Hills before it heads into the Scottish Borders. Back on the south-west coast, the tidal mudflats and sandy beaches of the Solway Firth are dotted with attractive villages and seaside towns including Kirkcudbright, with it's long artistic tradition as well as a thriving current arts scene. Dumfries is the main town in the region. Sometimes known as Queen of the South, this handsome red sandstone town has strong associations with Robert Burns. Other outstanding attractions are Caerlaverock Castle with four bird reserves nearby, Gretna Green and the Famous Old Blacksmith's Shop Visitor Centre, Threave Gardens and its new Countryside Centre, Wigtown (now a celebrated 'Book Town') and Sweetheart Abbey.

THE AYRSHIRE COAST has some excellent holiday attractions for all the family, including Vikingar! in Largs, and The Big Idea and the Magnum Leisure Centre both at Irvine Harbourside. For those interested in Scotland's national poet, Robert Burns, you can visit many attractions including his birthplace in Alloway. And you can relive some of his dramatic life at the Tam O' Shanter Experience. Less than an hour's sail will take you to the Isle of Arran which offers fine mountains, quiet beaches, the famous Brodick Castle and the Isle of Arran Distillery, Scotland's newest. For those who prefer a sporting holiday, the region offers horse-racing and football, while with over forty golf courses, golf is one of the biggest attractions. There are world famous courses at Troon, Turnberry and Prestwick.

Goat Fell, seen from Brodick, Isle of Arran

Quiet road near New Galloway, Dumfries and Galloway

FIRST IMPRESSIONS of the Scottish Borders are of a surprisingly wild area, though river valleys with their woodlands and farms soon give a softer appearance. These borderlands were fought over until the 17th century and as a result there are many magnificent ruined abbeys and towered castles to visit. There are also many fine stately homes such as the magnificent Edwardian mansion of Manderston and the superb Georgian house of Mellerstain. Market towns such as Kelso, Selkirk, Hawick and Melrose offer good shopping and accommodation facilities. Close by are the magnificent ruins of Melrose Abbey and the distinctive triple peaks of the Eildon Hills, a landmark for miles around. Below is the Tweed, one of Scotland's most famous salmon-fishing rivers. Sir Walter Scott's fascinating home of Abbotsford and the secluded Dryburgh Abbey where he is buried are just a few of the fascinating historical sites throughout this region.

The colourful past of the border towns is brought to life each year when the local residents re-enact the Common Ridings by dressing up in period costume and riding around the burgh boundaries. The landscape to the east is a beautiful mosaic of farmland and finally ends at the dramatic cliffs of St Abbs, a favourite place for bird watching.

EVENTS
SOUTH OF SCOTLAND
(AYRSHIRE AND ARRAN,
DUMFRIES AND GALLOWAY,
SCOTTISH BORDERS)

14 APRIL
Venue-Arran
Isle of Arran Rugby Sevens
Annual Rugby Tournament.
TEL: 01770 302565

*25 MAY-3 JUNE
Dumfries & Galloway Arts
Festival
Various venues,
Dumfries & Galloway
Unique Arts Festival with
various events.
Contact: Mrs Ruth Bell
TEL: 01387 260447

9-16 JUNE
Guid Nychburris
Various venues, Dumfries
Annual burgh festival with street
entertainment's, annual ride out
and crowning of
the Queen.
Contact: Stanley McEwen
TEL: 01387 254952

15 JUNE
Selkirk Common Riding
Town Centre, Selkirk
The battle of Flodden in 1513 is
commemorated with the casting
of colours in the town market
place plus the traditional riding
of the marches.
Contact: Allan Douglas
TEL: 01750 21954

9-14 JULY
Ayrshire Golf Classic
Various courses including the
Ailsa Craig Course, Turnberry
4 day amateur golf event.
Contact: Celtic Links
TEL: 01292 671500
EMAIL:
info@ayrshiregolfclassic.co.uk

16-27 AUGUST
Marymass Festival
Various venues, Irvine
Traditional festival featuring
activities for all ages, including
folk and other music events.
TEL: 01294 324482

*
MID AUGUST - SEPTEMBER
Gaelforce
Various venues,
Dumfries & Galloway
Arts festival celebrating Scottish
and Irish culture, featuring
music, dance, theatre,
exhibitions and much more.
Contact: Gracefield
Arts Centre
TEL: 01387 262084

8-15 SEPTEMBER
Borders Walking Festival
West Linton, Scottish Borders
Choice of guided walks
each day plus evening
entertainment.
Contact: Walking Development
Officer, Tweed Horizons
TEL: 01835 824632

*9-10 JUNE
Prestwick International Airshow
Prestwick Airport
2 day international airshow with
the Red Arrows, parachute
display teams, wing walkers, jet
fighters, funfair and public
catering.
Contact: The Airshow Office
TEL: 07769 974050

*provisional dates

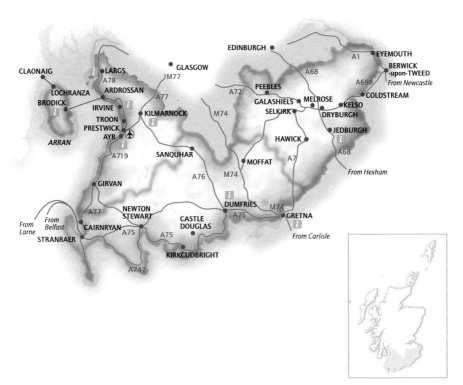

AYRSHIRE AND ARRAN
TOURIST BOARD
Ayr Tourist Information
Centre
22 Sandgate
AYR
KA7 1BW   Jan – Dec

TEL: **01 292 28 86 88**
FAX: **01 292 28 86 86**
www.ayrshire-arran.com

DUMFRIES AND GALLOWAY
TOURIST BOARD
64 Whitesands
Dumfries
DG1 2RS

TEL: **01 387 25 38 62**
FAX: **01 387 24 55 31**
www.dumfriesandgalloway.co.uk

SCOTTISH BORDERS
TOURIST BOARD
Tourist Information Centre
Murray's Green
Jedburgh   TD8 6BE

TEL: **08 70 60 70 250**
     (Brochure)
     01 835 86 40 99
     (Information)
FAX: **01 835 86 40 99**
www.scot-borders.co.uk

AYRSHIRE AND ARRAN TOURIST BOARD

AYR
22 Sandgate
TEL: **(01292) 288688**
Jan-Dec

BRODICK
The Pier
Isle of Arran
TEL: **(01770) 302140/302401**
Jan-Dec

GIRVAN
Bridge Street
TEL: **(01465) 714950**
Easter-Oct

IRVINE
New Street
TEL: **(01294) 313886**
Jan-Dec

KILMARNOCK
62 Bank Street
TEL: **(01563) 539090**
Jan-Dec

LARGS
Promenade
TEL: **(01475) 673765**
Jan-Dec

MILLPORT
28 Stuart Street
Isle of Cumbrae
TEL: **(01475) 530753**
Easter-Oct

DUMFRIES AND GALLOWAY TOURIST BOARD

CASTLE DOUGLAS
Markethill Car Park
TEL: **(01556) 502611**
Easter-Oct

DUMFRIES
Whitesands
TEL: **(01387) 253862**
Jan-Dec

GATEHOUSE OF FLEET
Car Park
TEL: **(01557) 814212**
Easter-Oct

GRETNA GREEN
Old Blacksmith's Shop
TEL: **(01461) 337834**

KIRKCUDBRIGHT
Harbour Square
TEL: **(01557) 330494**
Easter-end Oct

MOFFAT
Ladyknowe
TEL: **(01683) 220620**
Easter-end Oct

NEWTON STEWART
Dashwood Square
TEL: **(01671) 402431**
Easter-Oct

STRANRAER
Burns House
28 Harbour Street
TEL: **(01776) 702595**
Jan-Dec

SCOTTISH BORDERS TOURIST BOARD

COLDSTREAM
High Street
TEL: **(01890) 882607**
Easter-Oct

EYEMOUTH
Auld Kirk, Manse Road
TEL: **(018907) 50678**
April-Oct

GALASHIELS
St John Street
TEL: **(01896) 755551**
Easter-Oct

HAWICK
Drumlanrig's Tower
TEL: **(01450) 372547**
Easter-Oct

JEDBURGH
Murray's Green
TEL: **(01835) 863435/863688**
Jan-Dec

KELSO
Town House, The Square
TEL: **(01573) 223464**
Easter-Oct

MELROSE
Abbey House
TEL: **(01896) 822555**
Easter-Oct

PEEBLES
High Street
TEL: **(01721) 720138**
Jan-Dec

SELKIRK
Halliwell's House
TEL: **(01750) 20054**
Easter-Oct

Annan, Dumfriesshire | Map Ref: 2C10

Warmanbie Country House Hotel & Restaurant
Annan, Dumfriesshire DG12 5LL
Telephone: 01461 204015   Fax: 01461 204015
e.mail: info@warmanbie.co.uk   web: www.warmanbie.co.uk

Owned/run by the Duncan family. Creative cooking, friendly service, peace and quiet, huge breakfasts. Romantic breaks (four posters) – in-house weddings. Gretna Green nearby. Log fires, good selection malts. Free private fishing. Walled garden. Golf nearby. Special rates midweek/festive season. The Good Hotel Guide recommended.

★★★

HOTEL

Warmanbie Country House Hotel & Restaurant
Annan, Dumfriesshire, DG12 5LL
Tel/Fax: 01461 204015
E-mail: info@warmanbie.co.uk
Web: www.warmanbie.co.uk

Family run Georgian country house in wooded grounds overlooking River Annan. Own Salmon and Trout fishing. Traditional and creative menus, using herbs from the walled garden plus an excellent breakfast selection.

1 Single	All En Suite	B&B per person	Open Jan-Dec
2 Twin		from £47.00 Single	
5 Double		from £34.00 Dbl/Twn	

Blackwaterfoot, Isle of Arran | Map Ref: 1E7

★★

SMALL
HOTEL

Blackwaterfoot Hotel
Blackwaterfoot, Isle of Arran, KA27 8EU
Tel/Fax: 01770 860202

Situated 50 yards from the picturesque harbour at Blackwaterfoot this family run hotel seeks to provide a warm & welcoming home from home during your holiday. Recently built spacious conservatory overlooking the delightful garden.

2 Single	8 En Suite fac	B&B per person	Open Jan-Dec
3 Twin	1 Pub Bath/Show	from £25.00 Single	B&B + Eve.Meal
3 Double		from £30.50 Dbl/Twn	from £42.00
2 Family			

Important: Prices stated are estimates and may be subject to amendments

Blackwaterfoot, Isle of Arran Map Ref: 1E7

Kinloch Hotel

Blackwaterfoot, Isle of Arran KA27 8ET
Tel: 01770 860444   e.mail: kinloch@cqm.co.uk
Fax: 01770 860447 Web: www.kinloch-arran.com

The **Kinloch Hotel** has 44 rooms with private bathrooms, colour TV, tea-making facilities and direct-dial telephones. There are also 7 suites, each with a small kitchen area adjoining their lounge. Hotel facilities include a heated indoor swimming pool, sauna, solarium, full-size snooker table, multi-gym and squash court. There is a passenger lift to the 1st and 2nd floors and the hotel has full central heating. Ground-floor rooms and disabled facilities. Ideally situated for exploring the Island and observing the varied wildlife from *Golden Eagles* to *Red Deer* or simply watching the beautiful sunsets. *From £35 per person per night.*

★★★

HOTEL

Kinloch Hotel
Blackwaterfoot, Isle of Arran, KA27 8ET
Tel: 01770 860444 Fax: 01770 860447
E-mail: kinloch@cqm.co.uk
Web: www.kinloch-arran.com

On the sea front with views of the Mull of Kintyre. Extensive leisure facilities, indoor pool. Ideal for families and open to non-residents.

10 Single	All En Suite	B&B per person	Open Jan-Dec
31 Twin	Suites avail	£35.00-£49.00	B&B + Eve.Meal
3 Double			£48.00-£64.00

Brodick, Isle of Arran Map Ref: 1F7

★★★

GUEST HOUSE

Allandale House
Brodick, Isle of Arran, KA27 8BJ
Tel: 01770 302278

Comfortable guest house in south facing postion with well laid out garden, on the outskirts of Brodick. Only a few minutes walk from the ferry and Brodick centre yet in a peaceful location. Some ground floor annexe accommodation.

1 Single	5 En Suite fac	B&B per person	Open 20Jan-Oct
1 Twin	1 Priv.NOT ensuite	£20.00-£26.00 Single	B&B + Eve.Meal
1 Double		£20.00-£26.00 Dbl/Twn	£34.00-£38.00
3 Family		Room only	
		£18.00-£24.00	

★★★★

HOTEL

Auchrannie Country House Hotel
Brodick, Isle of Arran, KA27 8BZ
Tel: 01770 302234 Fax: 01770 302812
Web: www.auchrannie.co.uk

The hospitality offered at Auchrannie confirms its popular reputation as Arran's flagship hotel. Close to Brodick village, beach and golf course, Auchrannie offers a choice of cuisine from award winning Garden Restaurant and Brambles Cafe Bar. The extensive leisure club incorporates superb 20 m swimming pool, sauna/steam, gym, aromatherapy and shiatsu.

10 Twin	All En Suite	B&B per person	Open Jan-Dec
16 Double		from £45.00 Single	B&B + Eve.Meal
2 Family		from £35.00 Dbl/Twn	from £52.50

VAT is shown at 17.5%: changes in this rate may affect prices. | *Key to symbols is on back flap.*

Brodick, Isle of Arran   Map Ref: 1F7

**GUEST
HOUSE**

★★★★

Dunvegan House
Shore Road, Brodick, Isle of Arran, KA27 8AJ
Tel/Fax: 01770 302811
Web: www.dunveganhouse-arran.co.uk

3 Twin	8 En Suite fac	B&B per person	Open Jan-Dec excl
5 Double		from £35.00 Single	Xmas/New Year
1 Family		from £29.00 Dbl/Twn	B&B + Eve.Meal
			from £45.00

Superb sea and mountain views, conveniently situated for ferry terminal. Licensed. Dinner using fresh local produce when available. Private parking. Ground floor bedrooms available.

TV 📺 📷 P ☕ ⌇ ⚒ ✕ ⌐ 🍷 🏠

C V

**GUEST
HOUSE**

★★★

Glen Cloy Farmhouse
Glen Cloy Road, Brodick, Isle of Arran, KA27 8DA
Tel: 01770 302351
Web: www.SmoothHound.co.uk/hotels/glencloy.html

1 Single	2 En Suite fac	B&B per person	Open Jan-Dec
2 Twin	1 Pub Bath/Show	from £22.00 Single	
2 Double		£22.00-£27.00 Dbl/Twn	

Farmhouse full of character set in peaceful glen with views of hills and sea. Within easy reach of Brodick ferry. Mark and Vicki produce memorable breakfasts with homemade jams and bread, and eggs from their own hens. Embroidery courses held in spring and autumn.

TV 📺 P ☕ ⚒ 🍽 ⌐

C 🐕 ♿ V

**GUEST
HOUSE**

★★★★

The Invercloy
Brodick, Isle of Arran, KA27 8AJ
Tel: 01770 302225 Fax: 01770 302495

2 Twin	All En Suite	B&B per person	Open Mar-Oct
8 Double		from £34.00 Single	B&B + Eve.Meal
		from £29.00 Dbl/Twn	from £44.00

Superbly appointed guest house run personally by the owners Terry and Liz McManus. Ideally situated for exploring beautiful Arran, 'Quality is our Policy' at affordable prices. Choose one of our deluxe rooms and admire the views from your own balcony.

TV 📺 ☕ ⌇ ⚒ ✕ ⌐ 🍷 🍴 🏠

♿ W

HOTEL

★★

Kingsley Hotel
Brodick, Isle of Arran, KA27 8AJ
Tel: 01770 302226 Fax: 01770 302319
E-mail: kingsleyhotel@connectfree.co.uk

8 Single	All En Suite	B&B per person	Open Mar-Sep
11 Twin		from £30.00 Single	B&B + Eve.Meal
6 Double		from £30.00 Dbl/Twn	from £45.00
2 Family		Room only per person	
		from £24.00	

Family run for over 50 years. On Brodick seafront with views of Goatfell and Brodick Castle. Specialising in good home cooking using fresh Scottish produce and locally caught fish. Golf packages. Families welcome. 400 yards from ferry terminal.

TV 📞 📻 📺 P ☕ ⌇ ⚒ 🍽 ⚲ 🍷

C 🐕 ♿ V

**SMALL
HOTEL**

★★

Ormidale Hotel
Brodick, Isle of Arran, KA27 8BY
Tel: 01770 302293 Fax: 01770 302098
E-mail: reception@ormidale-hotel.co.uk
Web: www.ormidale-hotel.co.uk

1 Single	4 En Suite fac	B&B per person	Open Mar-Oct
3 Twin	1 Pub Bath/Show	from £23.00 Single	
2 Double		from £23.00 Dbl/Twn	
1 Fam/Trpl		Room only per person	
		from £18.00	

Family run, set in mature woodland by the golf course. Excellent home cooked bar meals, children welcome. CAMRA approved. Good pub atmosphere.

TV 📺 P ☕ 🍽 🍷

C 🐕 ♿ V

Important: Prices stated are estimates and may be subject to amendments

---

Corrie, Isle of Arran

Map Ref: 1F6

★★

GUEST HOUSE

Blackrock Guest House
Corrie, Isle of Arran, KA27 8JP
Tel: 01770 810282

2 Single	3 En Suite fac	B&B per person	Open Mar-Nov
1 Twin	1 Pub Bath/Show	from £18.00 Single	
1 Double		from £18.00 Dbl/Twn	
4 Family			

Where the mountains meet the sea... that is where we are, on the outskirts of 'the Prettiest village in Europe'. Come and enjoy our traditional Scottish guesthouse, established on shore edge in the 1930's. Ensuite accommodation; panoramic views; natural garden; red squirrels; otters and birdlife. Groups welcome - constant hot water. Boat Hire.

Lamlash, Isle of Arran

Map Ref: 1F7

★★★

HOTEL

Glenisle Hotel
Shore Road, Lamlash, Isle of Arran, KA27 8LS
Tel: 01770 600559/600258 Fax: 01770 600966

2 Single	All En Suite	B&B per person	Open Mar-4 Jan
5 Twin		£27.00-£34.00 Single	B&B + Eve.Meal
4 Double		from £34.00 Dbl/Twn	£40.00-£47.00
2 Family			

Situated on seafront with attractive garden and easy access to the shore. Personal attention, ample parking. October to April special package rates available.

★★★★

GUEST HOUSE

Lilybank Guest House
Shore Road, Lamlash, Isle of Arran, KA27 8LS
Tel/Fax: 01770 600230
E-mail: colin369.richardson@virgin.net
Web: SmoothHound.co.uk/hotels/lilybank

3 Twin	All Ensuite fac	B&B per person	Open Jan-Dec
4 Double		from £25.00 Single	
		from £25.00 Dbl/Twn	

A small family-run guest house overlooking Holy Island and Lamlash Bay. Ground floor bedrooms. Private parking. All rooms en-suite or with private facilities.

Lochranza, Isle of Arran

Map Ref: 1E6

★★★★

GUEST HOUSE

Apple Lodge
Lochranza, Isle of Arran, KA27 8HJ
Tel/Fax: 01770 830229
E-mail: applelodge@easicom.com

1 Twin	All En Suite	B&B per person	Open Jan-Dec excl
2 Double		from £30.00 Dbl/Twn	Xmas/New Year
1 Suite			B&B + Eve.Meal
			from £47.00

A charming intimate country house set amidst spectacular scenery countryside where deer and eagles are often sighted. Taste of Scotland.

★★★★

HOTEL

Butt Lodge Country House Hotel
Newton Shore, Lochranza, Isle of Arran, KA27 8JF
Tel/Fax: 01770 830240

1 Twin	All En Suite	B&B per person	Open Mar-Jan
3 Double		£38.00-£47.00 Single	B&B + Eve.Meal
1 Family		£28.00-£37.00 Dbl/Twn	£43.00-£52.00

A warm welcome awaits you at this former hunting lodge in a secluded position with magnificent views all around. Varied and imaginative dishes, using only the best of local produce. Home Baking. Residential license.

VAT is shown at 17.5%: changes in this rate may affect prices.

Key to symbols is on back flap.

Whiting Bay, Isle of Arran | Map Ref: 1F7

SMALL HOTEL

Burlington Hotel & Licensed Restaurant
Shore Road, Whiting Bay, Isle of Arran, KA27 8PZ
Tel: 01770 700255 Fax: 0374 595327
E-mail: burlhotel@aol.com
Web: www.milford.co.uk/scotland/accom/h-a-1737.html

2 Single	8 En Suite fac	B&B per person	Open Apr-Oct
3 Twin	1 Priv.NOT ensuite	£27.00-£37.00 Single	B&B + Eve.Meal
4 Double		£25.00-£34.00 Dbl/Twn £40.00-£53.00	
		Room only per person	
		£19.00-£30.00	

Enjoy the Arran experience and traditional Scottish hospitality in this
seafront Edwardian Hotel. A delightful culinary experience using local
produce organically orientated. Fine wines specially selected from
international lists. A member of the Arran Taste Trail.

GUEST HOUSE

View Bank House
Golf Course Road, Whiting Bay, Isle of Arran, KA27 8QT
Tel/Fax: 01770 700326

1 Single	4 En Suite fac	B&B per person	Open Jan-Dec excl
1 Twin	2 Pub Bath/Show	from £20.00 Single	Xmas/New Year
2 Double		from £20.00 Dbl/Twn	B&B + Eve.Meal
3 Family			from £32.00

Beautifully privately owned house where you can relax and enjoy superb
home cooked fresh food, large garden with magnificent views across the
Clyde. 500 yards down a country lane brings you onto the shore. Open
most of the year with full central heating and warm atmosphere.
Viewbank charms its guests back time and time again.

Auchencairn, by Castle Douglas, Kirkcudbrightshire | Map Ref: 2A10

Balcary Bay Hotel
Auchencairn, near Castle Douglas, Dumfries & Galloway DG7 1QZ
Telephone: 01556 640217/640311   Fax: 01556 640272
e.mail: reservations@balcary-bay-hotel.co.uk
Web: www.balcary-bay-hotel.co.uk
Family-run country house in three acres of garden. A magnificent and peaceful
setting on the shores of the bay. Ideal base for all leisure facilities or a relaxing
holiday with warm hospitality, good food and wine.
AA/RAC ★★★. One of Scotland's Hotels of Distinction.
★★★★ HOTEL

HOTEL

Balcary Bay Hotel
Auchencairn, by Castle Douglas,
Kirkcudbrightshire, DG7 1QZ
Tel: 01556 640217/640311 Fax: 01556 640272
e.mail: reservations@balcary-bay-hotel.co.uk
Web: www.balcary-bay-hotel.co.uk

3 Single	All En Suite	B&B per person	Open Mar-Nov
6 Twin		from £61.00 Single	B&B + Eve.Meal
10 Double		from £54.00 Dbl/Twn	from £54.00
1 Family			

A lovely country house hotel, with past smuggling associations dating back
to 1625. Stands in over 3 acres of garden in a secluded and enchanting
situation on the shores of the bay. Cuisine based on local delicacies:
Galloway beef, lamb, lobster and of course, Balcary Bay salmon.

INN

Old Smugglers Inn
Main Street, Auchencairn, by Castle Douglas,
Kirkcudbrightshire, DG7 1QU
Tel: 01556 640331

1 Twin	All En Suite	B&B per person	Open Jan-Dec
2 Double		from £20.00 Single	
		from £20.00 Dbl/Twn	

Cosy Inn dating from 17th Century located in picturesque village on
Solway Coast. Secluded Beer Garden with children's play area and burn
running through it. Extensive menu with daily specials using fresh local
produce.

Important: Prices stated are estimates and may be subject to amendments

Ayr | Map Ref: 1G7

GUEST HOUSE
★★

Belmont Guest House
Mr Andrew Hillhouse (Proprietor),
15 Park Circus, Ayr, KA7 2DJ
Tel: 01292 265588 Fax: 01292 290303
E-mail: belmontguesthouse@btinternet.com
Web: www.belmontguesthouse.co.uk

Victorian townhouse in a quiet tree lined conservation area, within easy walking distance of town centre. Ground-floor bedrooms, all with ensuite facilities. Guest lounge with extensive book collection. On street and private car parking.

1 Twin	All En Suite
2 Double	
2 Family	

B&B per person
£20.00-£24.00 Single
from £20.00 Dbl/Twn
Room only per person
£15.00-£19.00

Open Jan-Dec excl Xmas/New Year

SILVER

GUEST HOUSE
★★★★

Craggallan Guest House
8 Queen's Terrace, Ayr, Ayrshire, KA7 1DU
Tel/Fax: 01292 264998
E-mail: craggallan@aol.com
Web: www.craggallan.com

A warm welcome awaits you at this delightful Guest House. Ideally located in a quiet conservation area close to the shore front & promenade, less than 10 minutes walk from Ayr town centre.

1 Single	All En Suite
1 Twin	
1 Double	
2 Family	

B&B per person
£22.00-£25.00 Single
£18.00-£22.00 Dbl/Twn

Open Jan-Dec

HOTEL
★★★★
&

Fairfield House Hotel
Fairfield Road, Ayr, KA7 2AR
Tel: 01292 267461 Fax: 01292 261456
Web: www.fairfieldhotel.co.uk

Victorian building lovingly restored, commanding views of Arran. Renowned for food, hospitality and leisure. Modern air conditioned function suite available.

1 Single	All En Suite
12 Twin	
40 Double	
3 Family	

B&B per person
from £80.00 Single
from £95.00 Dbl/Twn

Open Jan-Dec
B&B + Eve.Meal
from £130.00

INN
★★

Finlayson Arms Hotel
Hillhead, Coylton, Ayr, Ayrshire, KA6 6JT
Tel/Fax: 01292 570298
Web: www.finlaysonarmshotel.co.uk

Friendly village hotel, offering comfortable ensuite accommodation. Excellent food served in either the bar lounge or the dining room. Ideally situated (4 miles) for Ayr Races, golf and Robert Burns enthusiasts.

8 Twin	All En Suite
1 Double	

B&B per person
from £30.00 Single
from £26.00 Dbl/Twn

Open Jan-Dec

HOTEL
★★★
&

Horizon Hotel
Esplanade, Ayr, Ayrshire, KA7 1DT
Tel: 01292 264384 Fax: 01292 264011
E-mail: mail@horizonhotel.com
Web: www.horizonhotel.com

Ayr's only sea front hotel has panoramic views over the Clyde to the Isle of Arran. The hotel has a spacious conservatory restaurant, which serves food all day, and a comfortable lounge with open fire to relax in. First class en suite and budget accommodation, some with sea views. Highly recommended for golf breaks, complimentary golf booking service available to guests. Ground floor bedrooms, one with full disabled facilities.

7 Twin	15 En Suite fac
2 Double	3 Priv.NOT ensuite
13 Family	4 Pub Bath/Show

B&B per person
from £25.00 Single
from £25.00 Dbl/Twn

Open Jan-Dec
B&B + Eve.Meal
from £35.00

VAT is shown at 17.5%: changes in this rate may affect prices. | **Key to symbols is on back flap.**

Ayr		Map Ref: 1G7		

★★★★
SMALL
HOTEL

The Ivy House
2 Alloway, Ayr, KA7 4NL
Tel: 01292 442336 Fax: 01292 445572
Web: www.theivyhouse.com
Substantial investment by new owners, George and Eli Whillock, has already been recognised by the Scottish Tourist Board awarding 4 stars just four months after they acquired the property. The Ivy House is a relaxed country house with views across the golf course. The public areas are bright and light, the food really rather good, the hospitality warm and the five bedrooms have been refurbished to the highest levels of comfort. A jewel in the Ayrshire crown.

2 Twin   All En Suite
3 Double

B&B per person
from £79.00 Single
from £70.00 Dbl/Twn

B&B + Eve.Meal
from £95.00

Jarvis Caledonian Hotel
DALBLAIR ROAD, AYR KA7 1UG
Telephone: 01292 269331   Fax: 01292 610722
Modern 118-bedroom hotel is ideally located in the town centre yet minutes from Ayr's sandy beach and opposite Ayr's Gaiety Theatre. Hudson's Bar and Grill offers a selection of international dishes including "A Taste of Burns". Leisure club has an indoor pool, 2 gymnasiums, sauna and solarium.
Golfing and special breaks can be arranged.

★★★
HOTEL

Jarvis Caledonian
Dalblair Road, Ayr, Ayrshire, KA7 1UG
Tel: 01292 269331 Fax: 01292 610722
Web: www.jarvis.co.uk

40 Single   All En Suite
60 Twin
6 Double
12 Family

B&B per person
from £37.50

Open Jan-Dec excl
Xmas/New Year
B&B + Eve.Meal
from £42.50 per person

Comfortable modern hotel and conference centre in town centre. Minutes from beach. 22 golf courses within easy reach. 5 miles Prestwick airport. 35 miles Glasgow airport.

★★★
GUEST
HOUSE

Langley Bank Guest House
39 Carrick Road, Ayr, Ayrshire, KA7 2RD
Tel: 01292 264246 Fax: 01292 282628
Web: www.accommodation-ayr.co.uk

2 Twin   4 En Suite fac
3 Double   2 Pub Bath/Show
1 Family

B&B per person
£16.00-£25.00 Dbl/Twn

Open Jan-Dec

Elegantly refurbished Victorian house close to all amenities. Most rooms have en-suite facilities and all have telephones. Good base for touring Ayrshire.

★★★
HOTEL

Pickwick Hotel
19 Racecourse Road, Ayr, KA7 2TD
Tel: 01292 260111 Fax: 01292 285348
E-mail: info@pickwickhotel.freeserve.co.uk

2 Single   All En Suite
9 Twin
4 Double

B&B per person
from £39.50 Single
from £35.00 Dbl/Twn

Open Jan-Dec

Traditional stone built house with extensive car park. In residential area within 0.5 miles (1km) of town centre and beach.

Important: Prices stated are estimates and may be subject to amendments

Ayr   Map Ref: 1G7

GUEST HOUSE
★★★

Queens Guest House
10 Queens Terrace, Ayr, KA7 1DU
Tel: 01292 265618 Fax: 01292 880918
E-mail: hannah@waterloo21.freeserve.co.uk

1 Single	All En Suite	B&B per person
1 Twin		from £20.00 Single
1 Double		from £19.00 Dbl/Twn
2 Family		Room only per person
		from £17.00

Open Jan-Dec excl
Xmas/New Year
B&B + Eve.Meal
from £27.00

The Queen's extends the warmest of welcomes to its guests from near and far. This terraced house is situated in a conservation area only a few minutes walk from the seafront yet convenient for the town centre and various golf courses. Evening meal by prior arrangement.

GUEST HOUSE
★★★

The Richmond
38 Park Circus, Ayr, Ayrshire, KA7 2DL
Tel: 01292 265153 Fax: 01292 288816
E-mail: Richmond38@btinternet.com
Web: www.richmond-guest-house.co.uk

2 Double	5 En Suite fac	B&B per person
4 Family	1 Priv.NOT ensuite	from £25.00 Single
		from £22.00 Double

Open Jan-Dec

Traditional stone built town house with many period features. Easy walking distance to sea front and town centre with all its amenities including a variety of eating establishments.

HOTEL
★★

St Andrews Hotel
7 Prestwick Road, Ayr, Ayrshire, KA8 8LD
Tel: 01292 263211 Fax: 01292 440477
E-mail: st_andrews_ayr@yahoo.com

1 Single	3 En Suite fac	B&B per person
3 Double		from £20.00 Single
3 Family		from £17.00 Dbl/Twn

Open Jan-Dec

St Andrews is a family run hotel, recently upgraded. The hotel has a lounge bar, public bar, games room and a newly fitted dining room. The hotel is close to Ayr town centre, railway station and Prestwick Airport. Private parking.

Savoy Park Hotel
16 Racecourse Road, Ayr KA7 2UT
Tel: 01292 266112 Fax: 01292 611488
e.mail: mail@savoypark.com Web: www.savoypark.com

Discover Ayr's leading family-run hotel. Experience friendly professional service and relax in homely surroundings. Comfortable, inviting and excellent value.

SMALL HOTEL
★★★

Savoy Park Hotel
16 Racecourse Road, Ayr, KA7 2UT
Tel: 01292 266112 Fax: 01292 611488
E-mail: mail@savoypark.com
Web: www.savoypark.com

6 Twin	All En Suite	B&B per person
6 Double		from £55.00 Single
3 Family		from £37.50 Dbl/Twn
		Room only per person
		from £45.00 Single

Open Jan-Dec

A classic Scottish home, recently refurbished to today's quality standards. Ideally located in Ayr's premier residential area. Relax in homely surroundings and experience friendly service. Comfortable inviting and excellent value.

VAT is shown at 17.5%: changes in this rate may affect prices.

Key to symbols is on back flap.

Ayr

Map Ref: 1G7

★★★

**GUEST
HOUSE**

Mrs Muriel Sullivan
Miller House, 36 Miller Road, Ayr, Ayrshire, KA7 2AY
Tel: 01292 282016/611903

2 Twin	5 En Suite fac	B&B per person	Open Jan-Dec
2 Double	2 Pub Bath/Show	£22.00-£30.00 Single	
3 Family		£22.00-£30.00 Dbl/Twn	

Miller House is a superior Victorian villa which has been converted to two apartments. The upper half houses the majority of comfortable bedrooms, there are three bedrooms on the ground floor. Conveniently situated for beach and town centre which has a vast range of restaurants. Personal attention assured at all times in this family run guest house. Ample private parking.

★★★

B&B

Tramore Guest House
17 Eglinton Terrace, Ayr, Ayrshire, KA7 1JJ
Tel/Fax: 01292 266019

2 Twin	1 Pub Bath/Show	B&B per person	Open Jan-Dec
1 Double		from £18.00 Single	B&B + Eve.Meal
		from £17.00 Dbl/Twn	from £24.00

Set in a quiet conservation area in a Victorian terraced house – a two minute walk from either town centre or beach. Evening meals available.

Broughton, by Biggar, Peeblesshire

Map Ref: 2B6

★★★

**GUEST
HOUSE**

The Glenholm Centre
Broughton, by Biggar, Tweeddale, ML12 6JF
Tel/Fax: 01899 830408
E-mail: glenholm@dircon.co.uk

2 Twin	All En Suite	B&B per person	Open Feb-Dec excl Xmas
1 Double		from £25.20 Single	B&B + Eve.Meal
1 Family		from £22.50 Dbl/Twn	from £34.50

A warm welcome awaits you at our family run guest house set on a farm at The Heart of Glenholm in the Scottish Borders. Close to Broughton, 30 miles South of Edinburgh - it is the perfect location to come to unwind and enjoy the hills, glens, nature and history of the valley. Full board available.

Canonbie, Dumfriesshire

Map Ref: 2D9

★★★

HOTEL

Cross Keys Hotel
Canonbie, Dumfriesshire, DG14 0SY
Tel: 013873 71205 Fax: 013873 71878

2 Single	9 En Suite fac	B&B per person	Open Jan-Dec
4 Twin	1 Priv bathroom	from £27.00 Single	
3 Double		from £26.00 Dbl/Twn	
1 Family			

An 'Olde Worlde' 17th century coaching inn situated in the centre of the picturesque village of Canonbie just off the main A7 road to Edinburgh. Ideal for those seeking peace and solitude backed up by the comfort, service and hospitality of a traditional coaching inn.

Castle Douglas, Kirkcudbrightshire

Map Ref: 2A10

★★★

HOTEL

Douglas Arms Hotel
King Street, Castle Douglas, Kirkcudbrightshire,
DG7 1DB
Tel: 01556 502231 Fax: 01556 504000
E-mail: doughot@aol.com

4 Single	All En Suite	B&B per person	Open Jan-Dec
9 Twin		from £37.50 Single	B&B + Eve.Meal
10 Double		from £34.25 Dbl/Twn	from £40.00
1 Family		Room only per person	
		from £30.00	

Centrally located within the picturesque market town of Castle Douglas, the Douglas Arms was originally a coaching inn and dates back to 1779. The hotel has been tastefully modernised without losing any of the original charm from those bygone days. Secure undercover parking.

Important: Prices stated are estimates and may be subject to amendments

Castle Douglas, Kirkcudbrightshire   Map Ref: 2A10

★★★
HOTEL

The Imperial Hotel
King Street, Castle Douglas, Kirkcudbrightshire, DG7 1AA
Tel: 01556 502086 Fax: 01556 503009
Web: www.thegolfhotel.co.uk

2 Single	All En Suite	B&B per person	Open Jan-Dec excl
5 Twin	1 Pub Bath/Show	from £37.50 Single	Xmas/New Year
5 Double		from £28.00 Dbl/Twn	B&B + Eve.Meal
			from £37.50

Privately owned hotel in market town, close to local leisure facilities. Ideal base for touring Galloway. Golfing holidays. Private secure parking.

★★
HOTEL

The Kings Arms Hotel
St Andrews Street, Castle Douglas, Kirkcudbrightshire, DG7 1EL
Tel: 01556 502626 Fax: 502097
E-mail: david@galloway-golf.co.uk
Web: www.galloway-golf.co.uk

2 Single	9 En Suite fac	B&B per person	Open Jan-Dec excl
4 Twin	1 Priv.NOT ensuite	from £35.00 Single	Xmas/New Year
2 Double	1 Pub Bath/Show	from £28.00 Dbl/Twn	B&B + Eve.Meal
2 Family			from £37.50

Former coaching inn in town centre. Ideal for touring Galloway. Private secure parking.

★★★★
SMALL
HOTEL

Longacre Manor
Ernespie Road, Castle Douglas, Kirkcudbrightshire, DG7 1LE
Tel: 01556 503576 Fax: 01556 503886
E-mail: ball.longacre@btinternet.com
Web: www.aboutscotland.co.uk/south/longacre.html

2 Twin	All En Suite	B&B per person	Open Jan-Dec
2 Double		£40.00-£50.00 Single	B&B + Eve.Meal
		£35.00-£50.00 Dbl/Twn	£52.50-£67.50

A small private country manor hotel surrounded by woodland gardens overlooking green fields on the edge of Castle Douglas. A traditional scottish country town in one of the most beautiful and undiscovered areas of southern Scotland.

★★★
GUEST
HOUSE

Rose Cottage Guest House
'Rose Cottage', Gelson, Castle Douglas
Kirkcudbrightshire, DG7 1SH
Tel/Fax: 01556 502513

1 Single	1 En Suite fac	B&B per person	Open Jan-Dec excl
1 Twin	1 Pub Bath/Show	from £20.00 Single	Xmas/New Year
2 Double		from £18.00 Dbl/Twn	B&B + Eve.Meal
			from £29.00

Friendly welcome in personally run guest house, situated in quiet village. Ideal for walkers and birdwatchers. Ample private parking. All rooms on ground floor. 1 1/2 miles from Threave Gardens - National Trust for Scotland.

★★
HOTEL

The Urr Valley Hotel
Ernespie Road, Castle Douglas, Kirkcudbrightshire, DG7 3JG
Tel: 01556 502188 Fax: 01556 504055

3 Single	All En Suite	B&B per person	Open Jan-Dec
5 Twin	2 Priv.NOT ensuite	£25.00-£49.50 Single	
6 Double		£32.50-£37.50 Dbl/Twn	
5 Family			

Friendly welcome in a family run hotel with fine views, in a peaceful rural setting. 1 mile (1.5km) from town centre.

 VAT is shown at 17.5%: changes in this rate may affect prices.   *Key to symbols is on back flap.*

Coldingham Bay, Berwickshire — Map Ref: 2F5

★★★★

GUEST HOUSE

Cul-na-Sithe
Coldingham Bay, nr Eyemouth, Berwickshire, TD14 5PA
Tel: 018907 71355 Fax: 018907 71565
E-mail: culnasithe@clara.co.uk

1 Twin	All En Suite	B&B per person	Open Feb-Nov
2 Double		from £23.00 Dbl/Twn	B&B + Eve.Meal
			from £39.50

Friendly, family run guest house with attractive garden overlooking Coldingham Sands with superb sea views. Open log fire in lounge. French and German spoken. Home cooked evening meals using the best local produce. All rooms en-suite.

★★★★

GUEST HOUSE

Dunlaverock Country House
Coldingham Bay, nr Eyemouth, Berwickshire, TD14 5PA
Tel/Fax: 018907 71450
E-mail: dunlaverock@lineone.net

2 Twin	All En Suite	B&B + Eve.Meal	Open Feb-Nov
4 Double		from £56.00	

Find peace and comfort in our beautiful villa. Spectacularly situated over sandy beach and rocky coastline. Large, comfortable ensuite bedrooms and delicious award winning food.

Colvend, Kirkcudbrightshire — Map Ref: 2A10

★★

HOTEL

Clonyard House Hotel
Colvend, Dalbeattie, Kirkcudbrightshire, DG5 4QW
Tel: 01556 630372 Fax: 01556 630422
E-mail: nickthompson@clara.net

8 Twin	All En Suite	B&B per person	Open Jan-Dec
3 Double		from £35.00 Single	B&B + Eve.Meal
3 Family		from £27.50 Dbl/Twn	from £40.00
		Room only per person	
		from £25.00	

Situated in 7 acres of mature gardens and woodlands, in a secluded position on the Solway Coast between Rockcliffe and Kippford. Choice of modern or traditional rooms, many on the ground floor, with their own private patio.

Millport, Isle of Cumbrae — Map Ref: 1F6

★

GUEST HOUSE

The College of the Holy Spirit
The College, Millport, Isle of Cumbrae, KA28 0HE
Tel: 01475 530353 Fax: 01475 530204
E-mail: tccumbrae@argyll.anglican.org

4 Single	7 Pub Bath/Show	B&B per person	Open Jan-Dec excl
7 Twin		from £17.00 Single	Xmas/New Year
5 Double		from £17.00 Dbl/Twn	B&B + Eve.Meal
3 Family		Room only per person	from £26.00
		from £12.50	

Unique opportunity to stay in the smallest working cathedral in Europe. Some seperate accommodation in North college. Refectory style dining. Library. All the buildings are grade 'A' listed.

Dalrymple, Ayrshire — Map Ref: 1G7

★★

INN

The Kirkton Inn
1 Main Street, Dalrymple, Ayrshire, KA6 6DF
Tel: 01292 560241 Fax: 01292 560835
E-mail: kirkton@cqm.co.uk
Web: www.kirktoninn.co.uk

7 Twin	All En Suite	B&B per person	Open Jan-Dec
4 Family		from £26.00 Single	B&B + Eve.Meal
		from £26.00 Twin	from £35.00
		Room only per person	
		from £20.00	

This refurbished Inn, dating from 1879, is situated in a rural conservation village in the heart of the Ayrshire countryside, yet only 5 miles from Ayr. In addition, there are 8 studios with limited cooking facilities adjacent to the Inn which are ideal for families or groups. Occupants of the studios have full access to all the Inn's amenities which include the traditional village pub, Malt Room and lounge bar.

Important: Prices stated are estimates and may be subject to amendments

HOTEL ★★

Aberdour Hotel
16-20 Newall Terrace, Dumfries, DG1 1LW
Tel: 01387 252060 Fax: 01387 262323

Family run hotel in quiet position, close to the town centre and railwat station. Home produced food and bar meals, all Scottish Galloway Beer served here. 9 rooms en-suite, 3 with private bathroom. Car park.

1 Single	9 En Suite fac
6 Twin	3 Priv.NOT ensuite
1 Double	
4 Family	

B&B per person
from £35.00 Single
from £27.50 Dbl/Twn
Room only per person
from £24.00

Open Jan-Dec excl
Xmas/New Year
B&B + Eve.Meal
£36.00-£45.00

Cairndale Hotel and Leisure Club

English Street, Dumfries DG1 2DF
Tel: 01387 254111 Fax: 01387 250555
e.mail: sales@cairndale.fsnet.co.uk   Web: www.cairndalehotel.co.uk

Regular entertainment in this popular hotel includes dinner dances (Saturdays), ceilidhs (Sundays, May to October) and cabaret evenings throughout the year. Superb leisure facilities including heated indoor pool and spa. Leisure breaks from £40 pp D,B&B. Golf, inclusive rate from £62.50 pp. 'Twixmas', Christmas, Hogmanay, Valentines and Easter packages also available.

HOTEL ★★★

Cairndale Hotel and Leisure Club
English Street, Dumfries, DG1 2DF
Tel: 01387 254111 Fax: 01387 250555
E-mail: sales@cairndale.fsnet.co.uk
Web: www.cairndalehotel.co.uk

Family run hotel in town centre. Executive rooms with jacuzzis. Extensive leisure facilities. Range of dining options.

14 Single	All En Suite
15 Twin	
40 Double	
22 Family	

B&B per person
from £55.00 Single
from £52.50 Dbl/Twn

Open Jan-Dec
B&B + Eve.Meal
from £45.00

GUEST HOUSE ★★★

Fulwood Hotel
30 Lovers Walk, Dumfries, DG1 1LX
Tel/Fax: 01387 252262

An impressive Victorian villa of red sandstone situated opposite the railway station, and in easy walking distance of the town centre. Refurbished to a high standard offering very comfortable accommodation, most with en-suite bathrooms, all with colour televisions, wash basins and tea and coffee making facilities.

1 Single	3 En Suite fac
2 Twin	2 Priv NOT ensuite
2 Double	
1 Family	

B&B per person
£21.00-£30.00 Single
£17.00-£22.00 Dbl/Twn

Open Jan-Dec excl
Xmas

HOTEL ★★★

Huntingdon House Hotel & Restaurant
18 St Marys Street, Dumfries, DG1 1LZ
Tel: 01387 254893 Fax: 01387 262553
E-mail: acame45046@aol.com

Traditional stone built house personally run by proprietor. Ideal base for touring. All rooms en-suite, ample private parking. 150 meters railway station, 10 mins walk to city centre.

2 Single	All En Suite
3 Twin	
2 Double	
1 Family	

B&B per person
£36.00-£49.00 Single
£27.00-£29.00 Dbl/Twn
Room only per person
£22.00-£25.00

Open Jan-Dec
B&B + Eve.Meal
£36.00-£49.00

Dumfries				Map Ref: 2B9

Moreig Hotel
★★★ HOTEL

67 Annan Road, Dumfries, DG1 3EG
Tel: 01387 255524 Fax: 01387 267105

2 Single	All En Suite	B&B per person	Open Jan-Dec
3 Double		£35.00-£40.00 Single	B&B + Eve.Meal
3 Family		from £27.50 Double	£37.50-£45.00

Small family run hotel, close to centre of Dumfries and local amenities.

Station Hotel
★★★ HOTEL

49 Lovers Walk, Dumfries, DG1 1LT
Tel: 01387 254316 Fax: 01387 250388

7 Single	All En Suite	B&B per person	Open Jan-Dec
11 Twin		from £60.00 Single	B&B + Eve.Meal
14 Double		from £35.00 Dbl/Twn	from £40.00 ppn

A imposing Victorian, sandstone building convenient both for railway station and all town centre facilities. Enterprising use of local fish and game in both the Pullman a la carte restaurant and bistro. All rooms en-suite. Lift available. Private parking.

by Dumfries				Map Ref: 2B9

Comlongon Castle Country House Hotel
★★★ HOTEL

Clarencefield, Dumfriesshire, DG1 4NA
Tel: 01387 870283 Fax: 01387 870266

2 Single	12 En Suite fac	B&B per person	Open Feb-Dec
2 Twin		£50.00-£70.00 Single	
7 Double		£50.00-£75.00 Dbl/Twn	
1 Family		Room only per person	
		£45.00-£60.00	

18th century mansion house adjoining medieval castle set in 120 acres of parkland. A popular location for small weddings which may be performed in the Great Hall of the castle. Bridal suite with 4 poster bed, spacious, historically themed rooms.

Trigony House Hotel
★★★★ SMALL HOTEL

Closeburn, Thornhill, Dumfriesshire, DG3 5EZ
Tel: 01848 331211 Fax: 01848 331303

1 Single	All En Suite	B&B per person	Open Jan-Dec
3 Twin		from £37.50 Single	B&B + Eve.Meal
4 Double		from £37.50 Dbl/Twn	from £45.00

An attractive red sandstone Edwardian country house situated close to A76 in 4 acres of secluded gardens and woodland. Taste of Scotland. Chef proprietor uses fresh local produce, much of it organic, plus own grown vegetables.

by Duns, Berwickshire				Map Ref: 2E5

Allanton Inn
★★★ INN

Allanton, Nr Chirnside, Berwickshire, TD11 3JZ
Tel: 01890 818260 Fax: 01890 817186
E-mail: allantoninn@supanet.com

1 Twin	3 Ensuite fac	B&B per person	Open Jan-Dec
2 Double	1 Priv.NOT ensuite	from £46.00 Single	B&B + Eve.Meal
1 Family-Suite		from £40.00 Dbl/Twn	from £48.00

Early 19c traditional village coaching Inn, near the Rivers Whiteadder and Blackadder. 1 mile (2kms) south of Chirnside. Real ale and home produced food served in cosy restaurant specialising in fish and game. Private Tweed salmon beat available.

Important: Prices stated are estimates and may be subject to amendments

Ecclefechan, Dumfriesshire — Map Ref: 2C9

HOTEL ★★★

Kirkconnel Hall
Ecclefechan, nr Lockerbie, Dumfriesshire, DG11 3JH
Tel: 01576 300277 Fax: 01576 300402
Web: www.kirkconnelhall.com

8 Double	11 En Suite fac	B&B per person	Open Jan-Dec
3 Family		£35.00-£60.00 Single	B&B + Eve.Meal
		£50.00-£105.00 Double	£60.00-£63.50

Kirkconnel Hall is a family run hotel, the oldest part of which was built in 1720. Tastefully modernised, it offers a high standard of accommodation, cuisine and personalised service. Conveniently situated next to the M74, at junction 19, it is ideal for those wishing to explore Southern Scotland. Numerous golf courses in the area. Function suite for weddings/conferences/ dinner dances

Ettrickbridge, by Selkirk, Selkirkshire — Map Ref: 2D7

SMALL HOTEL ★★★★

Ettrickshaws Country House Hotel
Ettrickbridge, by Selkirk, Selkirkshire, TD7 5HW
Tel/Fax: 01750 52229
E-mail: jenny@ettrickshaws.co.uk
Web: www.ettrickshaws.co.uk

1 Twin	All En Suite	B&B per person	Open Jan-Dec
4 Double		from £35.00 Dbl/Twn	B&B + Eve.Meal
			from £57.50

Victorian Country house in 12 acre woodland setting. Elegant, spacious accommodation and home cooked food. Salmon fishing - guest concessions. Walking.

Eyemouth, Berwickshire — Map Ref: 2F5

INN ★★★

Dolphin Hotel
North Street, Eyemouth, Berwickshire, TD14 5ES
Tel: 018907 50280 Fax: 018907 51087

1 Twin	5 En Suite fac	B&B per person	Open Jan-Dec
2 Double	1 Priv.NOT ensuite	from £36.00 Single	
3 Family		from £27.50 Dbl/Twn	

A small family run hotel on the seafront with beer garden. Convenient for local shops and amenities.

INN ★★

Ship Hotel
Harbour Road, Eyemouth, Berwickshire, TD14 5HT
Tel: 018907 50224

1 Single	3 En Suite fac	B&B per person	Open Jan-Dec
1 Twin	2 Pub Bath/Show	£18.00-£28.00 Single	
3 Double		£18.00-£21.00 Dbl/Twn	
1 Family		Room only per person	
		£16.00-£20.00	

Friendly pub on the harbour front in small fishing town, offering good hospitality and food.

Galashiels, Selkirkshire — Map Ref: 2D6

HOTEL ★★

Abbotsford Arms Hotel
63 Stirling Street, Galashiels, Selkirkshire,
TD1 1BY
Tel: 01896 752517 Fax: 01896 750744

2 Single	All En Suite	B&B per person	Open Jan-Dec excl
5 Twin		from £39.00 Single	Xmas/New Year
5 Double		from £30.00 Dbl/Twn	
2 Family			

Family run hotel, with both bar and restaurant meals, food available all day. Good base for touring the Borders and golfing. Convenient town centre location and just 1 hour to Edinburgh.

VAT is shown at 17.5%: changes in this rate may affect prices.

Key to symbols is on back flap.

Galashiels, Selkirkshire | **Map Ref: 2D6**

HOTEL
★★

King's Hotel
56 Market Street, Galashiels, TD1 3AN
Tel/Fax: 01896 755497
E-mail: kingshotel@talk21.com

1 Single	All En Suite	B&B per person	Open Jan-Dec excl
5 Twin		from £35.00 Single	Xmas/New Year
3 Double		from £25.00 Dbl/Twn	B&B + Eve.Meal
2 Family			from £40.00

Family run hotel centrally situated in the heart of market town. Restaurant offers traditional Scottish fayre with emphasis on fresh local produce.

HOTEL
★★★

Kingsknowes Hotel
1 Selkirk Road, Galashiels, Selkirkshire, TD1 3HY
Tel: 01896 758375 Fax: 001896 750377
E-mail: enquiries@kingsknowes.co.uk
Web: www.kingsknowes.co.uk

7 Twin	All En Suite	B&B per person	Open Jan-Dec
6 Double		from £49.00 Single	B&B + Eve.Meal
3 Family		from £37.00 Dbl/Twn	from £47.00

Family owned and run hotel, built 1860 overlooking the River Tweed and Eildon Hills. 'A' listed former mansion house with original conservatory and set in 3.7 acres of grounds. Ample parking. Sporting activities can be arranged nearby, golf, fishing, riding, walking, shooting etc.

HOTEL
★★★

Woodlands House Hotel
Windyknowe Road, Galashiels, Selkirkshire, TD1 1RG
Tel: 01896 754722 Fax: 01896 754892
E-mail: woodlands.uk@virgin.net

2 Single	All En Suite	B&B per person	Open Jan-Dec
1 Twin		from £50.50 Single	B&B + Eve.Meal
6 Double		from £36.00 Dbl/Twn	from £48.00
1 Family			

Woodlands House Hotel, a Victorian Gothic Mansion, set in two acres of picturesque grounds. A private mill owners house, a Polish Hospital, then a Church of Scotland children's home. Now a country house hotel. Informal dining in the Oak Wood Bar, or more formally in Alexanders Restaurant.

---

by Galashiels, Selkirkshire | **Map Ref: 2D6**

HOTEL
★★

Clovenfords Hotel
1 Vine Street, Clovenfords, by Galashiels,
Selkirkshire, TD1 3LU
Tel/Fax: 01896 850203

2 Twin	All En Suite	B&B per person	Open Jan-Dec
2 Double		from £30.00 Single	
1 Family		from £25.00 Dbl/Twn	

18c Coaching Inn situated in small village 3 miles from Galashiels. Real ale bars, restaurant and close to golf, fishing, walking, clay pigeon shooting and stalking can be arranged. Conveniently located for visiting many visitor attractions of the Borders.

Gatehouse of Fleet, Kirkcudbrightshire | **Map Ref: 1H10**

HOTEL
★★

Bank O'Fleet Hotel
47 High Street, Gatehouse-of-Fleet,
Kirkcudbrightshire, DG7 2HR
Tel: 01557 814302

1 Twin	5 En Suite fac	B&B per person	Open Jan-Dec
3 Double	1 Pub Bath/Show	£30.00 Single	B&B + Eve.Meal
2 Family		£23.50 Dbl/Twn	£35.50-£42.00
		Room only per person	
		£20.00-£25.00	

Resting in the heart of this picturesque and historic town of Gatehouse, the home of The Mill on the Fleet Visitor Centre, the Bank of Fleet Hotel is a central base for hillwalking, shooting and fishing. The area is renowned for its outstanding sandy beaches.

Important: Prices stated are estimates and may be subject to amendments

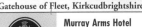

Gatehouse of Fleet, Kirkcudbrightshire — Map Ref: 1H10

HOTEL ★★

Murray Arms Hotel
Ann Street, Gatehouse of Fleet, Castle Douglas
Kirkcudbrightshire, DG7 2HY
Tel: 01557 814207 Fax: 01557 814370

1 Single	All En Suite	B&B per person	Open Jan-Dec
5 Twin		from £49.50 Single	B&B + Eve.Meal
5 Double		from £44.50 Dbl/Twn	from £125.00
2 Family			

Built c1760, an attractive old Posting Inn where Robert Burns is known to have written 'Scots Wha Hae'. Discounted golf, fishing and tennis for residents. Warm friendly service.

Girvan, Ayrshire — Map Ref: 1F8

HOTEL ★★

Hotel Westcliffe
15 Louisa Drive, Girvan, Ayrshire, KA26 9AH
Tel/Fax: 01465 712128

5 Single	All En Suite	B&B per person	Open Jan-Dec
8 Twin	3 Pub Bath/Show	from £25.00 Single	B&B + Eve.Meal
5 Double		from £22.00 Dbl/Twn	from £29.00
6 Family			

A family hotel, run by the Jardine family for 34 years, situated on the seafront and overlooking the promenade, putting green and boating lake. Views across the Firth of Clyde to Ailsa Craig, Isle of Arran, Kintyre and Irish coast. Ground floor accommodation. Relax after a days sightseeing, golfing, fishing, walking, in the whirlpool spa, steam room, toning table or exercise gym. Limited secure private parking, unrestricted street parking.

GUEST HOUSE ★★

Thistleneuk Guest House
19 Louisa Drive, Girvan, Ayrshire, KA26 9AH
Tel/Fax: 01465 712137
E-mail: reservations@thistleneuk.freeserve.co.uk

1 Single	All En Suite	B&B per person	Open Easter-Oct
2 Twin		from £23.00 Single	B&B + Eve.Meal
2 Double		from £23.00 Dbl/Twn	from £31.00
2 Family			

A warm welcome from George and Margaret at Thistleneuk which is situated on the sea front with views of Ailsa Craig and is central for all Girvans amenities. In their Robert Burns dining room the emphasis is on traditional Scottish food using local produce when possible. Over the years Thistleneuk has established a reputation for comfort and good food.

Glenluce, Wigtownshire — Map Ref: 1G10

HOTEL ★★★

Kelvin House Hotel
53 Main Street, Glenluce, Wigtownshire, DG8 0PP
Tel: 01581 300303 (office)/300528 (for residents u
se only) Fax: 01581 300303
E-mail: kelvinhouse@lineone.net
Web: www.kelvin-house.co.uk

2 Twin	5 En Suite fac	B&B per person	Open Jan-Dec
4 Double	1 Priv.NOT ensuite	from £25.00 Single	B&B + Eve.Meal
		from £22.50 Dbl/Twn	from £35.00
		Room only per person	
		from £20.00	

Located in tranquil village centre with easy access to major routes. Convenient for touring, either by car or bicycle, golfing, fishing, shooting and Irish ferries. Large family rooms available.

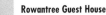

GUEST HOUSE ★★

Rowantree Guest House
38 Main Street, Glenluce, Wigtownshire, DG8 0PS
Tel: 01581 300244 Fax: 01581 300366

1 Twin	4 En Suite fac	B&B per person	Open Jan-Dec
2 Double	1 Priv.NOT ensuite	from £16.50 Single	
2 Family	1 Pub Bath/Show	from £15.50 Dbl/Twn	
		Room only per person	
		from £12.50	

Family run house, popular with fishermen, golfers, tourists and ferry passengers. In village 15 minutes from Stranraer. Disabled facilities. Evening meal by prior arrangement.

VAT is shown at 17.5%: changes in this rate may affect prices.　　　　*Key to symbols is on back flap.*

Gretna, Dumfriesshire | Map Ref: 2C10

HOTEL

The Gables Hotel
1 Annan Road, Gretna, Dumfriesshire, DG16 5DQ
Tel/Fax: 01461 338300
Web: www.gretna-weddings.co.uk/accom/gables.htm

2 Twin	All En Suite	B&B per person	Open Jan-Dec excl
8 Double		from £45.00 Single	Xmas/New Year
2 Family		from £30.00 Dbl/Twn	

Turn of the century grade II listed building retaining many of its original architectural features. Well kept gardens with spacious lawns sheltered by trees and shrubs. Located 300 yards from Gretna village centre and within easy reach of many of the areas attractions.

HOTEL

Hunters Lodge Hotel
Annan Road, Gretna, Dumfriesshire, DG16 5DL
Tel: 01461 338214
E-mail: reception@HuntersLodgeHotel.co.uk
Web: www.HuntersLodgeHotel.co.uk

2 Single	10 En Suite fac	B&B per person	Open Jan-Dec
2 Twin	1 Limited ensuite	£35.00-£37.00 Single	
5 Double	1 Pub Bath/Show	£27.00-£34.00 Dbl/Twn	
2 Family			

Closest hotel to the famous Gretna Registration Office. Cross the border into Scotland. Hunters Lodge Hotel is close to major routes. A qualified chef creates freshly prepared dishes in attractive dining room with it's tartan carpet giving a real flavour of Scotland. Staff are warm and welcoming as are the many different malt whiskies in the well stocked bar. Rooms are ensuite and well appointed. Full disabled facilities available.

HOTEL

Solway Lodge Hotel
97-99 Annan Road, Gretna, Dumfriesshire, DG16 5DN
Tel: 01461 338266 Fax: 01461 337791
Web: www.solwaylodge.co.uk

4 Twin	All En Suite	B&B per person	Open Jan-Dec excl
6 Double		from £39.50 Single	Xmas
		from £29.00 Dbl/Twn	
		Room only per person	
		from £25.00	

Family run hotel situated in gateway village to Scotland. Some superior rooms fitted with whirlpool baths. Some annexe accommodation.

---

nr Gretna Green, Dumfriesshire | Map Ref: 2C10

LODGE

The Mill
Grahamshill, Kirkpatrick Fleming, Dumfriesshire, DG11 3BQ
Tel: 01461 800344 Fax: 01461 800255
Web: www.themill.co.uk

2 Single	All En Suite	B&B per person	Open Jan-Dec
12		from £48.00 Single	
Dbl/Twn		from £34.00 Dbl/Twn	
9 Family			
4 Bridal			

Converted farm steading and mill with stone built chalet style, en-suite accommodation. Just off the M74 near Gretna Green. Fully licensed bar /restaurant and function room. Purpose built, churchlike Forge building for marriage ceremonies in attractive grounds.

Hawick, Roxburghshire | Map Ref: 2D7

SMALL HOTEL

Elm House Hotel
17 North Bridge Street, Hawick, Roxburghshire, TD9 9BD
Tel: 01450 372866 Fax: 01450 374175

2 Single	All En Suite	B&B per person	Open Jan-Dec excl
6 Twin		from £30.00 Single	Xmas/New Year
4 Double		from £22.00 Dbl/Twn	
3 Family			

Family run, centrally situated in old town. Ideal base for touring the Borders. Fishing, bowling, golfing and shooting available. 8 annexe bedrooms.

Important: Prices stated are estimates and may be subject to amendments

Hawick, Roxburghshire | Map Ref: 2D7

★★★
SMALL
HOTEL

Kirklands Hotel
West Stewart Place, Hawick, Roxburghshire, TD9 8BH
Tel: 01450 372263 Fax: 01450 370404

3 Twin	All En Suite	B&B per person	Open Jan-Dec
6 Double	1 Pub Bath/Show	£30.00-£52.00 Single	B&B + Eve.Meal
		£30.00-£40.00 Dbl/Twn	£47.50-£57.50

Victorian House Hotel quietly situated in a one acre garden with good views over town and countryside. Children and babies welcome. Pets by arrangement. Three hundred yards from modern well equipped leisure centre.

TV ☏ 🍴 P ☕ 🍷 ✕ ⭐ 🍽 ♨ ♟

C 🐾 ⛱ V

★★★
SMALL
HOTEL

Mansfield House Hotel
Weensland Road, Hawick, Roxburghshire, TD9 9EL
Tel: 01450 373988 Fax: 01450 372007

5 Twin	All En Suite	B&B per person	Open Jan-Dec
4 Double		£42.00-£55.00 Single	B&B + Eve.Meal
3 Family		£30.00-£42.50 Dbl/Twn	£45.00-£75.00
		Room only per person	
		£25.00-£35.00	

Fine family run hotel in extensive grounds with an outstanding reputation for excellent food and friendly atmosphere. Function/conference facility for up to 200. Taste of Scotland.

TV ☏ 🍴 P ☕ 🍷 🍽 ♨ ♟

C 🐾 ⛱ V

Innerleithen, Peeblesshire | Map Ref: 2C6

★★★★
SMALL
HOTEL

Caddon View Small Hotel
14 Pirn Road, Innerleithen, Peeblesshire, EH44 6HH
Tel: 01896 830208

2 Twin	6 En Suite fac	B&B per person	Open Jan-Dec
2 Double		£25.00-£40.00 Single	B&B + Eve.Meal
1 Family		£25.00-£32.00 Dbl/Twn	from £36.00
1 Single			

A warm welcome and excellent fine dining at this substantial Victorian house, with many period features. Ideal for touring the Borders. Two en-suite rooms on ground floor.

TV 🍴 P ☕ ✕ ♟

C 🐾 ⛱ W V

★★★
HOTEL

Traquair Arms Hotel
Traquair Road, Innerleithen, Peeblesshire, EH44 6PD
Tel: 01896 830229 Fax: 01896 830260
E-mail: traquair.arms@scotborders.co.uk
Web: www.s-h-systems.co.uk/hotels/traquair.html

3 Single	All En Suite	B&B per person	Open Jan-Dec excl
2 Twin		from £45.00 Single	Xmas/New Year
3 Double		from £29.00 Dbl/Twn	B&B + Eve.Meal
2 Family			from £47.00

Friendly Victorian country hotel in historic Borders village, near the River Tweed. Traditional cuisine provided by chef/proprietor, winners of Best Bar Food in the Borders award.

TV ☏ 🍴 P ☕ 🍽 ♨ ♟

C 🐾 ⛱ W V

Irvine, Ayrshire | Map Ref: 1G6

★★★
HOTEL

Annfield House Hotel
6 Castle Street, Irvine, Ayrshire, KA12 8RJ
Tel: 01294 278903 Fax: 01294 278904

2 Single	All En Suite	B&B per person	Open Jan-Dec
1 Twin		from £49.50 Single	
6 Double		from £35.00 Dbl/Twn	

Country house in residential area near town centre. Overlooking River Irvine and Clyde and Arran hills beyond.

TV 🎣 ☏ 🍴 P ☕ 🍷 ✕ 🍽 ℹ ♨ ♟

C 🐾 ⛱ V

VAT is shown at 17.5%: changes in this rate may affect prices. | **Key to symbols is on back flap.**

Irvine, Ayrshire　　　　　　　　　　　Map Ref: 1G6

★★

B&B

Mayfield Guest House
62 East Road, Irvine, Ayrshire, KA12 0BS
Tel: 01294 279045

1 Twin	1 Ensuite fac	B&B per person	Open Jan-Dec excl
1 Double	1 Pub Bath/Show	from £22.00 Twin	Xmas/New Year
		from £20.00 Double	Eve. meal Avail.

Traditional stone built house in residential area, close to the town centre.
Private parking. 8mls from Prestwick Airport.

Thistle Irvine
46 Annick Road, Irvine, Ayrshire, KA11 4LD
Tel: 01294 272272 Fax: 01294 277287
Web: www.thistlehotels.com

★★★★

HOTEL

&

52 Twin	All En Suite	B&B per person	Open Jan-Dec
76		from £49.00 Single	B&B + Eve.Meal
Dbl/Fam		from £40.00 Dbl/Twn	from £64.00
		Room only per person	
		from £40.00	

Modern hotel, convenient for Prestwick Airport. With conference and
banqueting facilities. Lagoon and swimming pool.

BRONZE

Isle of Whithorn, Wigtownshire　　　　　　Map Ref: 1H11

★

INN

The Steampacket Hotel
Harbour Row, Isle of Whithorn, Wigtownshire, DG8 8LL
Tel: 01988 500334 Fax: 01988 500627

1 Twin	All En Suite	B&B per person	Open Jan-Dec excl
3 Double		from £22.50 Single	Xmas/New Year
1 Family		from £22.50 Dbl/Twn	

Personally run, on harbour front. Sea fishing. Access to walks, birdwatching
and archaeological sites. Children and dogs welcome. Excellent value food
with the emphasis on fresh local seafood, meat and game. Separate
children's menu. Extensive wine list and range of malt whiskies. Real ales.
Traditional Sunday lunches and buffet. Lunches served 12-2pm. Bar meals
and restaurant 7-9.30pm. Conservatory and beer garden. No smoking
areas. Open fires.

Jedburgh, Roxburghshire　　　　　　　Map Ref: 2E7

★★★

HOTEL

Glenfriars Country House
The Friars, Jedburgh, Roxburghshire, TD8 6BN
Tel/Fax: 01835 862000
Web: member.visitscotland.com/glenfriarsjedburgh

2 Single	All En Suite	B&B per person	Open Jan-Dec excl
1 Twin		from £33.00 Single	Xmas
2 Double		from £29.50 Dbl/Twn	B&B + Eve.Meal
1 Family			from £50.50

Large Georgian house set above Jedburgh and centrally situated for
touring the Borders. Special deals available on short breaks. Some four
poster beds. All ensuite.

★★★★

HOTEL

Jedforest Hotel
Camptown, Jedburgh, TD8 6PJ
Tel: 01835 840222 Fax: 01835 840226
E-mail: mail@jedforesthotel.freeserve.co.uk
Web: www.jedforesthotel.freeserve.co.uk

2 Twin	All En Suite	B&B per person	Open Jan-Dec
6 Double		from £60.00 Single	B&B + Eve.Meal
		from £47.50 Dbl/Twn	from £67.50

First hotel in Scotland on A68 route. High quality accommodation. All
rooms en-suite. Taste of Scotland restaurant. Country setting, in 35 acres
of grounds with 1 mile of trout fishing on the Jed Water. Scottish
hospitality with a continental flavour.

Important: Prices stated are estimates and may be subject to amendments

Jedburgh, Roxburghshire

Map Ref: 2E7

★★★

GUEST
HOUSE

Meadhon House
48 Castlegate, Jedburgh, Roxburghshire, TD8 6BB
Tel/Fax: 01835 862504

16c building with panoramic views overlooking Jedburgh Abbey and Castle Jail. Spacious accommodation all ensuite, very close to town centre. Attractive landscaped garden. No children under twelve.

2 Double	All En Suite	B&B per person	Open Jan-Dec
3 Family		from £25.00 Single	
		from £20.00 Double	

★★★

GUEST
HOUSE

Willow Court
The Friars, Jedburgh, Roxburghshire, TD8 6BN
Tel: 01835 863702 Fax: 01835 864601

Set in 2 acres of garden above the town, with excellent views. Peaceful setting, yet close to all amenities including Abbey Castle and a good selection of restaurants. All rooms are either ensuite or with private bathroom or shower-room. Most rooms are on the ground floor.

1 Twin	3 En Suite fac	B&B per person	Open Jan-Dec
2 Double	1 Priv.NOT ensuite	from £25.00 Single	
1 Family		from £19.00 Dbl/Twn	
		Room only per person	
		from £18.00	

---

by Jedburgh, Roxburghshire

Map Ref: 2E7

★

GUEST
HOUSE

Ferniehirst Mill Lodge
by Jedburgh, Roxburghshire, TD8 6PQ
Tel/Fax: 01835 863279

Personally run, modern guest house, all rooms ensuite. Secluded riverside location, just two and a half miles South of Jedburgh. Haven for bird watchers and walkers. Specialists in home cooking using local produce. Trail riding centre.

1 Single	All En Suite	B&B per person	Open Jan-Dec
4 Twin	1 Pub Bath/Show	from £23.00 Single	B&B + Eve.Meal
3 Double		from £23.00 Dbl/Twn	from £37.00
1 Family		Room only per person	
		from £20.00	

Kelso, Roxburghshire

Map Ref: 2E6

★★★

HOTEL

Cross Keys Hotel
36-37 The Square, Kelso, Roxburghshire, TD5 7HL
Tel: 01573 223303 Fax: 01573 225792
Web: www.cross-keys-hotel.co.uk

One of Scotland's oldest coaching Inns, recently re-furbished to a high standard. Enjoying prominent position overlooking the cobbled Flemish style square. A la carte restaurant and Bistro specialising in both local and continental cuisine. 1999 winner of best eating place in the Borders.

4 Single	All En Suite	B&B per person	Open Jan-Dec excl
11 Twin		from £44.50 Single	Xmas
10 Double		from £29.90 Dbl/Twn	B&B + Eve.Meal
1 Family			from £41.90

★★★

GUEST
HOUSE

The Old Priory & Coach House
12 Abbey Row, Kelso, TD5 7JF
Tel: 01573 223030 Fax: 01573 228246
Web: http://home.btclick.com/borderhost/
oldpriory.html

18th Century coachhouse, set within large walled garden in the very heart of Kelso. Private parking. All rooms en-suite.

3 Twin	All En Suite	B&B per person	Open Mar-Nov
3 Double		from £32.50 Single	B&B + Eve.Meal
2 Family		from £22.50 Dbl/Twn	from £37.00

VAT is shown at 17.5%: changes in this rate may affect prices.

Key to symbols is on back flap.

by Kelso, Roxburghshire | Map Ref: 2E6

The Roxburghe
Hotel & Golf Course

HEITON, BY KELSO, ROXBURGHSHIRE TD5 8JZ
Tel: 01573 450331 Fax: 01573 450611
e.mail: hotel@roxburghe.net
Web: www.roxburghe.net

Majestically set in the Scottish Borders, The Roxburghe Hotel, under the careful ownership of The Duke and Duchess of Roxburghe, boasts superb cuisine and delightfully individual rooms. Open fires, oil paintings and four-poster beds, combined with attentive service, add to the unique atmosphere of The Roxburghe. One hour from Edinburgh and Newcastle, this luxury hotel stands in a beautiful 200-acre estate on the banks of the River Teviot. Facilities include an all-weather tennis court, croquet lawn, trout pond, shooting school, luxury beauty salon and 18-hole championship standard Roxburghe Golf Course designed by Dave Thomas.

★★★★

HOTEL

The Roxburghe Hotel & Golf Course
Heiton, by Kelso, Roxburghshire, TD5 8JZ
Tel: 01573 450331 Fax: 01573 450611
E.mail: hotel@roxburghe.net
Web: www.roxburghe.net

Country house hotel owned by the Duke And Duchess of Roxburghe. Set in two hundred acres of woodland and park. Log fires and fresh produce. Shooting school, fishing and eighteen hole championship golf course.

2 Single	All En Suite	B&B per person	Open Jan-Dec excl Xmas
7 Twin		from £120.00 Single	B&B + Eve.Meal
7 Double		from £60.00 Dbl/Twn	from £85.00
4 Family			

Kilmarnock, Ayrshire | Map Ref: 1G6

★★★★

GUEST
HOUSE

Burnside Hotel
18 London Road, Kilmarnock, Ayrshire, KA3 7AQ
Tel: 01563 522952 Fax: 01563 573381
E-mail: djd@burnsidehotel.co.uk
Web: www.burnsidehotel.co.uk

Early 19th century private hotel, conveniently located for town centre. Private parking. Opposite museum and art gallery. No pets.

3 Single	5 En Suite fac	B&B per person	Open Jan-Dec
3 Twin	3 Pub Bath/Show	from £25.00 Single	B&B + Eve.Meal
3 Double		from £23.00 Dbl/Twn	from £36.00
1 Family			

SILVER 🏅

★★

GUEST
HOUSE

Eriskay House
2 Dean Terrace, Kilmarnock, Ayrshire, KA3 1RJ
Tel: 01563 532061 Fax: 01563 544262
E-mail: eriskayhouse@hotmail.com

Detached villa conveniently situated on main bus route and close to Dean Park and Castle. Enclosed secure car park. Ideal base for touring Burns Country, Culzean Castle or taking the ferry to Arran.

2 Single	4 En Suite fac	B&B per person	Open Jan-Dec
3 Twin	1 Pub Bath/Show	from £15.00 Single	B&B + Eve.Meal
1 Double		from £15.00 Dbl/Twn	from £23.00
1 Family		Room only per person	
		from £15.00	

Important: Prices stated are estimates and may be subject to amendments

Kilmarnock, Ayrshire — Map Ref: 1G6

Fenwick Hotel
A77 Ayr Road, Fenwick, by Kilmarnock, Ayrshire, KA3 6AU
Tel: 01560 600478 Fax: 01560 600334
Web: www.fenwickhotel.co.uk

4 Single
14 Twin
10 Double
3 Family

All En Suite

B&B per person
£45.00-£72.00 Single
£25.00-£46.00 Sharing
Room only per person
£40.00-£65.00

Open Jan-Dec
B&B + Eve.Meal
£45.00 Sharing

In conservation village, half an hour from the Ayrshire coast and its championship golf courses. Seafood and game specialities. AA rosette for food.

nr Kilwinning, Ayrshire — Ref: 1G6

Montgreenan Mansion House Hotel
Montgreenan Estate, nr Kilwinning, Ayrshire, KA13 7QZ
Tel: 01294 557733 Fax: 01294 850397
Web: www.montgreenanhotel.com

2 Single
6 Twin
6 Double
3 Suites
4 Exec

All En Suite

B&B per person
from £50.00 Single
from £49.50 Double
Room only per person
from £40.00

Open Jan-Dec
B&B + Eve.Meal
from £65.00

Country house in 48 acres of garden. Near championship golf courses - Royal Troon, Old Prestwick and Turnberry. Tennis courts and 5 hole practice golf course. Billiard room. Ideal base for touring Burns Country, Arran and the isles. Extensive refurbishment in last 2 years.

Kirkbean, Dumfriesshire — Ref: 2B10

Cavens Country House Hotel
Kirkbean, Dumfriesshire, DG2 8AA
Tel: 01387 880234 Fax: 01387 880467
E-mail: enquiries@cavens-hotel.co.uk
Web: www.cavens-hotel.co.uk

4 Twin
4 Double

All En Suite

B&B per person
£35.00-£40.00 Single
£30.00-£35.00 Dbl/Twn

Open Jan-Dec
4 course dinner £18.50

Built by Robert Oswald, one of the Glasgow 'Tobacco Barons' who had close connections with Benjamin Franklin. Cavens offers comfortable, stylish accommodation and quality dining in a peaceful rural setting within 6 acres of mature gardens. Central base for exploring the picturesque villages of the Solway Firth.

Kirkcudbright — Map Ref: 2A10

Selkirk Arms Hotel
High Street, Kirkcudbright, DG6 4JG
Tel: 01557 330402 Fax: 01557 331639

3 Single
5 Twin
6 Double
2 Family

16 En Suite fac

B&B per person
from £62.00 Single
from £45.00 Dbl/Twn

Open Jan-Dec
B&B + Eve.Meal
£65.00-£75.00

Family run 18c hotel, in historic town, where Burns wrote the Selkirk Grace. New restaurant and Bistro serving Taste of Scotland menus. Real ales.

Kirk Yetholm, Roxburghshire — Map Ref: 2E7

Border Hotel
The Green, Kirk Yetholm, Kelso, Roxburghshire, TD5 8PQ
Tel: 01573 420237 Fax: 01573 420549
E-mail: theborderhotel@tinyonline.co.uk
Web: www.theborderhotel.co.uk

4 Double
1 Family

All En Suite

B&B per person
from £20.00 Single
from £25.00 Double

Open Jan-Dec
B&B + Eve.Meal
from £35.00

Famous Border hotel ideally situated for both St Cuthbert's and Pennine Way walkers. Quality accommodation, with meals available lunchtimes and evenings.

Langholm, Dumfriesshire — Map Ref: 2D9

★★★

INN

The Reivers Rest
81 High Street, Langholm, Dumfriesshire, DG13 0DJ
Tel: 013873 81343
E-mail: paul@reivers-rest.demon.co.uk

Small family run Inn. Centre of the historic Borders town of Langholm.
Personally managed by the proprietors Paul and Betty Hayhoe. There is
always a warm welcome and the very best in Borders hospitality, locally
brewed real ale, extensive wine list, innovative, informal menu using fresh
local produce wherever possible. Open fire. Ample public car parking in
the immediate vicinity. The area is steeped in history and there is plenty to
see and do.

2 Twin	All En Suite	B&B per person
3 Double		£32.00-£34.00 Single
		£26.00-£28.00 Dbl/Twn

Open Jan-Dec
B&B + Eve.Meal
from £35.00

Largs, Ayrshire — Map Ref: 1F5

★★

GUEST
HOUSE

Carlton Guest House
10 Aubery Crescent, Largs, Ayrshire, KA30 8PR
Tel: 01475 672313 Fax: 01475 676128
E-mail: carlton.guesthouse@usa.net
Web: www.carltonguesthouse.com

On a quiet cul de sac on Largs promenade with full views to the ferries
and the islands. Lounge with superb views situated on the first floor, has
satellite T.V.

1 Single	1 En Suite fac	B&B per person
1 Twin		from £17.00 Single
1 Double		from £17.00 Dbl/Twn
1 Family		

Open Jan-Dec

★★★★

B&B

Stonehaven Guest House
8 Netherpark Crescent, off Routenburn Road, Largs, KA30 8QB
Tel: 01475 673319
E-mail: stonehaven.martin@virgin.net

Situated in quiet residential area in front of Routenburn Golf Course,
overlooking the Largs Bay, Isle of Cumbrae with the Isle of Arran and Ailsa
Craig in the distance.

1 Single	1 En Suite fac	B&B per person
1 Twin	1 Pub Bath/Show	from £20.00 Single
1 Double		from £23.00 Dbl/Twn

Open Jan-Dec excl
Xmas/New Year

★★★

HOTEL

Willow Bank Hotel
96 Greenock Road, Largs, Ayrshire, KA30 8PG
Tel: 01475 672311/675435 Fax: 01475 672311

Modern hotel offering bedrooms on ground floor and 1st floor only, in
tree-lined location on edge of town. Mid week and weekend
entertainment. Bar meals, high teas and dinner available daily.

2 Single	All En Suite	B&B per person
15 Twin		£50.00-£60.00 Single
9 Double		£40.00-£50.00 Dbl/Twn
3 Family		

Open Jan-Dec

Lauder, Berwickshire — Map Ref: 2D6

★★

SMALL
HOTEL

Black Bull Hotel
3 Market Place, Lauder, Berwickshire, TD2 6SR
Tel: 01578 722208 Fax: 01578 722419
E-mail: blackbullhotel@hotmail.com

Historic Coaching Inn circa 1500, traditionally furnished retaining its old
world charm. In village centre on the A68 , only 25 miles south of
Edinburgh centre.

6 Single	5 En Suite fac	B&B per person
2 Double	1 Pub Bath/Show	from £25.00 Single
1 Family		from £20.00 Dbl/Twn

Open Jan-Dec

Important: Prices stated are estimates and may be subject to amendments

Lauder, Berwickshire

Map Ref: 2D6

★★★★

SMALL
HOTEL

The Lodge, Carfraemill
Lauder, Berwickshire, TD2 6RA
Tel: 01578 750750 Fax: 01578 750751
Web: www.carfraemill.co.uk

2 Twin	All En Suite	B&B per person	Open Jan-Dec
6 Double		from £48.00 Single	B&B + Eve.Meal
2 Family		from £35.00 Dbl/Twn	from £50.00

Delightful country lodge situated at the junction of the A68/A697 – perfect for touring the Scottish Borders and visiting Edinburgh. Excellent food and accommodation.

Lockerbie, Dumfriesshire

Map Ref: 2C9

The Dryfesdale Country House Hotel

Dryfebridge, Lockerbie, Dumfriesshire DG11 2SF
Tel: 01576 202427 Fax: 01576 204187
e.mail: reception@DryfesdaleHotel.co.uk

A relaxing family run hotel only 4 minutes drive and clearly seen from J17 of the M74. The hotel nestles in an elevated position with superb views over rolling countryside. The bedrooms are all luxurious and well-equipped. Our award winning rosetted restaurant looks forward to welcoming you.

★★★

HOTEL

Dryfesdale Hotel
Lockerbie, Dumfriesshire, DG11 2SF
Tel: 01576 202427 Fax: 01576 204187
E.mail: reception@DryfesdaleHotel.co.uk

4 Single	All En Suite	B&B per person	Open Jan-Dec
5 Twin		£55.00-£65.00 Single	
5 Double		£84.00-£87.00 Dbl/Twn	
1 Family		Room only per person	
		£46.00-£56.00	

Family run country house in 5 acres of ground, yet close to M74. Interesting menu serving fresh local produce. Ideal for business or pleasure. Ground floor rooms available and all rooms en-suite.

★

HOTEL

Lockerbie Manor Country Hotel
Boreland Road, Lockerbie, Dumfriesshire, DG11 2RG
Tel: 01576 202610/203939 Fax: 01576 203046

7 Single	All En Suite	B&B per person	Open Jan-Dec
8 Twin		£40.00-£75.00 Single	
12 Double		£30.00-£49.00 Dbl/Twn	
1 Family		Room only per person	
		£26.00-£51.50	

Am impressive Georgian mansion house (circa 1814) in 78 acres of grounds offering comfortable accommodation in a secluded and peaceful setting. Approx 1 km north east of Lockerbie.

★★

HOTEL

Ravenshill House Hotel
12 Dumfries Road, Lockerbie, Dumfriesshire, DG11 2EF
Tel/Fax: 01576 202882
E-mail: Ravenshillhouse.hotel@virgin.net

3 Twin	7 En Suite fac	B&B per person	Open Jan-Dec excl
3 Double	1 Priv.NOT ensuite	£25.00-£35.00 Single	Xmas/New Year
2 Family		£22.50-£25.00 Dbl/Twn	B&B + Eve.Meal
		Room only per person	from £32.00
		from £20.00	

A family run hotel set in 2.5 acres of garden in a quiet residential area, yet convenient for town centre and M6/M74. With a chef proprietor the hotel enjoys a reputation for good food, comfortable accommodation and friendly service. Weekend, short and golfing breaks.

VAT is shown at 17.5%: changes in this rate may affect prices.

Key to symbols is on back flap.

Lockerbie, Dumfriesshire — Map Ref: 2C9

★★★

GUEST
HOUSE

Rosehill Guest House
9 Carlisle Road, Lockerbie, Dumfriesshire,
DG11 2DR
Tel/Fax: 01576 202378

1 Single	3 En Suite fac	B&B per person	Open Jan-Dec excl
2 Twin	2 Priv.NOT ensuite	£18.00-£20.00 Single	Xmas/New Year
1 Double		£18.00-£20.00 Dbl/Twn	
1 Family		Room only per person	
		£16.00-£18.00	

Family guest house in residential area, 5 minutes walk from town centre.
Ample car parking. Walking distance for a choice of restaurants

---

★★★

HOTEL

Somerton House Hotel
Carlisle Road, Lockerbie, Dumfriesshire, DG11 2DR
Tel: 01576 202583/202384 Fax: 01576 204218
E-mail: somerton@somerton.co.uk
Web: www.somertonhotel.co.uk

1 Single	All En Suite	B&B per person	Open Jan-Dec
2 Twin		from £41.00 Single	
6 Double		from £25.00 Dbl/Twn	
2 Family		Room only per person	
		from £20.00	

Sandstone, Victorian building standing in one acre of grounds. Comfortable
accommodation and excellent food. Taste of Scotland member. Some
rooms annexed.

Melrose, Roxburghshire — Map Ref: 2D6

★★★★

SMALL
HOTEL

Burts Hotel
Market Square, Melrose, Scottish Borders, TD6 9PL
Tel: 01896 822285 Fax: 01896 822870
Web: www.burtshotel.co.uk

7 Single	All En Suite	B&B per person	Open Jan-Dec
9 Twin		from £52.00 Single	B&B + Eve.Meal
4 Double		from £46.00 Dbl/Twn	from £65.00

Family owned and run town house hotel in the heart of the Scottish
Borders specialising in imaginative food in award winning Taste of
Scotland restaurant. Scottish Borders chef of the year 2000.

★★★★

GUEST
HOUSE

Dunfermline House
Buccleuch Street, Melrose, TD6 9LB
Tel/Fax: 01896 822148
E-mail: bestaccom@dunmel.freeserve.co.uk
Web: www.dunmel.freeserve.co.uk

1 Single	4 En Suite fac	B&B per person	Open Jan-Dec
2 Twin	1 Priv.NOT ensuite	from £23.00 Single	
2 Double		from £23.00 Dbl/Twn	

Overlooking Melrose Abbey. A highly respected and well established guest
house offering very high standards. All rooms (except one) with en-suite
facilities, the single room has a private bathroom. Traditional Scottish
breakfasts with interesting variations. Non-smoking house.

BRONZE

Melrose, Roxburghshire

Map Ref: 2D6

THE GEORGE & ABBOTSFORD HOTEL
HIGH STREET, MELROSE TD6 9PD
Tel: 01896 822308 Fax: 01896 823363
e.mail: enquiries@georgeandabbotsford.co.uk
Web: www.georgeandabbotsford.co.uk

Set in the heart of the Scottish Borders, we have 30 en-suite bedrooms,
comfortable bar and dining room. Table d'hote and bar meals served daily
offering the finest of local ingredients. Activity holiday packages can all be
tailored to requirements. (Golf, salmon and trout fishing, walking and cycling).

★★

HOTEL

The George & Abbotsford Hotel
High Street, Melrose, Roxburghshire, TD6 9PD
Tel: 01896 822308 Fax: 01896 823363
E.mail: enquiries@georgeandabbotsford.co.uk
Web: www.georgeandabbotsford.co.uk

Former coaching inn, of character in the centre of town, with large car
park to the rear. Close to Abbey and River Walks. All rooms en-suite.
Full restaurant as well as spacious bar offering a good range of meals.

6 Single	All En Suite	B&B per person	Open Jan-Dec
13 Twin		from £30.00 Single	B&B + Eve.Meal
8 Double		from £30.00 Dbl/Twn	from £45.00
3 Family			

★★★

INN

Kings Arms Hotel
High Street, Melrose, Roxburghshire, TD6 9PB
Tel: 01896 822143 Fax: 01896 823812
E-mail: enquiries@kingsarmsmelrose.co.uk

Former coaching Inn dating back some 300 years, in centre of historic
Border town. Cosy lounge bar with open fires.

1 Twin	All En Suite	B&B per person	Open Jan-Dec
3 Single	Suite available	from £37.50 Single	
1 Double		from £28.75 Dbl/Twn	
2 Family			

★★★

SMALL HOTEL

Millars Hotel
Market Square, Melrose, Roxburghshire, TD6 9PQ
Tel: 01896 822645 Fax: 01896 823474

Situated in heart of historic Borders town, this delightful family run hotel
offers excellent food and wines and best local produce. 10 well-appointed
bedrooms. Ideally located for fishers, walkers and cyclists (facilities
available). Direct access to St Cuthberts and Southern Upland Ways.

1 Twin	All En Suite	B&B per person	Open Jan-Dec
7 Double		from £45.50 Single	B&B + Eve.Meal
1 Family		from £37.50 Dbl/Twn	from £54.00
1 Four Poster			

---

by Melrose, Roxburghshire

Map Ref: 2D6

★★★★

B&B

Whitehouse
St Boswells, Melrose, Roxburghshire, TD6 0ED
Tel: 01573 460343 Fax: 01573 460361
E-mail: angela.whitehouse@bun.com

Spacious former Dower house, decorated to a high standard. Full of
character, relaxed atmosphere, log fires, home cooked dinners, baking
and preserves. Kelso Dryburgh and Melrose within 10 minuites.

2 Twin	All En Suite	B&B per person	Open Jan-Dec
1 Double		from £27.00 Dbl/Twn	B&B + Eve.Meal
			from £47.00

VAT is shown at 17.5%: changes in this rate may affect prices.

Key to symbols is on back flap.

Moffat, Dumfriesshire   Map Ref: 2B8

INN ★

Allanton Hotel
20-22 High Street, Moffat, Dumfriesshire, DG10 9HL
Tel: 01683 220343 Fax: 01683 220914

1 Single	3 En Suite fac
4 Double	2 Pub Bath/Show
2 Family	

B&B per person
from £30.00 Single
from £20.00 Double
Room only per person
from £20.00

Open Jan-Dec
B&B + Eve.Meal
from £27.00

Small family owned hotel situated within Moffat town centre and close to all amenities. Pleasant service, good food.

HOTEL ★★

Annandale Arms Hotel
High Street, Moffat, Dumfriesshire, DG10 9HF
Tel: 01683 220013 Fax: 01683 221395
E-mail: Reception@AnnandaleArmsHotel.co.uk
Web: www.AnnandaleArmsHotel.co.uk

1 Single	All En Suite
4 Twin	
4 Double	
2 Family	

B&B per person
from £45.00 Single
from £35.00 Dbl/Twn

Open Jan-Dec excl
Xmas and Boxing Day

Award winning two hundred and forty year old former Coaching Inn located in the centre of Moffat. Privately owned, chef proprietor uses fresh local produce. Many outdoor sporting activities available locally, excellent walking in the lovely unspoilt countryside. Large car park.

GUEST HOUSE ★★

Barnhill Springs Country Guest House
Moffat, Dumfriesshire, DG10 9QS
Tel: 01683 220580

2 Twin	1 Priv.NOT ensuite
2 Double	2 Pub Bath/Show
1 Family	

B&B per person
from £22.00 Single
from £22.00 Dbl/Twn

Open Jan-Dec
B&B + Eve.Meal
from £36.00

Barnhill Springs is an early victorian country house standing in its own grounds overlooking upper Annandale. It is a quiet family run guest house situated 1/2 a mile from the A74/M at the Moffat junction no.15. Barnhill Springs is ideally situated as a centre for touring Southern Scotland, for walking and cycling on the Southern Upland Way or for a relaxing overnight stop for holiday makers heading North or South. AA 3 Diamonds.

HOTEL ★★

The Famous Star Hotel
44 High Street, Moffat, Dumfriesshire, DG10 9EF
Tel: 01683 220156 Fax: 01683 221524
E-mail: info@famousstarhotel.com
Web: www.famousstarhotel.com

3 Twin	All En Suite
4 Double	
1 Family	

B&B per person
from £40.00 Single
from £28.00 Dbl/Twn

Open Jan-Dec
B&B + Eve.Meal
from £52.00

A warm welcome is assured at this family run hotel in the centre of the popular Border town of Moffat. As the narrowest hotel in the United Kingdom, it is featured in the Guiness Book of Records. Popular with golfers.

GUEST HOUSE ★★★★

Hartfell House
Hartfell Crescent, Moffat, Dumfriesshire, DG10 9AL
Tel: 01683 220153
E-mail: robert.white@virgin.net
Web: http://freespace.virgin.net/robert.white/

1 Single	7 En Suite fac
1 Twin	1 Priv. fac
4 Double	
2 Family	

B&B per person
£25.00 Single
£23.00 Dbl/Twn

Open Jan-Dec excl
Xmas/New Year
B&B + Eve.Meal
from £35.50

Family run, in rural setting, within walking distance of the town centre. Large, well maintained garden and fine views. Evening meals by prior arrangement.

Important: Prices stated are estimates and may be subject to amendments

Moffat, Dumfriesshire   Map Ref: 2B8

Moffat House Hotel
High Street, Moffat, Dumfriesshire, DG10 9HL
Tel: 01683 220039 Fax: 01683 221288
Web: www.moffathouse.co.uk

3 Single	All En Suite	B&B per person	Open Jan-Dec
8 Twin		£45.00-£60.00 Single	Evening Meal
9 Double		£70.00-£90.00 Dbl/Twn	£17.00-£22.00
1 Family			

18c Adam mansion with magnificent staircase, set in own grounds with country views to rear, yet in the centre of the award winning 'Scotland in Bloom' village of Moffat. All rooms en suite, ground floor rooms available including a self contained cottage. Lounge food plus fine dining in Hopetown's Restaurant.

Morlich House
Ballplay Road, Moffat, Dumfriesshire, DG10 9JU
Tel: 01683 220589 Fax: 01683 221032
Web: www.morlich-house.ndirect.co.uk

1 Single	4 En Suite fac	B&B per person	Open Feb-Nov
1 Twin	1 Priv.NOT ensuite	from £19.00 Single	B&B + Eve.Meal
2 Double		from £20.00 Dbl/Twn	from £28.50
1 Family			

Small family run guest house set in 1/2 acre of mature grounds, in quite a secluded area, yet only 5 minutes walk from town centre. Ideal base for touring, hill walking, riding and bird-watching. Warm friendly atmosphere. Laundry facilities.

Rockhill Guest House
14 Beechgrove, Moffat, Dumfriesshire, DG10 9RS
Tel: 01683 220283
Web: www.moffatown.com/moffat/accommodation

2 Single	5 En Suite fac	B&B per person	Open Jan-Nov
1 Twin	2 Pub Bath/Show	£17.00-£21.00 Single	B&B + Eve.Meal
3 Double		£17.00-£21.00 Dbl/Twn	£26.00-£30.00
4 Family			

Victorian house overlooking bowling green and park, in quiet area close to town centre. Open outlook to hills. Own private carpark. Ensuite rooms; some rooms with colour television. Pets welcome by arrangement. Evening meals available also by prior arrangement.

Well View Hotel
Ballplay Road, Moffat, Dumfriesshire, DG10 9JU
Tel: 01683 220184 Fax: 01683 220088
Web: www.wellview.co.uk

2 Twin	All En Suite	B&B per person	Open Jan-Dec
4 Double		from £53.00 Single	B&B + Eve.Meal
		from £36.00 Dbl/Twn	from £64.00

Mid Victorian house converted to comfortable, family run hotel. Overlooking town and surrounding hills, with its own large garden. Innovative and original use of fresh local ingredients, in our attractive award winning restaurant.

Moniaive, Dumfriesshire   Map Ref: 2A9

Woodlea Hotel
Moniaive, Dumfriesshire, DG3 4EN
Tel: 01848 200209
E-mail: robin@woodlea43.freeserve.co.uk

1 Single	11 En Suite fac	B&B per person	Open Apr-Oct
3 Dbl/Twn		from £26.00 Single	B&B + Eve.Meal
8 Family		from £26.00 Dbl/Twn	from £41.00 pp

Friendly country hotel with indoor swimming pool, sauna, bowls, putting, croquet, tennis, badminton, clay pigeon shooting, bikes, golf, horse riding and sailing available close by.

VAT is shown at 17.5%: changes in this rate may affect prices.   Key to symbols is on back flap.

Monkton, by Prestwick, Ayrshire   Map Ref: 1G7

★★★

HOTEL

Manor Park Hotel
48 Kilmarnock Road, Monkton, KA9 2RJ
Tel/Fax: 01292 479365

12 Single	All En Suite	B&B per person	Open Jan-Dec
4 Twin		from £65.00 Single	B&B + Eve.Meal
7 Double		£45.00-£55.00 Dbl/Twn	from £45.00
1 Family		Room only per person	
		from £65.00	

This early 20th century hotel in rural setting has been completely
refurbished and is personally managed by the chef/proprietor. The
bedrooms are individually furnished and guests have a choice of dining in
the conservatory or in the more formal dining room. Convenient for
Prestwick Airport and the many famous local golf courses.

TV ℃ 🛏 P 🍷 🍴 🛈 🎾 ❢

C ♨ W V

Newcastleton, Roxburghshire   Map Ref: 2D9

★★

SMALL
HOTEL

The Liddlesdale Hotel
Douglass Square, Newcastleton, TD9 0QD
Tel: 013873 75255 Fax: 013873 75569

2 Twin	All En Suite	B&B per person	Open Jan-Dec
2 Double		from £28.00 Single	
1 Family		from £25.00 Dbl/Twn	

Family run, 18C coaching Inn, situated in main Square of attractive
village. Central for Borders sightseeing; scenic route to Edinburgh.

TV 🛏 🍷 ✕ 🍴 ❢

C 🐕 ♨ V

New Galloway, Kirkcudbrightshire   Map Ref: 1H9

AWAITING
INSPECTION

Leamington House Hotel
High Street, New Galloway, Castle Douglas,
Kirkcudbrightshire, DG7 3RN
Tel: 01644 420327 Fax: 01644 420778
E-mail: leamington@newgalloway.fsnet.co.uk
Web: www.leamington-hotel.com

1 Single	5 En Suite fac	B&B per person	Open Jan-Dec
1 Twin	2 Limited ensuite	£18.50-£20.00 Single	
3 Double		£20.00-£22.50 Dbl/Twn	
2 Family		£55.00-£60.00 Family	

Enjoy the warmest welcome at this 18thc family run hotel. Evening meals
available. Unspoiled scenic beauty The Galloway Forest Park which is
popular with walkers, cyclists and bird-watchers is just 5 minutes away.
New Galloway is ideally situated for excursions or sporting activities such
as golf, fishing and sailing. Private courtyard and parking. Pets welcome.

🐕 ♨ V

Newton Stewart, Wigtownshire   Map Ref: 1G10

Creebridge House Hotel
Newton Stewart, Dumfries and Galloway DG8 6NP
Tel: 01671 402121   Fax: 01671 403258
e.mail: info@creebridge.co.uk   Web: www.creebridge.co.uk

Country house hotel with award-winning cuisine. 19 bedrooms, choice
of two restaurants, log fires, elegant public lounges. Ideal base for
exploring the south west of Scotland. Golf, salmon fishing, walking,
mountain biking all arranged. Come and unwind, slow down and enjoy
our renowned hospitality at an unhurried pace.

★★★

HOTEL

Creebridge House Hotel
Newton Stewart, Wigtownshire, DG8 6NP
Tel: 01671 402121 Fax: 01671 403258
E-mail: info@creebridge.co.uk
Web: www.creebridge.co.uk

2 Single	All En Suite	B&B per person	Open Jan-Dec
8 Twin	Suites avail	£49.50-£59.50 Single	B&B + Eve.Meal
5 Double		£39.50-£49.50 Dbl/Twn	£55.00-£70.00
4 Family			

Traditional Scottish country house hotel, offering modern comforts, situated in 3
acres of gardens, yet close to town centre. Relax in the elegant lounges with log
fires in winter. Chef Proprietor Chris Walker and his team produce innovative
meals in either the Brasserie or the Restaurant using fresh, local produce when
available. Ideal base for golfers and walkers with Galloway Forrest nearby.
CAMRA Good Beer Guide. Taste of Scotland.

TV 🎣 ℃ 🛏 P 🍷 🦮 🍴 🛈 🎾 ❢

C 🐕 ♨ W V

Important: Prices stated are estimates and may be subject to amendments

Newton Stewart, Wigtownshire   Map Ref: 1G10

★★★

GUEST
HOUSE

Flowerbank Guest House
**Millcroft Road, Minnigaff, Newton Stewart,
Wigtownshire, DG8 6PJ
Tel: 01671 402629**

Geoff and Linda Inker welcome you to Flowerbank, a charming 18th century house where the River Cree runs alongside our 1 acre landscaped gardens, just 1/2 mile from Newton Stewart. Warm, comfortable, non-smoking accommodation with colour TVs, tea/coffee, lounge with log fire and ample parking. Spacious dining room, separate tables, good home cooking. Quiet and friendly - a warm welcome awaits you.

1 Twin	4 En Suite fac	B&B per person	Open Jan-Dec excl
2 Double	1 Priv.NOT ensuite	from £18.50 Dbl/Twn	Xmas/New Year
2 Family			B&B + Eve.Meal
			from £28.50

★

HOTEL

Galloway Arms Hotel
**54/58 Victoria Street, Newton Stewart,
Wigtownshire, DG8 6DB
Tel/Fax: 01671 402653
E-mail: gordon@gallowayarmshotel.Freeserve.co.uk
Web: www.gallowayarms.co.uk**

Old coaching inn, being totally refurbished and greatly enlarged with the purchase of the building next door. Situated in centre of town. Bar, lounge, coffee shop and RAC dining award restaurant.

6 Single	17 En Suite fac	B&B per person	Open Jan-Dec
5 Twin	1 Pub Bath	£25.00-£27.50 Single	B&B + Eve.Meal
5 Double		£25.00-£27.50 Dbl/Twn	£37.50-£39.00
2 Family			

Alex - Moira Jackson
**Duncree House, Girvan Road, Newton Stewart,
Wigtownshire, DG8 6DP
Tel/Fax: 01671 402792**

★★

GUEST
HOUSE

Stone built former Dower House dating from 1850's with 2 acres of mature gardens, peacefully situated on the edge of town, where there is a good choice of eating establishments. Centrally situated for exploring the south west of Scotland. There are several good gardens, hill and forest walks, cycling, birdwatching and several golf courses readily available.

1 Single	4 En Suite fac	B&B per person	Open Jan-Dec
2 Twin	1 Priv.NOT ensuite	from £18.50 Single	
1 Double	1 Pub Bath/Show	£20.00 Dbl/Twn	
2 suitable		Room only per person	
family/double/		from £14.00	
single			

Peebles   Map Ref: 2C6

★★★★

HOTEL

Castle Venlaw Hotel
**Edinburgh Road, Peebles, EH45 8QG
Tel: 01721 720384 Fax: 01721 724066
E-mail: enquiries@venlaw.co.uk
Web: www.venlaw.co.uk**

Family owned, fully refurbished baronial castle overlooking Peebles and the Moorfoot Hills. Large rooms with spectacular views, oak panelled library and 4 acres of wooded grounds.

2 Single	All En Suite	B&B per person	Open Jan-Dec
2 Twin		from £65.00 Single	B&B + Eve.Meal
4 Double		from £55.00 Dbl/Twn	from £65.00
2 Family			

★★★★

HOTEL

Cringletie House Hotel
**Eddleston, Peebles, Peebles-shire, EH45 8PL
Tel: 01721 730233 Fax: 01721 730244
E-mail: enquiries@cringletie.com
Web: www.cringletie.com
A member of the Wren's Group**

Stunning baronial mansion set in 28 acres of grounds and woodland. Only 2 miles from picturesque market town of Peebles and 30 minutes from Edinburgh. Sublime cuisine and attentive service in a relaxed environment.

1 Single	All En Suite	B&B per person	Open Jan-Dec
8 Twin		£70.00-£75.00 Single	B&B + Eve.Meal
4 Double		£75.00-£90.00 Dbl/Twn	£90.00-£98.00
1 Family			

VAT is shown at 17.5%: changes in this rate may affect prices.

Key to symbols is on back flap.

Peebles			Map Ref: 2C6	

Glentress Hotel & Country Inn
Kirnlaw, Peebles, EH45 8NB
Tel/Fax: 01721 720100

AWAITING INSPECTION

A friendly privately owned hotel under the personal supervision of the owners. Handily situated on the A72 2 miles from Peebles, 25 miles from Edinburgh, The Glentress is the idyllic place to escape the rigours of city life. Set among the mills of the Scottish borders next to The Glentress Forest it offers easy access for fishing, walking, tour mountain biking, cyclists or just a relaxing break. The restaurant offers an excellent choice of foods from a varied menu using local produce whenever possible. It is well frequented by the locals.

3 Twin	All En Suite	B&B per person	Open Jan-Dec
6 Double		£30.00 Single	B&B + Eve.Meal
1 Family		£28.00 Dbl/Twn	from £38.00
		£60.00 Family	

Kingsmuir Hotel

SPRINGHILL ROAD, PEEBLES, BORDERS EH45 9EP
Telephone: 01721 720151   Fax: 01721 721795   ★★★ HOTEL
e.mail: chrisburn@kingsmuir.scotborders.co.uk
Web: www.scotborders.co.uk/kingsmuir

Kingsmuir is a charming 1850's style country mansion in leafy grounds. Resident proprietors specialise in traditional Scottish cooking and have won many awards. All bedrooms are tastefully decorated with private bathrooms, TV and telephone. Peebles is a Royal and Ancient Burgh famous for Tweeds and Woollens, golf, fishing, walking and mountain biking.

★★★

HOTEL

Kingsmuir Hotel
Springhill Road, Peebles, EH45 9EP
Tel: 01721 720151 Fax: 01721 721795
E-mail: chrisburn@kingsmuir.scotborders.co.uk
Web: www.scotborders.co.uk/kingsmuir

A 19c mansion in its own grounds with ample parking, situated in a quiet corner of Peebles near the River Tweed. A warm welcome and friendly service are a feature of this personally run hotel. Restaurant and bar meals available.

2 Single	All En Suite	B&B per person	Open Jan-Dec
4 Twin		£36.00-£44.00 Single	B&B + Eve.Meal
3 Double		£32.00-£38.00 Dbl/Twn	£43.00-£55.00
1 Family			

★★★

HOTEL

The Park Hotel
Innerleithen Road, Peebles, EH45 8BA
Tel: 01721 720451 Fax: 01721 723510
E-mail: reserve@parkpeebles.co.uk

Quiet and comfortable, with extensive gardens and fine hill views. Ideal touring centre, and only 22 miles (35kms) from Edinburgh.

4 Single	All En Suite	B&B per person	Open Jan-Dec
10 Twin		from £54.00 Single	B&B + Eve.Meal
10 Double		from £48.00 Dbl/Twn	from £64.00

Portpatrick, Wigtownshire			Map Ref: 1F10	

★★

GUEST HOUSE

Braefield Guest House
Portpatrick, Wigtownshire, DG9 8TA
Tel: 01776 810255

A warm friendly welcome awaits you at Braefield Guest House, which is a large detached Victorian house in an excellent position overlooking the harbour, with extensive sea views. A short walk takes you to the centre of the village with its variety of eating places, bowling and putting greens and tennis courts, 100 yds from the golf course.

1 Single	5 En Suite fac	B&B per person	Open Jan-Dec
2 Twin	2 Priv.NOT ensuite	from £20.00 Single	
4 Double	1 Pub Bath/Show	from £21.00 Dbl/Twn	
1 Family			

Important: Prices stated are estimates and may be subject to amendments

Portpatrick, Wigtownshire — Map Ref: 1F10

HOTEL ★★

Downshire Arms Hotel
Main Street, Portpatrick, Wigtownshire, DG9 8JJ
Tel: 01776 810300 Fax: 01776 810620
E-mail: info@downshire-arms-hotel.co.uk
Web: www.downshire-arms-hotel.co.uk

This family run hotel is conveniently situated only 75 yards from the sea front of this picturesque harbour village. Shops and amenities nearby. Fully refurbished public areas and bedrooms for the 2000 season. Most bedrooms have sea views. With a chef/proprietor the hotel offers a choice of menus using fresh local produce when available. Friendly Scottish hospitality. CAMRA Good Beer Guide. Golf parties our speciality.

3 Single	13 En Suite fac
11 Twin	3 Priv.NOT ensuite
7 Double	4 Pub Bath/Show
2 Family	

B&B per person
from £28.00 Single
from £30.00 Dbl/Twn
Room only per person
from £25.00

Open Jan-Dec excl Xmas
B&B + Eve.Meal
from £45.00

SMALL HOTEL ★★★★★

Knockinaam Lodge
Portpatrick, Wigtownshire, DG9 9AD
Tel: 01776 810471 Fax; 01776 810435
E-mail: reservations@knockinaamlodge.com

Situated at the waters edge, this small and unique country house enjoys one of Scotland's most romantic settings. Guests can marvel at the changing sea views, relax in the comfortable lounges with log fires in winter, or savour the proprietors famous and vast collection of single malt whiskies. To complement the international cuisine using the finest fresh ingredients. The wine list has over 500 varieties.

1 Single	All Ensuite
2 Twin	
7 Double	

D.B&B per person
£105.00-£140.00 Sgl
£85.00-£165.00 Dbl

Open Jan-Dec

HOTEL ★★

Torrs Warren Hotel
Stoneykirk, Stranraer, Wigtownshire, DG9 9DH
Tel: 01776 830204 Fax: 01776 830298
Web: www.torrswarren.co.uk

Friendly, family run Country House Hotel on the edge of small rural Village, 5 miles from Stranraer and the Ferry Terminal to Ireland. You will be made most welcome, whether you are staying to enjoy golf, sea angling or a relaxing short break.

1 Single	All En Suite
1 Twin	
3 Double	
1 Family	

B&B per person
from £28.00 Single
from £24.00 Dbl/Twn
Room only per person
from £19.50

Open Jan-Dec
B&B + Eve.Meal
from £34.00

---

by Port William, Wigtownshire — Map Ref: 1G11

HOTEL ★★★★

Corsemalzie House Hotel
Port William, Wigtownshire, DG8 9RL
Tel: 01988 860254 Fax: 01988 860213
E-mail: corsemalzie@ndirect.co.uk
Web: www.corsemalzie-house.ltd.uk

Victorian country mansion set in 40 acres of parkland with its own small burn, The Malzie Burn within the garden and woodland walks. Corsemalzie has its own fishing on both river and loch. Fresh game from the estate and fresh vegetables from kitchen garden.

6 Twin	All En Suite
6 Double	
2 Family	

B&B per person
£39.00-£63.00 Single
£39.00-£49.00 Dbl/Twn

Open Mar-Jan
B&B + Eve.Meal
£49.50-£67.50

VAT is shown at 17.5%: changes in this rate may affect prices.

Key to symbols is on back flap.

Powfoot, by Annan, Dumfriesshire   Map Ref: 2C10

POWFOOT HOTEL

POWFOOT, ANNAN, DUMFRIESSHIRE DG12 5PN
TEL: 01461 700254 FAX: 01461 700288
E.MAIL: info@powfoothotel.co.uk WEB: www.powfoothotel.co.uk

Endless beaches, panoramic sea and mountain views, sunsets together with its unique coastal location make Powfoot special. Cooking is from local produce with an emphasis on seafood. Roaring log fires and caring attentive staff will ensure that your stay in our family owned and managed Victorian hotel is memorable.

★★

HOTEL

The Powfoot Hotel
Powfoot, nr Annan, Dunfriesshire, DG12 5PN
Tel: 01461 700254 Fax: 01461 700288
E-mail: info@powfoothotel.co.uk
Web: www.powfoothotel.co.uk

Privately owned Hotel in peaceful village on the shore of the Solway Firth with South-facing views to Cumbria and Lake District Hills. Situated adjacent to 18-hole Golf Course - golfing packages can be arranged. Activity Breaks include watercolour painting & fishing.

12 Twin	All En Suite	B&B per person	Open Jan-Dec
5 Double		from £55.00 Single	B&B + Eve.Meal
1 Family		from £37.00 Dbl/Twn	from £47.50

Prestwick, Ayrshire   Map Ref: 1G7

GUEST
HOUSE

★★★★

The Fairways
19 Links Road, Prestwick, Ayrshire, KA9 1QG
Tel/Fax: 01292 470396
E-mail: anne@thefairways.co.uk
Web: www.thefairways.co.uk

Impressive Victorian house with private parking in quiet location overlooking Prestwick Golf Course. Close to town centre amenities, railway station and Prestwick International Airport.

2 Single	4 En Suite fac	B&B per person	Open Jan-Dec excl
2 Twin	1 Priv.NOT ensuite	£30.00 Twin/Single	Xmas/New Year
1 Dbl/Twn			

Bronze

GUEST
HOUSE

★★★

Fernbank Guest House
213 Main Street, Prestwick, Ayrshire, KA9 1LH
Tel/Fax: 01292 475027/01292 678944
E-mail: bandb@fernbank.co.uk

Modernised Edwardian villa near beach and local sports facilities, close to many golf courses including Troon and Prestwick. 1 mile (2kms) from Prestwick airport. 0.5 mile from Centrum Arena.

2 Single	5 En Suite fac	B&B per person	Open Jan-Dec
3 Twin	1 Priv.NOT ensuite	£18.00-£23.00 Single	
1 Fam/Dbl		from £18.50 Dbl/Twn	
		Room only per person	
		£16.00-£21.00	

B&B

★★★

Fionn Fraoch
64 Ayr Road, Prestwick, KA9 1RR
Tel: 01292 478029

Comfortable and homely accommodation close to Prestwick Airport with pick up/drop off facilities. Walking distance of ice rink, beach, golf courses, swimming pool and bowling. Numerous restaurants & bars nearby. Pets by arrangement.

1 Twin	2 En Suite fac	B&B per person	Open Jan-Dec
1 Double	1 Pub Bath/Show	from £16.00 Single	
1 Family		from £16.00 Dbl/Twn	

Important: Prices stated are estimates and may be subject to amendments

Prestwick, Ayrshire   Map Ref: 1G7

★★★★

**GUEST
HOUSE**

Golf View Private Hotel
17 Links Road, Prestwick, Ayrshire, KA9 1QG
Tel: 01292 671234 Fax: 01292 671244
Web: www.golfviewhotel.com

1 Single	All En Suite
4 Twin	1 Pub Bath/Show
1 Dbl/Fam	

B&B per person
from £28.00 Single
from £28.00 Dbl/Twn

Open Jan-Dec excl
Xmas/New Year

Stylish west coast Victorian house, tastefully decorated and furnished
offering superb B&B accommodation under the management of the
owners Christine and Allan Heslop.

★★★

HOTEL

North Beach Hotel
5-7 Link's Road, Prestwick, Ayrshire, KA9 1QG
Tel: 01292 479069 Fax: 01292 671521
E-mail: info@northbeach.co.uk

2 Single	All En Suite
6 Twin	
4 Double	
1 Family	

B&B per person
from £35.00
from £35.00 Dbl/Twn

Open Jan-Dec excl
Xmas/New Year
B&B + Eve.Meal
from £45.00

Family run hotel, overlooking the 18th green at Old Prestwick. Close to
seafront and convenient for Royal Troon. Locally popular Bistro. Ideally
situated for railway and Prestwick Airport.

★★★

HOTEL

Parkstone Hotel
Central Esplanade, Prestwick, Ayrshire, KA9 1QN
Tel: 01292 477286 Fax: 01292 477671
Web: www.parkstonehotel.co.uk

7 Single	All En Suite
7 Twin	
6 Double	
2 Family	

B&B per person
£41.50-£48.50 Single
£33.50-£36.50 Dbl/Twn

Open Jan-Dec

On the seafront overlooking a sandy beach on the Firth of Clyde. Close to
many good golf courses and local amenities, and the town centre. Ideally
situated for railway station and Prestwick airport.

St Boswells, Roxburghshire   Map Ref: 2D7

★★★

HOTEL

Buccleuch Arms Hotel
The Green, St Boswells, Roxburghshire, TD6 0EW
Tel: 01835 822243 Fax: 01835 823965
E-mail: bucchotel@aol.com

4 Single	All En Suite
5 Twin	
8 Double	
2 Family	

B&B per person
from £44.00 Single
from £37.50 Dbl/Twn
Room only per person
from £25.00

Open Jan-Dec excl
Xmas
B&B + Eve.Meal
from £39.00

A former 17c coaching inn, situated on the main A68. Ideally located for
business or pleasure, with function facilities for up to 100 guests. Good
restaurant plus bar food served all day.

VAT is shown at 17.5%: changes in this rate may affect prices. | *Key to symbols is on back flap.*

St Boswells, Roxburghshire   Map Ref: 2D7

Dryburgh Abbey Hotel
St Boswells, Melrose TD6 0RQ
Tel: 01835 822261 Fax: 01835 823945
e.mail: enquiries@dryburgh.co.uk
Web: www.dryburgh.co.uk

Peacefully set in 10 acres of grounds and gardens, the Dryburgh Abbey Hotel stands on the banks of the River Tweed adjacent to the historic ruins of Dryburgh Abbey. This splendid baronial mansion is owned and managed by the Grose family who have over 100 years experience in providing hospitality. The hotel has been beautifully restored to a very high standard. Each of the 38 bedrooms have been elegantly furnished and all include the facilities you would expect from a leading hotel. An ideal base for all manner of country pursuits. We offer excellent service, award winning cuisine and extensive wine list.

★★★★

HOTEL

Dryburgh Abbey Hotel			
St Boswells, Roxburghshire, TD6 0RQ	6 Single	All En Suite	B&B per person	Open Jan-Dec
Tel: 01835 822261 Fax: 01835 823945	28 Dbl/Twn		from £55.00 Single	B&B + Eve.Meal
E-mail: enquiries@dryburgh.co.uk	2 Double		from £40.00 Dbl/Twn	from £55.00
Web: www.dryburgh.co.uk	2 Family			

Country house hotel on banks of River Tweed overlooked by 12c Dryburgh Abbey. Ideal base for fishing, shooting or exploring this historic area. Indoor pool, putting green and mountain bikes, trout rights on the Tweed.

Seamill, Ayrshire   Map Ref: 1F6

★★★

HOTEL

Seamill Hydro			
Ardrossan Road, Seamill, Ayrshire, KA23 9NB	6 Single	All En Suite	B&B per person	Open Jan-Dec
Tel: 01294 822217 Fax: 01294 823939	16 Twin		from £42.50 Single	B&B + Eve.Meal
Web: www.seamillhydro.co.uk	32 Double		from £42.50 Dbl/Twn	from £44.00
	30 Family			

Family-owned hotel, overlooking Firth of Clyde to Arran. Access to the beach. Swimming pool and leisure facilities. Some annexe accommodation.

Selkirk   Map Ref: 2D7

★★

HOTEL

County Hotel			
3-5 High Street, Selkirk, TD7 4BZ	1 Single	All En Suite	B&B per person	Open Jan-Dec
Tel/Fax: 01750 21233	1 Twin		from £32.50 Single	
	3 Double		from £27.50 Dbl/Twn	
	1 Family			

Small family run hotel in centre of this historic Borders town. Popular function room. Bar lunches, coffee shop plus extensive evening menu.

Important: Prices stated are estimates and may be subject to amendments

Selkirk

Map Ref: 2D7

★★★

SMALL HOTEL

The Glen Hotel
Yarrow Terrace, Selkirk, TD7 5AS
Tel/Fax: 01750 20259
E-mail: glenhotel@hotmail.com

1 Single	All En Suite	B&B per person	Open Jan-Dec
4 Double	1 Pub Bath/Show	£38.00-£40.00 Single	
3 Family		£31 Double	

Beautifully refurbished small hotel set in pleasant gardens overlooking the River Ettrick.

PHILIPBURN COUNTRY HOUSE HOTEL
Linglie Road, Selkirk TD7 5LS
Tel: 01750 20747   Fax: 01750 21690
e.mail: info@philipburnhousehotel.co.uk
Web: www.philipburnhousehotel.co.uk

★★★★
HOTEL

Philipburn Country House Hotel re-opened after complete refurbishment in May 1998, the resulting hotel can only be described as stunning. Situated in the beautiful Scottish borders, the hotel is perfect for an activity based holiday or merely for relaxing. Our dining areas – Charlie's Bar and Bistro and '1745' cater for all tastes.

★★★★

HOTEL

Philipburn Country House Hotel
Selkirk, TD7 5LS
Tel: 01750 20747 Fax: 01750 21690
E.mail: info@philipburnhousehotel.co.uk
Web: www.philipburnhousehotel.co.uk

1 Single	All En Suite	B&B per person	Open Jan-Dec
6 Twin	Suites avail	£80.00-£125.00 Single	B&B + Eve.Meal
9 Double		£50.00-£70.00 Dbl/Twn	£95.00
1 Family			

Set amidst beautiful Borders scenery. Unique, tasteful accommodation in historic manor house. Recently refurbished. Innovative and interesting cuisine. Also garden rooms available by outdoor heated pool.

---

by Selkirk

Map Ref: 2D7

★★

INN

Tibbie Shiels Inn
St Mary's Loch, Selkirkshire, TD7 5LH
Tel: 01750 42231

1 Twin	All En Suite	B&B per person	Open Jan-Dec excl
2 Double		to £28.00 Single	Mon/Wed low season
2 Family		to £25.00 Dbl/Twn	

Historical coaching inn on the shores of beautiful St Marys Loch. Fishing, sailing, walking and birdwatching. Imaginative cooking.

Skirling, by Biggar, Peeblesshire

Map Ref: 2B6

★★★★★

B&B

Skirling House
Skirling, by Biggar, Peebles-shire, ML12 6HD
Tel: 01899 860274 Fax: 01899 860255
Web: www.skirlinghouse.com

2 Twin	All En Suite	B&B per person	Open Mar-Dec
2 Double		from £45.00 Single	B&B + Eve.Meal
		from £35.00 Dbl/Twn	from £55.00

Open fires, peaceful gardens, rolling hills, fine cuisine. Unique Arts & Crafts house by village green. All rooms overlooking secluded gardens and woods.

VAT is shown at 17.5%: changes in this rate may affect prices.

Key to symbols is on back flap.

Sorbie, Wigtownshire — Map Ref: 1H11

★★★★

GUEST HOUSE

Birchtrees Guesthouse
Reiffer Park Road, Sorbie, Wigtownshire, DG8 8EH
Tel: 01988 850391

2 Twin	2 En Suite fac	B&B per person	Open Mar-Oct incl
1 Double	1 Priv.NOT ensuite	from £24.00 Single	B&B + Eve.Meal
		from £24.00 Dbl/Twn	£32.00

Pauline and John welcome you to Birchtrees which is an attractive bungalow set in a 1/2 acre garden in a peaceful location amidst beautiful scenery in the heart of Galloway countryside. 12 miles south of Newton Stewart, 6 miles from Wigtown, Scotland's book town. Non smoking home.

Stranraer, Wigtownshire — Map Ref: 1F10

★★

GUEST HOUSE

Harbour Guest House
Market Street, Stranraer, Wigtownshire, DG9 7RF
Tel: 01776 704626
E-mail: reservations@harbourguesthouse.com
Web: www.Harbourguesthouse.com

3 Dbl/Twn	En Suite fac	B&B per person	Open Jan-Dec excl
1 Family	Private fac	£20.00-£25.00 Single	Xmas/New Year
	1 Pub.Bath/Show	£19.00-£23.00 Twin	
		Room only per person	
		£17.00-£19.00	

The Harbour Guest House offers spacious and luxurious accommodation for the ultimate in relaxation. Within easy walking distance you will find the town centre should you require shops, restaurants, leisure facilities, pubs. Ideally situated for bus, train and ferry terminals for the scheduled traveller. Private secure parking available by arrangement. Family pets welcome by prior arrangement.

nr Stranraer, Wigtownshire — Map Ref: 1F10

★★★★

SMALL HOTEL

Corsewall Lighthouse Hotel
Kirkcolm, by Stranraer, DG9 0QG
Tel: 01776 853220 Fax: 01776 854231
E-mail: corsewall-lighthouse@msn.com

4 Twin	5 En Suite fac	B&B per person	Open Jan-Dec
2 Double	1 Priv.NOT ensuite	£80.00-£120.00 Single	B&B + Eve.Meal
		£50.00-£100.00 Dbl/Twn	£55.00-£130.00

Corsewall Lighthouse Hotel offers the charm and romance of an 1815 functional lighthouse with its cosy bedrooms each individually furnished. Spectacular sea views. The award winning restaurant caters for a wide range of tastes including local beef, lamb, seafood and vegetarian dishes. Additionally there are 3 properties in the grounds.

Swinton, Berwickshire — Map Ref: 2E6

★★★★

RESTAURANT WITH ROOMS

The Wheatsheaf at Swinton
Main Street, Swinton, Berwickshire, TD11 3JJ
Tel: 01890 860257 Fax: 01890 860688

2 Twin	All En Suite	B&B per person	Open Jan-Dec excl
4 Double		from £50.00 Single	Xmas/New Year
		from £40.00 Dbl/Twn	

Attractive country inn, owned and personally run, by Alan Reid and his wife Julie. Emphasis on hospitality and customer care and high class cuisine using local produce creatively. Convenient location for touring the Borders. All rooms en-suite.

Troon, Ayrshire   **Map Ref: 1G7**

HOTEL

Marine Hotel
Crosbie Road, Troon, Ayrshire, KA10 6HE
Tel: 01292 314444 Fax: 01292 316922

The Marine Hotel is located adjacent to Royal Troon Golf Course with views out to sea and the Isle of Arran. The hotel has two restaurants and business centre with all facilities available. A Conference and Banqueting Centre and the Marine Health and Fitness Club.

16 Single	All En Suite	B&B per person	Open Jan-Dec
31 Twin	Suites avail	£95.00-£100.00 Single	
25 Double		£76.00-£80.00 Dbl/Twn	

HOTEL

Piersland House Hotel
Craigend Road, Troon, Ayrshire, KA10 6HD
Tel: 01292 314747 Fax: 01292 315613
E-mail: reception.piersland@talk21.com
Web: www.piersland.com

Unique and historic house built for Sir Alexander Walker with 13 cottage suites set in beautifully landscaped grounds and situated on the Southwest Coast - a haven for golfers. Family owned hotel. Many historic attractions including Robert Burns Cottage and Culzean Castle nearby.

1 Single	All En Suite	B&B per person	Open Jan-Dec
21 Twin		£62.50-£90.00 Single	B&B + Eve.Meal
6 Double		£59.50-£82.50 Dbl/Twn	£79.50 Single
			£102.50 Dbl/Twn

HOTEL

South Beach Hotel
South Beach, Troon, Ayrshire, KA10 6EG
Tel: 01292 312033 Fax: 01292 318438

Privately owned hotel facing the sea on main road and about 0.5 miles (1km) from town centre. Convenient for Troon championship golf course.

3 Single	All En Suite	B&B per person	Open Jan-Dec
20 Twin		from £41.50 Single	B&B + Eve.Meal
6 Double		from £37.50 Dbl/Twn	from £45.00
4 Family			
1 Suite			

Turnberry, Ayrshire   **Map Ref: 1G8**

MALIN COURT
TURNBERRY, AYRSHIRE KA26 9PB
Telephone: 01655 331457   Fax: 01655 331072
e.mail: info@malincourt.co.uk   Web: www.malincourt.co.uk

Malin Court is situated in the heart of Burns Country, close to Culzean Castle, overlooking Turnberry's famous Open Championship golf course and the Firth of Clyde. It offers a perfect blend of informality, congeniality, the best of local produce cooked to perfection and the warmest of Scottish welcomes.

HOTEL

Malin Court
Turnberry, Ayrshire, KA26 9PB
Tel: 01655 331457 Fax: 01655 331072
E-mail: info@malincourt.co.uk
Web: www.malincourt.co.uk

Totally refurbished modern hotel with views over Turnberry Golf Course and Ailsa Craig, near Culzean Castle. Patio garden. AA 2 rosettes restaurant.

7 Twin	All En Suite	B&B per person	Open Jan-Dec
3 Double		£72.00-£82.00 Single	B&B + Eve.Meal
7 Family		£52.00-£62.00 Dbl/Twn	from £85.00 Sgl
1 Suite			from £65.00 Dbl

SILVER

Turnberry, Ayrshire   Map Ref: 1G8

★★★★★

INTERNATIONAL
RESORT HOTEL

Turnberry Hotel & Golf Courses & Spa
Turnberry, Ayrshire, KA26 9LT
Tel: 01655 331000 Fax: 01655 331706

221 rooms	All En Suite	B&B per person	Open Jan-Dec
including	Suites avail	£158.00-£250.00	B&B + Eve.Meal
Cottages+		Single	£137.00-£197.50
Lodges		£92.00-£142.50	
		Dbl/Twn	

Luxury hotel, overlooking the famous golf courses with stunning coastal views. Choice of restaurants and fine dining. Superb health spa and gymnasium facilities, together with newly opened Colin Montgomerie Links Golf Academy.

W ITH A CITY SKYLINE EVERY BIT AS SPECTACULAR AS THE POSTCARDS SUGGEST, SCOTLAND'S CAPITAL IS SIMPLY OUTSTANDING IN WORLD TERMS.

Linlithgow Palace, West Lothian

IT IS NOW ALSO home to the new Scottish Parliament. Edinburgh Castle is one of the most famous symbols of Scotland, but it is only one of a whole range of attractions stretching down the Royal Mile in the heart of the Old Town. The city is steeped in history and culture, from the Palace of Holyroodhouse, where the tragic story of Mary Queen of Scots unfolded, to the narrow alleyways of the Old Town which were the inspiration for Robert Louis Stevenson's novel Dr Jekyll and Mr Hyde. Our Dynamic Earth, the Royal Yacht Britannia and the Museum of Scotland are just three of the city's newest visitor attractions.

THE MOST FAMOUS EVENTS the city host are the spectacular International Festival and the Festival Fringe, but it remains the liveliest of cities all year round with other events such as the Science Festival, Film Festival and the biggest New Year street party in the world. As a major cultural centre, Edinburgh has many art galleries, theatres and cinemas. There are many street cafés and restaurants specialising in both international and modern Scottish cuisine, while over 700 bars in the city offer fine locally brewed beers and, of course, a wide range of malt whiskies.

Edinburgh Skyline from Calton Hill

Firth of Forth and East Lothian landscape seen from the Lammermuir Hills

THIS FAST-PACED and cosmopolitan city offers superb shopping in the many department stores along the famous thoroughfare of Princes Street as well as Princes Mall and the many designer shops along elegantly proportioned George Street in the heart of the 18-century New Town. The village-like suburbs of Stockbridge and Bruntsfield offer small shops where a friendly welcome is guaranteed. A relaxing alternative within the bustling city are the many quiet green spaces including Holyrood Park, Calton Hill, the Dean Village and the Royal Botanic Garden, which features Britain's tallest palm house and the world-famous Rock Garden.

WITHIN A FEW MILES of the city centre are the Lothians. This is soft rolling farmland with splendid hill-walking in the surrounding Pentland, Moorfoot and Lammermuir Hills. There are almost 70 miles of coastline along the Firth of Forth combining nature reserves, sandy beaches and seaside resorts. Dunbar has been officially recorded as Scotland's driest and sunniest town. The new Scottish Seabird Centre in North Berwick uses the latest technology to allow all the family to view the famous gannet colony on the nearby Bass Rock. To the west, South Queensferry is set in a dramatic location immediately below the gigantic structures of the famous Forth Bridges.

EXPERIENCE AND ENJOY one of Europe's most exciting regions, by combining city and countryside. With easy access by air, rail and road, Edinburgh and the Lothians is a year-round destination for everyone.

EVENTS
EDINBURGH AND
LOTHIANS

17 FEBRUARY
Scotland v Wales
Murrayfield Stadium, Edinburgh
As part of the Six Nation
Championship.
Contact: Scottish Rugby Union
TEL: **0131 346 5000**
www.sru.org.uk

17 MARCH
Scotland v Italy
Murrayfield Stadium, Edinburgh
As part of the Six Nation
Championship.
Contact: Scottish Rugby Union
TEL: **0131 346 5000**
www.sru.org.uk

1-12 APRIL
Edinburgh International
Science Festival
Various venues, Edinburgh
Worlds largest event devoted to
celebration of science. Lots of
events for children.
Contact: Science Festival Office
TEL: **0131 530 2001**
www.edinburghfestivals.co.uk
/science/

7 APRIL
Scotland v Ireland
Murrayfield Stadium, Edinburgh
As part of the Six Nation
Championship.
Contact: Scottish Rugby Union
TEL: **0131 346 5000**
www.sru.org.uk

21-24 JUNE
Royal Highland Show
Royal Highland Centre,
Edinburgh
The spectacular highlight of
Scotland's country calendar,
with a Scottish food exhibition,
pedigree livestock, flower show,
show jumping, craft fair and
much more.
Contact: Royal Highland Centre
TEL: **0131 333 3036**

3-25 AUGUST
Edinburgh Military Tattoo
Edinburgh Castle Esplanade,
A unique blend of music,
ceremony and theatre set against
the magnificent backdrop of
Edinburgh Castle, featuring
display teams and bands from all
over the World.
Contact: The Tattoo Office
TEL: **0131 225 1188**
www.edintattoo.co.uk

5-27 AUGUST
Edinburgh Festival Fringe
Various venues, Edinburgh
One of the largest arts festivals
in the World, comprising three
weeks of theatre, dance, music
and comedy, with up to 1000
different shows a day played in
over 200 venues throughout
the city.
Contact: The Fringe Office
TEL: 0131 226 5257
EMAIL: admin@edfringe.com
www.edfringe.com

11-27 AUGUST
Edinburgh International Book
Festival
Charlotte Square Gardens,
Edinburgh
Annual celebration where
writers and readers meet to
celebrate the written word.
Lectures, talks, discussions,
readings and daily events for
children.
Contact: Edinburgh
International Book Festival
TEL: **0131 228 5444**
EMAIL: admin@edbookfest.co.uk
www.edbookfest.co.uk

12 AUGUST-1 SEPTEMBER
Edinburgh International
Festival
Various venues, Edinburgh
For three weeks Edinburgh plays
hosts to some of the World's
finest theatre, opera, music and
dance companies in one of
Europe's premier arts festivals.
Contact: The Hub, Edinburgh's
Festival Centre
TEL: **0131 473 2001**
(information)
TICKET LINE: **0131 473 2000**
www.eif.co.uk

THE OFFICIAL WHERE TO STAY G

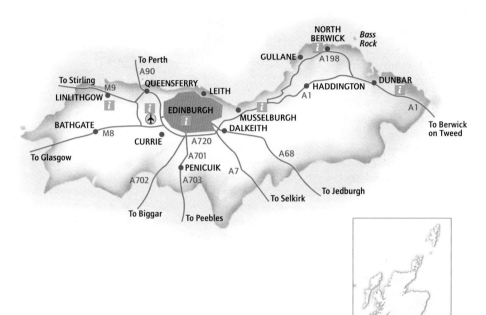

EDINBURGH AND
LOTHIANS TOURIST
BOARD
Edinburgh and Scotland
Information Centre
3 Princes Street
Edinburgh
EH2 2QP

TEL: **0131 473 3800**
FAX: **0131 473 3881**
www.edinburgh.org

EDINBURGH AND
LOTHIANS TOURIST BOARD

DUNBAR
143 High Street
TEL: **(01368) 863353**
Jan-Dec

EDINBURGH
Edinburgh and Scotland
Information Centre
3 Princes Street
TEL: **(0131) 473 3800**
Jan-Dec

EDINBURGH AIRPORT
Tourist Information Desk
TEL: **(0131) 333 2167**
Jan-Dec

NEWTONGRANGE
Scottish Mining Museum
Lady Victoria Colliery
TEL: **(0131) 663 4262**
Easter-Oct

NORTH BERWICK
Quality Street
TEL: **(01620) 892197**
Jan-Dec

OLD CRAIGHALL
Granada Service Area
A1
Musselburgh
TEL: **(0131) 653 6172**
Jan-Dec

PENICUIK
Edinburgh Crystal
Visitor Centre
Eastfield
TEL: **(01968) 673846**
Easter-Sept

Aberlady, East Lothian — Map Ref: 2D4

★★★ HOTEL

Kilspindie House Hotel
Main Street, Aberlady, Longidday, East Lothian, EH32 0RE
Tel: 01875 870682 Fax: 01875 870504
E-mail: info@kilspindie-golfscotland.com

6 Single
16 Twin
4 Double

All En Suite

B&B per person
from £40.00 Single
from £33.00 Dbl/Twn

B&B + Eve.Meal
from £50.00

Family run hotel in coastal conservation village of Aberlady. Ample parking and all rooms en-suite. Within easy reach of 17 local golf courses. 25 mins drive from Edinburgh. Full restaurant plus bar meals and high teas. Lovely area for walking, bird watching and interesting hillviews.

by Dalkeith, Midlothian — Map Ref: 2C5

★★ INN

Laird & Dog Hotel
5 High Street, Lasswade, Midlothian, EH18 1NA
Tel/Fax: 0131 663 9219

1 Single
4 Twin
3 Double
1 Family

All En Suite

B&B per person
from £25.00 Single
from £20.00 Dbl/Twn

Open Jan-Dec

One mile from city bypass, ten minutes Edinburgh centre. Old coaching inn, conservatory restaurant, real ales, ample parking, all ensuite.

Dirleton, East Lothian — Map Ref: 2D4

★★★★ SMALL HOTEL

The Open Arms Hotel
Dirleton, East Lothian, EH39 5EG
Tel: 01620 850241 Fax: 01620 850570
E-mail: openarms@clara.co.uk
Web: http://home.clara.net/openarms

3 Single
6 Twin
1 Double

All En Suite

B&B per person
£65.00-£90.00 Single
£50.00-£90.00 Dbl/Twn

Open Jan-Dec

Dating from 1185, this family run hotel stands at the foot of the village green overlooking the 13th Century Castle. Quiet lounges with open fires add to the warmth of personal welcome. All bedrooms are highly decorated, and as one would expect of a building of this huge variety in size and style. Dine in Deveau's Brasserie or the more formal restaurant.

Dunbar, East Lothian — Map Ref: 2E4

★★ SMALL HOTEL

Bayswell Hotel
Bayswell Park, Dunbar, East Lothian, EH42 1AE
Tel/Fax: 01368 862225

4 Twin
5 Double
4 Family

All En Suite

B&B per person
£49.50-£55.00 Single
£35.00-£39.50 Dbl/Twn

Open Jan-Dec

Town house by the sea, situated on the cliff top overlooking the Firth of Forth. Only half an hour by car or train to Edinburgh.

★★ SMALL HOTEL

The Goldenstones Hotel
Queens Road, Dunbar, East Lothian, EH42 1LG
Tel: 01368 862356 Fax: 01368 865644
E-mail: goldenstones@cs.com

19 Rooms

All En Suite

B&B per person
from £32.00 Single
from £30.00 Double

Open Jan-Dec
B&B + Eve.Meal
from £37.00

Family run hotel centrally situated in Dunbar. Near town centre and beaches. Golfing packages available.

VAT is shown at 17.5%: changes in this rate may affect prices.

Key to symbols is on back flap.

Dunbar, East Lothian
Map Ref: 2E4

★

SMALL
HOTEL

Hillside Hotel
3 Queens Road, Dunbar, East Lothian, EH42 1LA
Tel/Fax: 01368 862071

4 Single	11 En Suite fac
5 Twin	5 Priv.NOT ensuite
4 Double	2 Pub Bath/Show
3 Family	

B&B per person
from £38.50 Single
from £29.50 Dbl/Twn

Open Jan-Dec

Personally run hotel with a reputation for good food using fresh local produce. Ideal for golf and touring East Lothian.

📺 📶 ☕ 🍽 🍷

Ⓒ ♨ Ⓥ

🏵
★★

GUEST
HOUSE

Overcliffe Guest House
11 Bayswell Park, Dunbar, EH42 1AE
Tel: 01368 864004

2 Double	3 En Suite fac
3 Family	1 Shared bathroom

B&B per room
£25.00-£30.00 Single
£40.00-£45.00 Double
£40.00-£50.00 Family

Open Jan-Nov
Open Hogmanay period

Family run guest house in quiet residential area close to cliff top trail, new swimming pool and town centre. 20 golf courses within 15 mile radius. Golf packages can be arranged. Edinburgh easily accessible by rail.

📺 🐕 📶 ☕ 💷 ✗ 🍷 📱

Ⓒ 🐕 Ⓥ

★★

GUEST
HOUSE

Springfield Guest House
Belhaven Road, Dunbar, East Lothian, EH42 1NH
Tel/Fax: 01368 862502
E-mail: smeed@tesco.net

1 Single	2 Priv.NOT ensuite
1 Twin	1 Pub Bath/Show
1 Double	
2 Family	

B&B per person
£20.00-£30.00 Single
£18.00-£22.00 Dbl/Twn
Room only per person
£16.00-£20.00

Open Jan-Nov excl
New Year
B&B + Eve.Meal
£28.00-£32.00

An elegant 19c villa with attractive garden. Family run with home-cooking. Ideal base for families, golf and touring.

📺 🎮 Ⓟ ☕ ✗ ✕ ⛺ 🍷 📱

Ⓒ 🐕 ♨ Ⓥ

Edinburgh
Map Ref: 2C5

🏵
★★★★

GUEST
HOUSE

Aaron Guest House
16 Hartington Gardens, Edinburgh, EH10 4LD
Tel: 0131 229 6459 Fax: 0131 228 5807
E-mail: aaron.guest.house@cableinet.co.uk
Web: www.aaron-guesthouse.com

1 Single	10 Ensuite fac
2 Twin	
5 Double	
2 Family	

B&B per person
£25.00-£50.00 Single
£20.00-£50.00 Dbl/Twn

Open Jan-Dec

Quality service in a thoughtfully restored 19th century Victorian house located in a quiet cul-de-sac in residential area in central Edinburgh with private parking. Within walking distance of all major attractions. Ground floor accommodation available. Non smoking establishment.

📺 🔌 Ⓟ ☕ 🔖 ✗ 📱

Ⓒ ♨ Ⓦ Ⓥ

★★

GUEST
HOUSE

Acorn Guest House
70 Pilrig Street, Edinburgh, EH6 5AS
Tel: 0131 554 2187

1 Twin	2 En Suite fac
2 Double	1 Priv.NOT ensuite
2 Family	2 Pub Bath/Show

B&B per person
£16.00-£25.00 Dbl/Twn

Open Jan-Dec excl
Xmas/New Year

Terraced house on bus route to city centre, close to Playhouse Theatre, restaurants and main tourist attractions.

📺 📶 ☕ ✗ 📱

🐕 Ⓥ

Important: Prices stated are estimates and may be subject to amendments

Edinburgh

Map Ref: 2C5

GUEST HOUSE ★★★★

Acorn Lodge Guest House
26 Pilrig Street, Edinburgh, EH6 5AJ
Tel: 0131 555 1557 Fax: 0131 555 4475
E-mail: info@acorn.co.uk
Web: www.acornlodge.co.uk

1 Single	All En Suite	B&B per person	Open Jan-Dec
2 Twin		£30.00-£55.00 Single	
2 Double		£30.00-£55.00 Dbl/Twn	
2 Family			

Refurbished Georgian town house centrally situated for all amenities. Personal attention assured. Extensive breakfast menu. Non smoking house.

SMALL HOTEL ★★★

The Adam Hotel
19 Lansdowne Crescent, Edinburgh, EH12 5EH
Tel: 0131 337 1148 Fax: 0131 337 1729

5 Single	All En Suite	B&B per person	Open Jan-Dec
2 Twin		£30.00-£65.00 Single	
5 Double		£30.00-£75.00 Dbl/Twn	
1 Family			

Georgian terraced house in quiet street close to Haymarket Station. Convenient for bus routes to city centre and airport. Evening meal available on request by prior arrangement. Bar service.

GUEST HOUSE ★★★★

Addison Hotel
2 Murrayfield Avenue, Edinburgh, EH12 6AX
Tel: 0131 337 4060 Fax: 0131 337 8030
E-mail: booking@addisonhotel.freeserve.co.uk
Web: www.addisonhotel.freeserve.co.uk

2 Single	All En Suite	B&B per person	Open Jan-Dec
2 Twin		£35.00-£65.00 Single	
4 Double		£27.50-£65.00 Dbl/Twn	
2 Family			

Family owned victorian terraced house situated in the tree lined avenue set back from the main road. Convenient for both city centre and airport. South facing patio and gardens.

GUEST HOUSE ★★★

Adria Hotel
11/12 Royal Terrace, Edinburgh, EH7 5AB
Tel: 0131 556 7875 Fax: 0131 558 7782
E-mail: manager@adriahotel.co.uk

2 Single	9 Ensuite fac	B&B per person	Open Feb-Nov
6 Twin	6 Pub Bath/Show	£25.00-£40.00 Single	
9 Double	1 Priv.NOT ensuite	£21.00-£35.00 Dbl/Twn	
6 Family			

Friendly family run private hotel in quiet Georgian terrace. Spacious bedrooms. Ten minutes walk from centre.

SMALL HOTEL ★★★

A-Haven Town House
180 Ferry Road, Edinburgh, EH6 4NS
Tel: 0131 554 6559 Fax: 0131 554 5252
E-mail: reservations@a-haven.co.uk
Web: www.a-haven.co.uk

3 Single	All En Suite	B&B per person	Open Jan-Dec excl
4 Twin		from £35.00 Single	Xmas
3 Double		from £30.00 Dbl/Twn	
2 Family			

Family run town house with secure private parking. Near city centre and on main bus route. Scottish welcome and hospitality including a hearty Highland breakfast. Variety of restaurants nearby or dinner by prior arrangement.

VAT is shown at 17.5%: changes in this rate may affect prices.

Key to symbols is on back flap.

Map Ref: 2C5

Ailsa Craig Hotel
24 Royal Terrace, Edinburgh EH7 5AH
Tel: 0131-556 1022/6055 Fax: 0131-556 6055
e.mail: ailsacraighotel@ednet.co.uk Web: www.townhousehotels.co.uk
Elegant Georgian townhouse hotel ideally situated in the city centre within walking distance to Princes Street, Waverley train station, Edinburgh Castle and the Playhouse Theatre. Combining traditional features with modern facilities, the hotel offers superb views, private gardens and friendly atmosphere together providing the perfect blend of history and hospitality.

HOTEL

Ailsa Craig Hotel
24 Royal Terrace, Edinburgh, EH7 5AH
Tel: 0131 556 1022/6055 Fax: 0131 556 6055
E-mail: ailsacraighotel@ednet.co.uk
Web: www.townhousehotels.co.uk

Elegant city centre Georgian townhouse hotel with tastefully decorated bedrooms, some offering views across Edinburgh to Firth of Forth and Fife coast, others overlooking landscaped gardens. Only a 10 minute walk to Waverley Station and Princes Street, the hotel is ideally situated to visit all histoeic attractions, theatres, restaurants and shopping. Large family rooms also available.

4 Single	15 En Suite fac	B&B per person	Open Jan-Dec
3 Twin	1 Priv.NOT ensuite	from £25.00 Single	B&B + Eve.Meal
5 Double	2 Pub Bath/Show	from £22.50 Dbl/Twn	from £35.50
5 Family			

**GUEST
HOUSE**

Airdenair Guest House
29 Kilmaurs Road, Edinburgh, EH16 5DB
Tel: 0131 668 2336
Web: http://airdenair.edinburghnet.co.uk/

Double upper flatted Victorian stonebuilt house situated in quiet residential area on south side of city. Near Royal Commonwealth Pool and Holyrood Park. Views to local hills of Arthurs Seat and Blackford Hill. Unrestricted street parking. Speciality diets catered for.

1 Single	All En Suite	B&B per person
2 Twin		from £25.00 Single
2 Double		from £22.00 Dbl/Twn
		Open Jan-Dec

**GUEST
HOUSE**

Airlie Guest House
29 Minto Street, Edinburgh, EH9 1SB
Tel: 0131 667 3562 Fax: 0131 662 1399
E-mail: airlieguesthouse@btinternet.com

Totally Non Smoking family run establishment offering a variety of clean comfortable rooms. Located on an excellent bus route. Private car park at rear of house.

1 Single	5 En Suite fac	B&B per person	Open Jan-Dec
3 Twin	1 Priv.NOT ensuite	from £18.00 Single	
3 Double	1 Pub Bath/Show	from £15.00 Dbl/Twn	
1 Family			

Important: Prices stated are estimates and may be subject to amendments

The Albany Town House Hotel

39 Albany Street, Edinburgh EH1 3QY
Tel: 0131-556 0397   Fax: 0131-557 6633
e.mail: info@albanyhoteledinburgh.co.uk
Web: www.albanyhoteledinburgh.co.uk

You will find the Albany Town House Hotel in the famous New Town less than 10 minutes' walk from the town centre. We have renovated the hotel so that you can enjoy superb comfort in a traditional environment, where you will be spoilt by our attentive and caring team.

HOTEL
★★★★

Albany Hotel

39/43 Albany Street, Edinburgh, EH1 3QY
Tel: 0131 556 0397 Fax: 0131 557 6633
E.mail: info@albanyhoteledinburgh.co.uk
Web: www.albanyhoteledinburgh.co.uk

An elegant Georgian terrace town house situated in a quiet street in Edinburgh's New Town. Retaining many original features and refurbished to a high standard of comfort. A charming intimate restaurant and county house lounge. All main visitor attractions within walking distance.

5 Single	All En Suite	Room only per person	Open Jan-Dec
8 Twin		£57.50-£90.00	
8 Double			

The Alexander Guest House

35 Mayfield Gardens, Edinburgh EH9 2BX
Tel: 0131 258 4028   Fax: 0131 258 1247
e.mail: alexander@guest68.freeserve.co.uk

Elegantly furnished 4-star Victorian villa, situated 1 mile from Edinburgh's famous Royal mile, Castle and Holyrood. Every detail has been thought of in our recently refurbished bedrooms to make your stay a memorable one. Breakfast time is special at the Alexander with a wide variety of dishes on offer.

GUEST HOUSE
★★★★

The Alexander Guest House

35 Mayfield Gardens, Edinburgh, EH9 2BX
Tel: 0131 258 4028 Fax: 0131 258 1247
E-mail: alexander@guest68.freeserve.co.uk

Elegantly furnished four star Victorian villa situated one mile from Edinburgh's famous Royal Mile, castle and Holyrood. Every detail has been thought of in our recently refurbished bedrooms, to make your stay a memorable one. Breakfast time is special at the Alexander with a wide variety of dishes on offer.

2 Single	4 En Suite fac	B&B per person	Open Jan-Dec
3 Twin	1 Pub Bath/Show	from £20.00 Single	
3 Double	1 Limited ensuite	from £20.00 Dbl/Twn	

HOTEL
★★★

Allison House Hotel

15-17 Mayfield Gardens, Edinburgh, EH9 2AX
Tel: 0131 667 8049 Fax: 0131 667 5001
E-mail: dh007ljh@msn.com
Web: www.allisonhousehotel.com

On main route into the city, convenient for all attractions, private parking and regular bus service. All rooms double glazed.

3 Single	All En Suite	B&B per person	Open Jan-Dec
8 Twin		from £25.00 Single	B&B + Eve.Meal
8 Double		from £20.00 Dbl/Twn	from £35.00
1 Family			

VAT is shown at 17.5%: changes in this rate may affect prices.

Key to symbols is on back flap.

Edinburgh

Map Ref: 2C5

Alloway Guest House
96 Pilrig Street, Edinburgh, EH6 5AY
Tel: 0131 554 1786

1 Single	2 En Suite fac	B&B per person	Open Jan-Dec
2 Twin	2 Pub Bath/Show	£22.00-£25.00 Single	
2 Double		£18.00-£25.00 Dbl/Twn	
1 Family			

Family run Victorian guest house, within easy reach of the city centre. Unrestricted street parking. Short stroll to Leith Walk offering many buses to city centre.

GUEST HOUSE ★★

Anvilla Guest House
1a Granville Terrace, Edinburgh, EH10 4PG
Tel: 0131 228 3381

1 Single	2 Pub Bath/Show	B&B per person	Open Jan-Dec
2 Twin		£22.00-£24.00 Single	
1 Double		£21.00-£23.00 Dbl/Twn	
2 Family			

A warm, friendly welcome at this detached Victorian villa noting many original features including spacious comfortable lounge with ornate plaster work. The house is centrally located, close to Kings Theatre and EICC and on bus route to city centre. Private car park.

GUEST HOUSE ★★

Ardgarth Guest House
1 St Mary's Place, Portobello, Edinburgh, EH15 2QF
Tel: 0131 669 3021 Fax: 0131 468 1221
Web: www.ardgarth.demon.co.uk

3 Single	4 En Suite fac	B&B per person	Open Jan-Dec
4 Twin		from £16.00 Single	
1 Double		from £16.00 Dbl/Twn	
2 Family			

Comfortable accommodation in quiet and friendly guest house. Close to beach and golf course. Special diets catered for, ground floor ensuite disabled facilities with roll-in showers. Unrestricted parking. Frequent buses give easy access to and from city centre. French spoken.

GUEST HOUSE ★★★

Ard Thor
10 Mentone Terrace, Newington, Edinburgh, EH9 2DG
Tel: 0131 667 1647

1 Twin	2 Pub Bath/Show	B&B per person	Open Jan-Dec excl Xmas
2 Double		from £24.00 Single	
		from £20.00 Dbl/Twn	

Victorian semi-detached villa in quiet residential area. Friendly and family run. Easy access to city centre by car and public transport.

GUEST HOUSE ★★★

Ashdene House
23 Fountainhall Road, Edinburgh, EH9 2LN
Tel: 0131 667 6026
E-mail: Ashdene_House_Edinburgh@Compuserve.com
Web: http://welcome.to/ashdene_house

1 Single	5 En Suite fac	B&B per person	Open Jan-Dec excl
1 Twin		£42.00-£58.00 Single	Xmas/New Year
2 Double		£24.00-£40.00 Dbl/Twn	
1 Family			

Very comfortable family run Edwardian town house retaining many features, in quiet residential conservation area. Convenient for bus route to city centre (10 minutes). Non-smoking establishment.

GUEST HOUSE ★★★★

GOLD

Important: Prices stated are estimates and may be subject to amendments

Edinburgh

Map Ref: 2C5

Ashlyn Guest House
42 Inverleith Row, Edinburgh, EH5 5PV
Tel/Fax: 0131 552 2954
E-mail: reservations@ashlyn-edinburgh.com

2 Single	4 Ensuite fac
2 Twin	2 Pub Bath/Show
3 Double	1 Priv.NOT ensuite
1 Family	

B&B per person
from £23.00 Single
from £24.00 Dbl/Twn

Open Jan-Dec excl
Xmas/New Year

★★★★
GUEST
HOUSE

Semi-detached Georgian family home, only 5 minutes walk from the beautiful Botanical Gardens. This listed building retains many original features with ornate cornicing and period fire places. 20 minute walk to Princes Street and the Castle with frequent bus service on the door step. Unrestricted free street parking nearby. Self Catering facilities also available.

Ashwood Guest House
20 Minto Street, Edinburgh, EH9 1RQ
Tel: 0131 667 8024 Fax: 0131 271 1646
E-mail: ashwood@ednet.co.uk
Web: www.ednet.co.uk/~ashwood

1 Twin	2 En Suite fac
1 Double	
2 Family	

B&B per person
from £25.00 Single
from £20.00 Dbl/Twn

Open Jan-Dec excl Xmas

★★★
GUEST
HOUSE

Small friendly guest house, ideally situated close to the city centre and tourist attractions. Private parking. Ensuite rooms.

Auld Reekie Guest House
16 Mayfield Gardens, Edinburgh, EH9 2BZ
Tel: 0131 667 6177 Fax: 0131 662 0033
E-mail: RHONA@auldreekiegh.freeserve.co.uk
Web: www.auldreekiegh.freeserve.co.uk

1 Single	All En Suite
2 Twin	
2 Double	
2 Family	

B&B per person
£25.00-£40.00 Single
£20.00-£35.00 Dbl/Twn

Open Jan-Dec

★★★
GUEST
HOUSE

Family run stone built house on south side of city centre. On main bus route to Princes Street.

Averon Guest House
44 Gilmore Place, Edinburgh, EH3 9NQ
Tel: 0131 229 9932
E-mail: info@averon.co.uk
Web: www.averon.co.uk

1 Single	6 En Suite fac
3 Twin	2 Pub Bath/Show
3 Double	
3 Family	

B&B per person
from £19.00 Single
from £19.00 Dbl/Twn

Open Jan-Dec

★
GUEST
HOUSE

Central location with private car park to rear. 10 minute walk to Princes Street and Castle. Near Kings Theatre and Conference Centre.

Avon Hotel
1-2 Spence Street, (off Dalkeith Road), Edinburgh, EH16 5AG
Tel: 0131 667 8681 Fax: 0131 667 9531
E-mail: info@avonhotel.co.uk

1 Single	5 Ensuite fac
2 Twin	3 Pub Bath/Show
3 Double	
4 Family	

B&B per person
£20.00-£39.00 Single
£19.00-£39.00 Dbl/Twn
Room only per person
£15.00-£35.00

Open Jan-Dec

★★
HOTEL

Privately owned Victorian town house, close to the Commonwealth Pool and Holyrood Park. All rooms with telephone and TV. Off street private and secure parking.

VAT is shown at 17.5%: changes in this rate may affect prices.

Key to symbols is on back flap.

Edinburgh   Map Ref: 2C5

HOTEL

The Balmoral Edinburgh
1 Princes Street, Edinburgh, EH2 2EQ
Tel: 0131 556 2414 Fax: 0131 557 8740
E-mail: reservations@thebalmoralhotel.com
Web: www.rfhotels.com

Edinburgh's landmark hotel, completely refurbished to international standard.

22 Twin	All En Suite	B&B per person	Open Jan-Dec
164		£82.50-£110.00	
Double		Single/Dbl/Twn	

GUEST HOUSE

Balmore House
34 Gilmore Place, Edinburgh, EH3 9NQ
Tel/Fax: 0131 221 1331
E-mail: Balmore@classicfm.net

Recently refurbished traditional Victorian terraced villa with conservatory dining room. 10 minutes to city centre. Close to Kings Theatre. Private parking.

1 Twin	All En Suite	B&B per person	Open Jan-Dec
3 Double		from £25.00 Dbl/Twn	
1 Family			

GUEST HOUSE

Balquhidder Guest House
94 Pilrig Street, Edinburgh, EH6 5AY
Tel: 0131 554 3377

Detached house in its own grounds overlooking public park and on bus routes to the city centre.

1 Single	5 En Suite fac	B&B per person	Open Jan-Dec excl
3 Twin	1 Limited ensuite	from £20.00 Single	Xmas/New Year
2 Double	1 Pub Bath/Show	from £20.00 Dbl/Twn	

INN

Bank Hotel
Royal Mile, 1 South Bridge, Edinburgh, EH1 1LL
Tel: 0131 622 6800 Fax: 0131 622 6822
E-mail: bank@festival-inns.co.uk
Web: www.festival-inns.co.uk

Central situation on the Royal Mile. Stylish accommodation in themed rooms based on famous Scots. Lively cafe/bar ambience with bar meals & bar breakfast.

1 Single	8 En Suite fac	B&B per person	Open Jan-Dec
4 Twin	1 Priv.NOT ensuite	from £65.00 Single	
3 Double		from £40.00 Dbl/Twn	
1 Family		per room	

GUEST HOUSE

Barrosa Guest House
21 Pilrig Street, Edinburgh, EH6 5AN
Tel: 0131 554 3700

Georgian house only ten minutes from city centre on bus route.

1 Twin	4 En Suite fac	B&B per person	Open Jan-Dec
2 Double	3 Pub Bath/Show	£21.00-£32.00 Dbl/Twn	
3 Family			

Important: Prices stated are estimates and may be subject to amendments

Edinburgh   Map Ref: 2C5

★★★★

GUEST
HOUSE

Ben Doran Guest House
11 Mayfield Gardens, Edinburgh, EH9 2AX
Tel: 0131 667 8488 Fax: 0131 667 0076
E-mail: info@bendoran.com
Web: www.bendoran.com

1 Single	6 En Suite fac	B&B per person	Open Jan-Dec
1 Twin	4 Priv.NOT ensuite	from £30.00 Single	B&B + Eve.Meal
3 Double	3 Pub Bath/Show	from £30.00 Dbl/Twn	from £53.00
5 Family			

Luxurious 4 star Georgian townhouse, beautifully refurbished. Central, on bus routes, close to city centre and Edinburgh attractions. Lovely city and hillside views and a warm welcome.

BERESFORD HOTEL
32 COATES GARDENS, EDINBURGH EH12 5LE
TEL: 0131 337 0850 FAX: 0131 538 7123
E.MAIL: bookings@beresford-edinburgh.com
WEB: www.beresford-edinburgh.com

Relax in this recently refurbished Victorian town-house. In a prime location only $1/2$ mile from Princes Street and all city centre amenities, an ideal base for your visit to Edinburgh. En-suite rooms with direct-dial phones and some with fridges. Children most welcome.

★★★

GUEST
HOUSE

Beresford Hotel
32 Coates Garden, Edinburgh, EH12 5LE
Tel: 0131 337 0850 Fax: 0131 538 7123
E-mail: bookings@beresford-edinburgh.com
Web: www.beresford-edinburgh.com

3 Twin	10 En Suite fac	B&B per person	Open Jan-Dec
4 Double	2 Pub Bath/Show	from £25.00 Single	
5 Family		from £35.00 Dbl/Twn	

Family run establishment close to city centre and Haymarket station. Most rooms en-suite. Children most welcome.

★★★

GUEST
HOUSE

Beverley Hotel
40 Murrayfield Avenue, Edinburgh, EH12 6AY
Tel: 0131 337 1128 Fax: 0131 313 3275
E-mail: bevedin@aol.com
Web: www.beverley-hotel.com

1 Single	7 En Suite fac	B&B per person	Open Jan-Dec
1 Twin		from £30.00 Single	
2 Double		from £25.00 Dbl/Twn	
3 Family			

An elegant Victorian terraced house, situated in a quiet tree-lined avenue offering ample free parking. Only minutes from Edinburgh's historic city centre and within fifteen minutes of all main coach, rail and air terminals.

★★

GUEST
HOUSE

Blossom House
8 Minto Street, Edinburgh, EH9 1RG
Tel: 0131 667 5353 Fax: 0131 667 2813

2 Twin	En Suite fac	B&B per person	Open Jan-Dec
2 Double	Pub Bath/Show	from £20.00 Single	
4 Family		from £17.50 Dbl/Twn	
En suite fac			

Comfortable, family run guest house. City centre within walking distance. Excellent bus service. Private car park. Close to commonwealth pool.

Edinburgh   Map Ref: 2C5

Boisdale Hotel
9 Coates Gardens, Edinburgh, EH12 5LG
Tel: 0131 337 1134 Fax: 0131 313 0048

GUEST HOUSE

| 2 Single | All En Suite | B&B per person | Open Jan-Dec |

2 Twin £25.00-£45.00 Single   B&B + Eve.Meal
3 Double £25.00-£40.00 Dbl/Twn from £40.00
3 Family Room only per person from £40.00

Victorian terraced house, close to Haymarket station. All rooms have full private facilities.

The Bonham
35 Drumsheugh Gardens, Edinburgh, EH3 7RN
Tel: 0131 623 6060 Fax: 0131 332 9631
E-mail: reserve@thebonham.com
Web: www.thebonham.com

HOTEL

10 Single All En Suite   B&B per person   Open Jan-Dec excl Xmas
38 Dbl/Twn   £135.00-£155.00 Sgle
£82.50-£147.50 Double

At Edinburgh's West End lies The Bonham designed in rich, bold colours to give a contemporary feel of the highest quality. All 48 bedrooms are fitted with eTV Interactive, the latest in modern equipment (including Internet/E-mail/DVD/CD/Microsoft Office applications) and the restaurant offers wholesome food with Californian influences.

Borthwick House
23 Mayfield Gardens, Edinburgh, EH9 2BX
Tel/Fax: 0131 667 8475
E-mail: borthwickhouse@scotland-hotels.com

GUEST HOUSE

1 Single All En Suite   B&B per person   Open Jan-Dec
3 Twin   from £25.00 Single
4 Double   from £20.00 Dbl/Twn
4 Family

An impressive detached Victorian villa with off road secure parking. Beautifully restored to a very high standard with decorative plasterwork and period cornices. Very comfortable spacious accommodation with easy access to city centre via main bus route.

Brae Guest House
119 Willowbrae Road, Edinburgh, EH8 7HN
Tel: 0131 661 0170
E-mail: braeguesthouse@tinyworld.co.uk

GUEST HOUSE

1 Single 3 En Suite fac   B&B per person   Open Jan-Dec
1 Twin   1 Priv.NOT ensuite from £20.00 Single
1 Double   from £20.00 Dbl/Twn
1 Family

Friendly family run guest house on bus route to city centre. 10 minutes walk from Meadowbank Stadium and Holyrood Palace.

Brodies Guest House
22 East Claremont Street, Edinburgh, EH7 4JP
Tel: 0131 556 4032 Fax: 0131 556 9739
Web: www.brodiesguesthouse.co.uk

GUEST HOUSE

1 Single 3 En Suite fac   B&B per person   Open Jan-Dec
1 Twin   1 Pub Bath/Show £24.00-£30.00 Single
1 Double   £24.00-£38.00 Dbl/Twn
2 Family

Small, friendly, family run Victorian town house in a cobbled street within 1/2 mile of Princes Street. Convenient for bus/railway station, playhouse theatre, pubs and restaurants nearby. Scottish breakfasts a speciality.

Important: Prices stated are estimates and may be subject to amendments

Edinburgh		Map Ref: 2C5		

GUEST HOUSE ★★

The Broughton Hotel
37 Brougton Place, Edinburgh, EH1 3RR
Tel: 0131 558 9792 Fax: 0131 558 9790

City centre accommodation with some car parking. All rooms ensuite with colour TV, tea and coffee making facilities. Restaurants, bars and Playhouse Theatre nearby.

1 Single	All En Suite	B&B per person	Open Jan-Dec
2 Twin		£25.00-£40.00 Single	
2 Double		£25.00-£40.00 Dbl/Twn	
1 Family		Room only per person from £20.00	

GUEST HOUSE ★★★

Brunswick Hotel
7 Brunswick Street, Edinburgh, EH7 5JB
Tel: 0131 556 1238 Fax: 0131 557 1404

Listed Georgian Building now under new ownership, situated close to London Road and main bus routes to City Centre and Playhouse Theatre. Free street parking available.

2 Twin	Ensuite	B&B per person	Open all year
4 Double	Ensuite	£25.00-£45.00 Single	
2 Family	Ensuite	£25.00-£45.00 Dbl/Twn	
2 Family	Shower/Whb		

HOTEL ★★★★

Bruntsfield Hotel
69 Bruntsfield Place, Edinburgh, EH10 4HH
Tel: 0131 229 1393 Fax: 0131 229 5634
Web: www.thebruntsfield.co.uk

Overlooking a park close to the city centre, the Bruntsfield is a well appointed townhouse hotel with friendly & professional service. The 75 comfortably furnished bedrooms offer all facilities & services required by both business & leisure travellers. The AA rosetted Potting Shed Restaurant serves modern scottish cusine in an elegant but informal atmosphere. A relaxing lounge & lively pub bar add to the distinctive character of The Bruntsfield.

11 Single	All En Suite	B&B per person	Open Jan-Dec
32 Twin		£65.00-£105.00 Single	B&B + Eve.Meal
30 Double		£90.00-£150.00 Double	£60.00-£80.00
4 Family			

Cairn Hotel
10-18 Windsor Street, Edinburgh EH7 5JR
Tel: 0131 557 0175 Fax: 0131 556 8221
Web: www.cairn-hotels.co.uk

Hotel is located close to famous Princes Street, shops, restaurants and theatres within walking distance. Free on street parking. All rooms are ensuite, with TV, direct dial telephone and hostess tray.

HOTEL ★

Cairn Hotel
10/18 Windsor Street, Edinburgh, EH7 5JR
Tel: 0131 557 0175 Fax: 0131 556 8221
Web: www.cairn-hotels.co.uk

Situated in quiet residential area, close to Princes Street, with easy access to city centre and all amenities. A good selection of restaurants nearby.

10 Single	All En Suite	B&B per person	Open Jan-Dec
20 Twin		from £45.00 Single	
17 Double		from £27.50 Dbl/Twn	
2 Family			

VAT is shown at 17.5%: changes in this rate may affect prices.

Key to symbols is on back flap.

Caledonian Hilton

PRINCES STREET, EDINBURGH EH1 2AB
Tel: 0131 459 9988   Fax: 0131 225 6632
e.mail: ednchhirm@hilton.com

Situated in the heart of the city in the shadow of
Edinburgh Castle, The Caledonian Hilton provides
the finest possible base from which to explore
Scotland's historic capital. The hotel's elegant decor
and it's long tradition of attentive and friendly
service have charmed guests from around the world
for almost a century. The Caledonian Hilton stands
as a proud symbol of Scottish hospitality.

★ ★ ★ ★ ★ HOTEL   Caledonian Hilton

HOTEL

The Caledonian
Princes Street, Edinburgh, EH1 2AB
Tel: 0131 459 9988 Fax: 0131 225 6632
E-mail: ednchhirm@hilton.com

43 Single	All En Suite	B&B per person	Open Jan-Dec
101 Twin		£170.00-£190.00 Single	
82 Double		£85.00-£170.00 Dbl/Twn	
23 Suites			

Traditional hotel with friendly atmosphere, elegantly furnished. Situated
on world famous Princes Street, affording spectacular views of the castle.

**GUEST
HOUSE**

Cameron Toll Guest House
299 Dalkeith Road, Edinburgh, EH16 5JX
Tel: 0131 667 2950 Fax: 0131 662 1987
E-mail: camerontoll@msn.com

3 Single	10 En Suite fac	B&B per person	Open Jan-Dec
2 Twin	1 Priv.NOT ensuite	from £30.00 Single	B&B + Eve.Meal
3 Double		from £22.00 Dbl/Twn	from £32.00
3 Family			

Andrew and Mary offer you a cosy bedroom in our friendly guest house
with some private parking. Situated on the A7, there is a frequent bus
service to the city centre. The Commonwealth Pool is nearby. Scottish
hospitality to ensure a memorable stay. Gold award for environmental
management.

GOLD

HOTEL

Carlton Hotel
North Bridge, Edinburgh, EH1 1SD
Tel: 0131 472 3000 Fax: 0131 556 2691

15 Single	All En Suite	B&B per room	Open Jan-Dec
64 Twin		£125.00-£140.00 Sngl.	B&B + Eve.Meal
50 Double		£193.00-£210.00 Dbl/Twn	£70.00-£105.00 ppn
10 Family		£210.00-£255.00 King size	
50 King size		Deluxe	
Deluxe			

Central, spacious, traditional style hotel with modern amenities. Leisure
complex including squash, aerobics, gym and swimming. Major
refurbishment underway during 2000.

Important: Prices stated are estimates and may be subject to amendments

Edinburgh | Map Ref: 2C5

GUEST HOUSE ★★

Carrington Guest House
38 Pilrig Street, Edinburgh, EH6 5AN
Tel: 0131 554 4769

3 Twin	4 En Suite fac	B&B per person	Open Jan-Dec
2 Double	2 Limited ensuite	£21.00-£30.00 Dbl/Twn	
2 Family	3 Pub Bath/Show		

Large family run guest house convenient for all city centre attractions. On street parking.

GUEST HOUSE ★

Castle Park Guest House
75 Gilmore Place, Edinburgh, EH3 9NU
Tel: 0131 229 1215 Fax: 0131 229 1223

1 Single	4 En Suite fac	B&B per person	Open Jan-Dec
2 Twin	1 Pub Bath/Show	from £17.50 Single	
3 Double		from £20.00 Dbl/Twn	
1 Family		Room only per person	
		from £10.00	

Family run guest house close to city centre. Convenient for Kings Theatre and Conference Hall. A variety of local restaurants and bistros. Children welcome.

CHANNINGS
South Learmonth Gardens, Edinburgh EH4 1EZ
Tel: 0131 332 3232 Fax: 0131 332 9631
e.mail: reserve@channings.co.uk Web: www.channings.co.uk

Channings is just a few minutes walk from the centre of Edinburgh, providing easy access to shops and Edinburgh Castle. Originally 5 Edwardian townhouses and facing onto a quiet cobbled street, Channings has 46 individually designed en-suite bedrooms all with traditional, restored period features, providing relaxing and comfortable surroundings.

HOTEL ★★★★

Channings
South Learmonth Gardens, Edinburgh, EH4 1EZ
Tel: 0131 332 3232 Fax: 0131 332 9631
E-mail: reserve@channings.co.uk
Web: www.channings.co.uk

5 Petite	All En Suite	B&B per person	Open Jan-Dec excl Xmas
41 Dbl/Twn		£120.00-£155.00 Sgle	
		£72.50-£120.00 Double	

On a peaceful street close to the city centre Channings is a stylish transformation of 5 Edwardian townhouses into an hotel of character and charm. A relaxed ambience pervades from restful firelit lounges to the individually designed guest rooms. Channings Restaurant serves distinctive contemporary Scottish cooking in elegant informal surroundings with terraced gardens and a new conservatory and wine bar creating a welcoming atmosphere.

GUEST HOUSE ★★

Mrs Judy Cheng
2 St Catherines Gardens, Corstorphine, Edinburgh, EH12 7AZ
Tel: 0131 334 6159

1 Twin	2 Pub Bath/Show	B&B per person	Open Jan-Dec
2 Double		£25.00-£30.00 Single	
2 Family		£20.00-£28.00 Dbl/Twn	

Close to Edinburgh Zoo and Murrayfield. On major bus route to city centre. Chinese evening meals available on request. Chinese language spoken. No smoking.

VAT is shown at 17.5%: changes in this rate may affect prices.   *Key to symbols is on back flap.*

Christopher North House Hotel

★★★
SMALL
HOTEL

6 Gloucester Place, Edinburgh EH3 6EF
Tel: 0131 225 2720 Fax: 0131 220 4706
e.mail: reservations@christophernorth.co.uk
Web: www.christophernorth.co.uk

Within the city centre set amid magnificent architecture, the
Christopher North House Hotel exudes an air of grace that favours
all who delight in the finer things in life. All our rooms and facilities
will have you waxing lyrical long after your visit.

★★★
SMALL
HOTEL

Christopher North House Hotel
6 Gloucester Place, Edinburgh, EH3 6EF
Tel: 0131 225 2720 Fax: 0131 220 4706
E-mail: reservations@christophernorth.co.uk
Web: www.christophernorth.co.uk

Georgian hotel, with new bistro being added now under new management
in Edinburgh's New Town, convenient for Princes Street and all city centre
amenities. The historic nature of the building procludes the provision of a
lift. Speciality traditional Austrian espresso available. All rooms en-suite.

1 Single	All En Suite	B&B per person	Open Jan-Dec
4 Twin		from £45.00 Single	
5 Double		from £30.00 Dbl/Twn	
4 Family			

★★
SMALL
HOTEL

Clan Campbell Hotel
11 Brunswick Street, Edinburgh, EH7 5JB
Tel: 0131 557 6910 Fax: 0131 557 6929
E-mail: clan.campbell:virgin.net

Former Black Watch Club, now family run hotel set in central Georgian
townhouse. Unrestricted street parking. Languages spoken.

1 Single	All En Suite	B&B per person	Open Jan-Dec
2 Twin		from £25.00 Single	
3 Double		from £20.00 Dbl/Twn	
2 Family			

★★
GUEST
HOUSE

Clashaidy Guest House
21 Kilmaurs Road, Edinburgh, EH16 5DA
Tel: 0131 667 2626 Fax: 0131 622 0942
E-mail: clashaidy@lineone.net

Quiet area of the city with free on street parking, central location.
Frequent bus service. Pleasant views from all bedrooms. Close to Queen's
Park and Arthur's Seat, University Residence and Royal Commonwealth
Pool. Walking distance to Cameron Toll Shopping Centre and a choice of
restaurants of different nationalities.

1 Twin	1 Priv.NOT ensuite	B&B per person	Open Jan-Dec
1 Double		£25.00-£30.00 Single	
2 Family		£16.00-£25.00 Dbl/Twn	

★★★
GUEST
HOUSE

Classic House
50 Mayfield Road, Edinburgh, EH9 2NH
Tel: 0131 667 5847 Fax: 0131 662 1016
E-mail: info@classichouse.demon.co.uk
Web: www.classichouse.demon.co.uk

Friendly welcome at this family home, recently refurbished to a high
standard. Attractive breakfast buffet offering a wide choice of traditional
and vegetarian dishes. Variety of local restaurants on a short bus ride to
city centre with all its amenities. Totally non-smoking house.

1 Single	All En Suite	B&B per person	Open Jan-Dec
2 Twin		from £18.00 Single	
3 Double		from £18.00 Dbl/Twn	
1 Family			

Important: Prices stated are estimates and may be subject to amendments

Edinburgh   Map Ref: 2C5

GUEST HOUSE ★★

Claymore Guest House
68 Pilrig Street, Edinburgh, EH6 5AS
Tel/Fax: 0131 554 2500

2 Twin	3 En Suite fac	B&B per person	Open Jan-Dec
2 Double	1 Priv.NOT ensuite	£18.00-£26.50 Dbl/Twn	
2 Family	1 Pub Show		

Red sandstone Victorian terraced villa, a former manse. Centrally situated with close proximity to all Edinburgh's main attractions. 10 minutes to Playhouse Theatre.

GUEST HOUSE ★★★

Craigelachie Hotel
21 Murrayfield Avenue, Edinburgh, EH12 6AU
Tel: 0131 337 4076 Fax: 0131 313 3305
E-mail: craig01@globalnet.co.uk
Web: http://come.to/edinburgh

3 Single	All En Suite	B&B per person	Open Jan-Dec
2 Twin		£30.00-£40.00 Single	
2 Double		£30.00-£40.00 Dbl/Twn	
2 Family			

Victorian terraced house in a quiet residential area with ample street parking. Near Murrayfield Stadium and bus services to the city centre.

GUEST HOUSE ★★

Crioch Guest House
23 East Hermitage Place, Edinburgh, EH6 8AD
Tel/Fax: 0131 554 5494
E-mail: welcome@crioch.com Web: www.crioch.com

1 Single	5 Ensuite fac	B&B per person	Open Jan-Dec
1 Twin	1 Priv.NOT ensuite	from £20.00 Single	
2 Double		from £18.50 Dbl/Twn	
2 Family			

Only 10 minutes from the city centre, Crioch overlooks the leafy park of Leith Links. Our recent major refurbishment means that all rooms now have ensuite shower or private bathroom, and you still receive the same warm welcome. Free parking and a frequent bus service leaves you to enjoy Edinburgh's sights on foot, and later a short stroll takes you to Leith's fine cafes, bars and restaurants.

CROWNE PLAZA EDINBURGH

80 High Street, The Royal Mile, Edinburgh EH1 1TH
Tel: 0131 557 9797 Fax: 0131 557 9789
e.mail: ResCPEdinburgh@AllianceUK.com Web: www.crowneplazaed.co.uk

Situated in the heart of the Old Town on the historic Royal Mile, the hotel lies halfway between Edinburgh Castle and Holyrood Palace, ideally placed for exploring Edinburgh's most famed attractions. Traditionally designed to blend with its ancient neighbours the heritage of its historic setting has been preserved on this medieval and world famous Royal Mile.

HOTEL ★★★★

Crowne Plaza Edinburgh
80 High Street, The Royal Mile, Edinburgh, EH1 1TH
Tel: 0131 557 9797 Fax: 0131 557 9789
E-mail: ResCPEdinburgh@AllianceUK.com
Web: www.crowneplazaed.co.uk

127 Twin	All En Suite	B&B per person	Open Jan-Dec excl Xmas
98 Double		from £120.00 Single	
3 Family		from £65.00 Dbl/Twn	
10 Suites			

This modern, 4 star city centre hotel offers first class facilities including 238 en-suite bedrooms, restaurant, lounge, bar, onsite parking for 135 cars, 12 meeting rooms, dedicated business centre, leisure club with indoor pool, fitness room, saunas, solarium and treatment room.

VAT is shown at 17.5%: changes in this rate may affect prices.   Key to symbols is on back flap.

Edinburgh

Map Ref: 2C5

★★

SMALL
HOTEL

Dean Hotel
10 Clarendon Crescent, Edinburgh, EH4 1PT
Tel: 0131 332 0308 Fax: 0131 315 4089
E-mail: deanhotel@aol.com
Web: www.deanhotel.co.uk

4 Single	5 En Suite fac	B&B per person	Open Jan-Dec
3 Twin	2 Pub Bath/Show	from £39.00 Single	
1 Double		from £35.00 Dbl/Twn	
1 Family			

Personally run hotel in traditional Edinburgh terrace. Close to West End and all amenities. Comfortable and popular lounge bar. No evening meal available, choice of eating places within 200 metres distance. Private garden by Water of Leith available to guests on request.

★★★

GUEST
HOUSE

Dene Guest House
7 Eyre Place, off Dundas Street, Edinburgh, EH3 5ES
Tel: 0131 556 2700 Fax: 0131 557 9876
E-mail: deneguesthouse@yahoo.co.uk

3 Single	5 En Suite fac	B&B per person	Open Jan-Dec
3 Twin	2 Pub Bath/Show	from £19.50 Single	
3 Double		from £19.50 Dbl/Twn	
2 Family			

Charming Georgian townhouse offering friendly service and a relaxed atmosphere. Perfectly located in city centre to experience Edinburgh's culture, history, restaurants and bars.

★★★

GUEST
HOUSE

Mr Derek Denham
Castle View Guest House, 30 Castle Street,
Edinburgh, EH2 3HT
Tel: 0131 226 5784 Fax: 0131 226 1603
E-mail: castleview@cableinet.co.uk
Web: http://www.castleviewgh.co.uk

2 Single	5 En Suite fac	B&B per person	Open Jan-Dec
1 Double	1 Priv.NOT ensuite	£30.00-£42.00 Single	
3 Family		£25.00-£40.00 Double	

Spacious Georgian 3rd floor flat with comfortable lounge area offering views to Castle and the Forth. Ideally positioned approximately 100 metres from Princes St yet a haven above the bustle of the city.

★★★★

GUEST
HOUSE

Dorstan Private Hotel
7 Priestfield Road, Edinburgh, EH16 5HJ
Tel: 0131 667 6721/5138 Fax: 0131 668 4644

5 Single	9 En Suite fac	B&B per person	Open Jan-Dec
1 Twin	3 Limited ensuite	£32.00-£48.00 Single	
6 Double	3 Pub Bath/Show	£36.00-£41.00 Dbl/Twn	
2 Family			

Victorian villa in quiet residential area. Own car parking. 1 mile (2 kms) on main bus route from city centre. Most rooms en suite. Golf course adjacent. Ideal for visiting tourist attractions and surrounding area.

★★

GUEST
HOUSE

'Dunedin' Private House
21-23 Colinton Road, Edinburgh, EH10 5DR
Tel: 0131 447 0679 Fax: 0131 446 9358
E-mail: H.FORT10560@aol.com

1 Single	3 En Suite fac	B&B per person	Open Jan-Dec
2 Twin	1 Priv.NOT ensuite	from £20.00 Single	
2 Double	1 limited ensuite	from £23.00 Dbl/Twn	
1 Family	2 Pub Bath/Show		

Listed Victorian town house retaining period ambience. Princes St. is approximately 15 minutes walk and close to the regular bus route. A bed and breakfast with basement annexe accommodation with independent front door entrance.

Important: Prices stated are estimates and may be subject to amendments

DUNSTANE HOUSE HOTEL

4 West Coates, Haymarket, Edinburgh EH12 5JQ
Tel/Fax: 0131-337 6169 e.mail: reservations@dunstanehousehotel.co.uk
Web: www.dunstanehousehotel.co.uk

Impressive Victorian mansion dating 1850's in elevated position in private garden grounds. All bedrooms luxuriously refurbished with four-poster deluxe rooms available. Only 10 mins walk to city centre and close to Murrayfield Stadium, conference centre and Edinburgh Airport. Traditional Scottish cuisine served. Lounge bar and private secluded car park.

★★★

SMALL HOTEL

Dunstane House Hotel
4 West Coates, Edinburgh, EH12 5JQ
Tel/Fax: 0131 337 6169
E-mail: reservations@dunstanehousehotel.co.uk
Web: www.dunstanehousehotel.co.uk

4 Single	All En Suite	B&B per person	Open Jan-Dec
2 Twin		from £35.00 Single	
5 Double		from £33.50 Dbl/Twn	
5 Family			

Impressive Listed Victorian mansion retaining many original features enjoying imposing position within large grounds on the A8 airport road (major bus route). 10 mins walk from city centre. Close to Edinburgh Conference Centre, Murrayfield and Edinburgh Zoo. Private secluded car park. Lounge bar. New seafood restaurant opening early 2001. Friendly service assured by proprietors Shirley and Derek Mowat.

Duthus Lodge

5 West Coates, Edinburgh EH12 5JG
Tel: 0131-337 6876 e.mail: Duthus.Lodge@ukgateway.net
Fax: 0131-313 2264 Web: http://members.edinburgh.org/duthuslodge

Splendid detached family-run Victorian establishment offering bed and breakfast in tastefully decorated and comfortable surroundings. The perfect base to explore Edinburgh. All rooms ensuite. Ten minutes from city centre, close to International Conference Centre and Murrayfield stadium. Private parking.

★★★

GUEST HOUSE

Duthus Lodge
5 West Coates, Edinburgh, EH12 5JG
Tel: 0131 337 6876 Fax: 0131 313 2264
E-mail: Duthus.Lodge@ukgateway.net
Web: http://members.edinburgh.org/duthuslodge

1 Single	All En Suite	B&B per person	Open Jan-Dec
2 Twin		£35.00-£45.00 Single	Evening meals on
2 Double		£25.00-£35.00 Dbl/Twn	request
2 Family			

Detached Victorian sandstone villa with attractive walled gardens. All rooms with garden or city outlook. Some with views to the Pentland Hills. Ideal base for exploring Edinburgh's historical attractions. Close to zoo. On main bus route to city centre.

★★

CAMPUS ACCOMMODATION

Edinburgh Conference Centre
Heriot-Watt University, Riccarton, Edinburgh, EH14 4AS
Tel: 0131 451 3669 Fax: 0131 451 3199
Web: www.ecc.scot.net

1493 Sngl	1231 Ensuite	B&B per person	Open Jan-Dec excl
98 Twin	465 Pub Bath/Show	from £26.00 Single	Xmas/New Year
35 Double		from £23.00 Dbl/Twn	B&B + Eve.Meal from £35.00

Situated in 370 acre picturesque campus of Heriot Watt University. 6 miles (10kms) west of the city centre, 3 miles (5kms) from Edinburgh Airport.

VAT is shown at 17.5%: changes in this rate may affect prices.

Key to symbols is on back flap.

Edinburgh

Map Ref: 2C5

Edinburgh First, *University of Edinburgh*

18 Holyrood Park Road, Edinburgh EH16 5AY
Tel: 0800 028 7118   Fax: 0131-667 7271
e.mail: Edinburgh.First@ed.ac.uk   Web: www.EdinburghFirst.com

Beautiful location only 10 minutes from Princes Street, Edinburgh First's Pollock Halls are one of Edinburgh's most popular accommodation centres for people of all ages. With 1,200 modern rooms (500 en-suite), restaurant, shop, bar, meeting facilities and free parking, Edinburgh First offers a complete centre in the heart of Edinburgh.

★★

HOTEL

Edinburgh First
The University of Edinburgh, 18 Holyrood Park Road,
Edinburgh, EH16 5AY
Tel: 0800 028 7118 Fax: 0131 667 7271
E-mail: Edinburgh.First@ed.ac.uk
Web: www.EdinburghFirst.com

On campus in Holyrood Park beside Arthur's Seat. Close to Royal Commonwealth Pool, 3 km from city centre. In beautiful surroundings, we offer comfortable accommodation with en-suite facilities. Particularly suitable for groups. Alternative annexe accommodation available. Conference and meeting facilities.

330 Rooms   All En Suite

B&B per person
£27.00-£46.00 Single
£69.00-£75.00 Double

Open Mar-Apr, Jun-Sep

★★★

GUEST HOUSE

Edinburgh House
11 McDonald Road, Edinburgh, EH7 4LX
Tel: 0131 556 3434

Small personally run guest house in a traditional tenement building approx 0.5 ml from Princes Street. Good bus service to city centre with all its amenities. Evening meal by prior arrangement or variety of restaurants nearby. Non-smoking house.

5 Double   All En Suite

B&B per person
£26.00-£37.00 Double

Open Jan-Dec

★★

HOTEL

Edinburgh's Minto Hotel
16-18 Minto Street, Edinburgh, EH9 9RQ
Tel: 0131 668 1234 Fax: 0131 662 4870

Family run hotel on main A701 road south, with private car park. On main bus route to city centre (10 minutes). Easy access to theatre and Commonwealth Pool.

5 Single   All En Suite
6 Twin
9 Double
3 Family

B&B per person
£30.00-£60.00 Single
£25.00-£47.50 Dbl/Twn

Open Jan-Dec

★★★★

GUEST HOUSE

Ellesmere Guest House
11 Glengyle Terrace, Edinburgh, EH3 9LN
Tel: 0131 229 4823 Fax: 0131 229 5285
E-mail: celia@edinburghbandb.co.uk
Web: www.edinburghbandb.co.uk

City centre Victorian terraced house in quiet location overlooking Bruntsfield Links with frontage overlooking golf links. Kings Theatre, Conference Centre and all amenities within walking distance. All rooms en suite. Full Scottish Breakfast.

1 Single   All En Suite
2 Twin
2 Double
1 Family

B&B per person
from £25.00 Single
from £25.00 Dbl/Twn

Open Jan-Dec excl Xmas

Important: Prices stated are estimates and may be subject to amendments

Map Ref: 2C5

EMERALD GUEST HOUSE

3 Drum Street, Gilmerton, Edinburgh EH17 8QQ
Tel: 0131 664 5918 or 664 1920
Mobile: 07930 889598

Family run Victorian villa within easy reach of city centre.
Convenient to city by-pass for all national routes.
Private parking. Good bus route. Warm welcome assured.

★★

B&B

Emerald Guest House
3 Drum Street, Gilmerton, Edinburgh. EH17 8QQ
Tel: 0131 664 5918 or 664 1920
Mobile: 07930 889598

1 Family	3 Ensuite fac	B&B per person	Open Jan-Dec
1 Double	1 Pub Bath/Show	£20.00-£35.00 Single	
2 Twin		£20.00-£31.00 Dbl/Twn	
1 Treble			

Family run bed and breakfast located on convenient bus route to city
centre. Private parking available.

★★★

HOTEL

Express By Holiday Inn, Edinburgh – Leith
Britannia Way, Ocean Drive, Edinburgh, EH6 6LA
Tel: 0131 555 4422 Fax: 0131 555 4646
Web: www.hiex-edinburgh.com

36 Twin	All En Suite	B&B per person	Open Jan-Dec
30 Double		from £52.50 Single	
36 Family		from £26.25 Dbl/Twn	

New quality hotel, 1.5 miles from city centre, overlooking Royal Yacht
Britannia. Continental breakfast included in room price. Children stay free.
Ample parking. In-house bar, power showers, in-room telephones, movies
and Sky TV.

★★★

**GUEST
HOUSE**

Fairholme Guest House
13 Moston Terrace, Edinburgh, EH9 2DE
Tel: 0131 667 8645 Fax: 0131 668 2435
E-mail: STB@fairholme.co.uk Web: www.fairholme.co.uk

1 Single	3 En Suite fac	B&B per person	Open Jan-Dec
1 Twin	1 Priv.NOT ensuite	from £20.00 Single	
1 Double		from £20.00 Dbl/Twn	
1 Family		Room only per person	
		from £20.00	

Look no further... Nestled away from noisy traffic yet close to the city
centre Fairholme provides facilities for restful relaxation after an eventful
day sightseeing. Unwind in an elegant home of comfort, charm and
character. Start the day refreshed and replenished after indulging in our
traditional Scottish breakfast. You'll be glad you did! Unrestricted parking.
Special winter breaks offer.

★

**GUEST
HOUSE**

Falcon Crest Guest House
70 South Trinity Road, Edinburgh, EH5 3NX
Tel: 0131 552 5294

1 Single	3 En Suite fac	B&B per person	Open Jan-Dec excl Xmas
2 Twin	2 Pub Bath/Show	from £16.00 Single	
2 Double		from £16.00 Dbl/Twn	
1 Family		Room only per person	
		from £15.00	

Victorian terraced family home in attractive residential area, near main
bus route to city centre. Free on street parking.

VAT is shown at 17.5%: changes in this rate may affect prices.

Key to symbols is on back flap.

Edinburgh   Map Ref: 2C5

HOTEL
★★★

Frederick House Hotel
42 Frederick Street, Edinburgh, EH2 1EX
Tel: 0131 226 1999 Fax: 0131 624 7064
E-mail: frederickhouse@ednet.co.uk
Web: www.townhousehotels.co.uk

5 Single	All En Suite	B&B per person	Open Jan-Dec
11 Twin		from £25.00 Single	
15 Double		from £25.00 Dbl/Twn	
13 Family		Room only per person	
		from £20.00	

Situated in the heart of Edinburgh close to all city centre amenities and with a wide variety of restaurants and bars in the immediate vicinity. Georgian building with all rooms recently refurbished to a high standard with en-suite facilities, fridges and modem points. Princes Street just 1 block away.

📺 ✎ 📞 🛏 ☕ 🏷

C ⏣

GUEST HOUSE
★★★

Galloway
22 Dean Park Crescent, Edinburgh, EH4 1TH
Tel/Fax: 0131 332 3672

1 Single	6 En Suite fac	B&B per person	Open Jan-Dec
2 Twin	1 Priv.NOT ensuite	from £25.00 Single	
2 Double		from £18.00 Dbl/Twn	
5 Family			

Friendly, family run guest house, beautifully restored and situated in a residential area, 10 minutes walk from Princes Street and convenient for Edinburgh International Conference Centre. Free street parking.

📺 📷 ☕ 🏷 🍴 📱

C 🐕 V

HOTEL
★★★★

The George Inter-Continental Hotel
19-21 George Street, Edinburgh, EH2 2PB
Tel: 0131 225 1251 Fax: 0131 226 5644
E-mail: edinburgh@interconti.com
Web: www.interconti.com

51 Single	All En Suite	B&B per person	Open Jan-Dec
94 Twin	Suites avail	£178.50-£203.50 Single	
47 Double		£106.00-£121.00 Dbl/Twn	
3 Family		Room only per person	
		£165.00-£215.00	

Located in heart of business and commercial centre of city. The hotel offers extensive Scottish and French cuisine in classically elegant surroundings.

📺 ✎ 📞 🛏 🅿 ☕ 📱 ✂ 🍴 🎦 🏰 🍸 🍷

C 🐕 ⏣ W V

GUEST HOUSE
★★★★

Gifford House
103 Dalkeith Road, Edinburgh, EH16 5AJ
Tel/Fax: 0131 667 4688
E-mail: giffordhotel@btinternet.com

1 Single	All En Suite	B&B per person	Open Jan-Dec
2 Twin		from £25.00 Single	
2 Double		from £20.00 Dbl/Twn	
2 Family		Room only per person	
		from £18.00	

A well appointed Victorian stone built house situated on one of the main routes into Edinburgh. Close to Holyrood Park and Arthur's Seat and only 300 metres from Royal Commonwealth Swimming Pool. Regular bus services to all city amenities. Well positioned for conference centre.

📺 🛏 ☕ 📱 ✂ 🍴 📱

C 🐕 ⏣ V

GUEST HOUSE
★★

Gilmour City Centre Guest House
51 Gilmore Place, Edinburgh, EH3 9NT
Tel/Fax: 0131 229 5008
E-mail: freddiedoreen@gilmourguesthouse.fsnet.co.uk

1 Single	3 En Suite fac	B&B per person	Open Jan-Dec
1 Twin	1 Pub Bath/Show	from £18.00 Single	
2 Double		from £18.00 Dbl/Twn	
1 Family			

Family run guest house, close to the city centre and most of the major tourist attractions. Assured of a warm friendly welcome. Private parking available.

📺 📷 ☕ ✂ 📱

C 🐕 ⏣ W V

Important: Prices stated are estimates and may be subject to amendments

Edinburgh | Map Ref: 2C5

GUEST HOUSE

★★★

Glenallan Guest House
19 Mayfield Road, Edinburgh, EH9 2NG
Tel: 0131 667 1667
E-mail: enquiries@Glenallan.co.uk
Web: www.Glenallan.co.uk

1 Single	3 En Suite fac	B&B per person	Open Jan-Dec
1 Twin	1 Priv.NOT ensuite	from £24.00 Single	
2 Double	1 Pub Bath/Show	from £22.00 Dbl/Twn	
1 Family			

Conveniently situated on main bus route into city centre. Private car parking. Recently refurbished. Completely non-smoking. Under new ownership. French, Spanish, German and Polish spoken.

GUEST HOUSE

★★★

Glenerne Guest House
4 Hampton Terrace, West Coates, Edinburgh, EH12 5JD
Tel/Fax: 0131 337 1210
E-mail: m-ballentyne@glenerne.co.uk

2 Twin	2 En Suite fac	B&B per person	Open Jan-Dec excl Xmas
1 Double	1 Priv.NOT ensuite	from £39.50 Single	
		from £27.50 Dbl/Twn	

Comfortable family home with off street parking within walking distance of city centre. All rooms with en suite or private facilities. Good bus service. Most bedrooms are at the rear of the house and overlook an attractive garden.

SMALL HOTEL

★★★

Glenora Hotel
14 Rosebery Crescent, Edinburgh, EH12 5JY
Tel: 0131 337 1186 Fax: 0131 337 1119
E-mail: edinburgh@purplenet.co.uk
Web: www.edinburgh.purplenet.co.uk

2 Single	All En Suite	B&B per person	Open Jan-Dec
3 Twin		from £17.50 Single	
3 Double		from £17.50 Dbl/Twn	
2 Family			

Victorian terraced house approximately a minutes walk to city centre and within easy reach of city's tourist attractions. Airport bus stops next to hotel.

GUEST HOUSE

★★★

Glenorchy Guest House
22 Glenorchy Terrace, Edinburgh, EH9 2DH
Tel: 0131 667 5708 Fax: 0131 667 1201

2 Twin	All En Suite	B&B per person	Open Jan-Dec
2 Double		£20.00-£30.00 Single	
2 Family		£20.00-£30.00 Dbl/Twn	

Privately owned Victorian house situated in quiet residential area, convenient for bus routes to city centre. Unrestricted parking.

HOTEL

★★★

Grange Hotel
8 Whitehouse Terrace, Edinburgh, EH9 2EU
Tel: 0131 667 5681 Fax: 0131 668 3300
Web: www.grange-hotel-edinburgh.co.uk

4 Single	All En Suite	B&B per person	Open Jan-Dec excl Xmas
3 Twin		from £80.00 Single	B&B + Eve.Meal
3 Double		from £67.00 Dbl/Twn	from £85.00
5 Family			

A large victorian mansion house set in a peaceful residential area just over one mile from Princes Street. Traditional architecture, and period features have been enhanced by the sympathetic decor and attention to modern comforts. The conservatory restaurant specialises in fresh Scottish Produce, while the extensive breakfast menu is a treat to look forward to.

VAT is shown at 17.5%: changes in this rate may affect prices. | *Key to symbols is on back flap.*

Greenside Hotel
9 Royal Terrace, Edinburgh EH7 5AB
TEL: 0131-557 0022/0121   FAX: 0131-557 0022
e.mail: greensidehotel@ednet.co.uk   Web: www.townhousehotels.co.uk
Elegant Georgian Townhouse hotel ideally situated in the city centre within
walking distance to Princes Street, Waverley train station, Edinburgh Castle and
The Playhouse Theatre combining traditional features with modern facilities, the
hotel offers superb views, private gardens and friendly atmosphere together
providing the perfect blend of history and hospitality.

HOTEL

Greenside Hotel
9 Royal Terrace, Edinburgh, EH7 5AB
Tel: 0131 557 0022/0121 Fax: 0131 557 0022
E-mail: greensidehotel@ednet.co.uk
Web: www.townhousehotels.co.uk

3 Single	All En Suite	B&B per person	Open Jan-Dec
4 Twin		from £25.00 Single	B&B + Eve.Meal
5 Double		from £22.50 Dbl/Twn	from £36.00
4 Family			

Elegant city centre Georgian townhouse hotel only a 10 minute walk from
Waverley Station and Princes Street. Ideally situated for all historic
attractions, theatres, restaurants and shopping. Tastefully decorated
ensuite bedrooms with family rooms also available.

GUEST HOUSE

Halcyon Hotel
8 Royal Terrace, Edinburgh, EH7 5AB
Tel: 0131 556 1033/2
Web: www.halcyon-hotel.com

4 Single	14 Ensuite fac	B&B per person	Open Jan-Dec
4 Twin	4 Pub Bath/Show	from £40.00 Single	
4 Double	2 Priv.NOT ensuite	from £40.00 Dbl/Twn	
4 Family			

Within walking distance of Princes Street, Georgian terrace property in
quiet area. 5 minutes walk from bus station, 10 minutes walk from
Waverly Station. Metered street parking available.

HOTEL

Harp Toby Hotel
114-116 St John's Road, Corstorphine, Edinburgh, EH12 8AX
Tel: 0131 334 8235 Fax: 0131 316 5012

6 Single	All En Suite	Room Rate of	Open Jan-Dec
7 Twin		£49.95 B&B	
10 Double			
2 Family			

Former coaching inn situated on main road, 3 miles W of city centre on
route to airport (3 miles). Ideal for business travellers and tourists alike.

SMALL HOTEL

Haymarket Hotel
1 & 3 Coates Gardens, Edinburgh, EH12 5LG
Tel: 0131 337 1775/1045 Fax: 0131 313 0330
E-mail: michael@haymarket-hotel.co.uk
Web: www.haymarket-hotel.co.uk

2 Single	All En Suite	B&B per person	Open Jan-Dec
4 Twin		from £35.00 Single	B&B + Eve.Meal
9 Double		from £27.70 Dbl/Twn	from £35.00
9 Family			

Personally run, privately owned hotel within short walk of Haymarket
railway station and Princes Street, 3 feature garden rooms with patio door,
comfortable lounge bar with large screen TV, friendly, informative staff.

Important: Prices stated are estimates and may be subject to amendments

Edinburgh				Map Ref: 2C5		

★★
HOTEL

Herald House Hotel
70 Grove Street, Edinburgh, EH3 8AP
Tel: 0131 228 2323 Fax: 0131 228 3101
E-mail: info@heraldhousehotel.co.uk
Web: www.heraldhousehotel.co.uk

9 Single
18 Twin
11 Double
8 Family

All En Suite

B&B per person
from £42.00 Single
from £30.00 Dbl/Twn

Open Jan-Dec excl
Xmas

Traditional Victorian stone faced building located close to city centre. Fully modernised but small enough to give individual attention. 500m from Edinburgh Conference Centre.

★★
HOTEL

Heriot-Watt University
Heriot-Watt University, Riccarton, Edinburgh, EH14 4AS
Tel: 0131 451 3669/3501 (eve) Fax: 0131 451 3199
E-mail: ecc@hw.ac.uk
Web: www.ecc.scot.net

1491
Single
98 Twin
35 Double

1918 En Suite fac
96 Pub Bath/Show

B&B per person
£26.00-£40.00 Single
£23.00-£30.00 Dbl/Twn

Open Jan-Dec
B&B + Eve.Meal
£35.00-£55.50

Situated in 370 acre picturesque campus of Heriot Watt University. 6 miles (10kms) west of city centre, 3 miles (5kms) from Edinburgh airport.

★★★
GUEST
HOUSE

Hermitage Guest House
16 East Hermitage Place, Leith Links, Edinburgh, EH6 8AB
Tel: 0131 555 4868 Fax: 0870 1249537
Web: www.guesthouse-edinburgh.com

1 Single
2 Twin
2 Double
1 Family

5 En Suite fac
1 Priv.NOT ensuite

B&B per person
from £20.00 Single
from £20.00 Dbl/Twn

Open Jan-Dec

Brenda extends a warm and friendly welcome to you at her Victorian Terraced House overlooking historic Leith Links. Excellent restaurants nearby or city centre only 10 minutes journey by bus. Unrestricted street parking. Business support service available on request.

★★★★
HOTEL

♿

Hilton Edinburgh Grosvenor Hotel & Grosvenor Club
Grosvenor Street, Edinburgh, EH12 5EF
Tel: 0131 226 6001 Fax: 0131 220 2387

38 Single
62 Twin
67 Double
22 Family

189 En Suite fac
Suites avail

B&B per person
£65.00-£145.00 Single
£55.00-£85.00 Dbl/Twn
Room only per person
£50.00-£110.00

Open Jan-Dec
B&B + Eve.Meal
£65.00-£160.00

Part of an attractive Georgian terrace situated at West End of Princes St. Convenient for city centre and Haymarket Station. Conference facilities.

★★★★
GUEST
HOUSE

House O'Hill Guest House
7 House O'Hill Terrace, Blackhall, Edinburgh, EH4 2AA
Tel: 0131 332 3674 Fax: 0131 343 3446
E-mail: chrissy@houseohill.co.uk

2 Twin
1 Double
1 Family

All En Suite

B&B per person
from £25.00 Single
from £23.00 Dbl/Twn

Open Jan-Dec

Family run semi-detached Victorian house situated approx 1.5 miles (2.5kms) from West End. Convenient access to city via Queensferry Road. City bypass, airport, train stations, sports stadiums, shopping complexes, leisure clubs and zoo witin a 2 mile radius. Parking. Children welcome.

VAT is shown at 17.5%: changes in this rate may affect prices.

Key to symbols is on back flap.

Edinburgh	Map Ref: 2C5

★★★★★

SMALL
HOTEL

The Howard
34 Great King Street, Edinburgh, EH3 6QH
Tel: 0131 315 2220 Fax: 0131 332 9631
E-mail: reserve@thehoward.com
eWeb: www.thehoward.com

2 Single   All En Suite
13 Dbl/Twn

B&B per person
£135.00-£175.00 Sgle
£122.50-£162.50 Dble

Open Jan-Dec excl Xmas

Made up of three beautifully and traditionally restored Georgian town houses, The Howard is a gem amongst small hotels. Ideally located, just ten minutes walk from city centre. In direct contrast to the traditional feel of the hotel, the contemporary and individual '36', housed by The Howard, is firmly positioned as one of Edinburgh's top restaurants.

★

HOTEL

The Inverleith Hotel
5 Inverleith Terrace, Edinburgh, EH3 4NS
Tel: 0131 556 2745 Fax: 0131 557 0433
E-mail: Hotel@5inverleith.freeserve.co.uk

2 Single   All En Suite
2 Twin
2 Double
2 Family

B&B per person
from £30.00 Single
from £25.00 Dbl/Twn
Room only per person
from £25.00

Open Jan-Dec

Under new ownership this townhouse is situated a short walk from city centre. Excellent bus sevice. Free on-street parking. Close to botanical gardens. Group discount.

★★

HOTEL

Iona Hotel
17 Strathearn Place, Edinburgh, EH9 2AL
Tel/Fax: 0131 447 6264
E-mail: ronald.pugh@dial.pipex.com
Web: www.iona-hotel.com

6 Single   17 En Suite fac
3 Twin
5 Double
3 Family

B&B per person
from £40.00 Single
from £34.00 Dbl/Twn

Open Jan-Dec
B&B + Eve.Meal
from £45.00

Privately run hotel with own car park in residential area. Approx 2 miles (3kms) from city centre, convenient for bus routes. Meeting room.

★★★

HOTEL

Jarvis Ellersly House Hotel
Ellersly Road, Murrayfield, Edinburgh, EH12 6HZ
Tel: 0131 337 6888 Fax: 0131 313 2543

13 Single   All En Suite
30 Twin
14 Double

B&B per person
from £42.50 Single
from £42.50 Dbl/Twn

Open Jan-Dec

Formerly an Edwardian residence with refurbished bedrooms. Quietly situated in 2 acre grounds, only 1.5 miles west of the city centre and 5 miles from Edinburgh Airport. Summit conference rooms with full range of state of art audio/visual equipment.

Important: Prices stated are estimates and may be subject to amendments

Jewel and Esk Valley College
24 MILTON ROAD EAST, EDINBURGH EH15 2PP
TEL: 0131 657 7222/7253 FAX: 0131 657 7253

Student halls of residence located in quiet residential suburb, excellent bus route 15-20 minutes by bus to city centre, easy access to city bypass and motorways, open January to November, all rooms with washhand basin, tea and coffee making facilities, good parking, sport facilities, swimming pool.

★

CAMPUS ACCOMMODATION

Jewel & Esk Valley College
24 Milton Road East, Edinburgh, EH15 2PP
Tel: 0131 657 7222 Fax: 0131 657 7253

Student halls of residence in quiet residential suburb on excellent bus route to city centre. Ample parking. Leisure facilities.

244 Single	42 Pub Bath/Show
4 Twin	

B&B per person
£23.50-£25.50 Single
£23.50-£25.50 Twin

Open Jan-Nov

★★★

GUEST HOUSE

Joppa Turrets Guest House
1 Lower Joppa (at beachend of Morton St), Edinburgh, EH15 2ER
Tel/Fax: 0131 669 5806
Web: www.joppaturrets.demon.co.uk

What makes us special? Location right on sandy beach, sea views, fresh air and sounds of the waves, from our attractive, cosy bedrooms. Frequent nearby bus to beautiful city centre, returning to peace and quiet in our residential cul de sac and pretty private garden. Unrestricted on-street parking. NON SMOKING. Nearby are restaurants and pubs, plus indoor swimming, turkish baths and fitness centre. See our web-page.

4 Double	3 En Suite fac
1 Family	1 Pub Bath/Show

B&B per person
from £19.00 Single
from £19.00 Double
Room only per person
from £19.00

Open Jan-Dec excl Xmas

★★

GUEST HOUSE

Kariba Guest House
10 Granville Terrace, Edinburgh, EH10 4PQ
Tel: 0131 229 3773 Fax: 0131 229 4968

A Victorian house on major bus route to city centre about 10 minutes away. Restaurants, theatres and International Conference Centre all within easy reach. Private car parking.

3 Twin	6 En Suite fac
4 Double	1 Priv.NOT ensuite
2 Family	1 Pub Bath/Show

B&B per person
from £18.00 Dbl/Twn

Open Jan-Dec

★★★

GUEST HOUSE

Kelly's Guest House
3 Hillhouse Road, Queensferry Road, Edinburgh, EH4 3QP
Tel: 0131 332 3894 Fax: 0131 538 0925
E-mail: info@kellysguesthouse.cx
Web: www.kellysguesthouse.cx

Personally run Guest House in West Edinburgh (A90), with conservatory dining room over-looking garden. Easy access to city centre, airport and Forth Bridge and on main bus route - 10 minutes from City Centre.

1 Twin	3 En Suite fac
2 Double	1 Priv.NOT ensuite
1 Family	

B&B per person
£30.00-£40.00 Single
£23.00-£30.00 Dbl/Twn

Open Jan-Dec

VAT is shown at 17.5%: changes in this rate may affect prices.

Key to symbols is on back flap.

KENVIE GUEST HOUSE
16 Kilmaurs Road, Edinburgh EH16 5DA
Tel: 0131 668 1964 Fax: 0131 668 1926
e.mail: dorothy@kenvie.co.uk Web: www.kenvie.co.uk

Quiet and comfortable house situated in a residential area with easy access to City Centre on an excellent bus route. All rooms have tea and coffee-making facilities and TVs. Central heating throughout.
A warm and friendly welcome is guaranteed.

★★★

GUEST
HOUSE

Kenvie Guest House
16 Kilmaurs Road, Edinburgh, EH16 5DA
Tel: 0131 668 1964 Fax: 0131 668 1926
E-mail: dorothy@kenvie.co.uk
Web: www.kenvie.co.uk

A charming, comfortable, warm, friendly family run Victorian town house in a quiet residential street. Very close to bus routes and the city by-pass. We offer for your comfort, lots of caring touches including complimentary tea / coffee, colour TV and no-smoking rooms. En-suite available and vegetarians catered for. You are guranteed a warm welcome from Richard and Dorothy.

2 Twin	3 En Suite fac	B&B per person	Open Jan-Dec
1 Double	2 Pub Bath/Show	from £25.00 Single	
2 Family		from £23.00 Dbl/Twn	
		Room only per person	
		from £20.00	

★★★★

HOTEL

Kildonan Lodge Hotel
27 Craigmillar Park, Edinburgh, EH16 5PE
Tel: 0131 667 2793 Fax: 0131 667 9777
E-mail: kildonanlodge@compuserve.com
Web: www.kildonanlodgehotel.co.uk

Kildonan Lodge is an outstanding example of Victorian elegance beautifully restored to capture the atmosphere of a bygone era by resident owners, Maggie and Bruce Urquhart. Relax by an open fire in the splendid Residents Lounge whilst enjoying a dram from the honesty bar. Well equipped individually designed bedrooms some with spa baths or four-poster beds. Ideally situated close to city centre. Private car park.

2 Twin	All En Suite	B&B per person	Open Jan-Dec excl Xmas
7 Double		£45.00-£69.00 Single	
3 Family		£35.00-£49.00 Dbl/Twn	

★★★

GUEST
HOUSE

Kingsley Guest House
30 Craigmillar Park, Edinburgh, EH16 5PS
Tel: 0131 667 3177 Tel/Fax: 0131 667 8439
E-mail: lynredmayne@kingsleyguesthouse.co.uk

Friendly, comfortable and family run Victorian villa with own private car park. Excellent bus service for all major attractions in the city. Close to university area and Commonwealth Pool.

2 Twin	3 En Suite fac	B&B per person	Open Jan-Dec
1 Double	1 Priv.NOT ensuite	from £20.00 Dbl/Twn	
2 Family	1 Pub Bath/Show		

Important: Prices stated are estimates and may be subject to amendments

King's Manor Hotel
100 Milton Road East, Edinburgh EH15 2NP
Tel: 0131 669 0444 Fax: 0131 669 6650

Family owned and managed hotel in suburbs of Edinburgh.
70 well-appointed bedrooms. Two bars full service restaurant and bistro.
New extensive leisure club with 20-metre pool, sauna, solarium and full gym.
Short breaks and special interest holidays. Open to non-residents.

★★★

HOTEL

King's Manor Hotel
100 Milton Road East, Edinburgh, EH15 2NP
Tel: 0131 669 0444 Fax: 0131 669 6650
E-mail: reservations@kingsmanor.com

Family run hotel 4 miles (6kms) east of city centre, handy for beach and all major road routes. Extensive modern leisure facilities.

14 Single	All En Suite	B&B per person	Open Jan-Dec
39 Twin		from £68.00 Single	B&B + Eve.Meal
14 Double		from £60.00 Dbl/Twn	from £68.00
2 Family			

★★

GUEST HOUSE

Kingsview Guest House
28 Gilmore Place, Edinburgh, EH3 9NQ
Tel/Fax: 0131 229 8004
E-mail: kingsviewguesthouse@talk21.com
Web: www.kingsviewguesthouse.com.uk

Family run, city centre guest house conveniently situated near the Kings Theatre. Close to all main bus routes.

1 Single	3 En Suite fac	B&B per person	Open Jan-Dec
2 Twin	1 Pub Show	from £18.00 Single	
2 Double	1 Limited ensuite	from £18.00 Dbl/Twn	
3 Family			

★★

GUEST HOUSE

Kirklea Guest House
11 Harrison Road, Edinburgh, EH11 1EG
Tel: 0131 337 1129 Fax: 0131 337 6650
E-mail: vkielnar@compuserve.com

A family run guest house in Victorian terrace convenient for bus routes to city centre and all attractions. 1.25 miles (2kms) from Princes Street. Dutch, French, German and Italian spoken by the owners.

2 Single	En Suite fac	B&B per person	Open Jan-Dec
2 Double	Pub Bath/Show	from £26.00 Single	
2 Family		from £21.00 Dbl/Twn	

Edinburgh   Map Ref: 2C5

GUEST HOUSE

★★★

The Lairg
11 Coates Gardens, Edinburgh, EH12 5LG
Tel: 0131 337 1050 Fax: 0131 346 2167
E-mail: thelairg@aol.com
Web: http://members.aol.com/thelairg

A warm welcome at this personally run guest house within easy access to city centre and all tourist attractions.

2 Single	10 En Suite fac	B&B per person	Open Jan-Dec
4 Twin		from £25.00 Single	
4 Double		from £22.00 Dbl/Twn	
2 Family			

GUEST HOUSE

★★★★

Lauderville House
52 Mayfield Road, Edinburgh, EH9 2NH
Tel: 0131 667 7788 Fax: 0131 667 2636
E-mail: res@laudervilleguesthouse.co.uk
Web: www.LaudervilleGuestHouse.co.uk

Brian and Yvonne Marriott welcome visitors to their restored Victorian Town House, centrally situated with easy access to city centre. Comfortable rooms, excellent breakfast, including vegetarian. All bedrooms non-smoking.

1 Single	All En Suite	B&B per person	Open Jan-Dec
2 Twin		£28.00-£45.00 Single	
6 Double		£25.00-£40.00 Dbl/Twn	
1 Family			

GUEST HOUSE

★★★

Lindsay Guest House
108 Polwarth Terrace, Edinburgh, EH11 1NN
Tel: 0131 337 1580 Fax: 0131 337 9174
E-mail: bill@lindsay-polwarth.demon.co.uk

Listed semi-detached sandstone house in residential area on bus route to city centre. 1.5 miles (3 kms) from Princes St. Car parking. TVs in all bedrooms.

1 Single	3 En Suite fac	B&B per person	Open Jan-Dec
1 Twin	2 Pub Bath/Show	from £18.00 Single	
2 Double		from £18.00 Dbl/Twn	
3 Family			

SMALL HOTEL

★★★★

The Lodge Hotel
6 Hampton Terrace, West Coates, Edinburgh, EH12 5JD
Tel: 0131 337 3682
E-mail: thelodgehotel@btconnect.com
Web: www.thelodgehotel.co.uk

The Lodge Hotel is a private hotel which has been extended and refurbished yet has retained many features of an elegant Georgian residence. The lodge is situated on the main A8 Edinburgh to Glasgow road convenient for the city centre, conference centre and airport. Guests can relax in the cocktail bar before enjoying a freshly prepared dinner with emphasis on fresh local produce when available. Non smoking house. Private car park.

2 Single	All En Suite	B&B per person	Open Jan-Dec
2 Twin	1 Pub Bath/Show	£38.00-£48.00 Single	
6 Double		£29.00-£42.50 Dbl/Twn	

Lorne Villa Guest House
9 East Mayfield, Edinburgh EH9 1SD
Tel/Fax: 0131 667 7159
e.mail: lornevilla@cableinet.co.uk

Festival city centre guest house one mile to city centre. Excellent bus service, off-street parking available. Ground floor room available, children welcome. Reduced rates for children sharing parents' room. Under 5's go free. Dinners available on request. Prices £18-£35 pppn.

★★★

GUEST HOUSE

Lorne Villa Guest House
9 East Mayfield, Edinburgh, EH9 1SD
Tel/Fax: 0131 667 7159
E-mail: lornevilla@cableinet.co.uk

1 Single	3 En Suite fac
3 Twin	1 Priv.NOT ensuite
2 Double	1 Pub Bath/Show
1 Family	

B&B per person
from £18.00 Single
from £18.00 Dbl/Twn

Open Jan-Dec
B&B + Eve.Meal
from £30.00

Personally run guest house conveniently situated for city centre bus route with off street parking. Ground floor ensuite bedroom. Dinner available on request.

★★★

GUEST HOUSE

Maple Leaf Guest House
23 Pilrig Street, Edinburgh, EH6 5AN
Tel/Fax: 0131 554 7692

3 Single	All En Suite
2 Twin	
3 Double	
1 Family	

B&B per person
from £24.00 Single
from £23.00 Dbl/Twn
Room only per person
from £20.00

Open Jan-Dec excl
Xmas/New Year

Family run Georgian terraced house, conveniently situated 10 minutes from town centre. A good warm welcome here. Friendly, relaxed atmosphere. Free on-street parking.

Edinburgh

Map Ref: 2C5

★★

GUEST
HOUSE

Marrakech Guest House
30 London Street, Edinburgh, EH3 6NA
Tel: 0131 556 4444 Fax: 0131 557 3615
E-mail: marr@rapidial.co.uk
Web: www.hotels.co.uk/marr.htm

2 Single	with shared fac	B&B per person	Open Jan-Dec
3 Twin	All other rooms	from £25.00 Single	
3 Double	with private fac	from £20.00 Dbl/Twn	
3 Family			

A warm welcome at this guest house with its own restaurant serving many home made specialities. This Georgian house is situated in the heart of Edinburgh's New Town only a few minutes walk from Princes Street and close to Waverley Station and the bus station.

TV 📺 🍵 ✎ ✗ 🛏 📱

C £ V

★★★

GUEST
HOUSE
♿

Melville Guest House
2 Duddingston Crescent, Edinburgh, Lothian, EH15 3AS
Tel/Fax: 0131 669 7856
E-mail: melvillegh@aol.com
Web: http://members.aol.com/melvillegh

4 Twin	7 En Suite fac	B&B per person	Open Jan-Dec
3 Double		£17.00-£45.00 Single	
2 Family		£17.00-£32.50 Dbl/Twn	

Conveniently situated on the eastern approach road just 3 miles from city centre. A comfortable guest house offering accommodation of a high standard with off-road parking. Ground floor rooms, with wheelchair access.

TV 📺 P 🍵 ✎ 🛏 📱

C £ V

★★★

HOTEL

Melvin House Hotel
3 Rothesay Terrace, Edinburgh, EH3 7RY
Tel: 0131 225 5084 Fax: 0131 226 5085
E-mail: reservations@melvinhouse.demon.co.uk

6 Twin	All En Suite	B&B per person	Open Jan-Dec
10 Double		£60.00-£115.00 Single	B&B + Eve.Meal
6 Family		£40.00-£80.00 Dbl/Twn	£49.00-£75.00

Melvin House is ideally situated in the heart of Edinburgh's fashionable West End, within easy walking distance of Princes Street shopping area and all city attractions. Built in 1880, the hotel provides exceptional character with it's galleried library and elegant public rooms. You cannot fail to be transported from the hustle and bustle of the city to the calm nostalgia of a bygone era.

TV 📞 🛏 🍵 ✎ 🍴 🎱 🍷

C 🐕 £ V

★★

GUEST
HOUSE

Meriden Guest House
1 Hermitage Terrace, Edinburgh, EH10 4RP
Tel: 0131 447 5152
E-mail: meriden@ukgateway.net

2 Twin	1 En Suite fac	B&B per person	Open Jan-Dec
2 Double	2 Pub Bath/Show	£19.00-£28.00 Single	
1 Family		£19.00-£21.00 Dbl/Twn	
		Room only per person	
		£18.00-£20.00	

Stone built Victorian terraced house in quiet residential area. Theatres, restaurants, shops and universities nearby. Central location with bus service to city centre. Completely non-smoking. Dogs welcome.

TV 📺 🍵 ✎ 📱

C 🐕 V

★★★

GUEST
HOUSE

Milton House
24 Duddingston Crescent, Edinburgh, EH15 3AT
Tel: 0131 669 4072
E-mail: winenbru@supanet.com

1 Twin	2 En Suite	B&B per person	Open Jan-Dec
3 Double		from £20.00 Single	
		from £20.00 Dbl/Twn	

Friendly family atmosphere with off street parking and easy access to the city centre. Adjacent to 9 hole golf course. Dog friendly household.

TV 📺 P 🍵 ✎ 🛏 📱

C 🐕 £ V

Important: Prices stated are estimates and may be subject to amendments

Edinburgh | Map Ref: 2C5

Mingalar
2 East Claremont St, Edinburgh, EH7 4JP
Tel: 0131 556 7000 Fax: 0131 556 4907
Web: www.criper.com/mingalar

GUEST HOUSE

3 Double   All En Suite
3 Family   1 Pub Bath/Show

B&B per person   Open Feb-Dec
from £22.50 Single
from £20.00 Double

Refurbished Georgian terraced house, 10 minutes from the city centre and all its ammenities. Surrounding streets have metered or free parking.

Muffin Guest House
164 Ferry Road, Edinburgh, EH6 4NS
Tel: 0131 554 4162 Fax: 0131 554 4827

GUEST HOUSE

2 Single   2 En Suite fac
1 Twin   2 Pub Bath/Show
3 Double
1 Family

B&B per person   Open Jan-Dec
£18.00-£25.00 Single
£16.00-£30.00 Dbl/Twn

Personally run, situated on main bus route with easy access to town centre and all amenities. Short distance to Britannia visitor attraction.

Murrayfield Hotel
18 Corstorphine Road, Edinburgh, EH12 6HN
Tel: 0131 337 1844 Fax: 0131 346 8159

HOTEL

18 Single   All En Suite
7 Twin
7 Double
1 Family

B&B per person   Open Jan-Dec
£54.00-£59.00 Single   B&B + Eve.Meal
£37.00-£39.50 Dbl/Twn £40.00-£60.00

Stone built Victorian house with restaurant and lounge, also garden for alfresco dining. Some annexe accommodation.

Murrayfield Park Guest House
89 CORSTORPHINE ROAD, EDINBURGH EH12 5QE
Telephone: 0131 337 5370   Fax: 0131 337 3772
e.mail: murrayfieldpark@yahoo.com
A warm and friendly welcome awaits you at this family-run *Guest House* which is situated in a residential area five minutes by bus to the City Centre. According to our visitors' book all our previous guests have found us extremely comfortable and many return again and again. Contact proprietors *Dale and Gordon Scott.*
AA LISTED – ◆◆◆ CLASS.   ★★★★ GUEST HOUSE

Murrayfield Park Guest House
89 Corstorphine Road, Murrayfield, Edinburgh, EH12 5QE
Tel: 0131 337 5370 Fax: 0131 337 3772
E-mail: murrayfieldpark@yahoo.com

GUEST HOUSE

1 Single   6 En Suite fac
5 Twin   1 Priv.NOT ensuite
3 Double   1 Pub Bath/Show

B&B per person   Open Jan-Dec
from £25.00 Single
from £25.00 Dbl/Twn
Room only per person
from £25.00

A warm welcome at this comfortable Guest House, 10 minutes by bus from the city centre. Ideal location for enjoying the attractions of Edinburgh. Convenient for the airport and Edinburgh Zoo. Private car park with security lighting.

VAT is shown at 17.5%: changes in this rate may affect prices. | *Key to symbols is on back flap.*

Edinburgh	Map Ref: 2C5

GUEST HOUSE

Newington Guest House
18 Newington Road, Edinburgh, EH9 1QS
Tel: 0131 667 3356 Fax: 0131 667 8307
E-mail: newington.guesthouse@dial.pipex.com
Web: www.newington-gh.co.uk

Interestingly furnished Victorian house on main road into city from south. Easy access to centre. Most rooms double glazed.

1 Single	6 Ensuite fac	B&B per person	Open Jan-Dec excl
3 Twin	1 Pub Bath/Show	from £30.00 Single	Xmas
3 Double		from £24.50 Dbl/Twn	
2 Family		Room only per person	
		from £22.50	

HOTEL

Nova Hotel
5 Bruntsfield Crescent, Edinburgh, EH10 4EZ
Tel: 0131 447 6437/7349 Fax: 0131 452 8126
E-mail: jamie@scotland-hotels.demon.co.uk
Web: www.novahotel.F9.com

Recently refurbished hotel, in the city centre located in a quiet position overlooking ancient golf links. Easy parking. Close to cinemas, theatres and IECC.

2 Single	All En Suite	B&B per person	Open Jan-Dec excl
2 Twin		from £35.00 Single	Xmas/New Year
3 Double		from £35.00 Dbl/Twn	
6 Family		pp sharing	

HOTEL

Old Waverley Hotel
43 Princes Street, Edinburgh, EH2 2BY
Tel: 0131 556 4648 Fax: 0131 557 6316

City centre hotel overlooking Princes Street Gardens within 100 yards of Waverley station. Views of castle and Scott Monument.

11 Single	All En Suite	B&B per person	Open Jan-Dec
32 Twin		£95.00-£99.00 Single	
20 Double		£76.00-£79.00 Dbl/Twn	
3 Family			

Important: Prices stated are estimates and may be subject to amendments

Osbourne Hotel

51-59 York Place, Edinburgh EH1 3JD
Tel: 0131 556 5577   Fax: 0131 556 1012
e.mail: reservations@osbourne-hotel.com
Web: www.osbourne-hotel.com

Ideal city centre location within easy
walking distance of Edinburgh's main
attractions and rail and coach stations.
With 46 ensuite rooms, restaurant, bar, lift,
night porter, etc. Start your holiday with
us. Low season £38; high season £52 per
ensuite single including fully cooked buffet
breakfasts. We book tickets and tours.
Friendly service and reasonable rates.

★

HOTEL

Osbourne Hotel
51-59 York Place, Edinburgh, EH1 3JD
Tel: 0131 556 5577 Fax: 0131 556 1012
E-mail: reservations@osbourne-hotel.com
Web: www.osbourne-hotel.com

Personally run hotel close to city centre and all amenities. Short distance
from railway and bus stations. Restaurant closed on Sundays.

13 Single	46 En Suite fac	B&B per person	Open Jan-Dec
13 Twin	3 Pub Bath/Show	from £29.00 Single	
13 Double		from £28.00 Dbl/Twn	
10 Family		Room only per person	
		from £29.00	

★★★

GUEST HOUSE

Parklands Guest House
20 Mayfield Gardens, Edinburgh, EH9 2BZ
Tel: 0131 667 7184 Fax: 0131 667 2011
E-mail: parklands_guesthouse@yahoo.com

Look forward to a warm welcome at this late Victorian house with fine
woodwork and ceilings. Situated on the south side, on main bus routes to
city centre. Close to University.

2 Twin	Ensuite fac	B&B per person	Open Jan-Dec
2 Double	Ensuite fac	from £20.00 Dbl/Twn	
1 Family	Ensuite fac		
1 Single	Private fac		

★★★

HOTEL

Parliament House Hotel
15 Calton Hill, Edinburgh, EH1 3BJ
Tel: 0131 478 4000 Fax: 0131 478 4001
Web: www.scotland-hotels.co.uk

New town house hotel, city centre location, situated on historic Calton Hill a
few minutes walk from Princes Street and the Playhouse Theatre. 3
minutes walk from Waverley Train Station.

2 Single	All En Suite	B&B per person	Open Jan-Dec
26 Twin		from £50.00 Single	
25 Double		from £35.00 Dbl/Twn	

VAT is shown at 17.5%: changes in this rate may affect prices. | *Key to symbols is on back flap.*

Edinburgh | Map Ref: 2C5

★★
HOTEL

Piries Hotel
4-8 Coates Gardens, Edinburgh, EH12 5LB
Tel: 0131 337 1108 Fax: 0131 346 0279

4 Single	All En Suite	B&B per person	Open Jan-Dec
6 Twin		from £28.00 Single	Evening Meal
10 Double		from £22.50 Dbl/Twn	from £7.00
10 Family			

Comfortably furnished privately owned, stone terraced building in West End of city. City centre location, within walking distance of Princes Street, and EICC. Selection of bar meals available.

★★★
HOTEL

The Point Hotel
34 Bread Street, Edinburgh, EH3 9AF
Tel: 0131 221 5555 Fax: 0131 221 9929
Web: www.point-hotel.co.uk

8 Single	140 En Suite fac	B&B per person	Open Jan-Dec
87 Twin		from £80.00 Single	
32 Double		from £50.00 Dbl/Twn	
6 Family		from £75.00 Suite	
4 Suites			

Stylishly modern. Within its classical framework, the Point Hotel reflects the cosmopolitan character of this majestic city. Close to Edinburgh Castle, all major tourist attractions and Princes Street.

★★★★
HOTEL

Posthouse Edinburgh
Corstorphine Road, Edinburgh, EH12 6UA
Tel: 0870 400 9026 Fax: 0131 334 9237

48 Single	All En Suite	Room only per person	Open Jan-Dec
100 Twin		£109.00-£129.00	B&B + Eve.Meal
120 Double			from £76.00
35 Family			

Modern hotel situated on the main route to airport with easy access to the city centre. 303 bedrooms including family and disabled rooms. The hotel has a choice of two award winning restaurants including an oriental restaurant. There is a choice of meeting rooms in the Roof Top Academy Conference Centre.

★★★
HOTEL

The Quality Commodore Hotel
Marine Drive, Cramond Foreshore, Edinburgh, EH4 5EP
Tel: 0131 336 1700 Fax: 0131 336 4934
E-mail: admin@gb625.u-net.com

1 Single	All En Suite	B&B per person	Open Jan-Dec
55 Twin		£33.00-£83.75 Single	B&B + Eve.Meal
23 Double		£33.00-£57.50 Dbl/Twn	£43.00-£93.75
7 Family		Room only per person	
		£66.50-£96.00	

Quietly situated opposite golf course, with fine views over Firth of Forth. Grassy walkway to shore. Ample and free parking and easy access to city centre.

★★★
HOTEL

Quality Hotel
Edinburgh Airport, Ingliston Road, Edinburgh, EH28 8AU
Tel: 0131 333 4331 Fax: 0131 333 4124

4 Single	All En Suite	Room only	Open Jan-Dec excl
38 Twin		from £55.00	Xmas/New Year
53 Double			B&B + Eve.Meal
			from £80.00

Modern recently built hotel on Royal Highland Agricultural Show Grounds adjacent to Edinburgh Airport (terminal 0.5 mile) and 8 miles from Edinburgh city centre. Bistro style restaurant. Ample car parking. Shuttle bus all day to/from airport.

Important: Prices stated are estimates and may be subject to amendments

Edinburgh

Map Ref: 2C5

HOTEL
★★

Ritz Hotel
14-18 Grosvenor Street, Edinburgh, EH12 5EG
Tel: 0131 337 4315 Fax: 0131 346 0597

4 Single	All En Suite	B&B per person	Open Jan-Dec
19 Twin		£47.00-£65.00 Single	
9 Double		£37.50-£45.00 Dbl/Twn	
4 Family			

On five floors, each room of individual character, some featuring four poster beds. Within easy walking distance of Haymarket railway station and West End of Princes Street. There is a wide range of restaurants available in the city centre, or evening meals are available by prior arrangement.

GUEST HOUSE
★★★

Robertson Guest House
9 Hartington Gardens, Edinburgh, EH10 4LD
Tel: 0131 229 2652

1 Single	1 En Suite fac	B&B per person	Open Jan-Dec
1 Twin	1 Pub Bath/Show	£22.50-£35.00 Single	
2 Double	2 Priv.NOT ensuite	£22.50-£35.00 Dbl/Twn	
2 Family			

Choose the 'Robertson' for a warm welcome and a comfortable stay. Quiet location close to city centre attractions. Excellent breakfast.

HOTEL
★★★

Rosehall Hotel
101 Dalkeith Road, Edinburgh, EH16 5AJ
Tel/Fax: 0131 667 9372
E-mail: RosehallH@aol.com

1 Single	7 En Suite fac	B&B per person	Open Jan-Dec
2 Twin	1 Priv.NOT ensuite	from £25.00 Single	B&B + Eve.Meal
3 Double		from £22.00 Dbl/Twn	from £30.00
2 Family			

This quality, independant hotel has been recently refurbished, and many fine period features have been restored to their original Victorian splendour. All rooms have been tastefully furnished, with a beautiful Four Poster bedroom also available. The hotel is conveniently located 1.5 miles from Princes Street. Waveley Station, Castle, Holyrood Palace and the New Scottish Parliment are all within 20 mins walk. Cosy lounge bar.

GUEST HOUSE
★★★★

Roselea House
11 Mayfield Road, Edinburgh, EH9 2NG
Tel: 0131 667 6115 Fax: 0131 667 3556
E-mail: roselea11@aol.com
Web: www.roselea-guesthouse.com

1 Single	4 En Suite fac	B&B per person	Open Jan-Dec
1 Twin	1 Priv.NOT ensuite	£35.00-£50.00 Single	
2 Double		£30.00-£45.00 Dbl/Twn	
1 Family			

A warm welcome at personally run guest house close to city centre on main bus route. Ideal touring base. Non smoking house. Satellite TV including Italian satellite available.

VAT is shown at 17.5%: changes in this rate may affect prices.

Key to symbols is on back flap.

Royal British Hotel

20 Princes Street, Edinburgh EH2 2AN
Tel: 0131 556 4901 Fax: 0131 557 6510
e.mail: royalbritish@hotmail.com

Situated in the heart of the city, on world famous Princes Street – a popular attraction particularly with shoppers – and adjacent to Waverley mainline rail station, the Royal British Hotel provides an ideal location for the business traveller and tourist alike. A warm welcome awaits your arrival.

HOTEL

Royal British Hotel
20 Princes Street, Edinburgh, EH2 2AN
Tel: 0131 556 4901 Fax: 0131 557 6510
E-mail: royalbritish@hotmail.com

17 Single	All En Suite
37 Twin	
9 Double	
9 Family	

B&B per person
from £70.00 Single
from £50.00 Dbl/Twn

Open Jan-Dec excl Xmas

City centre hotel situated on Princes Street and 100 yards from Waverley railway station. Ideally situated for shopping, sightseeing, airport, bus terminal and business outlets.

Royal Garden Apartments

York Building, Queen Street, Edinburgh EH2 1HY
Tel: 0131 625 1234 Fax: 0131 625 5678
e.mail: reservations@royal-garden.co.uk

Luxury serviced apartments in a Georgian building located in the city centre offering one or two bedrooms with a spacious lounge, dining area, kitchen and bathroom. Two penthouse apartments with balcony offering spectacular views over Edinburgh. Minimum one nights stay. Café offering breakfast, 24 hour reception and limited car parking available. £62.50-£80.00 sharing per person per night.

SERVICED APARTMENTS

Royal Garden Apartments
York Buildings, Queen Street, Edinburgh, EH2 1HY
Tel: 0131 625 1234 Fax: 0131 625 5678
E.mail: reservations@royal-garden.co.uk
Web: www.royal-garden.co.uk

1 pub room	Min let 1 night	From £42.50
1-2 bedrms	30 luxury serviced	
sleeps 1-6	Apartments	

Open Jan-Dec

Conveniently situated near the city centre this large 'B' listed Georgian building offers a range of luxury one or two bedroom Serviced Apartments. 24 hour reception, cleaning service, laundry & stylish cafe for breakfast and lunch. Lift to all floors, modern kitchens, cable TV, fax modem points, dishwashers, microwaves and traditional oven & hob.

GUEST HOUSE

St Bernards Guest House
22 St Bernards Crescent, Edinburgh, EH4 1NS
Tel: 0131 332 2339 Fax: 0131 332 8842

1 Single	4 En Suite fac	
4 Twin	2 Pub Bath/Show	
3 Double		

B&B per person
£28.00-£35.00 Single
£22.00-£30.00 Dbl/Twn

Open Jan-Dec

Elegant terrace house in Georgian New Town area of the city. Convenient for Princes Street. Many excellent restaurants within walking distance. A warm and friendly welcome.

Important: Prices stated are estimates and may be subject to amendments

Edinburgh Map Ref: 2C5

The St Valery
36 Coates Gardens, Haymarket, Edinburgh, EH12 5LE
Tel: 0131 337 1893 Fax: 0131 346 8529
Web: www.stvalery.com

1 Single	All En Suite
3 Twin	
3 Double	
4 Family	

B&B per person
from £25.00 Single
from £25.00 Dbl/Twn
Room only per person
from £25.00

Open Jan-Dec
B&B + Eve.Meal
from £30.00

Tradional guest house, centrally situated in West End of Edinburgh. 1/2 mile from Princes Street. 3 minutes walk from Haymarket Station. Evening meal on request.

Sakura House
18 West Preston Street, Edinburgh, EH8 9PU
Tel/Fax: 0131 668 1204

1 Single	3 En Suite fac
1 Twin	1 Pub Bath/Show
1 Double	1 Priv.NOT ensuite
3 Family	

B&B per person
from £15.00 Single
from £15.00 Dbl/Twn
Room only per person
from £15.00

Open Jan-Dec

Victorian house in central location, close to castle and shopping centre. Continental breakfast only. Numerous good restaurants and pubs in immediate vicinity. On main bus route.

Salisbury View Hotel
64 Dalkeith Road, Edinburgh, EH16 5AE
Tel/Fax: 0131 667 1133
E-mail: enquiries@salisburyviewhotel.co.uk
Web: www.salisburyviewhotel.co.uk

1 Single	All En Suite
2 Twin	
6 Double	
1 Family	

B&B per person
from £32.00 Single
from £32.00 Dbl/Twn

Open Jan-Dec excl Xmas

Small privately run Georgian hotel in historical conservation area. Opposite Holyrood Park, Pollock Halls and Commonwealth Swimming Pool. Easy access to city centre. Approx 15 min walk to Royal Mile. Award winning chef and highly acclaimed restaurant. Private car park. Ground floor rooms available.

Sandaig Guest House
5 East Hermitage Place, Leith Links, Edinburgh, EH6 8AA
Tel: 0131 554 7357/7313 Fax: 0131 467 6389
E-mail: marina-ferbej@email.msn.com
Web: www.smoothhound.co.uk/hotels/sandaig.html

1 Single	6 En Suite fac
2 Twin	1 Priv.NOT ensuite
5 Double	2 Pub Bath/Show
2 Family	

B&B per person
from £26.00 Single
from £23.00 Dbl/Twn

Open Jan-Dec

Marina and Derek personally welcome you to their comfortable Victorian terraced villa overlooking historic Leith Links. Unrestricted street parking. Variety of restaurants nearby or 10 mins by bus or car to Princes Street with all its amenities. Some non-smoking bedrooms.

Santa Lucia Guest House
14 Kilmaurs Terrace, Edinburgh, EH16 5DR
Tel: 0131 667 8694

1 Single	3 Ensuite fac
4 Twin	2 Pub Bath/Show
1 Double	1 Toilet

B&B per person
£15.00-£25.00 Single
£15.00-£25.00 Dbl/Twn
Room only per person
£12.00-£20.00

Open Jan-Dec excl Xmas/New Year

Situated in very quiet residential area of city. Convenient for bus services to the city centre. Close to Commonwealth Swimming Pool.

VAT is shown at 17.5%: changes in this rate may affect prices. | *Key to symbols is on back flap.*

SHERATON GRAND HOTEL

1 FESTIVAL SQUARE, EDINBURGH EH3 9SR
Telephone: 0131 229 9131 Fax: 0131 228 4510
e.mail: sue_finlay@sheraton.com Web: www.sheraton.com

Nestling in the shadow of Edinburgh Castle, the Sheraton Grand combines the excellence of an international hotel with a warm luxurious Scottish style and superior modern facilities. State of the art spa opening 2001. Within easy walking distance of theatres, shops, restaurants and visitor attractions.

★★★★★

HOTEL

&

Sheraton Grand Hotel Edinburgh
1 Festival Square, Edinburgh, EH3 9SR
Tel: 0131 229 9131 Fax: 0131 228 4510
E-mail: sue_finlay@sheraton.com
Web: www.sheraton.com

Nestling in the shadow of Edinburgh Castle, the Sheraton Grand has a warm luxurious Scottish style and superior modern facilities. Within easy walking distance of shops, restaurants and visitor attractions.

102 Twin	All En Suite	B&B per person	Open Jan-Dec
131		from £50.00 Single	
Double		from £97.50 Dbl/Twn	
28 Family		Room only per person	
		from £130.00	

C ⓕ V   SILVER 🄿🄿

★★★

GUEST HOUSE

Sherwood Guest House
42 Minto Street, Edinburgh, EH9 2BR
Tel: 0131 667 1200 Fax: 0131 667 2344
E-mail: sherwdedin@aol.com
Web: http://members.aol.com/sherwdedin/index.htm

A friendly and hospitable welcome is assured from Mrs Greig. The guest house has been fully refurbished throughout to a high standard. On main bus route to city centre 1.5 miles distance (2.5 kms). Limited parking.

2 Twin	5 En Suite fac	B&B per person	Open Jan-Dec
2 Double	1 Priv.NOT ensuite	£25.00-£55.00 Dbl/Twn	
2 Family			

C ⓕ V

SIMPSONS

79 LAURISTON PLACE, EDINBURGH EH3 9HZ
TEL: 0131 622 7979 FAX: 0131 622 7900
WEB: www.simpsons-hotel.com

Situated in the centre of Edinburgh, Simpsons is conveniently located close to all major attractions and shopping areas. Constructed in 1879, the hotel is full of character and history. 51 superior en-suite rooms all with satellite TV, hairdryer, trouser press and much more. New in-house restaurant opening in July 2000.

★★★

HOTEL

&

Simpsons
79 Lauriston Place, Edinburgh, EH3 9HZ
Tel: 0131 622 7979 Fax: 0131 622 7900
Web: www.simpsons-hotel.com

Formerly Simpsons Memorial maternity hospital, completely refurbished in 1998 to provide 51 rooms and suites furnished to a high standard in a quiet location 0.5 mile from Princes Strreet. All bedrooms with refridgerators.

7 Single	All En Suite	B&B per person	Open Jan-Dec
14 Twin		from £70.00 Single	B&B + Eve.Meal
24 Double		from £40.00 Dbl/Twn	from £59.50
6 Family			

C ⓕ V

Important: Prices stated are estimates and may be subject to amendments

Edinburgh

Map Ref: 2C5

GUEST HOUSE

Six Marys Place Guesthouse
Raeburn Place, Stockbridge, Edinburgh, EH4 1JD
Tel: 0131 332 8965 Fax: 0131 624 7060
E-mail: sixmarysplace@btinternet.com

3 Single	1 En Suite fac
2 Twin	2 Pub Bath/Show
3 Double	1 Limited ensuite

B&B per person
from £30.00 Single
from £30.00 Dbl/Twn

Open Jan-Dec
B&B + Eve.Meal
from £40.00

Restored Georgian townhouse in central location with period furnishings in bedrooms. Vegetarian cuisine served in the conservatory with the opportunity to relax in the homely atmosphere of the spacious TV lounge afterwards.

GUEST HOUSE

Smiths' Guest House
77 Mayfield Road, Edinburgh, EH9 3AA
Tel: 0131 667 2524 Fax: 0131 668 4455
E-mail: mail@smithsgh.com
Web: www.smithsgh.com

2 Single	2 En Suite fac
2 Twin	3 Pub Bath/Show
2 Double	
1 Family	

B&B per person
from £16.00 Single
from £16.00 Dbl/Twn
Room only per person
from £16.00

Open Jan-Dec
B&B + Eve.Meal
from £21.00

Victorian town house, recently refurbished. Free on street parking. Near to city centre.

GUEST HOUSE

Southdown Guest House
20 Craigmillar Park, Edinburgh, EH16 5PS
Tel: 0131 667 2410 Fax: 0131 667 6056
E-mail: muriel@southdownguesthouse.fsnet.co.uk
Web: www.southdownguesthouse.co.uk

2 Twin	6 En Suite fac
4 Double	
2 Family	

B&B per person
from £18.00 Dbl/Twn

Open mid Jan-Nov,
New Year

Victorian terraced house in residential area on main A701 road, with many bus routes to city centre. Friendly and family run. Private car park. Cable TV in lounge.

GUEST HOUSE

Strathallan Guest House
44 Minto Street, Edinburgh, EH9 2BR
Tel/Fax: 0131 667 6678
E-mail: strathalan@aol.com
Web: http://www.SmoothHound.co.uk/hotels/strathallan.html

2 Twin	All En Suite
3 Double	
2 Family	

B&B per person
£25.00-£45.00 Single

Open Jan-Dec excl Xmas

Recently refurbished elegant detached Georgian Villa (1820) with spacious ensuite rooms and easy access to city centre. Private parking. All city amenities within a short walk. Close to Queen's Park and Arthur's Seat.

HOTEL

Swallow Royal Scot Hotel
111 Glasgow Road, Edinburgh, EH12 8NF
Tel: 0131 334 9191 Fax: 0131 316 4507
E-mail: edinburgh@swallowhotels.co.uk

19 Single	All En Suite
130 Twin	
106 Double	
4 Family	

B&B per person
from £110.00 Single
from £62.50 Dbl/Twn
Room only per person
from £55.00

Open Jan-Dec

Modern hotel in outskirts of city and only 5 minutes drive from Edinburgh Airport.

VAT is shown at 17.5%: changes in this rate may affect prices.

Key to symbols is on back flap.

Edinburgh	Map Ref: 2C5

★★
HOTEL

Tailors Hall Hotel
139 Cowgate, Edinburgh, EH1 1JS
Tel: 0131 622 6800 Fax: 0131 622 6822
E-mail: tailors@festival-inns.co.uk
Web: www.festival-inns.co.uk

Edinburgh's liveliest hotel offering three star facilities in modern bedrooms and the famous Three Sisters pub and disco.

14 Single	All En Suite
12 Twin	
12 Double	
4 Family	

B&B per person
from £60.00 Single
from £30.00 Dbl/Twn

Open Jan-Dec

★
GUEST
HOUSE

Tania Guest House
19 Minto Street, Edinburgh, EH9 1RQ
Tel: 0131 667 4144

Traditional Guest House, welcoming families, conveniently situated on main bus route, 10 minutes from city centre. Limited private parking. Choice of restaurants available locally.

1 Single	2 En Suite fac
1 Twin	2 Pub Bath/Show
1 Double	
3 Family	

B&B per person
from £20.00 Single
from £17.50 Dbl/Twn

Open Jan-Dec

★★
GUEST
HOUSE

Terrace Hotel
37 Royal Terrace, Edinburgh, EH7 5AH
Tel: 0131 556 3423 Fax: 0131 556 2520
E-mail: terracehotel@btinternet.com

Personally run guest house in impressive Georgian terrace close to city centre, shopping and all amenities. Excellent views.

2 Single	11 En Suite fac
3 Twin	2 Pub Bath/Show
2 Double	
7 Family	

B&B per person
£26.00-£38.00 Single
£22.50-£37.50 Dbl/Twn

Open Jan-Dec

★★★
SMALL
HOTEL

Thistle Court Hotel
5 Hampton Terrace, Edinburgh, EH12 3JP
Tel: 0131 313 5500 Fax: 0131 313 5511
Web: www.thistlecourt.co.uk

Privately owned Victorian house with easy access to Princes Street (10-15 minutes walk). 20 minutes drive from the airport. Car parking.

3 Twin	All En Suite
10 Double	
2 Family	

B&B per person
£35.00-£48.00 Single
£25.00-£45.00 Dbl/Twn

Open Jan-Dec

★★★★
HOTEL
&

Thistle Edinburgh
107 Leith Street, Edinburgh, EH1 3SW
Tel: 0131 556 0111 Fax: 0131 557 5333
Web: www.thistlehotels.com

Modern hotel in city centre location with friendly and efficient staff. Caledonian brassiere restaurant, Boston Bean cocktail bar.

10 Single	All En Suite
90 Twin	Suites avail
31 Double	
12 Family	

B&B per person
from £120.00 Single
from £85.00 Dbl/Twn
Room only per person
from £102.00

Open Jan-Dec
B&B + Eve.Meal
from £136.00

Important: Prices stated are estimates and may be subject to amendments

Edinburgh | Map Ref: 2C5

HOTEL ★★★

Thrums Private Hotel
14/15 Minto Street, Newington, Edinburgh, EH9 1RQ
Tel: 0131 667 5545 Fax: 0131 667 8707

2 Single	All En Suite	B&B per person	Open Jan-Dec excl Xmas
2 Twin	1 Pub Bath/Show	from £38.00 Single	B&B + Eve.Meal
5 Double		from £55.00 Dbl/Twn	from £45.00
5 Family		Room only per person	
		from £50.00	

A warm welcome at this privately owned hotel on main bus route to city centre. Secure parking in private gardens. All bedrooms in annexe house are of period style retaining many original features including fireplaces and ornate plasterwork. Families and pets welcome.

GUEST HOUSE ★★

Tiree Guest House
26 Craigmillar Park, Edinburgh, EH16 5PS
Tel: 0131 667 7477 Fax: 0131 662 1608
E-mail: reservations@tireeguesthouse.com
Web: www.tireeguesthouse.com

2 Twin	5 En Suite fac	B&B per person	Open Jan-Dec
2 Double	1 Limited ensuite	£18.00-£28.00 Dbl/Twn	
2 Family	2 Pub Bath/Show		

Victorian terraced house on bus route into city centre. Private parking. Close to shopping centre.

GUEST HOUSE ★★★★

The Town House
65 Gilmore Place, Edinburgh, EH3 9NU
Tel: 0131 229 1985
E-mail: Susan@thetownhouse.com
Web: www.thetownhouse.com

1 Single	All En Suite	B&B per person	Open Jan-Dec
1 Twin		from £25.00 Single	
2 Double		£25.00-£36.00 pppn	
1 Family			

A Victorian terraced town house c1876 in a residential area. Easy walking distance of West End, Princes Street and Kings Theatre. A skilful mix of modern and period furnishings enhanced by stylish decor makes for a very warm and comfortable stay.

GUEST HOUSE ★★★★

Turret Guest House
8 Kilmaurs Terrace, Edinburgh, EH16 5DR
Tel: 0131 667 6704 Fax: 0131 668 1368
Web: www.turret.clara.net

2 Single	4 En Suite fac	B&B per person	Open Jan-Dec excl Xmas
1 Twin	1 Priv.NOT ensuite	£21.00-£35.00 Single	
3 Double	1 Pub Bath/Show	£21.00-£35.00 Dbl/Twn	
1 Family			

Recently refurbished Listed Victorian house in quiet residential area. Convenient for buses to city centre. Commonwealth Pool nearby.

GUEST HOUSE ★

Valentine City Centre Guest House
19 Gilmore Place, Edinburgh, EH3 9NE
Tel/Fax: 0131 229 5622
E-mail: freddiedoreen@gilmoreguesthouse.fsnet.co.uk

2 Twin	2 Pub Bath/Show	B&B per person	Open Jan-Dec
2 Double		from £14.00 Single	
1 Family		from £14.00 Dbl/Twn	

Centrally situated family run guest house, situated on second floor level, 50 metres from King's Theatre. Approx. 1/2 mile (1 km) to Princes Street and West End. Variety of restaurants in the vicinity.

VAT is shown at 17.5%: changes in this rate may affect prices.

Key to symbols is on back flap.

Edinburgh   Map Ref: 2C5

**GUEST
HOUSE**

Villa Nina Guest House	2 Twin	4 Limited ensuite	B&B per person	Open Jan-Dec excl
39 Leamington Terrace, Edinburgh, EH10 4JS	2 Double	2 Pub Bath/Show	from £17.00 Dbl/Twn	Xmas/New Year
Tel: 0131 229 2644 Fax: 0131 229 2644				
E-mail: villanina@amserve.net				

Terraced house. Approximately 1/2 mile (1 kms) from city centre.
Near Kings Theatre, the Castle and International Conference Centre.
Showers in bedrooms.

📺 🍴 ⚐

🅆 🆅

**GUEST
HOUSE**

Zetland Guest House	1 Single	4 En Suite fac	B&B per person	Open Jan-Dec
186 St Johns Road, Edinburgh, EH12 8SG	4 Twin	2 Pub Bath/Show	from £20.00 Single	
Tel/Fax: 0131 334 3898	2 Double		from £20.00 Dbl/Twn	
E-mail: zetland@dial.pipex.com	1 Family		Room only per person	
			from £18.00	

Spacious, family run Victorian house. Private parking and convenient
for airport and city centre. Ensuite facilities available.

📺 🐾 🅿 🍴 ⚐

🆅

**GUEST
HOUSE**

Ashcroft Farmhouse	3 Twin	All En Suite	B&B per person	Open Jan-Dec
East Calder, West Lothian, EH53 0ET	1 Double		from £40.00 Single	
Tel: 01506 881810 Fax: 01506 884327	2 Family		from £28.00 Dbl/Twn	
E-mail: ashcroft30538@aol.com				

A warm Scottish welcome awaits you at this modern bungalow with
interesting landscaped garden and quality choice of breakfast. Half an
hour by bus to Edinburgh city centre, 5 miles from the airport and within
easy access to all major routes. Ample parking. Totally non-smoking.

📺 📠 🅿 🍴 ⚑ ✂ ⚐

🅲 💷 🅆 🆅

by Edinburgh   Map Ref: 2C5

Dalhousie Castle and Spa

Bonnyrigg, Nr Edinburgh, Midlothian EH19 3JB
Tel: 01875 820153 Fax: 01875 821936
e.mail: enquiries@dalhousiecastle.co.uk Web: www.dalhousiecastle.co.uk

Only 20 minutes from Edinburgh city centre this 13th century castle offers whole-
hearted Scottish hospitality. 10 of the 34 en-suite bedrooms are historically themed
including Robert the Bruce. The Aqueous Spa and Orangery, an alternative dining
area to the Dungeon restaurant complete the unique services of the castle.

HOTEL

Dalhousie Castle and Spa	2 Single	All En Suite	B&B per person	Open mid Jan-Dec
Bonnyrigg, Edinburgh, Midlothian, EH19 3JB	14 Twin		from £80.00 Single	B&B + Eve.Meal
Tel: 01875 820153 Fax: 01875 821936	15 Double		from £52.50 Dbl/Twn	from £78.00
E-mail: enquiries@dalhousiecastle.co.uk	3 Family		Room only per person	
Web: www.dalhousiecastle.co.uk			from £42.00	

Recently sympathetically converted 13c castle set in own parkland.
Only 9 miles (13kms) from the centre of Edinburgh. Restaurant in vaulted
dungeon. Helipad. 5 newly created bedrooms in a lodge within the
grounds. New Hydro Spa 'Aqueous' due for completion in October 2000.

📺 📞 🛏 📠 🅿 🍴 ⚑ ✂ 🍴 🎱 🎯 👶 🍺 🏆

🅲 🐕 💷 🅆 🆅

Important: Prices stated are estimates and may be subject to amendments

, East Lothian | Map Ref: 2D5

★

HOTEL

Goblin Ha' Hotel
Main Street, Gifford, by Haddington, East Lothian, EH41 4QH
Tel: 01620 810244 Fax: 01620 810718

2 Single	6 En Suite fac	B&B per person	Open Jan-Dec
3 Twin	1 Limited ensuite	£25.00-£35.00 Single	
2 Double	1 Pub Bath/Show	£25.00-£31.25 Dbl/Twn	

18C family run village inn of great character, with large beer garden and kids play area. Emphasis on fine cuisine and home baking. Fine wines and real ale, CAMRA listed. Twenty miles from Edinburgh city centre. With 18 golf courses in a 12 mile radius.

Gullane, East Lothian | Map Ref: 2D4

★★★★

HOTEL

Greywalls Hotel
Muirfield, Gullane, East Lothian, EH31 2EG
Tel: 01620 842144 Fax: 01620 842241

4 Single	All En Suite	B&B per person	Open Apr-Oct
17 Twin		from £105.00 Single	
2 Double		from £100.00 Dbl/Twn	

Renowned family owned Lutyens house with friendly atmosphere, gardens by Gertrude Jekyll. Adjacent to Muirfield Golf Course. Views over Forth.

Haddington, East Lothian | Map Ref: 2D4

BROWNS' HOTEL
1 West Road, Haddington EH41 3RD
Telephone: 01620 822254   Fax: 01620 822254
e.mail: info@browns-hotel.com Web: www.browns-hotel.com

Uninterrupted view of the Lammermuir Hills is afforded from this hotel, within easy access to Edinburgh, golf courses and many sports facilities. The bedrooms are furnished to the standard of the Hotel. The restaurant has an excellent reputation in the area with dinner available each evening and lunch Sundays.

★★★★

SMALL
HOTEL

Brown's Hotel
1 West Road, Haddington, East Lothian, EH41 3RD
Tel/Fax: 01620 822254
E-mail: info@browns-hotel.com
Web: http://www.browns-hotel.com

1 Single	All En Suite	B&B per person	Open Jan-Dec
2 Twin		from £65.00 Single	B&B + Eve.Meal
2 Double		from £47.50 Dbl/Twn	from £77.00

Regency town house, elegant furnishings and decor with contemporary Scottish paintings. Restaurant noted in many guides. Easy access to A1, only 20 minutes by car from Edinburgh on the outskirts of this historic market town.

VAT is shown at 17.5%: changes in this rate may affect prices. | *Key to symbols is on back flap.*

Haddington, East Lothian   Map Ref: 2B5

HOTEL
★★★

Maitlandfield Country House Hotel
24 Sidegate, Haddington, East Lothian, EH41 4BZ
Tel: 01620 826513 Fax: 01620 826713

A magnificent country house hotel privately owned and professionally
managed. Ideally located for golfing, shooting and fishing. Splendid
wedding and conference facilities also available.

3 Single	All En Suite	B&B per person	Open Jan-Dec
10 Twin		from £50.00 Single	B&B + Eve.Meal
6 Double		from £30.00 Dbl/Twn	from £60.00
3 Triple		from £60.00 Feature	
		Room	

Ingliston, by Edinburgh, Midlothian   Map Ref: 2B5

NORTON HOUSE HOTEL
INGLISTON • EDINBURGH • EH28 8LX
Tel: 0131-333 1275   Fax: 0131-333 5305
e-mail: events.nhh@arcadianhotels.co.uk

Norton House Hotel is a Victorian mansion traditionally furnished offering all
the facilities required of today's traveller. Set in 55 acres of parkland, the hotel
provides a secluded peaceful location and yet is the nearest country house hotel
to Edinburgh International Airport, with the city centre only 6 miles away.

HOTEL
★★★★

Norton House Hotel
Ingliston, Edinburgh, EH28 8LX
Tel: 0131 333 1275 Fax: 0131 333 3752
E-mail: events.nhh@arcadianhotels.co.uk
Web: www.arcadianhotels.co.uk

Ideally situated in wooded grounds, an elegant mansion house, 6 miles
(13kms) west of the city centre, close to the airport. Choice of restaurants.
Conference and banqueting facilities available.

30 Twin	All En Suite	B&B per person	Open Jan-Dec
17 Double		from £125.00 Single	
		from £75.00 Dbl/Twn	

Kirknewton, Midlothian   Map Ref: 2B5

HOTEL
★★★★

Marriott Dalmahoy Hotel & Country Club
Kirknewton, Midlothian, EH27 8EB
Tel: 0131 333 1845 Fax: 0131 333 1433

Centred around Georgian mansion house with full range of business and
leisure facilities including two mature golf courses.

40 Twin	All En Suite	B&B per person	Open Jan-Dec
104	Suites avail	from £59.00 Dbl/Twn	B&B + Eve.Meal
Double	Rooms		£93.00-£195.00
58 Family			

Berwick, East Lothian | Map Ref: 2D4

SMALL HOTEL
★★

Belhaven Hotel
28 Westgate, North Berwick, East Lothian, EH39 4AH
Tel: 01620 893009 Fax: 01620 895882
Web: www.belhavenhotel.co.uk

2 Single	5 En Suite fac
5 Twin	
2 Triple	

B&B per person
from £20.00 Single
from £20.00 Twin

Open Dec-Oct excl
Xmas
B&B + Eve.Meal
from £32.50

Family run hotel overlooking the 18th green and 1st tee of West Links Golf course. 5 minutes walk from town centre and railway station. Extensive sea views. Half an hour by road or rail to Edinburgh.

SMALL HOTEL
★

Blenheim House Hotel
14 Westgate, North Berwick, East Lothian, EH39 4AF
Tel: 01620 892385 Fax: 01620 894010

2 Single	All En Suite
4 Twin	
5 Family	

B&B per person
from £28.00 Single
from £28.00 Twin

Open Jan-Dec
B&B + Eve.Meal
from £38.00

Family run, Victorian stone built house on shore of Firth of Forth, 200 yards from first tee of Westlinks Golf Course. 14 golf courses within a half hour drive. Beer garden available.

SMALL HOTEL
★

Golf Hotel
34 Dirleton Avenue, North Berwick, East Lothian, EH39 4BH
Tel: 01620 892202 Fax: 01620 892290

4 Single	10 En Suite fac
3 Twin	2 Pub Bath/Show
2 Double	
4 Family	

B&B per person
£25.00-£36.50 Single
£22.50-£32.00 Dbl/Twn

Open Jan-Dec
B&B + Eve.Meal
£36.00-£46.00

Family run Victorian hotel on outskirts of town. Close to all of East Lothian's 18 golf courses. Five minutes walk to children's golf course. Ground floor accommodation. Birdwatching and boat trips to Bass Rock from town harbour.

HOTEL
★★★

Marine Hotel
Cromwell Road, North Berwick, East Lothian, EH39 4LZ
Tel: 0870 400 8129 Fax: 01620 894480

52 Twin	All En Suite
24 Double	Suites avail
7 Family	

B&B per person
£40.00-£79.00 Single
£31.00-£69.00 Dbl/Twn
Room only per person
£80.00-£200.00

Open Jan-Dec
B&B + Eve.Meal
£45.00-£84.00

Traditional golf and conference hotel, with superb views over golf course and Firth of Forth. Leisure break and incentive rates.

SMALL HOTEL
★★

Nether Abbey
Dirleton Avenue, North Berwick, EH39 4BQ
Tel: 01620 892802 Fax: 01620 895298
E-mail: bookings@netherabbey.co.uk
Web: www.netherabbey.co.uk

10 Twin	All En Suite
1 Double	
3 family	

B&B per person
from £29.00 Single
from £29.00 Dbl/Twn

Open Jan-Dec
B&B + Eve.Meal
from £39.00

Stone built hotel with character, situated in attractive grounds. 2 minutes walk to sandy beach and west links. 19 golf courses within 10 mile radius. 30 minute train service to Edinburgh.

VAT is shown at 17.5%: changes in this rate may affect prices.

Key to symbols is on back flap.

North Middleton, Midlothian | Map Ref: 2C5

★★★

SMALL HOTEL

Borthwick Castle Hotel
North Middleton, Gorebridge, Midlothian EH23 4QY
Tel: 01875 820514 Fax: 01875 821702

3 Twin	All En Suite	B&B per person	Open Mar-Jan excl
7 Double		from £80.00 Single	Xmas/New Year
		from £67.50 Dbl/Twn	B&B + Eve.Meal
			from £150.00

Unique twin tower fortified keep c.1430 with great hall and state room retaining medieval atmosphere. Dine by log fires and candlelight. Only 12 miles South of Edinburgh in a pastoral valley, this romantic Castle stands on the summit of a knoll.

Uphall, West Lothian | Map Ref: 2B5

★★★

GUEST HOUSE

Coille-Mhor House
20 Houston Mains Holdings, Uphall, West Lothian, EH52 6PA
Tel: 01506 854044 Fax: 01506 855118
E-mail: michaelfisher@cmgh.freeserve.co.uk

1 Twin	All En Suite	B&B per person	Open Jan-Dec
4 Double		£32.00-£37.00 Single	
1 Family		£44.00-£50.00 Dbl/Twn	
		Room only per person	
		from £35.00	

Characteristically converted small holding, furnished to a high standard. Close to Edinburgh airport and Glasgow motorway. Private parking. All accommodation on ground floor level. Strictly non-smoking.

★★★★

HOTEL

Houstoun House Hotel & Country Club
Uphall, West Lothian, EH52 6JS
Tel: 01506 853831 Fax: 01506 854220
E-mail: info@houstoun.macdonald-hotels.co.uk
E-mail: events.houstoun@macdonald-hotels.co.uk

4 Single	All En Suite	B&B per person	Open Jan-Dec
24 Twin		from £100.00 Single	B&B + Eve.Meal
34 Double		from £60.00 Dbl/Twn	from £80.00
10 Family			

Built in the early 17th century, this unique tower house offers 72 bedrooms, 26 of these in the original tower steading. Set in 20 acres of glorious gardens yet only 10 minutes from Edinburgh Airport. Our leisure club offers an extensive range of facilities, together with Italian restaurant and floodlit tennis court. Log fires, 8 conference suites and award winning dining room.

F OR SHEER EXCITEMENT, GLASGOW IS ONE OF THE TOP UK DESTINATIONS.
THIS FORWARD-THINKING AND STYLISH CITY OFFERS A CHOICE OF SHOPPING,
ENTERTAINMENT AND CULTURE THAT SHOULD NOT BE MISSED. THE LEGENDARY
GLASGOW FRIENDLINESS IS A BONUS, WHILE FIRST-TIME VISITORS WILL BE STRUCK
BY THE CITY'S PANACHE.

Kelvingrove Gallery, Glasgow

GLASGOW'S ARCHITECTURE ranges from the magnificent Gothic style of Glasgow Cathedral to the imposing Italian Renaissance of the Victorian City Chambers.
As Britain's finest Victorian city, Glasgow offers 19th-century grandeur in its streets, squares and gardens while the fashionable and elegant terraces of the West End have been restored. In the 18th-century Merchant city, you will find cafés and boutiques and the chic Italian Centre with its exclusive designer shops. You can explore the St Enoch's Shopping Centre which is the largest glass-covered building in Europe as well as the Buchanan Galleries and stylish Princes Square. If you have any money left, head for a bargain in the famous Barras Market.

GLASGOW HAS AN unrivalled selection of more than 20 art galleries a museums to discover from the innovative Gallery of Modern Art to the internationally acclaimed Burrell Collection. Throughout the city, the unmistakable influence of two of the city's greatest sons – the architects Charles Rennie Mackintosh and Alexander 'Greek' Thomson can been seen. Visit Mackintosh's outstanding Glasgow School of Art and Thomson's newly restored Holmwood House.

Gourock and the Firth of Clyde

World Heritage Site, New Lanark

A YEAR-ROUND PROGRAMME of events including Celtic Connections, the Glasgow Folk Festival and the International Jazz Festival complements the arts scene in the city which is also home to Scottish Opera, Scottish Ballet and the Royal Scottish National Orchestra. Glasgow's cafés, bars and nightclubs offer plenty of opportunities to enjoy the friendliness and colourful character of the locals.

FROM GLASGOW, there is easy access to the rolling hills of Renfrewshire, the Inverclyde coastline and the fertile Clyde valley. At Paisley, you can visit the restored 12th-century abbey and learn about the famous Paisley textile pattern. Head upriver and the River Clyde changes its character tumbling over waterfalls into a rocky gorge at New Lanark Industrial Heritage Village, which is now a World Heritage site.

The Italian Centre, Glasgow

EVENTS
GREATER GLASGOW AND CLYDE VALLEY

10–28 JANUARY
Celtic Connections
Various venues, Glasgow
Glasgow's annual celebration of
Celtic music featuring
international artists.
Contact: Celtic Connections
TEL: 0141 353 8050

13-18 FEBRUARY
**Scottish Curling
Championships**
Braehead Arena, Glasgow
The highlight of the Scottish
curling year.
Contact: Royal Caledonian
Curling Club
TEL: 0131 333 3003

26-27 MAY
**British Gold Panning
Championships**
Museum of Lead Mining,
Wanlockhead, Biggar
Gold panning championships in
Scotland's highest village –
veterans, novices, adults and
children alike can join the
Scottish gold rush.
Contact:
Museum of Lead Mining
TEL: 01659 74387
EMAIL:
wanlockhead@dial.pipex.com

*provisional dates

2 JUNE
Shotts Highland Games
Hannah Park, Dykehead
Traditional Highland games
including wrestling, side shows
and the Clan Chieftains parade.
Contact: Mr Alex Hamilton
TEL: 01501 820280

7 JUNE
Lanark Lanimer Day
Town centre, Lanark
Traditional procession and
crowning of Lanimer Queen
Contact: Mr L Reid
TEL/FAX: 01556 663251

9 JUNE
**Bearsden & Milngavie
Highland Games**
Burnbrae, Milngavie
Traditional Highland Games,
pipe bands, tug-o-war, athletics,
heavy events and children's
events.
Contact: Cameron Wallace
TEL: 0141 942 5177

*9-24 JUNE
West End Festival
Various venues, Glasgow
Music, theatre, exhibitions and
free events, food, drink, and the
midsummer Carnival Parade, in
the West End of Glasgow
Contact: Festival Office
TEL: 0141 341 0844

*4-8 JULY
Glasgow Jazz Festival
Various venues, Glasgow
Glasgow's annual Jazz Festival,
now in it's 15th Year.
Contact: Glasgow International
Jazz Festival
TEL: 0141 287 5511 -
TICKETLINE 0141 552 3592
EMAIL: glasgow@jazzfest.co.uk
www.jazzfest.co.uk

*11 AUGUST
**World Pipe Band
Championships**
Glasgow Green, Glasgow.
The most prestigious event in
the annual pipe band calendar,
attracting some 200 bands from
around the World.
Contact: Royal Scottish Pipe
Band Association
TEL: 0141 221 5414

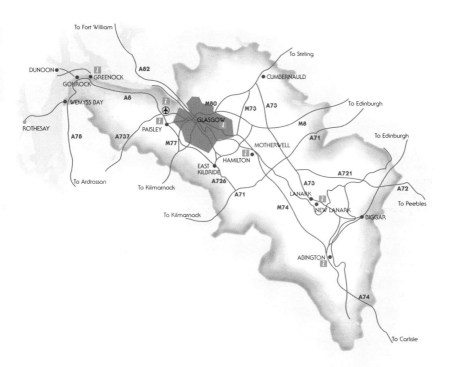

GREATER GLASGOW AND CLYDE VALLEY TOURIST BOARD

11 George Square
Glasgow
G2 1DY

TEL: **0141 204 4400**

FAX: **0141 204 4772**

www.seeglasgow.com

**GREATER GLASGOW AND
CLYDE VALLEY
TOURIST BOARD**

ABINGTON
Welcome Break Service Area
Junction 13, M74
TEL: **(01864) 502436**
Jan-Dec

BIGGAR
155 High Street
TEL: **(01899) 221066**
Easter-Oct

GLASGOW
11 George Square
TEL: **(0141) 204 4400**
Jan-Dec

GLASGOW AIRPORT
Tourist Information Desk
TEL: **(0141) 848 4440**
Jan-Dec

HAMILTON
Road Chef Services
M74 Northbound
TEL: **(01698) 285590**
Jan-Dec

LANARK
Horsemarket
Ladyacre Road
TEL: **(01555) 661661**
Jan-Dec

PAISLEY
9a Gilmour Street
TEL: **(0141) 889 0711**
Jan-Dec

Abington, Lanarkshire — Map Ref: 2B7

HOTEL
★★

Abington Hotel
Abington, by Biggar, Lanarkshire, ML12 6SD
Tel: 01864 502467 Fax: 01864 502223
E-mail: info@abington-hotel.ndirect.co.uk

5 Single	All En Suite	B&B per person	Open Jan-Dec
6 Twin		from £45.00 Single	B&B + Eve.Meal
11 Double		from £25.00 Dbl/Twn	from £39.00
6 Family		Room only per person	
		from £22.50	

Personally run family hotel situated in centre of village at the start of the Clyde Valley Tourist Route. All bedrooms en-suite. Easy to find, M74, junction 13. Good touring base for central Scotland - within one hours drive of Glasgow, Stirling, Edinburgh and Ayrshire Coast.

Airdrie, Lanarkshire — Map Ref: 2A5

GUEST HOUSE
★★

Rosslee Guest House
107 Forrest Street, Airdrie, Lanarkshire, ML6 7AR
Tel: 01236 765865 Fax: 01236 748535
E-mail: alan@rossleeguest.demon.co.uk

2 Single	4 En Suite fac	B&B per person	Open Jan-Dec
3 Twin	2 Pub Bath/Show	from £20.00 Single	
1 Family		from £20.00 Twn/Fam	
		Room only per person	
		from £18.00	

Former church manse, now family run guest house with comfortable rooms. Central situation for Edinburgh or Glasgow.

Biggar, Lanarkshire — Map Ref: 2B6

HOTEL
★★★

Cornhill House
Cornhill Road, Biggar, Lanarkshire, ML12 6QE
Tel: 01899 220001 Fax: 01899 220112

6 Double	All En Suite	B&B per person	Open Jan-Dec
1 Twin		from £50.00 Single	
		from £33.00 Double	

A late 19th Century building designed by William Leiper, in the style of a 'Rennaisance French Chateau'. Sensitively restored to a country house hotel offering both formal evening and informal bistro food and high teas.

Coatbridge, Lanarkshire — Map Ref: 2A5

SMALL HOTEL
★★

The Georgian Hotel
26 Lefroy Street, Coatbridge, Lanarkshire, ML5 1LZ
Tel: 01236 421888 Fax: 01236 421173

2 Single	6 En Suite fac	B&B per person	Open Jan-Dec
6 Twn/Dbl	1 Pub Bath/Show	£25.00-£35.00 Single	B&B + Eve.Meal
		£20.00-£25.00 Dbl/Twn	£34.00-£49.00

Family run hotel in quiet residential area near the Time Capsule. Easy access to motorway network. Ideal venue for weddings and conferences.

VAT is shown at 17.5%: changes in this rate may affect prices.

Key to symbols is on back flap.

East Kilbride, Lanarkshire   Map Ref: 1H6

HOTEL

The Stuart Hotel
2 Cornwall Way, Town Centre, East Kilbride
G74 1JR
Tel: 01355 221161 Fax: 01355 264410

13 Single	All En Suite	B&B per person	Open Jan-Dec
7 Twin		from £62.00 Single	B&B + Eve.Meal
17 Double		from £40.00 Dbl/Twn	from £77.00
1 Family			

Centrally located for all town centre attractions, featuring Jellowicki's - an American/Red Indian themed a la carte restaurant. Full business and conference facilities, also various function/meeting rooms. Weddings catered for also.

Glasgow   Map Ref: 1H5

**GUEST
HOUSE**

Alamo Guest House
46 Gray Street, Kelvingrove, Glasgow, G3 7SE
Tel: 0141 339 2395

2 Single	2 En Suite fac	B&B per person	Open Jan-Dec
1 Twin	1 Priv.NOT ensuite	from £21.00 Single	
1 Double	2 Pub Bath/Show	from £18.00 Dbl/Twn	
5 Family			
1 Triple			

Friendly family run Victorian house, in quiet location overlooking park. Easy access to centre and within walking distance of SECC, galleries, Transport Museum, Glasgow University and a range of restaurants.

HOTEL

Albion Hotel
405-407 North Woodside Road, Glasgow, G20 6NN
Tel: 0141 339 8620 Fax: 0141 334 8159
Web: www.glasgowhotelsandapartments.co.uk

6 Single	All En Suite	B&B per person	Open Jan-Dec
4 Twin		from £38.00 Single	
4 Double		from £24.00 Dbl/Twn	
2 Family			

Privately owned hotel in residential area close to Kelvingrove Park, University and underground station. All rooms with private facilities.

HOTEL

Ambassador Hotel
7 Kelvin Drive, Glasgow, G20 8QG
Tel: 0141 946 1018 Fax: 0141 945 5377
Web: www.glasgowhotelsandapartments.co.uk

8 Single	All En Suite	B&B per person	Open Jan-Dec
4 Twin		from £38.00 Single	
4 Double		from £24.00 Dbl/Twn	

Small privately run Victorian townhouse quietly located in West End, convenient for city centre, museums, art galleries and the Botanic Gardens. The ideal base for a business or pleasure stop over in the city.

**GUEST
HOUSE**

Angus Hotel
966-970 Sauchiehall Street, Glasgow, G3 7TH
Tel: 0141 357 5155 Fax: 0141 339 9469
E-mail: info@angushotelglasgow.co.uk
Web: www.angushotelglasgow.co.uk

2 Single	All En Suite	Rates per person	Open Jan-Dec excl
2 Twin		from £27.00 sharing	Xmas
7 Double			
7 Family			

Refurbished, privately owned Guest House situated on bus route to city centre. Within walking distance of Glasgow University and Kelvin Hall sports arena and Kelvingrove Art Gallery & Museum.

Important: Prices stated are estimates and may be subject to amendments

Glasgow			Map Ref: 1H5	

HOTEL ★★★

Argyll Hotel
973 Sauchiehall Street, Glasgow, G3 7TQ
Tel: 0141 337 3313 Fax: 0141 337 3283
E-mail: info@argyllhotelglasgow.co.uk
Web: www.argyllhotelglasgow.co.uk

Half a mile (1 km) from city centre, next to Kelvingrove Park. On main bus routes. Traditional hotel with bar and restaurant. Close to SECC, Glasgow University, art gallery and museums.

9 Single
10 Twin
12 Double
7 Family

All En Suite

B&B per person
from £35.00 sharing

Open Jan-Dec

HOTEL ★

The Buchanan Hotel
185 Buchanan Street, Glasgow, G1 2JY
Tel: 0141 332 7284 Fax: 0141 333 6635

City centre hotel near to Queen Street Station and Buchanan Street Bus Station.

13 Single
25 Twin
17 Double
4 Family

All En Suite

B&B per person
from £29.00 Single
from £29.00 Dbl/Twn
Room only per person
from £25.00

Open Jan-Dec
B&B + Eve.Meal
from £39.00

GUEST HOUSE ★

Chez Nous Guest House
33 Hillhead Street, Glasgow, G12 8PX
Tel: 0141 334 2977
E-mail: enquiries@cheznousguesthouse.co.uk
Web: www.cheznousguesthouse.co.uk

Situated in West End of city, close to Glasgow University and Art Gallery. Within easy reach of M8 and all amenities. Limited private parking.

12 Single
5 Twin
7 Double
7 Family

19 En Suite fac

B&B per person
from £20.50 Single
from £20.50 Dbl/Twn

Open Jan-Dec

CAMPUS ACCOMMODATION ★

Dalrymple Hall
Conference & Visitor Services, No 3 The Square,
University of Glasgow, Glasgow, G12 8QQ
Tel: 0800 027 2030 Fax: 0141 334 5465
Web: www.gla.ac/uk/vacationaccommodation

Hall of residence, part of Victorian terrace in West End of Glasgow, close to Botanic Gardens.

35 Single
21 Twin
1 Family

16 Pub Bath/Show

B&B per person
from £22.50 Single

Open Mar, Apr, Jul, Sep
B&B + Eve.Meal
from £31.25

SMALL HOTEL ★★★★★

Devonshire Hotel
No 5 Devonshire Gardens, Glasgow, G12 0UX
Tel: 0141 339 7878 Fax: 0141 339 3980
E-mail: devonshir5@aol.com
Web: www.the-devonshire.co.uk

The Devonshire is a distinctive town house, quietly standing in a grand leafy terrace just 10 minutes from Glasgow's impressive city centre, 45 minutes from Loch Lomond and 20 minutes from Glasgow Airport. An extremely tastful combination of modern hotel facilities with period features, rich designer fabrics, traditional furnishings and antique pine provide an understated effect. The bedrooms are large and luxurious but unfussy.

4 Twin
8 Double
2 Family

All En Suite

Room only per person
from £100.00 Single
from £60.00 Dbl/Twn

Open Jan-Dec

VAT is shown at 17.5%: changes in this rate may affect prices.

Key to symbols is on back flap.

Glasgow   Map Ref: 1H5

HOTEL ★★

Dunkeld Hotel
10 Queen's Drive, Glasgow, G42 8BS
Tel: 0141 424 0160 Fax: 0141 423 4437
E-mail: dunkeldhot@aol.com
Web: www.dunkeld-hotel.co.uk

Privately owned hotel on south side of city centre in residential area
overlooking Queens Park. Ample parking. Conservatory coffee lounge.

3 Single	All En Suite
5 Twin	
8 Double	
2 Family	

B&B per person
from £39.50 Single
from £27.50 Dbl/Twn

Open Jan-Dec
B&B + Eve.Meal
from £38.50

GUEST HOUSE ★★

Enterprize Hotel
144 Renfrew Street, Glasgow, G3 6RF
Tel/Fax: 0141 332 8095

Town house style guest house in quiet street behind Sauchiehall Street.
Convenient for motorway, shops, theatres and restaurants.

1 Single	All En Suite
1 Twin	
2 Double	
2 Family	

B&B per person
from £45.00 Single
from £30.00 Dbl/Twn

Open Jan-Dec
B&B + Eve.Meal
from £55.00

EWINGTON HOTEL
132 Queen's Drive, Queen's Park, Glasgow G42 8QW
Tel: 0141 423 1152   Fax: 0141 422 2030
e.mail: info@countryhotels.co.uk

A classic Victorian townhouse style hotel overlooking the beautiful
Queen's Park and only minutes from the city centre. Forty one
individually designed bedrooms and suites.
Award-winning restaurant and bar. Ample free parking.

HOTEL ★★★

Ewington Hotel
132 Queens Drive, Glasgow, G42 8QW
Tel: 0141 423 1152 Fax: 0141 422 2030
E-mail: info@countryhotels.co.uk
Web: www.countryhotels.co.uk

Victorian town house hotel situated in residential area overlooking Queens
Park, 1 mile south of city centre. Unrestricted on lane parking.
Individually designed bedrooms offering all modern day comforts.
Minstrels Restaurant offers the discerning diner a true flavour of Scotland.
Conference and banqueting facilities available.

8 Single	All En Suite
15 Twin	
17 Double	
1 Suite	

B&B per person
from £60.50 Single
from £40.50 Dbl/Twn
Room only per person
from £50.00

Open Jan-Dec
B&B + Eve.Meal
from £78.00

HOTEL ★★★★

Garfield House Hotel
Cumbernauld Road, Stepps, Glasgow, G33 6HW
Tel: 0141 779 2111 Fax: 0141 779 9799

Country house with refurbished modern wing close to main Glasgow-
Stirling road. Large car park.

2 Single	All En Suite
20 Twin	
22 Double	
2 Family	

B&B per person
£50.00-£76.00 Single
£30.00-£50.00 Dbl/Twn

Open Jan-Dec
B&B + Eve.Meal
from £40.00

Important: Prices stated are estimates and may be subject to amendments

Glasgow	Map Ref: 1H5

GUEST HOUSE ★★

Hillhead Hotel
32 Cecil Street, Hillhead, Glasgow, G12 8RJ
Tel: 0141 339 7733 Fax: 0141 339 1770
Web: www.hillheadhotel.co.uk

2 Single	All En Suite	
4 Twin		
1 Double		
4 Family		

B&B per person
from £34.00 Single
from £24.00 Dbl/Twn
Room only per person
from £30.00

Open Jan-Dec
Evening meal
from £4.00

Based in fashionable west end, privately owned hotel. Convenient for Glasgow University, Hillhead Underground Station and SECC. Within a five minute walk of many restaurants and shops.

HOLIDAY INN – GLASGOW
161 West Nile Street, Glasgow G1 2RL
Tel: 0141 352 8305 Fax: 0141 352 8311

Ideally located in the heart of the city's theatreland, the Holiday Inn Glasgow offers 113 superbly appointed bedrooms including executive rooms and penthouse suites. Recently benefiting from a £2 million reinvestment, the Holiday Inn delivers comfort and relaxation with an undertone of unassuming style and a focus on guest service.

HOTEL ★★★★ &

Holiday Inn Glasgow
161 West Nile Street, Glasgow, G1 2RL
Tel: 0141 352 8305 Fax: 0141 332 7447

32 Twin	All En Suite	
60 Double		
18 Executive	Suites	
3 Penthouse		

B&B per person
£35.00-£60.70 Dbl/Twn
Room only per person
£45.00-£60.00

Open Jan-Dec
B&B + Eve.Meal
£50.00-£105.00

In the heart of the city, five minutes walk from theatres and transport. Brasserie style restaurant. Penthouse suites now available along with a small mini gym.

HOTEL ★★★

Jarvis Glasgow Hotel
201 Ingram Street, Glasgow, G1 1DQ
Tel: 0141 248 4401 Fax: 0141 226 5913

38 Twin	All En Suite	
51 Double		
2 Suites		

B&B per person
from £50.00 Single
from £35.00 Dbl/Twn

Open Jan-Dec

Modern hotel in city centre. Car parking. Satellite TV. Conference facilities.

HOTEL ★★★

Jurys Glasgow Hotel
Great Western Road, Glasgow, G12 0XP
Tel: 0141 334 8161 Fax: 0141 334 3846
Web: www.jurysdoyle.com

72 Twin	All En Suite	
40 Double		
24 Family		

B&B per person
from £60.00 Single
from £70.00 Dbl/Twn

Open Jan-Dec
B&B + Eve.Meal
On request

Modern hotel, on main Glasgow/Loch Lomond road, convenient for Botanic Gardens and City Centre. Leisure centre. Large car park. Convenient for Glasgow airport and the M8 for day trips to Edinburgh.

VAT is shown at 17.5%: changes in this rate may affect prices.

| Key to symbols is on back flap. |

601
GLASGOW

C

GREATER GLASGOW
AND CLYDE VALLEY

Glasgow

Map Ref: 1H5

KELVINGROVE HOTEL

944 Sauchiehall Street, Glasgow G3 7TH
Tel: 0141-339 5011/0141-569 1121 Fax: 0141 339 6566
e.mail: kelvingrove.hotel@business.ntl.com
Web: www.kelvingrovehotel.co.uk

Quality rooms at low prices, fully refurbished, close to S.E.C.C., art gallery, parks, transport museum, university, transport to town takes 5 minutes. Central heating, 23 en-suite rooms, double glazing throughout, colour TV in all rooms, direct dial phone, satellite and cable TV. Tea and coffee making facilities in all rooms. No parking restrictions. 10 mins walk to International Conference Centre. Tremendous value for money.

★★★

GUEST
HOUSE

Kelvingrove Hotel
944 Sauchiehall Street, Glasgow, G3 7TH
Tel: 0141 339 5011 Fax: 0141 339 6566
E-mail: kelvingrove.hotel@business.ntl.com
Web: www.kelvingrovehotel.co.uk

2 Single	23 En Suite fac	B&B per person
6 Twin	1 Pub Bath/Show	from £33.00 Single
14 Double	2 Priv.NOT ensuite	from £26.50 Dbl/Twn
5 Family		Room only per person
		from £24.00

Open Jan-Dec

City centre hotel with mainly ensuite rooms, TV, tea and coffee facilities. 15 minutes walk to shopping centre. SECC nearby. Kelvingrove Art Gallery, Kelvin Hall, The Western Infirmary and Glasgow University and all a short walk away.

★★

GUEST
HOUSE

Kelvin Hotel
15 Buckingham Terrace, Gt Western Road, Glasgow, G12 8EB
Tel: 0141 339 7143 Fax: 0141 339 5215
Web: www.scotland2000.com/lomondkelvin

10 Single	9 En Suite fac	B&B per person
4 Twin	6 Pub Bath/Show	£22.00-£39.00 Single
2 Double		£20.00-£28.00 Dbl/Twn
4 Family		Room only per person
		£19.00-£31.00

Open Jan-Dec

Victorian terraced house in the west end. Close to the BBC, Botanical Gardens and Glasgow University. On main bus routes to city centre and five minutes walk from underground, restaurants and shops.

★

GUEST
HOUSE

McLays Guest House
264-276 Renfrew Street, Glasgow, G3 6TT
Tel: 0141 332 4796 Fax: 0141 353 0422
Web: www.mclays.com

18 Single	39 En Suite fac	B&B per person
20 Twin	9 Pub Bath/Show	from £22.00 Single
12 Double		from £19.00 Dbl/Twn
12 Family		

Open Jan-Dec

Family run guest house in city centre near Charing Cross. Close to Universities and Kelvingrove Park, shopping and all amenities.

★★★★

HOTEL

Malmaison Hotel
278 West George Street, Glasgow, G2 4LL
Tel: 0141 572 1000 Fax: 0141 572 1002
E-mail: glasgow@malmaison.com
Web: www.malmaison.com

10 Twin	All En Suite	B&B per room
50 Double		from £115.75 Single
8 Suites		from £126.50 Double
4 Disabled		Room only rate
		from £105.00 Sgl/Dbl

Open Jan-Dec

Elegant 'Brasserie with rooms', originally a Greek Orthodox church. Lively atmosphere, interesting wines and French style cuisine using natural ingredients. All bedrooms with TV's, CD players and modem points.

Important: Prices stated are estimates and may be subject to amendments

Glasgow		Map Ref: 1H5	

HOTEL

The Millennium Hotel, Glasgow
George Square, Glasgow, G2 1DS
Tel: 0141 332 6711 Fax: 0141 332 4264
Web: www.stay.with-us.com

Recently refurbished landmark hotel in the heart of Scotland's commercial capital. Ideal for city centre attractions and amenities.

15 Single   All En Suite
38 Twin
58 Double
1 Family
5 Suites

B&B per person
from £90.00 Single
from £48.00 Dbl/Twn

Open Jan-Dec
B&B + Eve.Meal
from £55.00 pp

HOTEL

One Devonshire Gardens
1 Devonshire Gardens, Great Western Rd, Glasgow, G12 0UX
Tel: 0141 339 2001 Fax: 0141 337 1663
E-mail: onedevonshire@btconnect.com
Web: www.one-devonshire-gardens.co.uk

Adjoining Victorian town houses, elegantly refurbished to a high standard. Award winning restaurant, interesting cuisine complemented by fine wines.

3 Twin   All En Suite
24 Double

B&B per person
from £130.00 Single
from £130.00 Dbl/Twn

Open Jan-Dec

HOTEL
&

Posthouse Glasgow City
Bothwell Street, Glasgow, G2 7EN
Tel: 0870 400 9032 Fax: 0141 221 8986
E-mail: gm1786@forte-hotels.com

City centre location with easy access from M8. Choice of dining in Carvery or the recently opened 'Jules' themed restaurant and bar. Part of Forte Posthouse

61 Twin   All En Suite
166   Suite avail
Double
10 Family

B&B per person
£79.00-£99.00 Single
£50.00-£70.00 Dbl/Twn
Room only per person
£79.00-£99.00

Open Jan-Dec
B&B + Eve.Meal
£104.00-£114.00

GUEST HOUSE

Reidholme Guest House
36 Regent Park Square, Glasgow, G41 2AG
Tel: 0141 423 1855

B Listed terraced town house in quiet residential area on south side of city centre near Queens Park. Under 2 miles (3kms) from the Burrell Collection and Pollok Park. Convenient bus routes to city centre..

1 Single   1 Priv.NOT ensuite
3 Twin   2 Pub Bath/Show
1 Double
1 Family

B&B per person
from £20.00 Single
from £20.00 Dbl/Twn

Open Jan-Dec
B&B + Eve.Meal
from £28.00

GUEST HOUSE

Seton Guest House
6 Seton Terrace, Glasgow, G31 2HU
Tel: 0141 556 7654 Fax: 0141 402 3655
Web: www.vacations-scotland.co.uk/seton.html

Stone built townhouse c.1850 in conservation area of East End. Close to city centre and all amenities. Public transport of rail & bus a 2 minute walk away.

1 Single   3 Pub Bath/Show
2 Twin
2 Double
4 Family

B&B per person
from £17.00 Single
from £17.00 Dbl/Twn

Open Jan-Dec

VAT is shown at 17.5%: changes in this rate may affect prices.

Key to symbols is on back flap.

Glasgow   Map Ref: 1H5

HOTEL

Sherbrooke Castle Hotel
11 Sherbrooke Avenue, Glasgow, G41 4PG
Tel: 0141 427 4227 Fax: 0141 427 5685

7 Single	All En Suite	B&B per person	Open Jan-Dec
7 Twin		from £55.00 Single	B&B + Eve.Meal
9 Double		from £32.50 Dbl/Twn	from £42.50
2 Family			sharing Dbl/Twn

Situated in the leafy, up-market suburb of Pollokshields. This magnificent baronial building crafted in rich red sandstone, combines traditional grace with modern efficiency. The fully air conditioned restaurant serves fresh local produce, prepared by award winning chefs, complimented with an interesting wine cellar. Some annex accommodation.

GUEST
HOUSE

Smiths Hotel
963 Sauchiehall Street, Glasgow, G3 7TQ
Tel: 0141 339 7674 Fax: 0141 334 1892

17 Single	Limited ensuite	B&B per person	Open Jan-Dec
8 Twin		from £20.00 Single	
6 Double		from £17.50 Dbl/Twn	
2 Family			

Family run bed and breakfast hotel 3/4 mile (1 km) from city centre. On main bus routes. Near to Kelvin Hall, Art Gallery and SECC.

University of Strathclyde Graduate School of Business
199 Cathedral Street, Glasgow G4 0QU
Tel: 0141-553 6000   Fax: 0141-553 6137
Web: www.sgbs.strath.ac.uk/hotel

Strathclyde Graduate Business School Hotel is a modern establishment with 107 fully appointed ensuite bedrooms, conveniently located in the heart of Glasgow City Centre – only 5 mins walk from Buchanan Galleries. It is the perfect choice of accommodation for that special shopping spree, weekend break or theatre trip.

HOTEL

Strathclyde Graduate Business School
Hotel-Conference Centre, 199 Cathedral Street,
Glasgow, G4 0QU
Tel: 0141 553 6000 Fax: 0141 553 6137
Web: www.sgbs.strath.ac.uk/hotel

95 Single	All En Suite	B&B per person	Open Jan-Dec excl
10 Double		from £39.00 Single	Xmas/New Year
2 Twin		from £34.50 Dbl/Twn	

Very central, modern residential business school with conference facilities. All ensuite. Private parking. 5 minute walk from the Concert Hall and Buchanan Galleries shopping complex.

Important: Prices stated are estimates and may be subject to amendments

Glasgow   **Map Ref: 1H5**

★★★
HOTEL

Swallow Hotel
517 Paisley Road West, Glasgow, G51 1RW
Tel: 0141 427 3146 Fax: 0141 427 4059

Modern city centre hotel with a leisure complex including pool. Extensive conference and banqueting facilities. Spacious, free car parking.

7 Single	All En Suite	B&B per person	Open Jan-Dec
53 Twin		from £45.00 Single	B&B + Eve.Meal
57 Double		from £35.00 Dbl/Twn	from £45.00
		Room only	
		from £60.00	

★★★★
HOTEL

Thistle Glasgow
Cambridge Street, Glasgow, G2 3HN
Tel: 0141 332 3311 Fax: 0141 332 4050
Web. www.thistlehotels.com

Modern hotel situated in the heart of the city. 'Gengis' taste revolution restaurant. Banqueting and conference facilities. Private parking. New leisure centre opened January 2001.

115 Twin	All En Suite	B&B per person	Open Jan-Dec
119		from £80.00 Single	B&B + Eve.Meal
Double		from £51.00 Dbl/Twn	from £61.00
66 Family			

The Town House
4 Hughenden Terrace, Glasgow G12 9XR
Telephone: 0141 357 0862 Fax: 0141 339 9605
e.mail: hospitality@thetownhouseglasgow.com
Web: www.thetownhouseglasgow.com

Glasgow's long and established Victorian Town House, located in the fashionable West End. This small hotel offers a truly welcoming and comfortable stay. Its many amenities include ample parking and the use of neighbouring sports clubs. You are sure to enjoy the legendary breakfasts with a choice of local produce and seafood delights.

★★★
GUEST HOUSE

The Town House
4 Hughenden Terrace, Glasgow, G12 9XR
Tel: 0141 357 0862 Fax: 0141 339 9605
E.mail: hospitality@thetownhouseglasgow.com
Web: www.thetownhouseglasgow.com

Glasgow's original and long established town house, situated in the desirable west end, offers a peaceful and luxurious base from which to enjoy all that Glasgow has to offer. A fine example of Victorian architecture. Free and ample parking.

4 Twin	All En Suite	B&B per person	Open Jan-Dec
4 Double		from £60.00 Single	
2 Family		from £36.00 Dbl/Twn	

VAT is shown at 17.5%: changes in this rate may affect prices. | *Key to symbols is on back flap.* |

Glasgow   Map Ref: 1H5

University of Strathclyde

Residence and Catering Services, 50 Richmond St., Glasgow G1 1XP
Tel: 0141-553 4148   Fax: 0141-553 4149
e.mail: rescat@mis.strath.ac.uk
Web: www.strath.ac.uk/Departments/RESCAT/sales/index.htm

Strathclyde University offers a range of attractive accommodation in Glasgow city centre at affordable prices. En-suite and standard single rooms are located in the modern campus village adjacent to the Lord Todd bar/restaurant and twins and singles are available at Baird Hall in Sauchiehall Street.

★

CAMPUS
ACCOMMODATION

University of Strathclyde
Residence and Catering Services, 50 Richmond St.,
Glasgow, G1 1XP.
Tel: 0141 553 4148 Fax: 0141 553 4149
E-mail: rescat@mis.strath.ac.uk
Web: www.strath.ac.uk/Departments/RESCAT/sales/index.htm

Modern, purpose-built halls of residence on campus. Ideal centre for exploring the city.

833 Single	308 En Suite fac	B&B per person	Open Jun-Sep
135 Twin	679 Limited facs	from £24.00 Single	
17 Double		from £19.75 Dbl/Twn	
2 Family			

★★

HOTEL

Wickets Hotel
52 Fortrose Street, Glasgow, G11 5LP
Tel/Fax: 0141 334 9334
E-mail: wicketshotel@hotmail.com
Web: www.wicketshotel.com.uk

Privately owned, overlooks cricket ground. Close to Clydeside. Expressway to city. Near Scottish Exhibition Centre and Glasgow Airport. Beer garden and conservatory for dining and drinking.

4 Single	All En Suite	B&B per person	Open Jan-Dec excl
4 Twin		from £48.00 Single	Xmas/New Year
3 Double		from £29.00 Dbl/Twn	
		Room only	
		from £42.00	

★

CAMPUS
ACCOMMODATION

Wolfson Hall
Conference & Visitor Services
No 3 The Square, University of Glasgow, G12 8QQ
Tel: 0800 027 2030 Fax: 0141 334 5465
E-mail: vacation@gla.ac.uk

Modern property in quiet parkland, offering full Scottish breakfast. Located within easy commuting distance for Glasgow city centre. Sports facilities nearby. Facilities include 22 kitchens, 2 TV rooms, games room, public phones, 24 hr reception, Garescube sports facilities (extra charge).

131 Single	En Suite	B&B per person	Open mid Mar-mid
13 Twin	En Suite	from £22.50 Single	Apr, Jul-Sep
84 Single	WHB	from £31.00 Single Ensuite	
		from £26.00 Twin	

Glasgow Airport, Renfrewshire   Map Ref: 1H5

★★★★

HOTEL

Lynnhurst Hotel
Park Road, Johnstone, Renfrewshire, PA5 8LS
Tel: 01505 324331 Fax: 01505 324219
Web: www.lynnhurst.co.uk

Friendly family run hotel in residential area. Conservatory, function and conference facilities. Glasgow Airport 5 miles (8kms). Many Victorian features of the original mansions sympathetically retained.

11 Single	All En Suite	B&B per person	Open Jan-Dec excl
1 Twin		from £40.00 Single	Xmas/New Year
7 Double		from £35.00 Dbl/Twn	
2 Family			

Important: Prices stated are estimates and may be subject to amendments

Howwood, Renfrewshire | Map Ref: 1G5

Bowfield Hotel & Country Club

HOWWOOD · RENFREWSHIRE · PA9 1DB

Tel: 01505 705225   Fax: 01505 705230

Web: www.bowfieldcountryclub.co.uk

A refreshingly different country hotel offering a wealth of facilities including swimming pool, sauna, jacuzzi, squash courts, gymnasium and health and beauty spa. This perfect country retreat is only 20 minutes from Glasgow Airport. B&B from £37.50-£42.50 per person per night sharing a twin or double room. Two RAC blue ribbons.

AA ★★★ RAC ★★★   ★★★★ Hotel

★★★★

HOTEL

Bowfield Hotel & Country Club
Howwood, Renfrewshire, PA9 1DB
Tel: 01505 705225 Fax: 01505 705230
Web: www.bowfieldcountryclub.co.uk

A refreshingly different country retreat close to town and city attractions. A comprehensive leisure club with swimming pool and health & beauty spa and awarded restaurant.

8 Twin	All En Suite	B&B per person
12 Double		£50.00-£65.00 Single
3 Family		£37.50-£42.50 Dbl/Twn

Open Jan-Dec
T.d.H £19.50
Bar snacks+meals

Inverkip, Renfrewshire | Map Ref: 1F5

★★★

HOTEL

Inverkip Hotel
Main Street, Inverkip, Renfrewshire, PA16 0AS
Tel: 01475 521478 Fax: 01475 522065
Web: www.inverkip.co.uk

Family run hotel, on main tourist route adjacent to Scotland's No 1 yachting marina. Reputation for good food. Sports can be arranged. Busy restaurant and bars. Ideally positioned for the Clyde ferries to Dunoon and beyond or trips to Loch Lomond, Stirling and the Trossachs. 45 mins drive to Royal Troon.

2 Twin	All En Suite	B&B per person
2 Double		from £40.00 Single
1 Family		from £33.00 Dbl/Twn

Open Jan-Dec excl
Xmas/New Year

---

by Larkhall, Lanarkshire | Map Ref: 2A6

★★

LODGE

Shawlands Hotel
Ayr Road, Canderside Toll, by Larkhall,
Lanarkshire, ML9 2TZ
Tel: 01698 791111 Fax: 01698 792001

Privately owned and family run travel lodge with emphasis on quality food and drink at affordable prices. In central Scotland just off M74, 20 mins from Glasgow and 40 mins travel to Edinburgh.

1 Single	All En Suite	All rooms
16 Twin		£40.00
4 Double		

Open Jan-Dec

Motherwell, Lanarkshire   Map Ref: 1G5

DALZIEL PARK GOLF & COUNTRY CLUB

100 HAGEN DRIVE, DALZIEL PARK, MOTHERWELL ML1 5RZ
TEL: 01698 862862 FAX: 01698 862863
WEB: www.dalzielpark.co.uk

Situated in pleasant countryside estate 4 miles from Motherwell with
good access to M74 and M8 at junction 6 and midway between
Glasgow and Edinburgh. Convenient base for touring and relaxation.
Facilities include country club with 18-hole course and floodlit driving
range. Good food, modern, comfortable and excellent value for money.

★★★

**SMALL
HOTEL**

Dalziel Park Golf & Country Club	1 Single	All En Suite	B&B per person	Open Jan-Dec
100 Hagen Drive, Motherwell, ML1 5RZ	4 Double		from £45.00 Single	
Tel: 01698 862862 Fax: 01698 862863	4 Family		from £25.00 Dbl/Twn	
Web: www.dalzielpark.co.uk			Room only	
			from £39.95	

Newly built accommodation opposite the Clubhouse offering traditional
contemporary en-suite bedrooms. Set in picturesque clubhouse woodland
setting. Offering 15-bay floodlight driving range, hairdresser and 18 hole
golf course. Approximately 20 mins drive to Glasgow and Edinburgh.

📺 ⚲ 📞 🛏 🅿 🍳 ⌇ ✕ 🍴 ♿ 🍷

© 🐕 🚭 Ⓥ

★★★

HOTEL

♿

Moorings Hotel	2 Single	All En Suite	B&B per person	Open Jan-Dec
114 Hamilton Road, Motherwell, ML1 3DG	6 Twin		£30.00-£59.00 Single	B&B + Eve.Meal
Tel: 01698 258131 Fax: 01698 254973	20 Double		£25.00-£35.00 Dbl/Twn	£37.50-£66.50
	2 Family			

The Moorings House Hotel originates from a custom built 19th century
home of one of Scotlands foremost steel families (The Colvilles). Ideally
situated a few minutes from the M74 and M8 motorways. Ample parking.

📺 ⚲ 📞 🛏 🅿 🍳 ⌇ ✕ 🍴 ♿ 🍷

© 🐕 🚭 Ⓦ Ⓥ

★

**CAMPUS
ACCOMMODATION**

♿

Stewart Hall of Residence	45 Single	1 En Suite fac	B&B per person	Open Jan-Dec excl
Motherwell College, Dalziel Drive, Motherwell,		44 Pri.NOT ensuite	from £19.00 Single	Xmas/New Year
Lanarkshire, ML1 2PP			Room only per person	B&B + Eve.Meal
Tel: 01698 261890 Fax: 01698 232527			from £16.00	to £23.00

On college campus and all on one level. Close to Strathclyde Park and
M8/M74 motorway link for Glasgow and Edinburgh.

⚲ 🅿 ✕ ▥

🚭 Ⓦ Ⓥ

Paisley, Renfrewshire   Map Ref: 1H5

★★★

**GUEST
HOUSE**

🖼 🖼

Ardgowan Town House Hotel	2 Twin	7 En Suite fac	B&B per person	Open Jan-Dec
94 Renfrew Road, Paisley, Renfrewshire, PA3 4BJ	4 Double	1 Priv.NOT ensuite	from £40.00 Single	
Tel/Fax: 0141 889 4763	2 Family		from £25.00 Dbl/Twn	
Web: www.ardgowanhouse.com			Room only per person	
			from £20.00	

Spacious modern amenities in this town house off Junction 27 of the M8.
Large garden with fountains. Close to Glasgow airport with Glasgow city
centre only 7 miles away.

📺 🛏 🅿 🍳 ⌇ 🍷

🐕 🚭 Ⓦ Ⓥ

Important: Prices stated are estimates and may be subject to amendments

Paisley, Renfrewshire | Map Ref: 1H5

★★★

HOTEL

Brabloch Hotel
62 Renfrew Road, Paisley, Renfrewshire, PA3 4RD
Tel: 0141 889 5577 Fax: 0141 561 7012
E-mail: stay@brablochhotel.co.uk
Web: www.brablochhotel.co.uk

2 Single	All En Suite	B&B per person	Open Jan-Dec
13 Twin		from £63.00 Single	B&B + Eve.Meal
12 Double		from £42.50 Dbl/Twn	£58.00-£78.00
3 Family			

Privately owned hotel in its own grounds close to town centre and 2 miles
(3 kms) from Glasgow Airport. Conference and function rooms.

★

GUEST
HOUSE

Dryesdale Guest House
37 Inchinnan Road, Paisley, Renfrewshire, PA3 2PR
Tel: 0141 889 7178

2 Twin	2 Pub Bath/Show	B&B per person	Open Jan-Dec
2 Double		£20.00-£21.50 Single	
2 Family		£19.00-£20.00 Dbl/Twn	

Personally run guest house 0.5 mile (1km) from Glasgow Airport and M8
access. Close to Paisley with its station for the 15 minute journey to
Glasgow city centre. Ideal for touring Loch Lomond, Oban and Edinburgh.
Some ground floor rooms.

Renfrew | Map Ref: 1H5

★★★

HOTEL

The Glynhill Hotel & Leisure Club
169 Paisley Road, Renfrew, PA4 8XB
Tel: 0141 886 5555 Fax: 0141 885 2838
E-mail: GLYNHILLLEISUREHOTEL@MSN.COM
Web: www.glynhill.com

45 Twin	All En Suite	B&B per person	Open Jan-Dec
55 Double		from £64.00 Single	
25 Family		from £35.00 Dbl/Twn	

Set in own grounds on main Paisley-Renfrew road. Only 1mile (2kms)
from Glasgow Airport, courtesy coach available. Two restaurants, family
accommodation and leisure centre. Ample parking.

Uddingston, Lanarkshire | Map Ref: 2A5

★★★

HOTEL

Redstones Hotel
8/10 Glasgow Road, Uddingston, Glasgow,
Lanarkshire, G71 7AS
Tel: 01698 813774/814843 Fax: 01698 815319
E-mail: redstones@morris-inns.com

1 Single	14 En Suite fac	B&B per person	Open Jan-Dec
3 Twin		from £38.00 Single	
10 Double		from £50.00 Dbl/Twn	

Linked Victorian sandstone villas retaining original cornices and stained
glass windows. Situated at north end of M74 before Glasgow Zoo Park. 6
miles from city centre.

Uplawmoor, Renfrewshire | Map Ref: 1G6

★★★

HOTEL

Uplawmoor Hotel
Neilston Road, Uplawmoor, Glasgow, G78 4AF
Tel: 01505 850565 Fax: 01505 850689
Web: www.uplawmoor.co.uk

1 Single	All En Suite		Open Jan-Dec excl
3 Twin			Xmas/New Year
9 Double			
1 Family			

Quality eighteenth century Coaching Inn situated in quiet picturesque
village just twenty minutes from Glasgow City Centre and airport, gateway
to Burns Country. Taste of Scotland recommended.

VAT is shown at 17.5%: changes in this rate may affect prices.

| *Key to symbols is on back flap.* |

F ROM THE GREEN SLOPES OF THE OCHIL HILLS IN THE EAST TO THE FAR-FLUNG
HEBRIDEAN ISLANDS ON THE WESTERN SEABOARD, YOU WILL DISCOVER A
REMARKABLY DIVERSE REGION WHERE HISTORY IS SET WITHIN A GLORIOUS NATURAL
ENVIRONMENT.

Castle Stalker on Loch Linnhe, at Appin, north of Oban

IT IS HERE that the geological Highland boundary fault divides the lowland south from the mountainous north. Scenically, this area has everything, from the bonny banks of Loch Lomond, a playground for generations of visitors, to the bustling town of Stirling and western coastal resort of Oban.

A GOOD PLACE to begin is the Royal Burgh of Stirling. As a gateway to the Highlands and an important centre, Stirling has played a leading role in Scotland's story. Today, the castle with its newly restored Great Hall and the historic Old Town are just one of its many attractions. Nearby is the National Wallace Monument, telling the real story of Scotland's first freedom-fighter, William Wallace.

IN THE EARLY DAYS of tourism, the location of Loch Lomond and the Trossachs, a highly scenic area just beyond the Highland line, made them easy to reach. Often described as "The Highlands in Miniature", the Trossachs is still easy to reach with its gateway being the bustling and friendly town of Callander. At the Rob Roy and Trossachs Visitor Centre, you can uncover the legend of this celebrated folk hero. An excellent way to enjoy the captivating beauty of this area is on board the SS Sir Walter Scott which makes regular cruises across the placid waters of Loch Katrine. There are also plenty of cruising options on Loch Lomond, Scotland's largest loch (by surface area), which will shortly become part of Scotland's first national park.

Younger Botanic Gardens, by Dunoon, Cowal Peninsula

Castle Campbell, by Dollar

FURTHER WEST IS the delightful Cowal Peninsula with the fine Victorian resort of Dunoon and the lovely Isle of Bute with its magnificent Victorian gothic mansion, Mount Stuart and pleasant seaside resort of Rothesay. Across the sheltered waters of Loch Fyne sits the Georgian planned village of Inveraray and to the south the beautiful peninsula of Kintyre offering miles of shoreline and beaches with unsurpassed views of the islands. Regular ferry services cross to the lively island of Islay, world-famous for its peaty malt whiskies and then to Jura, which in contrast, has one road, one distillery, one hotel and lots of space.

THE ROAD WEST will take you through a panorama of dramatic mountains which sweep down to the coastal resort of Oban.

Romantic names and places such as Tobermory with its picture postcard harbour await the visitor to Mull and the island of Iona and Staffa are close by. You could venture further west for a real experience of island life and visit Colonsay, Tiree or Coll, but wherever you choose, you can be sure you will find a warm welcome in the heartland of Scotland.

EVENTS

WEST HIGHLANDS AND ISLANDS, LOCH LOMOND, STIRLING AND TROSSACHS

3-7 MAY
14th Isle of Bute Jazz Festival
Various venues, Bute
Annual jazz festival.
Contact: Ray & Linda Bruce
TEL: **01700 502800**

18-19 MAY
Alloa Ale Festival
Alloa Town Hall
Now in it's 5th year the Alloa
Real Ale Festival is back with
over forty real ales, scrumpy and
wine with live music nightly.
Contact: Speirs Booking Office
TEL: **01259 213131**

26-27 MAY
Loch Fyne Seafood Fair
Loch Fyne, Argyllshire
A feast of West Coast seafood,
plus live entertainment.
TEL: **01499 600264**

*15–17 JUNE
Royal Rothesay Regatta
Various venues, Rothesay
A celebration of the yacht clubs
of the Clyde and their friends
with plenty of shorebased
entertainment.
Contact: Rothesay, Tourist
Information Centre
TEL: **01700 502151**

28-29 JULY
Callander World Championship Highland Games
Callander Games Field,
Traditional Highland Games
with caber tossing, hammer
throwing, pipe bands, solo
piping and highland dancing.
Contact: Mr D McKirgan
TEL: **01877 330919**

24-25 AUGUST
Cowal Highland Gathering
Dunoon, Argylshire
The largest and most spectacular
Highland Games in the World,
featuring the World Highland
dancing championship, a major
pipe band championship with
over 150 pipe bands, also, solo
piping, track & heavy athletics,
shinty tournament together with
a variety of trade stands and
children's activities.
Contact: Janet Fletcher, Cowal
Highland Gathering
TEL: **01369 703206**
EMAIL:
info@cowalgathering.com
www.cowalgathering.com

*provisional dates

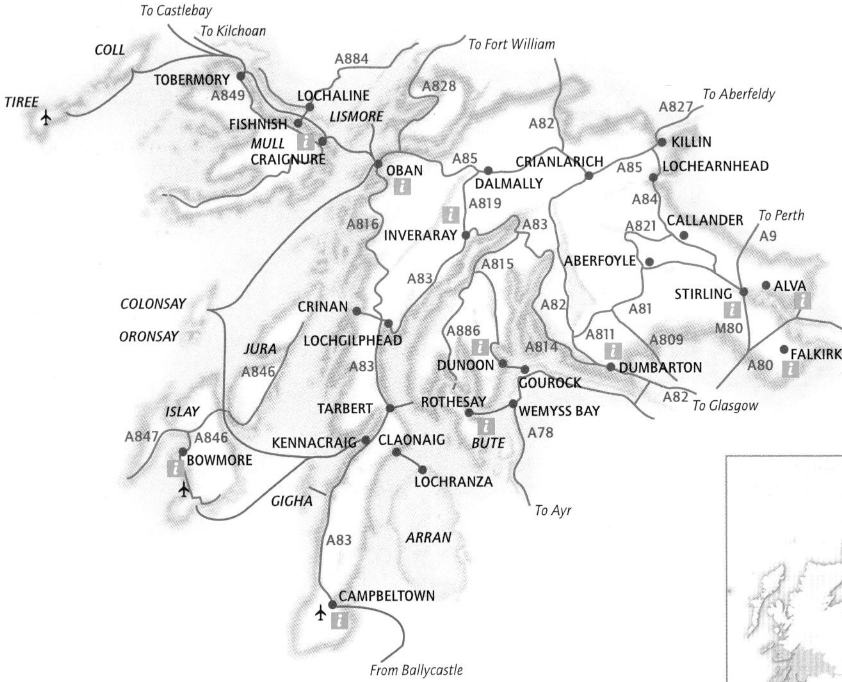

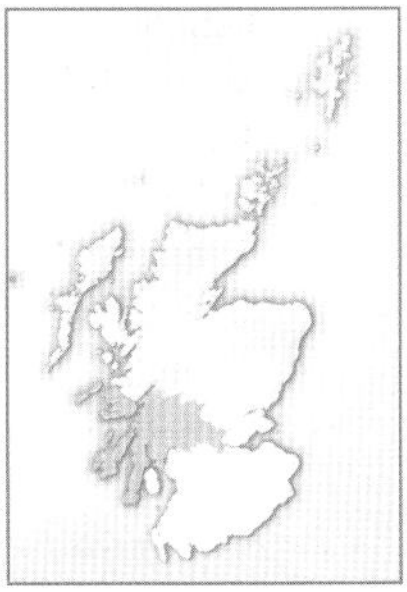

ARGYLL, THE ISLES,
LOCH LOMOND, STIRLING
AND TROSSACHS TOURIST
BOARD
Old Town Jail
St John Street
Stirling
FK8 1EA

TEL: **01786 445222**
FAX: **01786 471301/446325**
www.visitscottish.heartlands.org

**WEST HIGHLANDS,
LOCH LOMOND,
STIRLING AND
TROSSACHS
TOURIST BOARD**

ABERFOYLE
Trossachs Discovery
Centre
Main Street
TEL: **(01877) 382352**
Jan-Dec

ALVA
Mill Trail Visitor
Centre
TEL: **(01259) 769696**
Jan-Dec

ARDGARTAN
Arrochar
TEL: **(01301) 702432**
April-Oct

BALLOCH
Balloch Road
TEL: **(01389) 753533**
April-Oct

BO'NESS
Seaview Car Park
TEL: **(01506) 826626**
April-Sept

BOWMORE
Isle of Islay
TEL: **(01496) 810254**
Jan-Dec

CALLANDER
Rob Roy and Trossachs
Visitor Centre
Ancaster Square
TEL: **(01877) 330342**
Mar-Dec
Jan and Feb weekends
only

CAMPBELTOWN
Mackinnon House
The Pier
Argyll
TEL: **(01586) 552056**
Jan-Dec

CRAIGNURE
The Pier
Isle of Mull
TEL: **(01680) 812377**
Jan-Dec

DRYMEN
Drymen Library
The Square
TEL: **(01360) 660068**
May-Sept

DUMBARTON
Milton
A82 Northbound
TEL: **(01389) 742306**
Jan-Dec

DUNBLANE
Stirling Road
TEL: **(01786) 824428**
May-Sept

DUNOON
7 Alexandra Parade
Argyll
TEL: **(01369) 703785**
Jan-Dec

FALKIRK
2-4 Glebe Street
TEL: **(01324) 620244**
Jan-Dec

HELENSBURGH
The Clock Tower
TEL: **(01436) 672642**
April-Oct

INVERARAY
Front Street
Argyll
TEL: **(01499) 302063**
Jan-Dec

KILLIN
Breadalbane Folklore
Centre
TEL: **(01567) 820254**
March-end Oct
Feb weekends only

LOCHGILPHEAD
Lochnell Street
Argyll
TEL: **(01546) 602344**
April-Oct

OBAN
Argyll Square
Argyll
TEL: **(01631) 563122**
Jan-Dec

ROTHESAY
15 Victoria Street
Isle of Bute
TEL: **(01700) 502151**
Jan-Dec

STIRLING
Dumbarton Road
TEL: **(01786) 475019**
Jan-Dec

**STIRLING
(ROYAL BURGH)**
The Esplanade
TEL: **(01786) 479901**
Jan-Dec

STIRLING
Pirnhall Motorway
Service Area
Juntion 9, M9
TEL: **(01786) 814111**
April-Oct

TARBERT
Harbour Street
Argyll
TEL: **(01880) 820429**
April-Oct

**TARBET-LOCH
LOMOND**
Main Street
TEL: **(01301) 702260**
April-Oct

TOBERMORY
Isle of Mull
TEL: **(01688) 302182**
April-Oct

TYNDRUM
Main Street
TEL: **(01838) 400246**
April-Oct

Aberfoyle, Perthshire | Map Ref: 1H3

THE COVENANTERS INN
THE TROSSACHS · ABERFOYLE · PERTHSHIRE · FK8 3XD
Telephone: 01877 382347 Fax: 01877 382785
Web: www.covenantersinn.co.uk   ★★★ INN
A traditional country inn nestling in the splendid scenery of The Trossachs and steeped in the history of Scotland. Olde world charm combines with modern hotel comfort to create a hotel that's just a little different. Dinner, bed and breakfast from £39-£60 per person per night.

★★★

INN

The Covenanters Inn	5 Single	50 En Suite fac	B&B + Eve.Meal	Open Jan-Dec
Duchray Road, Aberfoyle, Perthshire, FK8 3XD	24 Twin	2 Priv.NOT ensuite	£35.00-£49.00	
Tel: 01877 382347 Fax: 01877 382785	18 Double			
Web: www.covenantersinn.co.uk	5 Family			

Overlooking Aberfoyle, on the edge of Queen Elizabeth Park. Ideal base for touring. Traditional coaching inn.

Creag-Ard House	2 Twin	All En Suite	B&B per person	Open Easter-Oct
Aberfoyle, Stirling, FK8 3TQ	4 Double		from £35.00 Single	B&B + Eve.Meal
Tel/Fax: 01877 382297			from £27.00 Dbl/Twn	from £47.00
E-mail: Creag-Ard@tinyonline.co.uk				

**GUEST
HOUSE**

Nestling in 3 acres of gardens this lovely Victorian house enjoys superb views over Loch Ard and Ben Lomond. Own trout fishing plus boat hire. A haven of peace and tranquility. Home baking and evening meals by arrangement.

Alloa, Clackmannanshire | Map Ref: 2A4

★★★

**SMALL
HOTEL**

The Royal Oak Hotel	1 Single	All En Suite	B&B per person	Open Jan-Dec
7 Bedford Place, Alloa, Clackmannanshire, FK10 1LJ	7 Twin		£37.50 Single	
Tel: 01259 722423 Fax: 01259 215523	2 Double		£27.00 Dbl/Twn	
	1 Family			

Friendly family owned 19c coaching inn, near town centre in quiet residential area.

Important: Prices stated are estimates and may be subject to amendments

Ardeonaig, by Killin, Perthshire — Map Ref: 1H2

Ardeonaig Hotel
South Loch, Tay Side, Perthshire, FK21 8SU
Tel: 01567 820400 Fax: 01567 820282
E-mail: ardeonaighotel@btinternet.com
Web: www.ardeonaighotel.co.uk

AWAITING INSPECTION

Situated amidst breathtaking scenery on the shore of the loch overlooking Ben Lawers and the mountains beyond. Ideal place to relax and enjoy excellent food in a comfortable and informal atmosphere. We have salmon and trout fishing on the loch with harbour, boats, rods and drying room. Several golf courses, stalking, horse riding and watersports available nearby. We are happy to arrange these for you.

3 Twin   All En Suite
7 Double
2 Family

B&B Single From £60.00
B&B Twn/Dbl from £45.00

Open Jan-Dec
B&B + Eve.Meal from £75.00

Ardfern, Argyll — Map Ref: 1E3

The Galley of Lorne Inn
by Lochgilphead, Argyll PA31 8QN
Telephone: 01852 500284   Fax: 01852 500284
Charming traditional inn, beautifully situated on the shores of Loch Craignish. Highest standards of comfort and service complemented by excellent food, with local seafood a speciality. Friendly pub with log fires, good company and a wide selection of malt whiskies. Bird and seal watching, riding, walking. Dogs most welcome.

★★★

HOTEL

The Galley of Lorne Inn
Ardfern, by Lochgilphead, Argyll, PA31 8QN
Tel/Fax: 01852 500284

Lively traditional Highland Inn, with open fires. Emphasis on charcoal grilled steaks and local seafood. Most bedrooms with loch views. Dogs welcome.

2 Twin   6 En Suite fac
5 Double 1 Priv.NOT ensuite

B&B per person from £43.50 Single
from £33.50 Dbl/Twn

Open Jan-Dec excl Xmas

Ardlui, Argyll — Map Ref: 1G3

★★

HOTEL

Ardlui Hotel
Ardlui, Loch Lomomd, Argyll, G83 7EB
Tel: 01301 704243 Fax: 01301 704268
Web: www.ardlui.co.uk

Former shooting lodge on A82 and on the banks of Loch Lomond with private gardens to shore. Caravan site adjacent. Moorings available. 1 hour from Glasgow or Oban & 1 1/2 hours from Fort William via Glencoe.

4 Twin   7 En Suite fac
5 Double 1 Pub Bath/Show
2 Family

B&B per person from £35.00 Single
from £25.00 Dbl/Twn

Open Jan-Dec

Ardrishaig, by Lochgilphead, Argyll — Map Ref: 1E4

★★★

GUEST HOUSE

'Allt-Na-Craig'
Tarbert Road, Ardrishaig, Argyll, PA30 8EP
Tel: 01546 603245

A Victorian Mansion set in picturesque grounds, with magnificent views across Loch Fyne. Entrance to Crinan Canal nearby. Home cooking. Hill-walking, bird-watching, fishing, golf, riding, diving, wind-surfing and many other outdoor activities are available in the area.

1 Single   All En Suite
2 Twin
2 Double
1 Family

B&B per person from £32.00 Single
from £32.00 Dbl/Twn
Room only per person from £27.00

Open Jan-Dec excl Xmas/New Year
B&B + Eve.Meal from £48.00

Ardrishaig, by Lochgilphead, Argyll Map Ref: 1E4

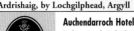

Auchendarroch Hotel

★★

SMALL HOTEL

Tarbert Road, Ardrishaig,by Lochgilphead, Argyll, PA30 8EP
Tel: 01546 602275 Fax: 01546 602555
Web: http://www.auchendarroch.co.uk

2 Twin	All En Suite	B&B per person	Open Apr-Oct
2 Double		from £22.00 Dbl/Twn	

Comfortable rooms and good food in our famil run small hotel with views over Loch Fyne to the Cowal Hills. Ideal base fortouring Kintyre and Argyll. 30 minutes drive to Islay Ferry terminal.

Arduaine, Argyll Map Ref: 1E3

LOCH MELFORT HOTEL
ARDUAINE, BY OBAN, ARGYLL PA34 4XG
Telephone: 01852 200233   Fax: 01852 200214
e.mail: LMhotel@aol.com   Web: www.loch-melfort.co.uk

The finest location for uninterrupted views of the west coast islands located on A816 between Oban and Inveraray beside the National Trust Gardens. Join our regular guests and enjoy excellent award winning cuisine in our 2AA Rosette restaurant or in the 'Skerry' cafe Bistro.

SEASONAL BREAKS AVAILABLE

B&B from £55.00 per person per night

Loch Melfort Hotel

★★★★

HOTEL

Arduaine, by Oban, Argyll, PA34 4XG
Tel: 01852 200233 Fax: 01852 200214
E-mail: LMhotel@aol.com Web: www.loch-melfort.co.uk

24 Dbl/Twn	All En Suite	B&B per person	Open Mid Feb-New Year
2 Superior Dbl		£75.00 Single	
		£55.00-£75.00 Dbl/Twn	

Family run hotel located 20 miles south from Oban in a magnificent location overlooking the Sound of Jura and many small islands. Spectacular views from all bedrooms, lounge and restaurant. Emphasis on locally caught seafood and shellfish and enjoying an excellent reputation for home cooking and fresh produce. Arduaine Gardens adjacent with many other glorious gardens in the area. Pony trekking and watersports nearby. Seasonal breaks available.

Balloch, Dunbartonshire Map Ref: 1G4

Anchorage Guest House

★

GUEST HOUSE

31 Balloch Road, Balloch, Loch Lomond, G83 8SS
Tel: 01389 753336

1 Twin	All En Suite	B&B per person	Open Jan-Dec
3 Double		from £20.00 Single	
1 Family		from £20.00 Dbl/Twn	
		Room only per person	
		from £18.00	

Extended cottage in centre of village, near river. Railway station and all other amenities nearby. Ideal touring base. All rooms ground floor.

Ms Lillian Biddulph

★★

B&B

Lachlan B&B, 15 Tullichewan Road, Balloch, G83 8SN
Tel: 01389 604402

1 Double	All En Suite	B&B per person	Open Jan-Dec excl
1		£16.00-£20.00 Double	Xmas/New Year
Family/Twn		Room only per person	
		from £14.00	

Family run B&B in the heart of Balloch, 5 minutes walk to Lomond shores. Ideally positioned for public transport by bus or train, stroll to pubs, restaurants, shops, Loch Lomond cruises and Balloch Castle Country Park or visit Glasgow 40 minutes by train with galleries, restaurants and shopping centres.

Important: Prices stated are estimates and may be subject to amendments

Balloch, Dunbartonshire — Map Ref: 1G4

★★★★ GUEST HOUSE

Gowanlea Guest House
Drymen Road, Balloch, Dunbartonshire, G83 8HS
Tel: 01389 752456 Fax: 01389 710543
Web: http://members.aol.com/gowanlea/gowanlea.htm

1 Twin
2 Double

All En Suite

B&B per person
from £20.00 Single
from £20.00 Dbl/Twn

Open Jan-Dec

Situated in residential area of Balloch, close to world famous Loch Lomond. Friendly welcome. All rooms ensuite.

★★★ GUEST HOUSE

Kinnoul House
Drymen Road, Balloch, Dunbartonshire, G83 8HS
Tel/Fax: 01389 721116
E-mail: kinnoul-guesthouse.scotland@virgin.net
Web: http://freespace.virgin.net/kinnoul-guesthouse.scotland

1 Twin
3 Double

3 En Suite fac
1 Priv.NOT ensuite

B&B per person
from £18.00 Dbl/Twn

Open Jan-Dec

Enjoy Scottish hospitality in this double Victorian house. Situated on an oak tree lined road at the quieter end of Balloch. Within walking distance of a variety of hotels, restaurants, Balloch Country Park and Loch Lomond itself. Within easy reach by car' Glasgow Airport 20 mins, Stirling 45 mins, Edinburgh 90 mins, Trossachs 30 mins. Oban 2 hrs. Balloch Railway Station has a half hourly service to and from Glasgow.

★★★ GUEST HOUSE

Norwood Guest House
60 Balloch Road, Balloch, Loch Lomond,
Dunbartonshire, G83 8LE
Tel: 01389 750309 Fax: 01389 710469
E-mail: norwoodgh@aol.com

2 Twin
3 Double

All En Suite

B&B per person
from £20.00 Single
from £18.00 Dbl/Twn

Open Jan-Dec

Centrally located overlooking Balloch Castle Country Park. Close to all local amenities including restaurants and shops.

★★★★ B&B

Sheildaig Farm
Upper Stoneymollen Road, Balloch, Alexandria
Dunbartonshire, G83 8QY
Tel: 01389 752459 Fax: 01389 753695
Mobile: 07711 317966
E-mail: sheildaig@talk21.com
Web: www.scotland2000.com/sheildaig

3 Double

All En Suite

B&B per person
from £40.00 Single
from £25.00 Double

Open Jan-Dec
B&B + Eve.Meal
from £40.00

Totally refurbished farm courtyard buildings in secluded setting. Conveniently situated for touring Loch Lomond and the Trossachs. Easy access to A82 and Glasgow Airport. Candlelit dinners, with table license. 5 minutes from Balloch station with its service into Glasgow city centre.

Balquhidder, Perthshire — Map Ref: 1H2

★★★ SMALL HOTEL

Monachyle Mhor
Balquhidder, Lochearnhead, Perthshire, FK19 8PQ
Tel: 01877 384622 Fax: 01877 384305

2 Twin
8 Double

All En Suite

B&B per person
£35.00-£45.00 Dbl/Twn

Open Jan-Dec

18c award winning house in 2000 acres. Magnificent situation overlooking 2 lochs. Open fires, antique furniture and country fabrics. Thoroughly relaxing quiet environment, ideal base for all seasonal rural pursuits or gently walking through our private lochside grounds.

VAT is shown at 17.5%: changes in this rate may affect prices.

Key to symbols is on back flap.

Bo'ness, West Lothian   Map Ref: 2B4

★★★

GUEST
HOUSE

Carriden House
Carriden Brae, Bo'ness, EH51 9SN
Tel: 01506 829811 Fax: 01506 826888
E-mail: carriden_house@compuserve.com

2 Twin	All En Suite	B&B per person	Open Jan-Dec
2 Double		£35.00-£40.00 Single	
1 Family		£30.00-£35.00 Dbl/Twn	

16th century turreted mansion house set in 5 acres of mature parkland – an ideal quiet and peaceful setting. Only 15 mins drive to Edinburgh airport and easy access to all major routes in central Scotland.

★★★

HOTEL

Richmond Park Hotel
26 Linlithgow Road, Bo'ness, West Lothian, EH51 0DN
Tel: 01506 823213 Fax: 01506 822717
Web: www.s-h-systems.co.uk/hotels/richmond.html

1 Single	All En Suite	B&B per person	Open Jan-Dec
21 Twin		from £58.00 Single	
18 Double		from £36.00 Dbl/Twn	
6 Family			

Privately owned hotel, overlooking the river Forth centrally located between Stirling and Edinburgh. A la carte restaurant and popular lounge-diner. Residents conservatory and fitness room. Occasional Scottish entertainment.

Bridge of Orchy, Argyll   Map Ref: 1G1

★★★★

SMALL
HOTEL

Bridge of Orchy Hotel
Bridge of Orchy, Argyll, PA36 4AD
Tel: 01838 400208 Fax: 01838 400313
E-mail: bridgeoforchy@onyxnet.co.uk

2 Twin	All En Suite	B&B per person	Open Jan-Dec excl
6 Double		from £45.00 Single	Xmas/New Year
2 Family		from £39.75 Dbl/Twn	B&B + Eve.Meal
			from £54.50

A hotel of character offering high quality rooms and service, conveniently located on the main A82 trunk road, 6 miles north of Tyndrum. Popular with walkers and outdoor enthusiasts. Spectacular scenery surrounds. Bar full of adventurous spirit. One AA rosette for food.

Rothesay, Isle of Bute   Map Ref: 1F5

★★★

HOTEL

The Ardyne-St Ebba Hotel and Restaurant
37-38 Mountstuart Road, Rothesay, Isle of Bute, PA20 9EB
Tel: 01700 502052 Fax: 01700 505129
E-mail: ardyne.hotel@virgin.net
Web: www.rothesay-scotland.com

1 Single	All En Suite	B&B per person	Open Jan-Dec excl
7 Twin	1 Pub Bath/Show	from £28.00 Single	Xmas
5 Double		from £25.00 Dbl/Twn	B&B + Eve.Meal
5 Family			from £38.95

Important: Prices stated are estimates and may be subject to amendments

Cairndow, Argyll

Map Ref: 1F3

Cairndow Stagecoach Inn

Cairndow, Argyll PA26 8BN
Tel: 01499 600286 Fax: 01499 600220
e.mail: cairndinn@aol.com

Across the 'Arrochar Alps' on Loch Fyne this historic coaching inn enjoys a delightful situation just off the A83. It is a haven of sparkling views, high mountains and magnificent woodlands and rivers.
We offer excellent accommodation in 14 bedrooms, all en-suite, in a relaxed country atmosphere. All have TV, radio, telephone, central heating etc.
Two deluxe bedrooms with two-person spa baths. Stables Restaurant with conservatory and bar meals served all day. Ideal centre for touring the Western Highlands from Glencoe to Kintyre and Loch Lomond and The Trossachs. Lochside beer garden, sauna and solarium, golf discounts.

★★★

INN

Cairndow Stagecoach Inn
Cairndow, Argyll, PA26 8BN
Tel: 01499 600286 Fax: 01499 600220
E-mail: cairndinn@aol.com

5 Twin	All En Suite	B&B per person	Open Jan-Dec
6 Double		from £25.00 Single	B&B + Eve.Meal
2 Family		from £20.00 Dbl/Twn	from £27.50
		Room only per person	
		from £20.00	

Old Coaching Inn on Loch Fyne. Ideal centre for touring Western Highlands. 9 bedrooms with loch view - all en-suite - all fully appointed. 2 rooms with 2 person spa baths. Stables restaurant and lounge meals all day. Half-price golf at Inveraray. Beer garden. Sauna, solarium and multi-gym.

Callander, Perthshire

Map Ref: 1H3

★★★

HOTEL

Abbotsford Lodge Hotel
Stirling Road, Callander, Perthshire, FK17 8DA
Tel/Fax: 01877 330066

1 Single	12 En Suite fac	B&B per person	Open Jan-Dec
3 Twin	2 Pub Bath/Show	from £19.50-£34.75 Single	B&B + Eve.Meal
5 Double		from £19.50-24.50	£32.50-£37.25
8 Family		Dbl/Twn	

Family run Victorian house set in its own grounds, with private parking. Ground floor en-suite accommodation available. Short walk to town centre. Our restaurant menu changes daily using a choice of fresh local produce. Be tempted by our selection of home-made desserts and fresh baking.

★★★

GUEST HOUSE

Annfield Guest House
North Church Street, Callander, Perthshire, FK17 8EG
Tel: 01877 330204

2 Twin	4 En Suite fac	B&B per person	Open mid Jan-Dec
5 Double	1 Priv.NOT ensuite	from £25.00 Single	excl Xmas
1 Family	2 Pub Bath/Show	from £21.00 Dbl/Twn	

Centrally situated in a quiet area of the town in close proximity to shops and restaurants. Stepping stone to the Highlands.

| Callander, Perthshire | | | | Map Ref: 1H3 | | | |

GUEST HOUSE
★★★★

Arden House
Bracklinn Road, Callander, Perthshire, FK17 8EQ
Tel/Fax: 01877 330235
Web: www.SmoothHound.co.uk/hotels/arden.html

1 Single
2 Twin
2 Double
1 Suite

All En Suite

B&B per person
from £30.00 Single
from £27.50 Dbl/Twn

Open Mar-Nov

Elegant Victorian country house, peacefully set in attractive gardens with marvellous views of hills and countryside. Home of BBC TV's 'Dr Finlay's Casebook'. Ideal base for touring the Trossachs and western highlands.

INN
★★

Bridgend House Hotel
Bridgend, Callander, Perthshire, FK17 8AH
Tel: 01877 330130 Fax: 01877 331512
E-mail: bridgendhotel@hotmail.com
Web: www.bridgendhotel.co.uk

1 Twin
4 Double

All En Suite
1 Pub Bath/Show

B&B per person
from £37.50 Single
from £27.50 Dbl/Twn

Open Jan-Dec excl Xmas

Small family run 18c hotel of character, offering a la carte dinner and bar meals. Children and pets welcome. Secluded rear garden offering views to Ben Ledi. Live music over weekends and family quiz Thursdays.

SMALL HOTEL
★★

Coppice Hotel
Leny Road, Callander, Perthshire, FK17 8AL
Tel: 01877 330188

1 Twin
3 Double
1 Family

All En Suite

B&B per person
from £25.00 Single
from £22.00 Dbl/Twn

Open Jan-Dec

Personally run hotel with emphasis on cuisine using fresh local produce when available.

HOTEL
★★

Dalgair House Hotel
113-115 Main Street, Callander, FK17 8BQ
Tel: 01877 330283 Fax: 01877 331114
E-mail: nieto@btinternet.com

3 Twin
4 Double
1 Family

All Ensuite fac

B&B per person
from £35.00 Single
from £25.00 Dbl/Twn

Open Jan-Dec excl
Xmas/New Year
B&B + Eve.Meal
from £39.50

Family run, main street hotel of character with informal friendly service. Good food using local ingredients; Bistro and Restaurant. Ample car parking.

B&B
★★★★

Invertrossachs Country House
Invertrossachs, by Callander, Perthshire, FK17 8HG
Tel: 01877 331126
Fax: 01877 331229
E-mail: res@invertrossachs.freeserve.co.uk
Web: www.invertrossachs.co.uk

2 Rooms

Suites available

B&B per person
£55.00-£85.00 Single
£39.50-£75.00 Dbl/Twn

Open Jan-Dec

Comfortable large rooms and suites within an Edwardian mansion offering country house bed & breakfast and enjoying privacy and seclusion by the shores of Loch Venachar. Spacious accommodation with outstanding loch and mountain views.

Important: Prices stated are estimates and may be subject to amendments

Callander, Perthshire			Map Ref: 1H3		

The Knowe

GUEST HOUSE

Ancaster Road, Callander, Perthshire, FK17 8EL
Tel: 01877 330076 Fax: 01877 331776
E-mail: knowefk17@aol.com

2 Twin	5 Ensuite fac	B&B per person	Open Jan-Dec
4 Double	1 Priv.NOT ensuite	from £21.00 Dbl/Twn	B&B + Eve.Meal
			from £33.00

Family run with a friendly welcome and good cooking. Quietly situated off the main road with magnificent views. We regret we do not accept children. Ideal for a relaxing & peaceful holiday. Ground floor accommodation.

Lubnaig Hotel

SMALL HOTEL

Leny Feus, Callander, Perthshire, FK17 8AS
Tel/Fax: 01877 330376
Web: www.lubnaighotel.co.uk

5 Twin	All En Suite	B&B per person	Open Apr-Oct
5 Double		from £30.00 Dbl/Twn	

A relaxing family run country house, enhanced by its secluded location, large garden, private parking and within easy walking distance of the town centre. A genuine Scottish welcome awaits all guests. We offer a stress free holiday to enjoy Scotland.

Riverview Guest House

GUEST HOUSE

Leny Road, Callander, Perthshire, FK17 8AL
Tel/Fax: 01877 330635
Web: www.nationalparksscotland.co.uk

1 Single	All En Suite	B&B per person	Open Feb-Dec
2 Twin		from £21.00 Single	B&B + Eve.Meal
2 Double		from £21.00 Dbl/Twn	from £32.00

Detached stone built Victorian house set in its own garden with private parking. Close to town centre, leisure complex and local amenities. Within easy walking distance of pleasant riverside park and cycle track. Ideal base for exploring the beautiful Trossachs. Cycle storage available.

ROMAN CAMP COUNTRY HOUSE HOTEL

Off Main Street, Callander FK17 8BG
Tel: 01877 330003 Fax: 01877 331533
e.mail: mail@roman-camp-hotel.co.uk
Web: www.roman-camp-hotel.co.uk

Built as a hunting lodge in 1625 and idyllically set in 20 acres of secluded gardens on the banks of the river Teith. The house with its oak-panelled library; silk-lined drawing room and tapestry hung restaurant all warmed by roaring log fires make this country retreat the perfect hideaway.

Roman Camp Country House Hotel

HOTEL

off Main Street, Callander, Perthshire, FK17 8BG
Tel: 01877 330003 Fax: 01877 331533
E.mail: mail@roman-camp-hotel.co.uk
Web: www.roman-camp-hotel.co.uk

6 Twin	All En Suite	B&B per person	Open Jan-Dec
8 Double		from £85.00 Single	B&B + Eve.Meal
		from £55.00 Dbl/Twn	from £94.00

Dating from 1625 and reminiscent of a miniature chateau, with 20 acres of beautiful gardens bordering the River Teith.

VAT is shown at 17.5%: changes in this rate may affect prices.

Key to symbols is on back flap.

Callander, Perthshire — Map Ref: 1H3

Southfork Villa
★★★★ GUEST HOUSE

25 Cross Street, Callander, Perthshire, FK17 8EA
Tel: 01877 330831

2 Twin	All Ensuite fac	B&B per person	Open Jan-Dec
2 Double		from £25.00 Single	B&B + Eve.Meal
2 Family		from £20.00 Dbl/Twn	from £32.50

Detached modern family home in centre of Callander. Ample secure private off-street parking. Local amenities and leisure centre close by. Ideal base for exploring the Trossachs. Outdoor activities including pony trekking, cycling and hillwalking. A warm welcome awaits.

TV 🖭 P 🍵 🗲 🖥 🍷

C 🐾 V

Campbeltown, Argyll — Map Ref: 1D7

Argyll Arms Hotel
★★ HOTEL

Campbeltown, Argyll, PA28 6AB
Tel: 01586 553431 Fax: 01586 553594
E-mail: argyllarms@aol.com

17 Twin	All En Suite	B&B per person	Open Jan-Dec excl
6 Double		from £38.00 Single	Xmas/New Year
2 Family		from £30.00 Dbl/Twn	B&B + Eve.Meal
			from £50.00

Family owned and run hotel offering traditional Scottish hospitality in town centre location, convenient for Irish Ferry. Families welcome, connecting rooms and kids menus available. TV lounge with video also available for residents.

TV 📞 🖭 P 🍵 🍴 🍷

C £ W V

Dellwood Hotel
★★ HOTEL

Drumore, Campbeltown, Argyll, PA28 6HD
Tel: 01586 552465

3 Single	9 En Suite fac	B&B per person	Open Jan-Dec
3 Twin	1 Pub Bath/Show	£18.00-£28.00 Single	B&B + Eve.Meal
3 Double		£18.00-£23.00 Dbl/Twn	£26.50-£31.50
3 Family			

Small family-run hotel close to town centre. Some annexe accommodation. Honeymoon suite available. Adequate parking.

TV 🖭 P 🍵 🍴 🍷

C 🐾 V

Seafield Hotel
★★ HOTEL

Kilkerran Road, Campbeltown, Argyll, PA28 6JL
Tel: 01586 554385 Fax: 01586 552741

2 Twin	All En Suite	B&B per person	Open Jan-Dec
7 Double		from £45.00 Single	
		from £32.50 Dbl/Twn	

On seafront overlooking Campbeltown Loch and within walking distance of town centre. Family run. Some annexe accommodation. 2 minutes walk to Irish ferry terminal.

TV 📞 🖭 P 🍵 🗲 🍴 🖥 🍷

🐾 £ V

Westbank Guest House
★★★ GUEST HOUSE

Dell Road, Campbeltown, PA28 6JG
Tel/Fax: 01586 553660

1 Single	5 En Suite fac	B&B per person	Open Jan-Dec
2 Twin	2 Priv.NOT ensuite	from £23.00 Single	
3 Double		from £18.00 Dbl/Twn	
1 Family			

A well maintained Victorian villa in a quiet residential area, near to Machrihanish Golf Course. An ideal base for touring. 3 minutes walk to all town centre restaurants, shops and attractions.

TV 🖭 🍵 🍷 🖥 🍷

C 🐾 £ W V

Carradale, Argyll   Map Ref: 1E6

★★

SMALL HOTEL

Ashbank Hotel			
Carradale, Argyll, PA28 6RY			
Tel/Fax: 01583 431650			

1 Single	3 En Suite fac	B&B per person	Open Easter-Oct
2 Twin	1 Priv.NOT ensuite	from £23.50 Single	B&B + Eve.Meal
1 Double		from £21.50 Dbl/Twn	from £33.50
		Room only per person	
		from £19.00	

Family hotel with compact rooms in small village with views from the rear across the Kilbrannan Sound to Arran and Ailsa Craig. Overlooking Carradale Golf Course and close to safe and sandy beach (10 minutes walk). 25 minutes drive to Campbeltown and Ireland ferry terminal.

Carradale Hotel
Carradale, Nr. Campbeltown, Argyll PA28 6RY
Telephone and Fax: 01583 431223
e.mail: carradaleh@aol.com
Overlooking Arran, this Taste of Scotland recommended family run hotel specialises in local fish and game, fine wines, local malts and cask ales. Golf on the adjacent course, sauna, bikes, fishing, riding, forest walks and sandy beaches. We provide an ideal base for exploring Kintyre and the Islands.

★★★

HOTEL

Carradale Hotel			
Carradale, Argyll, PA28 6RY			
Tel/Fax: 01583 431223			
E-mail: carradaleh@aol.com			

3 Twin	All En Suite	B&B per person	Open Jan-Dec
8 Double		from £25.00 Single	B&B + Eve.Meal
1 Family		from £25.00 Dbl/Twn	from £41.50

Family run hotel, overlooking Arran. Beautiful scenery, golf, fishing, beaches, mountain bikes, hillwalking and sauna. Taste of Scotland recommended.

★★★

B&B

Kiloran Guest House			
Carradale, Argyll, PA28 6QG			
Tel: 01583 431795			

3 Twin	2 Ensuite fac	B&B per person	Open Jan-Dec excl
1 Double	1 Priv.NOT ensuite	from £20.00 Single	Xmas/New Year
1 Family		from £18.50 Dbl/Twn	B&B + Eve.Meal
		Room only per person	from £25.00
		from £20.00	

Traditional Scottish hospitality awaits at this Victorian villa on the outskirts of the village. Evening meal by arrangement.

Carronbridge, Stirlingshire   Map Ref: 2A4

★

INN

Carronbridge Hotel			
Carronbridge, by Denny, Stirlingshire, FK6 5JG			
Tel: 01324 823459			

1 Twin	All En Suite	B&B per person	Open Jan-Dec
1 Double		from £25.00 Single	
1 Family		from £20.00 Dbl/Twn	

Family run hotel situated in picturesque Carron Valley. Ideal base for touring.

VAT is shown at 17.5%: changes in this rate may affect prices.   **Key to symbols is on back flap.**

Clydebank, Dunbartonshire   Map Ref: 1H5

★★★

GUEST
HOUSE

Tudor House
10 Drumry Road, Clydebank, Glasgow. G81 2LJ
Tel: 0141 941 3171 Fax: 0141 951 3662
Web: www.guesthouseglasgow.co.uk

2 Single	En suite fac	B&B per person	Open Jan-Dec
1 Twin	Pub Bath/Show	from £20.00 Single	
1 Double		from £18.00 Dbl/Twn	
1 Family		Room only per person	
		from £16.00	

Family guest house with cable TV in bedrooms. Situated in residential area.
Convenient for the Clydebank College, train station, shopping centre
business park and HCI Hospital. Communication in most foreign languages
available. 5 miles from Glasgow airport. 15 minute drive from Loch
Lomond.

Colintraive, Argyll   Map Ref: 1F5

★★

SMALL
HOTEL

The Colintraive Hotel
Colintraive,by Dunoon, Argyll, PA22 3AS
Tel/Fax: 01700 841207
E-mail: kyleshotel@aol.com

2 Twin	All En Suite	B&B per person	Open Jan-Dec
1 Double		from £26.00 Single	B&B + Eve.Meal
1 Family		from £24.00 Dbl/Twn	from £33.00
		Room only per person	
		from £22.00	

A small family run hotel offering comfort and informality with magnificent
views of the Kyles of Bute. Built as a hunting lodge over 100 years ago,
The Colintraive Hotel offers tranquility and remoteness which belies a
mere 2 hour journey time from Glasgow. The road to Colintraive goes no
further, so the rumble of passing traffic quickly becomes a distant
memory, with only the bleating of sheep to disturb the silence.

Coll, Isle of, Argyll   Map Ref: 1B1

★★★

HOTEL

Coll Hotel
Arinagour, Isle of Coll, Argyll, PA78 6SZ
Tel: 01879 230334 Fax: 01879 230317
E-mail: joliphotel@aol.com

1 Single	All En Suite fac	B&B per person	Open Jan-Dec excl
1 Twin	2 Pub/Show	from £25.00 Single	Xmas/New Year
2 Double		from £25.00 Dbl/Twn	
2 Family			

17c building with panoramic sea views across Mull and the Treshnish Isles.
Under 1 mile (2kms) from the ferry terminal. Bar and restaurant meals
available, specialising in seafood and using the best of fresh local produce.

Colonsay, Isle of, Argyll   Map Ref: 1C4

★★★

HOTEL

Isle of Colonsay Hotel
Isle of Colonsay, PA61 7YP
Tel: 01951 200316 Fax: 01951 200353
E-mail: colonsay.hotel@pipemedia.co.uk
Web: www.colonsay.org.uk

2 Single	8 En Suite fac	B&B per person	Open all Year
4 Twin	2 Pub Bath/Show	£50.00-£65.00 Single	B&B + Eve.Meal
2 Double			£60.00-£80.00
2 Family			

Charming island hotel blending a rich mixture of wildlife, outdoor pursuits
and total relaxation with comfort, good food and warm hospitality.

Connel, Argyll   Map Ref: 1E2

★★★★

GUEST
HOUSE

Ronebhal Guest House
Connel, by Oban, Argyll, PA37 1PJ
Tel: 01631 710310/813 Fax: 01631 710310
E-mail: ronebhal@btinternet.com
Web: www.argyllinternet.co.uk/ronebhal

1 Twin	4 En Suite fac	B&B per person	Open Feb-Nov
3 Double	1 Priv.NOT ensuite	£20.00-£30.00 Single	
1 Family		£20.00-£28.50 Dbl/Twn	
		Room only per person	
		£18.00-£24.50	

Victorian house with private parking. Magnificent views of Loch Etive and
mountains beyond. Oban 5 miles (8kms).

Important: Prices stated are estimates and may be subject to amendments

Crianlarich, Perthshire   Map Ref: 1G2

Ben More Lodge Hotel

Crianlarich, Perthshire FK20 8QS
Tel: 01838 300210 Fax: 01838 300218 e.mail: john@ben-more.demon.co.uk
Surrounded by spectacular scenery, adjacent to the road to the North West Highlands. This family run lodge hotel offers ensuite accommodation with colour TV and hospitality trays. Enjoy a drink or a meal prepared by our chef from the finest Scottish game and fish from either table d'hôte or extensive bar meal menus. An ideal centre for touring, walking, skiing, golf or simply relaxing.
B&B from £25, D,B&B from £35.

★★

INN

Ben More Lodge Hotel
Crianlarich, Perthshire, FK20 8QS
Tel: 01838 300210 Fax: 01838 300218
E-mail: john@ben-more.demon.co.uk
Web: www.ben-more.co.uk

Pine lodges of a high standard with restaurant and bar adjacent. Ideal base for touring, hillwalking and fishing.

1 Twin	All En Suite	B&B per person	Open Jan-Dec
7 Double		from £30.00 Single	B&B + Eve.Meal
2 Family		from £25.00 Dbl/Twn	from £35.00

★★★

GUEST HOUSE

Glenardran House
Crianlarich, Perthshire, FK20 8QS
Tel/Fax: 01838 300236
Web: www.championinternet.com/glenardran/

Very comfortable late Victorian house in centre of village close to West Highland Way. Excellent base for touring, walking or climbing. Non-smoking.

2 Twin	All En Suite	B&B per person	Open Jan-Dec excl
2 Double		from £30.00 Single	Xmas/New Year
		from £20.00 Dbl/Twn	

★★★★

GUEST HOUSE

The Lodge House
Crianlarich, Perthshire, FK20 8RU
Tel/Fax: 01838 300276
E-mail: Admin@lodgehouse.co.uk

2 Twin	All En Suite	B&B per person	Open Mar-Dec
3 Double		from £30.00 Single	B&B + Eve.Meal
1 Family		from £25.00 Dbl/Twn	from £40.00

★

HOTEL

Suie Lodge Hotel
Glendochart, Crianlarich, Perthshire, FK20 8QT
Tel: 01567 820417 Fax: 01567 820092
E-mail: jreillysuie@aol.com

Family run hotel in former Shooting Lodge, in scenic Glendochart. Offering a relaxed atmosphere, comfortable bedrooms. Many en-suite. Good Scottish food. Excellent centre for touring. Property available on self-catering basis for larger groups during the winter.

1 Single	7 En Suite fac	B&B per person	Open Mar-Oct
6 Twin	1 Pub Bath/Show	from £22.00 Single	B&B + Eve.Meal
3 Double		from £22.00 Dbl/Twn	from £28.00
1 Family		Room only per person	
		from £17.00	

VAT is shown at 17.5%: changes in this rate may affect prices.

Key to symbols is on back flap.

Crinan, by Lochgilphead, Argyll — Map Ref: 1E4

Crinan Hotel
Crinan, by Lochgilphead, Argyll, PA31 8SR
Tel: 01546 830261 Fax: 01546 830292
Web: www.crinanhotel.com

★★★★

HOTEL

2 Single	All En Suite
10 Twin	
10 Double	
1 Family	

Open Jan-Dec
B&B + Eve.Meal
from £70.00

Personally run hotel of great character and unique atmosphere in centre of fishing village at west end of Crinan Canal. Choice of restaurants including Lock 16 specialist seafood restaurant. Open Tue-Sat.

Dalmally, Argyll — Map Ref: 1F2

Craig Villa Guest House
Dalmally, Argyll, PA33 1AX
Tel/Fax: 01838 200255
Web: www.SmoothHound.co.uk/hotels/craigvilla.html

★★★

GUEST
HOUSE

2 Twin	5 En Suite fac
2 Double	1 Priv.NOT ensuite
2 Family	

B&B per person
from £25.00 Single
from £19.00 Dbl/Twn

Open Easter-Oct
B&B + Eve.Meal
from £31.50

Personally run guest house in own grounds amidst breathtaking scenery. Good touring base. Home cooking. Evening meal by arrangement.

Dollar, Clackmannanshire — Map Ref: 2B3

Castle Campbell Hotel
Bridge Street, Dollar, Clackmannanshire, FK14 7DE
Tel/Fax: 01259 742519
Web: www.castle/campbell.co.uk

★★★

SMALL
HOTEL

1 Single	All En Suite
1 Twin	
4 Double	
2 Family	

B&B per person
from £47.50 Single
from £30.00 Dbl/Twn

Open Jan-Dec

Personal attention from the owners at this friendly hotel in picturesque historic town. Emphasis on fresh Scottish produce.

Doune, Perthshire — Map Ref: 2A3

Creity Hall Hotel
Stirling Road, Doune, Perthshire, FK16 6AD
Tel: 01786 841215 Fax: 01786 841190

★★

HOTEL

2 Twin	All En Suite
2 Double	
1 Family	

B&B per person
£24.50-£30.00 Dbl/Twn

Open Jan-Dec

Charming Victorian country house with popular a la carte restaurant. Set in mature grounds on outskirts of village at start of the Trossachs Trail.

Important: Prices stated are estimates and may be subject to amendments

Drymen, Stirlingshire Map Ref: 1H4

The Buchanan Arms Hotel & Leisure Club
Drymen, by Loch Lomond, Stirlingshire G63 0BQ
Tel: 01360 660588 Fax: 01360 660943
Web: www.buchananarms.co.uk

In the heart of a conservation village by the 'bonnie banks' of Loch Lomond, the hotel seems to soak up the mood of the beautiful surrounding countryside. Comfort, fine dining and modern leisure facilities. Dinner, bed and breakfast from £48-£75 per person per night. AA ★★★ RAC ★★★

★★★
HOTEL

Buchanan Arms Hotel
Drymen, Loch Lomond, Stirlingshire, G63 0BQ
Tel: 01360 660588 Fax: 01360 660943
Web: www.buchananarms.co.uk

Refurbished Coaching Inn in picturesque village close to Loch Lomond and Trossachs. Leisure facilities with swimming pool and squash courts.

9 Single	All En Suite	B&B per person	Open Jan-Dec
30 Twin		£50.00-£82.00 Single	B&B + Eve.Meal
9 Double		£45.00-£60.00 Dbl/Twn	£53.00-£64.00
4 Family			

★★★
HOTEL

Winnock Hotel
The Square, Drymen, Loch Lomond, G63 0BL
Tel: 01360 660245 Fax: 01360 660136
E-mail: winnockhotel@ic24.net
Web: www.winnockhotel.com

Traditional coaching Inn, dating in parts from early 18th C, situated centrally on the village green.

4 Single	All En Suite	B&B per person	Open Jan-Dec
16 Twin		from £49.00 Single	
21 Double		from £32.50 Dbl/Twn	
6 Family			

Dunblane, Perthshire Map Ref: 2A3

★★★
HOTEL

Hilton Dunblane Hydro
Perth Road, Dunblane, Perthshire, FK15 0HG
Tel: 01786 822551 Fax: 01786 825403
Web: www.hilton.com

Set within 40 acres of private landscaped grounds, this Victorian style hotel offers comfortable bedrooms, traditional Scottish cuisine in the Balmoral Restaurant, Caffè Cino, an indoor swimming pool and fitness suite.

26 Single	All En Suite fac	B&B + Eve.Meal per person	Open Jan-Dec
87 Twin		£70.00-£110.00 Single	
53 Double		£45.00-£70.00 Dbl/Twn	
38 Family			
5 Suite			

Dunoon, Argyll Map Ref: 1F5

★★★★
HOTEL

The Anchorage Hotel & Restaurant
Shore Road, Sandbank, Dunoon, Argyll, PA23 8QG
Tel: 01369 705108 Fax: 0870 7061099
E-mail: info@anchorage.co.uk

Stylish traditional stone villa c.1870 with magnificent open views over Holy Loch. Easy access from ferry terminal. High standard of service and accommodation.

| 1 Twin | All En Suite | B&B per person | Open Dec-Oct |
| 4 Double | | from £55.00 Dbl/Twn | |

VAT is shown at 17.5%: changes in this rate may affect prices. | *Key to symbols is on back flap.*

Dunoon, Argyll — Map Ref: 1F5

HOTEL

The Argyll Hotel
Argyll Street, Dunoon, Argyll, PA23 7NE
Tel: 01369 702059 Fax: 01369 704483
Web: www.argyll-hotel.co.uk

6 Single	All En Suite	B&B per person	Open Jan-Dec
12 Twin		from £45.00 Single	B&B + Eve.Meal
11 Double		from £32.50 Dbl/Twn	from £40.00
4 Family			

Enjoying panoramic views over the Clyde; centrally located and close to the Ferry Terminal. Family run hotel offering a friendly atmosphere with facilities ideally suited to both businessmen and holidaymakers. Full bar and restaurant facilities available, serving meals all day. Children welcome. Conference/function facilities. DBB Packages.

HOTEL

Enmore Hotel
Marine Parade, Kirn, Dunoon, Argyll, PA23 8HH
Tel: 01369 702230 Fax: 01369 702148
E-mail: enmorehotel@btinternet.com
Web: www.enmorehotel.co.uk

1 Single	All En Suite	B&B per person	Open Jan-Dec
3 Twin		from £35.00 Single	B&B + Eve.Meal
5 Double		from £35.00 Dbl/Twn	from £60.00
1 Family			

Personal attention assured at this elegant Georgian House set in its own garden overlooking the Firth of Clyde. Each room tastefully decorated and furnished to create a relaxing atmosphere. Award winning restaurant and Taste of Scotland member. Squash courts. Some bedrooms with their own double Jacuzzi/spa bath.

HOTEL

Lyall Cliff Hotel
141 Alexandra Parade, East Bay, Dunoon, Argyll, PA23 8AW
Tel/Fax: 01369 702041
Web: www.in-uk.com/lyallcliff

4 Twin	All En Suite	B&B per person	Open 27Dec-31Oct
4 Double		from £22.00 Single	B&B + Eve.Meal
2 Family		from £20.00 Dbl/Twn	from £30.00
		Room only per person	
		from £18.00	

Beautifully situated, family-run hotel on the sea-front, with lovely garden and private car-park. 3 ground-floor bedrooms, marvellous sea-views, and excellent food. Short breaks and music/themed weekends available spring and autumn. German spoken.

Duntocher, Glasgow, Dunbartonshire — Map Ref: 1H5

HOTEL

Duntocher Hotel
Dumbarton Road, Duntocher, Glasgow, Dunbartonshire, G81 6PO
Tel: 01389 875371 Fax: 01389 877373

14 Single	All En Suite	B&B per person	Open Jan-Dec
9 Twin		from £34.75 Single	B&B + Eve.Meal
2 Double		from £29.75 Dbl/Twn	from £44.75
2 Family		Room only per person	
		from £30.00	

Modern purpose built hotel with large car park on route from Glasgow to Loch Lomondside. Convenient for Glasgow Airport via Erskine Bridge. Recently purpose built function suite ideal for weddings and business conferences up to 200 people.

Falkirk, Stirlingshire — Map Ref: 2A4

GUEST HOUSE

Ashbank Guest House
105 Main Street, Redding, Falkirk, Stirlingshire, FK2 9UQ
Tel: 01324 716649 Fax: 01324 712431
E-mail: ashbank@guest-house.freeserve.co.uk
Web: www.bandbfalkirk.com

1 Twin	All En Suite fac	B&B per person	Open Jan-Dec
2 Double		£23.00-£35.00 Single	Evening meal on
		£20.00-£25.00 Dbl/Twn	request.

Victorian family home - all rooms recently refurbished. North facing with views over Forth Valley to Braveheart country. Situated midway between Edinburgh & Glasgow. Ample off street parking.

Important: Prices stated are estimates and may be subject to amendments

---

Falkirk, Stirlingshire Map Ref: 2A4

★★★

HOTEL

Park Lodge Hotel
Camelon Road, Falkirk, Stirlingshire, FK1 5RY
Tel: 01324 628331 Fax: 01324 611593
E-mail: park@queensferry-hotels.co.uk
Web: www.theparkhotel.co.uk

23 Twin	55 En Suite fac	B&B per room	Open Jan-Dec
28 Double		from £69.00 Single	B&B + Eve.Meal
4 Family		from £79.00 Dbl/Twn	from £44.00

An easily accessible, quality hotel providing three star comfort and service at value for money prices. La Bonne Auberge French, Mediterranean Brasserie offers casual gourmet dining in an informal atmosphere.

Fintry, Stirlingshire Map Ref: 1H4

Culcreuch Castle and Country Park

Culcreuch Castle, Fintry, Stirlingshire G63 0LW
Telephone: 01360 860555 Fax: 01360 860556
Web: www.culcreuch.com

Magnificent 1600-acre parkland estate in breathtaking scenery. 700-year-old Culcreuch is a unique opportunity to sample the historic atmosphere of Central Scotland's oldest inhabited castle. Comfortable accommodation, cosy bar, licensed restaurant, free fishing, adjacent squash courts, log fires, warm welcome. Central for all Scotland's attractions, including Edinburgh (55 minutes by road). For free accommodation brochure, free fishing and golf brochures:–
Contact: Laird of Culcreuch, Culcreuch Castle, Stirlingshire G63 0LW.
Tel: (01360) 860555 Fax: (01360) 860556

★★★

HOTEL

Culcreuch Castle Hotel
Fintry, Loch Lomond, Stirling & Trossachs, G63 0LW
Tel: 01360 860555 Fax: 01360 860556
Web: www.culcreuch.com

2 Twin	All En Suite	B&B per person	Open Jan-Dec
4 Double		from £58.00 Single	B&B + Eve.Meal
4 Family		from £38.00 Dbl/Twn	from £49.50

14c castle with Dungeon Bar set in 1600 acre estate, with impressive views of Campsie Hills. Good base for touring central Scotland.

VAT is shown at 17.5%: changes in this rate may affect prices. | *Key to symbols is on back flap.*

Grangemouth, Stirlingshire — Map Ref: 2B4

HOTEL ★★★

Leapark Hotel
130 Bo'ness Road, Grangemouth, Stirlingshire, FK3 9BX
Tel: 01324 486733 Fax: 01324 665412
E-mail: iain@leapark.com
Web: www.leapark.com

Privately owned family run Hotel in central Scotland. Large function suite ideal for weddings, social functions and conferences.

16 Single	All En Suite	B&B per person	Open Jan-Dec
14 Twin		£40.00-£65.00 Single	B&B + Eve.Meal
14 Double		£25.00-£42.00 Dbl/Twn	£42.50-£82.50
1 Family			

Helensburgh, Argyll — Map Ref: 1G4

GUEST HOUSE ★★

Ardmore Guest House by the Sea
98 West Clyde Street, Helensburgh, Dunbartonshire, G84 8BE
Tel: 01436 673461 Fax: 01436 675739
E-mail: ardmore@fsbdial.co.uk
Web: www.scoot.co.uk/ardmore_guest_house

On the seafront with views over the River Clyde. Close to the town centre with its shops and restaurants. Relaxed, informal atmosphere. Off street parking. Loch Lomond 8 miles. Near Helensburgh railway station with its frequent service to Glasgow city centre. Full board terms available.

4 Twin	3 En Suite fac	B&B per person	Open Jan-Dec
1 Double	3 Pub Bath/Show	from £20.00 Dbl/Twn	B&B + Eve.Meal
4 Family	3 Priv.NOT ensuite	Room only per person	from £28.00
		from £20.00	

GUEST HOUSE ★★★★

Kirkton House
Darleith Road, Cardross, Argyll, G82 5EZ
Tel: 01389 841951 Fax: 01389 841868
E-mail: stbh@kirktonhouse.co.uk
Web: www.kirktonhouse.co.uk

Olde Worlde converted farmstead, with panoramic Cylde view, in tranquil countryside. All modern amenities. Wine and dine by oil lamplight. Taste of Scotland member. Glasgow Airport only 25 minutes drive.

2 Twin	All En Suite	B&B per person	Open Feb-Nov
4 Family		from £43.50 Double	B&B + Eve.Meal
		from £33.50 Twin	from £49.50

GUEST HOUSE ★★★

Sinclair House
91/93 Sinclair Street, Helensburgh, Argyll+Bute, G84 8TR
Tel: 01436 676301
E-mail: bookings@sinclairhouse.com

Traditional Scottish villa built in early 1800s, centrally situated close to all the town amenities.

3 Double	2 En Suite fac	B&B per person	Open Jan-Dec
1 Family	1 Pub Bath/Show	from £25.00 Single	
	2 Limited ensuite	from £17.50 Dbl/Twn	
		Room only per person	
		from £17.50	

Important: Prices stated are estimates and may be subject to amendments

Inveraray, Argyll   Map Ref: 1F3

THE ARGYLL
FRONT STREET, INVERARAY PA32 8XB
Tel: 01499 302466 Fax: 01499 302389
With spectacular views over Loch Fyne, this impressive Grade A
listed hotel offers modernised, luxurious rooms.
Comfortable public areas with traditional log fires. Fully licensed
with a wide range of malt whiskies. Our quality restaurant
features the best of local produce.

★★★★

HOTEL

The Argyll
The Great Inn at Inveraray, Front Street,
Inveraray, Argyll, PA32 8XB
Tel: 01499 302466 Fax: 01499 302389

4 Single	36 En Suite fac	B&B per person	Open Jan-Dec
10 Twin	2 Pub Bath/Show	£38.00-£49.00 Single	B&B + Eve.Meal
16 Double		£28.00-£48.00 Dbl/Twn	£53.00-£64.00
6 Family			

Designed in 1750 by the famous Scottish builder John Adam, The Argyll
formed part of the total rebuilding of Inveraray commissioned by the 3rd
Duke of Argyll. Originally built to accommodate guests to the Castle,
The Argyll today offers standards of hospitality that more than live up to
its illustrious past.

★★★

**SMALL
HOTEL**

Fernpoint Hotel
Round by the Pier, Inveraray, Argyll, PA32 8UY
Tel: 01499 302170 Fax: 01499 302366
E-mail: fernpoint.hotel@virgin.net

1 Single	6 En Suite fac	B&B per person	Open Mar-Jan excl Xmas
2 Twin	2 Priv.NOT ensuite	from £35.00 Single	B&B + Eve.Meal
4 Double		from £32.50 Dbl/Twn	from £45.00
1 Family		Room only per person	
		from £28.00	

Delightful Georgian house nestling in lochside gardens. Rooms with
charming decor have breathtaking views of Loch Fyne and surrounding
mountains. Bar meals served all day in stable bar or garden. Evening
meal reflect Chef's interest in local produce and vegetarian food.
Children and pets welcome.

Inverbeg, Argyll   Map Ref: 1G4

★★★★

**SMALL
HOTEL**

Inverbeg Inn
Luss, Loch Lomomd, Dunbartonshire, G83 8PD
Tel: 01436 860678 Fax: 01436 860686
E-mail: inverbeg@onyxnet.co.uk

6 Twin	All En Suite	B&B per person	Open Jan-Dec excl Xmas
12 Double		from £30.00 Single	
2 Family		from £30.00 Dbl/Twn	

The Inverbeg Inn enjoys one of the most spectacular settings in Scotland.
The hotel has 20 ensuite bedrooms. 8 luxury bedrooms are located by the
shore of Loch Lomond. The dining room offers a fine selection of dishes
prepared from fresh local produce. Outstanding location. A warm welcome
awaits you. Some annexe accommodation.

Iona, Isle of, Argyll   Map Ref: 1B2

★★

HOTEL

Argyll Hotel
Isle of Iona, Argyll, PA76 6SJ
Tel: 01681 700334 Fax: 01681 700510
E-mail: reception@argyllhoteliona.co.uk
Web: www.argyllhoteliona.co.uk

6 Single	All En Suite	B&B per person	Open Apr-Oct
3 Twin	1 Pub Bath/Show	from £39.00 Single	B&B + Eve.Meal
5 Double		from £18.00 Dbl/Twn	from £54.00
1 Family			

BRONZE

Key to symbols is on back flap.

Iona, Isle of, Argyll — Map Ref: 1B2

St Columba Hotel

★★ HOTEL

Isle of Iona, Argyll, PA76 6SL
Tel: 01681 700304 Fax: 01681 700688
Web: www.stcolumba-hotel.co.uk

9 Single	All En Suite
11 Twin	
3 Double	
4 Family	

B&B per person
from £41.00 Single
from £36.00 Dbl/Twn
Room only per person
from £31.00

Open Apr-Oct
B&B + Eve.Meal
from £49.00

A haven for total freedom and relaxation on this exquisite Hebridean island. Close to Abbey. Outstanding views from our sun lounges and dining room, warm welcome, friendly staff, log fire. Our chef's provide imaginative home baking and delicious home-cooked meals using fresh Scottish produce, some from our own organically cultivated garden. Children welcome. Ideal setting for a relaxing holiday for young and old.

Ballygrant, Isle of Islay, Argyll — Map Ref: 1C5

Ballygrant Inn

★★ INN

Ballygrant, Isle of Islay, Argyll, PA45 7QR
Tel/Fax: 01496 840277
E-mail: ballygrant-inn@isle-of-islay.freeserve.co.uk

1 Single	1 Pub Bath/Show
1 Twin	
1 Double	
1 Family	

B&B per person
from £25.00 Single
from £22.50 Dbl/Twn

Open Jan-Dec
B&B + Eve.Meal
from £42.50

Village Inn set back from main road in its own grounds. Only 3 miles (5kms) from Port Askaig ferry terminal. No smoking in bedrooms and dining room.

BRONZE

Kilmeny Country Guest House

★★★★★ GUEST HOUSE

Ballygrant, Isle of Islay, Argyll, PA45 7QW
Tel/Fax: 01496 840668
Web: www.kilmeny.co.uk

1 Twin	All En Suite
2 Double	

B&B per person
£36.00 Dbl/Twn

Open Jan-Dec excl
Xmas/New Year
B&B + Dinner
£60.00

Traditional farmhouse on 300 acre beef farm. Comfort, friendliness and peace. Emphasis on personal service, in a country house atmosphere. Non-smoking.

Bowmore, Isle of Islay, Argyll — Map Ref: 1C6

The Harbour Inn

★★★ INN

The Square, Bowmore, Isle of Islay, Argyll, PA43 7JR
Tel: 01496 810330 Fax: 01496 810990
Web: www.harbour-inn.com

4 Single	6 En Suite fac
4 Double	2 Priv.NOT ensuite

B&B per person
from £39.00 Single
from £32.50 Double

Open Jan-Dec

Welcoming, traditional, Islay Inn with award winning restaurant. Scottish tourist Board Thistle Award winners 1998. Good food guide recommended. We use the best Islay seafood, shellfish, beef and lamb. Lighter Bistro style lunch-time alternative. Friendly, cosy bar, popular with locals and visitors. One or two Islay malts can often lead to a fine sing-a-long evening.

Lochside Hotel

★★ SMALL HOTEL

Shore Street, Bowmore, Isle of Islay, Argyll, PA43 7LB
Tel: 01496 810244 Fax: 01496 810390
E-mail: ask@lochsidehotel.co.uk
Web: www.lochsidehotel.co.uk ; www.whisky4u.co.uk

5 Single	All En Suite
1 Twin	
1 Double	
1 Family	

B&B per person
£25.00-£39.50 Single
£25.00-£34.50 Dbl/Twn

Open Jan-Dec

Personally run, on main street of the village with views over Loch Indaal from the bar and dining room. Ideal base for touring Islay.

Important: Prices stated are estimates and may be subject to amendments

Bridgend, Isle of Islay, Argyll Map Ref: 1C5

Bridgend Hotel
Bridgend, Isle of Islay, Argyll, PA44 7PQ
Tel: 01496 810212 Fax: 01496 810960

2 Single	All En Suite	B&B per person	Open Jan-Dec
3 Twin	1 Pub Bath/Show	from £43.50 Single	B&B + Eve.Meal
2 Double		from £43.50 Dbl/Twn	from £59.50
3 Family			

SMALL
HOTEL

Friendly hotel in small village, centrally situated and ideal for touring the island.

Port Charlotte, Isle of Islay, Argyll Map Ref: 1B6

The Port Charlotte Hotel & Restaurant
Main Street, Port Charlotte, Isle of Islay, Argyll PA48 7TU
Tel: 01496 850360 Fax: 01496 850361
e.mail: carl@portcharlottehot.demon.co.uk
Web: www.milford.co.uk/go/portcharlotte.html
Tastefully restored Victorian hotel with great sea views in attractive conservation
village. Ten ensuite rooms beautifully decorated and furnished with antiques.
Excellent restaurant featuring local seafood, beef and lamb. Sandy beach.
Rooms from £49-£85.
Please call for full colour brochure.

Port Charlotte Hotel
Main Street, Port Charlotte, Isle of Islay, Argyll, PA48 7TU
Tel: 01496 850360 Fax: 01496 850361
E-mail: carl@portcharlottehot.demon.co.uk
Web: www.milford.co.uk/go/portcharlotte.html

2 Single	All En Suite	B&B per person	Open Jan-Dec
2 Twin		£55.00 Single	
5 Double		£45.00 Dbl/Twn	
1 Family			

HOTEL

Restored Victorian hotel offering all modern facilities in an informal,
relaxed atmosphere, situated in this picturesque conservation village on
the west shore of Loch Indaal. Fresh local seafood, lamb and beef.
Distillery visits, fishing and golfing can be arranged.

Port Ellen, Isle of Islay, Argyll Map Ref: 1C6

Glenmachrie
Port Ellen, Isle of Islay, Argyll, PA42 7AW
Tel/Fax: 01496 302560
E-mail: glenmachrie@lineone.net

2 Twin	All En Suite	B&B per person	Open Jan-Dec
2 Double	1 Pub Bath/Show	from £40.00 Single	B&B + Eve.Meal
1 Family		from £30.00 Dbl/Twn	from £53.00

GUEST
HOUSE

Farmhouse in quiet location, fine views westwards across Laggan Bay
towards the Rhinns. Family run farm using the best of Islay's larder.
Private fishing for wild brown trout. Taste of Scotland.

GOLD

The Trout-Fly Guest House
8 Charlotte Street, Port Ellen, Isle of Islay, Argyll, PA42 7DF
Tel: 01496 302204 Fax: 01496 300076

1 Single	All with w.h.b	B&B per person	Open Jan-Dec excl
2 Twin	Double with shower	from £18.50 Dbl/Twn	Xmas/New Year
1 Double			

GUEST
HOUSE

Guest house in town centre. Evening meals on request. Convenient for
ferry terminal, airport, golf-course and fishing. Restaurant for guests only
B.Y.O.B. 3 distilleries within 3 miles.

Craighouse, Isle of Jura, Argyll   **Map Ref: 1D5**

★★

HOTEL

Jura Hotel
Craighouse, Isle of Jura, Argyll, PA60 7XU
Tel: 01496 820243 Fax: 01496 820249
E-mail: jura.hotel@aol.com
Web: http://stay.at/jurahotel

Family run hotel with gardens, overlooking Small Isles Bay and close to famous distillery. Showers and drying room for sailors and walkers.

7 Single	10 En Suite fac	B&B per person	Open Jan-Dec
6 Twin	Suite avail	£32.00-£38.00 Single	B&B + Eve.Meal
4 Double	4 Pub Bath/Show	£32.00-£38.00 Dbl/Twn	£42.00-£55.00
2 Family			

Killin, Perthshire   **Map Ref: 1H2**

AA Hotel ★★★   Scottish ★★★★ HOTEL

Dall Lodge Country House Hotel
Main Street, Killin, Perthshire FK21 8TN
Tel: 01567 820217 Fax: 01567 820726
e.mail: wilson@dalllodgehotel.co.uk Web: www.dalllodgehotel.co.uk
Century-old mansion modernised, commanding stunning views of mountains on outskirts of scenic Highland village. Perfect base for outdoor activities, golfing, fishing, touring. Hotel offers home cooking, ensuite rooms, colour TV, hairdryers, tea/coffee makers, four-poster bed. Conservatory, lounge, ground-floor rooms for families or wheelchair or guests finding stairs difficult. Dinner served.

★★★★

HOTEL

Dall Lodge Country House Hotel
Killin, Perthshire, FK21 8TN
Tel: 01567 820217 Fax: 01567 820726
E-mail: wilson@dalllodgehotel.co.uk
Web: www.dalllodgehotel.co.uk

Century old mansion recently modernised with old world charm retained. On outskirts of scenic Highland village commanding stunning views of mountain and moorland. Scottish home cooking with fresh local produce. Perfect base for outdoor activities, golf, fishing and hillwalking. Ground floor rooms available.

1 Single	All En Suite	B&B per person	Open Mar-Oct
2 Twin		from £42.50 Single	B&B + Eve.Meal
5 Double		from £32.50 Dbl/Twn	from £53.00
2 Family			

FAIRVIEW HOUSE
Main Street, Killin, Perthshire FK21 8UT
Telephone: 01567 820667
e.mail: info@fairview-killin.co.uk Web: www.fairview-killin.co.uk

Rick and Joan offer a warm welcome to their friendly, comfortable guest house set in a picturesque village. Relax by an open fire in the residents lounge with breathtaking views of the central highlands. Excellent off-street parking, good drying facilities, and home-cooked evening meals are also on offer.

★★★

GUEST
HOUSE

Fairview House
Main Street, Killin, Perthshire, FK21 8UT
Tel: 01567 820667
E-mail: info@fairview-killin.co.uk
Web: www.fairview-killin.co.uk

Family run guest house specialising in home cooking. Excellent touring centre, good walking and climbing area.

1 Single	5 En Suite fac	B&B per person	Open Jan-Dec
2 Twin	2 Private fac	£20.00-£24.00 Single	B&B + Eve.Meal
4 Double		£20.00-£24.00 Dbl/Twn	£35.00-£39.00

Important: Prices stated are estimates and may be subject to amendments

Killin, Perthshire

Map Ref: 1H2

GUEST HOUSE ★★★

Invertay House
Killin, Perthshire, FK21 8TN
Tel: 01567 820492 Fax: 01567 820013
E-mail: invertay@btinternet.com

A very warm welcome in our listed former Manse with walled gardens on outskirts of village and enjoying magnificent views. Emphasis on comfort and fresh food, including seasonal garden produce.

2 Twin	All En Suite	B&B per person	Open Mar-mid Nov
4 Double		from £21.00 Single	B&B + Eve.Meal
		from £21.00 Dbl/Twn	from £35.00

HOTEL ★★

Killin Hotel
Main Street, Killin, Perthshire, FK21 8TP
Tel: 01567 820296 Fax: 01567 820647
E-mail: killinhotel@btinternet.com
Web: www.killinhotel.com

Family run hotel in the village of Killin and overlooking the western end of Loch Tay. Trout and salmon fishing by arrangement. Come and experience our new Riverside Bistro.

6 Single	All En Suite	B&B per person	Open Jan-Dec
9 Twin		from £35.00 Single	B&B + Eve.Meal
13 Double		from £26.00 Dbl/Twn	from £35.00
4 Family		Room only per person	
		from £19.00	

by Killin, Perthshire

Map Ref: 1H2

HOTEL ★★★

Morenish Lodge Hotel
Morenish, by Killin, Perthshire, FK21 8TX
Tel/Fax: 01567 820258
Web: www.morenishlodgehotel.co.uk

Former shooting lodge enjoying superb views over Loch Tay in an area famed for natural history and outdoor pursuits.

1 Single	12 En Suite fac	B&B per person	Open Mar-Nov
6 Twin	1 Priv.NOT ensuite	from £31.00 Single	B&B + Eve.Meal
10 Double	1 Pub Bath/Show	from £31.00 Dbl/Twn	from £43.00
1 Family			

Kilmelford, by Oban, Argyll

Map Ref: 1E3

CUILFAIL HOTEL
KILMELFORD, BY OBAN PA34 4XA

Charming old Scottish Hotel, 14 miles south of Oban. Dine in the 'Tartan Puffer' restaurant – indoor barbecue and grill. Rare collection of old and valuable malt whiskies on display with many more to sample.
B&B from £20, with discounts for longer stays.
Catch the West Highland atmosphere!
For full details call (01852) 200274   Fax (01852) 200264
e.mail: davidbirrell@cuilfailhotel.freeserve.co.uk

SMALL HOTEL ★★

Cuilfail Hotel
Kilmelford, by Oban, Argyll, PA34 4XA
Tel: 01852 200274 Fax: 01852 200264
E.mail: davidbirrell@cuilfailhotel.freeserve.co.uk
Web: www.cuilfail.co.uk

Old coaching Inn situated in small village. Emphasis on traditional Scottish fare based on local produce. 'Tartan Puffer' restaurant with indoor barbecue and grill. Collection of rare malt whiskies on display, over 100 available in bar.

4 Twin	All En Suite	B&B per person	Open Jan-Dec
6 Double		from £20.00 Single	B&B + Eve.Meal
2 Family		from £20.00 Dbl/Twn	from £35.00

VAT is shown at 17.5%: changes in this rate may affect prices. | *Key to symbols is on back flap.*

Kilninver, by Oban, Argyll		Map Ref: 1E2	

HOTEL ★★★★

Knipoch Hotel
by Oban, Argyll, PA34 4QT
Tel: 01852 316251 Fax: 01852 316249
Web: www.knipochhotel.co.uk

16 rooms   All En Suite   B&B per person   Open Feb-Dec
from £37.00 Single
from £37.00 Dbl/Twn

Family run country house hotel standing in its own grounds, overlooking Loch Feochan. 6 miles (10kms) south of Oban.

📺 📞 🖨 🅿 🍴 ✂ 🍽 🎣 🎱 🏆

Ⓒ 🐕 ♿ Ⓥ

Lerags, by Oban, Argyll		Map Ref: 1E2	

GUEST HOUSE ★★★

Lerags House
Lerags, by Oban, Argyll, PA34 4SE
Tel/Fax: 01631 563381
E-mail: leragshouse@supanet.com

1 Single   All En Suite   B&B per person   Open Mar-Oct
2 Twin   from £22.50 Single   B&B + Eve.Meal
4 Double   from £22.50 Dbl/Twn   from £37.50

An enchanting Georgian country house standing in almost two acres of mature garden on the shores of a tidal inlet on the northern banks of Loch Feochan. The house is set in the tranquil and picturesque Lerags Glen, a perfect retreat with a sense of the remote, yet it is only a short drive from Oban with it's town facilities, shopping and ferry terminal for the Islands.

🖨 🅿 ☕ ⚒ ✗ 🍽 🖱 🕮

Ⓒ ♿ Ⓥ

BRONZE 📎

Lochearnhead, Perthshire		Map Ref: 1H2	

Lochearnhead Hotel

Lochearnhead, Perthshire FK19 8PU
Tel: 01567 830229 Fax: 01567 830364
e.mail: gus@lochhot.freeserve.co.uk

Family run hotel with stunning views over Loch Earn. Excellent golf and touring centre with water sports on our doorstep. Seven golf courses within 14 miles. All rooms have colour Sky TV and central heating. Some with loch views. Try our popular bar and dining room menus. Families and pets welcome.

HOTEL ★★

Lochearnhead Hotel
Lochearnhead, Perthshire, FK19 8PU
Tel: 01567 830229 Fax: 01567 830364
E-mail: gus@lochhot.freeserve.co.uk

1 Single   8 En Suite fac   B&B per person   Open Apr-Nov
6 Twin   2 Pub Bath/Show   from £30.00 Single   B&B + Eve.Meal
6 Double   from £24.00 Dbl/Twn   from £42.50

Privately owned, in elevated position overlooking Loch Earn. Water sports centre and sailing facilities adjacent. Ideal centre for touring, golfing, fishing and hillwalking.

📺 🏄 🖨 🅿 ☕ ✂ 🍽 🎱 🏆

Ⓒ 🐕 ♿ Ⓥ

Lochgair, by Lochgilphead, Argyll		Map Ref: 1E4	

SMALL HOTEL ★★
♿

Lochgair Hotel
Lochgair, by Lochgilphead, Argyll, PA31 8SA
Tel/Fax: 01546 886333
E-mail: LochgairHotel@aol.com

3 Twin   All En Suite   B&B per person   Open Jan-Dec
5 Double 2 Pub Bath/Show   from £30.00 Single   B&B + Eve.Meal
1 Family   from £20.00 Dbl/Twn   £25.00-£48.00
                            Room only per person
                            from £20.00

Lovely lochside village family run hotel, comfortable rooms. Good Bar Food, quality A la Carte menu. Restaurant. Residents lounge. 2 bars. Log fires, malt whiskies. Stunning scenery, walking, fishing, riding, golf. Special Offers.

📺 🖨 🅿 ☕ ✂ 🍽 ✗ 🛏 🏆 🖱 🕮

Ⓒ 🐕 ♿ Ⓥ

Important: Prices stated are estimates and may be subject to amendments

by Lochgilphead, Argyll   Map Ref: 1E4

Cairnbaan Hotel
CAIRNBAAN, NR LOCHGILPHEAD, ARGYLL PA31 8SJ
Telephone: 01546 603668   Fax: 01546 606045
Web: www.cairnbaan.com
Delightful 18th century coaching inn overlooking Lock 5 on
the Crinan Canal. Superb food served by our friendly team in
relaxed and unhurried environment, close to Inveraray, Oban
and ideal for discovering Argyll and the islands.

★★★★

HOTEL

Cairnbaan Hotel
by Lochgilphead, Argyll, PA31 8SJ
Tel: 01546 603668 Fax: 01546 606045
Web: www.cairnbaan.com

1 Single	All En Suite	B&B per person
3 Twin		£55.00-£65.00 Single
6 Double		£45.00-£55.00 Dbl/Twn

Open Jan-Dec

Privately owned, family run hotel in tranquil surroundings overlooking the
Crinan Canal at Lock 5.

Lochgoilhead, Argyll   Map Ref: 1F3

★

INN

Shore House Inn
Lochgoilhead, Argyll, PA24 8AJ
Tel/Fax: 01301 703340
E-mail: shorehouse.inn@fs13dial.co.uk

1 Single	3 En Suite fac	B&B per person
2 Twin	2 Pub Bath/Show	from £16.00 Single
2 Double		from £20.00 Dbl/Twn
2 Family		

Open Jan-Dec

Peacefully situated on the shore of Loch Goil, with open views down the
loch. Informal and friendly. Pets welcome. Bar and Restaurant.

Luss, Argyll & Bute   Map Ref: 1G4

★

HOTEL

Colquhoun Arms Hotel
Luss, Loch Lomond, Dunbartonshire, G83 8NY
Tel: 01436 860282 Fax: 01436 860309
Web: www.lochlomondarms.co.uk

4 Single	17 En Suite fac	B&B per person
4 Twin	2 Priv.NOT ensuite	from £30.00 Single
11 Double	1 Pub Bath/Show	from £25.00 Dbl/Twn

Open Jan-Dec

Family run hotel, with bar open all day situated 200 yards from the banks
of Loch Lomond. Glendarroch Tearoom and gift shop open during the
summer months.

Luss, Argyll & Bute Map Ref: 1G4

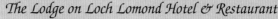

The Lodge on Loch Lomond Hotel & Restaurant

Tel: 01436 860201 www.loch-lomond.co.uk

★★★

HOTEL

Lodge on Loch Lomond Hotel
Rhu of Luss, Loch Lomond, Dunbartonshire, G83 8PA
Tel: 01436 860201 Fax: 01436 860203
E-mail: lusslomond@aol.com
Web: www.loch-lomond.co.uk

8 Twin	All En Suite	B&B per person	Open Jan-Dec
21 Double	Suite avail	£30.00-£63.00 Dbl/Twn	
		Room only per person	
		£25.00-£55.00	

Modern pine lodge situated on the serene banks of Loch Lomond close to
Luss village. Modern pine panelling character reflects the tranquility of the
surrounding scenery. All bedrooms ensuite with a sauna. Informal
Brasserie style restaurant with magnificent views across Loch Lomond.

Calgary, Isle of Mull, Argyll Map Ref: 1C1

★★★

**SMALL
HOTEL**

Calgary Farmhouse Hotel
Calgary, by Dervaig, Argyll, PA75 6QW
Tel/Fax: 01688 400256
Web: www.calgary.co.uk

1 Single	All En Suite	B&B per person	Open Apr-Oct
2 Twin		from £31.50 Single	
4 Double		from £35.00 Dbl/Twn	
2 Family			

Converted farmhouse and steading, close to the beautiful white sands of
Calgary Beach. Taste of Scotland restaurant. Our menu consists of local
Scottish produce skilfully prepared by our award-winning chef and served
in our original Dovecote restaurant. All bedrooms tastefully and
individually decorated. Some with TV's. Radio available.

Craignure, Isle of Mull, Argyll Map Ref: 1D2

★★★

INN

Craignure Inn
Craignure, Isle of Mull, Argyll, PA65 6AY
Tel: 01680 812305 Fax: 01680 812306
Web: www.craignure-inn.co.uk

1 Twin	All En Suite	B&B per person	Open Jan-Dec excl
1 Double		from £40.00 Single	Xmas/New Year
1 Family		from £29.50 Dbl/Twn	
		Room only per person	
		from £27.50	

Completely refurbished 17th century former drover's inn, conveniently
situated for ferry and bus tours. Characterful, friendly bars (including non-
smoking) popular with local trade. Bar meals available, non residents
welcome.

★★

**GUEST
HOUSE**

Pennygate Lodge
Craignure, Isle of Mull, Argyll, PA65 6AY
Tel: 01680 812333

3 Twin	En Suite fac	B&B per person	Open Jan-Dec excl
3 Double	2 Pub Bath/Show	from £22.00 Single	Xmas/New Year
2 Family	Priv.NOT ensuite	from £18.00 Dbl/Twn	

Former Georgian manse set in 4.5 acres of landscaped garden with
magnificent views of the Sound of Mull. Ideal base for touring, near main
bus route and ferry terminal. Three night special breaks available.

Important: Prices stated are estimates and may be subject to amendments

Dervaig, Isle of Mull, Argyll   Map Ref: 1C1

★★★★

SMALL
HOTEL

Druimard Country House
Dervaig, by Tobermory, Isle of Mull, PA75 6QW
Tel: 01688 400345/400291 Fax: 01688 400345
E-mail: druimard@hotels.activebooking.com
Web: www.druimard.co.uk

Small Victorian country house hotel, with elegant restaurant,(2 AA
Rosettes) Emphasis on using local produce. Adjacent to Mull Little Theatre.

1 Single	7 En Suite fac	D.B&B per person
3 Twin	1 Priv.NOT ensuite	from £77.00 Single
4 Double		from £62.00 Dbl/Twn
1 Family		

Open Apr-Oct

★★★

SMALL
HOTEL

Druimnacroish Hotel
Dervaig, Isle of Mull, Argyll, PA75 6QW
Tel/Fax: 01688 400274
E-mail: stay@druimnacrosh.co.uk
Web: www.druimnacroish.co.uk

Converted water mill set on a tranquil and secluded hillside offering a
relaxed, friendly atmosphere, spacious accommodation, extensive
gardens, good food, home made bread, superb views from every room.
Put your feet up by the fire or enjoy the view from the conservatory.
Well situated for Mull's many attractions including boat trips, wildlife,
walking and the Mull Little Theatre. Taste of Scotland Award.

3 Twin	All En Suite	B&B per person
3 Double		from £35.00 Single
		from £35.00 Dbl/Twn

Open Jan-Dec

B&B + Eve.Meal
from £49.50 pp

Fionnphort, Isle of Mull, Argyll   Map Ref: 1C2

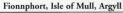

★★★

GUEST
HOUSE

Achaban House
Fionnphort, Isle of Mull, Argyll, PA66 6BL
Tel: 01681 700205 Fax: 01681 700649
Web: www.achabanhouse.co.uk

Former manse overlooking Loch Pottie. Imaginative cooking, emphasis on
fresh local produce. Ideal for Iona and Staffa.

1 Single	5 Ensuite fac	B&B per person
2 Twin	1 Priv.NOT ensuite	from £25.00 Single
2 Double		from £22.25 Dbl/Twn
1 Family		

Open Jan-Dec

Killiechronan, Isle of Mull, Argyll   Map Ref: 1D2

Killiechronan House
ISLE OF MULL, ARGYLL PA72 6JU
Telephone: 01680 300403 Fax: 01680 300463
e.mail: me@managed-estates.co.uk

Killiechronan House tastefully provides good food, comfortable accommodation
and a personal welcome, emulating its imposing situation at the head of Loch Na
Keal. The estate offers fishing, pony trekking, mountain biking, hillwalking and is
centrally situated on the island. All bedrooms have ensuite facilities. Special breaks
available. AA

★★★★

SMALL
HOTEL

Killiechronan House
Killiechronan, Isle of Mull, Argyll, PA72 6JU
Tel: 01680 300403 Fax: 01680 300463
E-mail: me@managed-estates.co.uk

At the head of Loch Na Keal this former Lodge (c.1840) offers peace and
tranquility and has been tastefully restored. Enjoy mouthwatering dishes
using the best of local produce and vegetables from the hotel's own walled
garden. 12 miles (19 km) from Craignure ferry.

1 Single	All En Suite
3 Twin	
2 Double	

Open Mar-Oct

B&B + Eve.Meal
£60.00-£85.00

VAT is shown at 17.5%: changes in this rate may affect prices.

Key to symbols is on back flap.

Pennyghael, Isle of Mull, Argyll   Map Ref: 1C2

Pennyghael Hotel and Cottages

Pennyghael, Isle of Mull, Argyll PA70 6HB
Tel: 01681 704288 Fax: 01681 704205

Originally a 17th century farmhouse this family-run hotel provides a warm friendly ambience in a lochside setting of unparalleled beauty. Ideally placed for visiting Iona and Staffa and overlooking 'Ben More', there is walking and wildlife in abundance. Wonderful home-cooking using local ingredients. Fabulous sunsets. No small children.

★★★
HOTEL

Pennyghael Hotel & Cottages
Pennyghael, Isle of Mull, Argyll, PA70 6HB
Tel: 01681 704288 Fax: 01681 704205

2 Twin	All En Suite	B&B per person	Open Late Mar-Oct
4 Double		from £42.50 Single	B&B + Eve.Meal
		from £32.50 Dbl/Twn	from £52.50

The Pennyghael is a small intimate hotel in a beautifully romantic setting (no small children to disturb the peace and quiet). High standards are in evidence throughout, but combined with a relaxed and friendly ambience.

Tobermory, Isle of Mull, Argyll   Map Ref: 1C1

★★★
**GUEST
HOUSE**

Baliscate Guest House
Salen Road, Tobermory, Isle of Mull, Argyll, PA75 6QA
Tel: 01688 302048 Fax: 01688 302666
Web: www.baliscate.com

2 Double	All En Suite	B&B per person	Open Jan-Dec
2 Family		from £20.00 Single	
		from £22.50 Double	

Recently refurbished Victorian house set in 1.5 acres of garden and woodland, with magnificent views over The Sound of Mull. 15 minute down hill walk to Tobermory front and all amenities. 'Request' bus stop at bottom of garden.

★★★
B&B

Copeland House
Jubilee Terrace, Tobermory, Isle of Mull, Argyll, PA75 6PZ
Tel: 01688 302049/302422
E-mail: EK@copeland2049.freeserve.co.uk
Web: www.skybusiness.com/copeland

1 Twin	All En Suite	B&B per person	Open Jan-Dec
1 Double		£23.00-£30.00 Single	
1 Family		£20.00-£23.00 Dbl/Twn	

Owner designed and built, this detached family house offers beautiful views overlooking the Sound of Mull and Tobermory Bay. 10 minutes walk to sea front. All local amenities nearby including Restaurants, Pubs, Museum, Whale and Dolphin Centre, Distillery and Arts & Craft Gallery.

★★★★
**GUEST
HOUSE**

Fairways Lodge
Golf Course, Tobermory, Isle of Mull, Argyll, PA75 6PS
Tel/Fax: 01688 302238
E-mail: derekmcadam@fairwaysmull.com
Web: www.fairwaysmull.com

1 Single	All En Suite	B&B per person	Open Jan-Dec excl
2 Twin		from £29.00 Single	Xmas
1 Double		from £29.00 Dbl/Twn	
1 Family			

Fairways Lodge enjoys an outstanding position on Tobermory golf course with wonderful views over Tobermory Bay and the Sound of Mull. All bedrooms have private bathrooms, colour TV, welcome tray and every luxury. Our conservatory lounge is available to guests all day. Ideal centre for golf, fishing and touring. Visit Staffa and Iona. To find us follow signs to the golf course.

Important: Prices stated are estimates and may be subject to amendments

Highland Cottage

Breadalbane Street, Tobermory, Isle of Mull PA75 6PD
Telephone: 01688 302030 Fax: 01688 302727
e.mail: davidandjo@highlandcottage.co.uk
Web: www.highlandcottage.co.uk

Intimate friendly family run hotel in quiet location in Upper Tobermory with reputation for hospitality and good food. 4-poster beds, satellite TV and books galore. Plentiful parking and only minutes from bustling main street and fisherman's pier. Come and relax. Colour brochure from David and Josephine Currie – resident owners.

★★★★

SMALL
HOTEL

&

Highland Cottage
Breadalbane Street, Tobermory, Isle of Mull, PA75 6PD
Tel: 01688 302030 Fax: 01688 302727
E.mail: davidandjo@highlandcottage.co.uk
Web: www.highlandcottage.co.uk

Newly built, family-run 'country house in the town' hotel located in the heart of upper Tobermory in conservation area. Well appointed bedrooms themed after local islands and including 2 with 4 poster beds. Imaginative cuisine using fresh, local ingredients served in our attractive, homely, dining room. High level of personal attention from resident owners.

1 Twin	All En Suite	B&B per person	Open Jan-Dec
5 Double		from £53.00 Single	B&B + Eve.Meal
		from £38.00 Dbl/Twn	from £57.50

BRONZE

The Western Isles Hotel

Tobermory, Isle of Mull, Argyllshire PA75 6PR
Tel: 01688 302012 Fax: 01688 302297
e.mail: wihotel@aol.com

This 28 bedroomed Victorian Hotel, built in 1883 majestically stands against the skyline overlooking picturesque Tobermory Bay and the Sound of Mull. With its backdrop of the Morven Hills and Tobermory's brightly coloured houses, the hotel has arguably one of the finest views in the Hebridean Islands. Offering standard, master and deluxe bedrooms, the hotel is a haven of comfort.

The dining room serves a four-course dinner and coffee in a formal atmosphere, plus a more casual form of dining, the Conservatory bar, offering an interesting range of bar meals for both lunch and evening. Non-residents most welcome.

★★★★

HOTEL

The Western Isles Hotel
Tobermory, Isle of Mull, Argyll, PA75 6PR
Tel: 01688 302012 Fax: 01688 302297
E-mail: wihotel@aol.com

Superbly situated overlooking Tobermory Bay, the hotel is a haven of peace and tranquility. Good food and comfort. Conservatory bar, serving bar meals. Non-residents very welcome. Small conferences, weddings and parties catered for.

3 Single	All En Suite	B&B per person	Open Jan-18 Dec
13 Twin		from £41.00 Single	B&B + Eve.Meal
12 Double		from £41.00 Double	from £54.50

Uisken, by Bunessan, Isle of Mull, Argyll   Map Ref: 1C3

ARDACHY HOUSE HOTEL
Uisken, by Bunessan, Isle of Mull PA67 6DS
Tel/Fax: 01681 700505
Web: http://members.xoom.com/ardachy

Beautifully presented and quietly located but only 20 minutes
drive from Iona and Staffa ferries. Overlooking the white sands
of Ardalanish to the Isles of Colonsay, Jura and Islay.
Dinner is by reservation. Prices for D,B&B £50-£55.

★★★

SMALL
HOTEL

Ardachy House Hotel			
Uisken, by Bunessan, Isle of Mull, Argyll, PA67 6DS			
Tel/Fax: 01681 700505			
Web: http://members.xoom.com/ardachy			

3 Single	7 En Suite fac	B&B per person	Open Apr-Sep
1 Twin	1 Pub Bath/Show	from £25.00 Single	B&B + Eve.Meal
3 Double		from £33.00 Dbl/Twn	from £43.00
1 Family			

Small, secluded, family-run licensed hotel, 7 miles (11 kms) from Iona.
Safe access to white sands of Ardalanish Beach. Spectacular views to
Colonsay, Jura and Islay.

📷 📶 🅿 ☕ ✕ 🍷

🏧 🅦 Ⓥ

Oban, Argyll   Map Ref: 1E2

★★★★

GUEST
HOUSE

Barriemore Hotel			
Esplanade, Oban, Argyll, PA34 5AQ			
Tel/Fax: 01631 566356			
E-mail: barriemore.hotel@dnet.co.uk			

| 4 Twin | All En Suite | B&B per person | Open Mar-Oct |
| 9 Double | | from £25.00 Dbl/Twn | |

Delightfully restored Victorian detached villa overlooking Oban Bay
offering the discerning holidaymaker a superior standard of style and
comfort. Personally run by proprietors.

📺 📶 🅿 ☕ 🍴 ✕ 🥢 🍷 📱

🐾 🏧

★★★★

GUEST
HOUSE

Beechgrove			
Croft Road, Oban, Argyll, PA34 5JL			
Tel: 01631 566111			
E-mail: BeechgroveGuesthouse@btinternet.com			

| 2 Double | All En Suite | B&B per person | Open Mar-Oct |
| 1 Family | | £19.00-£26.00 Double | |

'Beechgrove' is a family run modern Victorian house set within pleasant
gardens on an elevated position in a quiet, residential area of the town
with views of Oban Bay and Kerrera. Close to leisure facilities and only a
short walk to harbour, shops, esplanade. All rooms are comfortable and
tastefully decorated. Enjoy our breakfasts and warm hospitality.

📺 📶 🅿 ☕ 🥢 ✕ 🖥 📱

Important: Prices stated are estimates and may be subject to amendments

Oban, Argyll | Map Ref: 1E2

CALEDONIAN MILTON HOTEL

STATION SQUARE,
OBAN PA34 5RT
Freephone: 0808 100 55 56
Fax: 01786 469 400
Please quote ref HGH01

★★ Hotel

It's been standing here looking out to the isles for over 100 years. The views are just what you are looking for. So too is the hotel, AA 3 star, and very well furnished, comfy bedrooms, well-stocked bar and 2 very popular restaurants. It's in the town centre near shops, rail and ferry terminals.

Many holiday offers with our other hotels all over Scotland including Stirling, Fort William and Inverness.

e.mail: sales@miltonhotels.com
Web: www.miltonhotels.com

★★

HOTEL

Caledonian Milton Hotel
Station Square, Oban, Argyll, PA34 5RT
Milton Sales Centre: Freefone 0808 100 55 56
Fax: 01786 469 400
E-mail: sales@miltonhotels.com
Web: www.miltonhotels.com

Modernised 19c building adjacent to railway station and ferry pier, overlooking the harbour and the Isles of Kerrera and Mull.

13 Single	All En Suite	B&B per person	Open Jan-Dec
40 Twin		£61.00-£81.00 Single	
10 Double		£40.50-£80.50 Dbl/Twn	
7 Family			

★★★

GUEST HOUSE

Corrie Mar House
Corrarm, Esplanade, Oban, Argyll, PA34 5AQ
Tel: 01631 562476 Fax: 01631 564339
E-mail: Corriemar@tinyworld.co.uk

Situated on the seafront, this large Victorian family run Guest House is only 10 minutes walk along the prom to the town centre. Spectacular Oban sunsets looking from the lounge over to Kerrara with the hills of Mull beyond.

2 Single	All En Suite	B&B per person	Open Jan-Dec
4 Twin		£23.00-£35.00 Single	
5 Double		£18.00-£32.00 Dbl/Twn	
2 Family		Room only per person	
		from £15.00	

★★★

SMALL HOTEL

Dungallan House Hotel
Gallanach Road, Oban, Argyll, PA34 4PD
Tel: 01631 563799 Fax: 01631 566711
E-mail: welcome@dungallanhotel-oban.co.uk
Web: www.dungallanhotel-oban.co.uk

George and Janice Stewart's Victorian villa sits high above Oban at ease in 5 acres of lawns, cliffs and trees. Yet only 1/2 mile from town centre. Janice's renowned quality 'Taste of Scotland' style cooking must be experienced.

2 Single	11 En Suite fac	B&B per person	Open Jan,
5 Twin	2 Pub Bath/Show	£40.00-£48.00 Single	Mar-Oct
6 Double		£44.00-£48.00 Dbl/Twn	B&B + Eve.Meal
			£64.00-£73.00

Foxholes Hotel
Cologin, Lerags, Oban, Argyll PA34 4SE
Tel: 01631 564982 Fax: 01631 570890
Web: www.hoteloban.com

Enjoy peace and tranquility at Foxholes, situated in its own grounds in a quiet glen 3 miles south of Oban, with magnificent views of the surrounding countryside. An ideal spot for those who wish to "escape from it all". We offer tastefully furnished accommodation, a five-course table d'hôte menu and a large selection of wines and spirits. All bedrooms ensuite, colour TV and tea/coffee-making facilities. Send for colour brochure and tariff to Mrs S Dowson-Park at the above address. **Prices from £43.00 D,B&B pp per night. B&B from £27.50 pp per night. Single supplement £12 extra per night. OPEN ALL YEAR.**

★★★★
HOTEL

Foxholes Country Hotel
Cologin, Lerags, Oban, Argyll, PA34 4SE
Tel: 01631 564982 Fax: 01631 570890
Web: www.hoteloban.com

2 Twin	All En Suite	B&B per person	Open Jan-Dec
5 Double		from £37.50 Single	B&B + Eve.Meal
		from £27.50 Dbl/Twn	from £43.00
			Single sup £12.00

Peacefully situated in a quiet glen with magnificent views yet a mere 3 miles (5kms) south of Oban. Ideally placed for the ferries for day trips to the islands of the inner Hebrides, Mull and Iona in particular. Many scenic drives including Fort William are within an hour of the Hotel and gardens. Fresh local produce used in our Table D'Hote dinners.

★★★★
GUEST
HOUSE

Glenara Guest House
Rockfield Road, Oban, Argyll, PA34 5DQ
Tel: 01631 563172 Fax: 01631 571125
E-mail: glenara_oban@hotmail.com
Web: www.smoothhound.co.uk/hotels/glenara.html

1 Twin/	B&B per person	Open Mar-Oct
Triple	from £21.00 Single	
3 Double	from £21.00 Dbl/Twn	

Family run guest house close to the town centre and all amenities. Tastefully and comfortably appointed rooms. No detail spared in caring for guests individual needs. Excellent area for hillwalking, sailing, boat cruising, archaeology and simply enjoying outstanding scenery. No smokers.

★★★★
GUEST
HOUSE

Glenbervie Guest House
Dalriach Road, Oban, Argyll, PA34 5NL
Tel: 01631 564770 Fax: 01636 566723

2 Single	6 En Suite fac	B&B per person	Open Mar-Dec
1 Twin	1 Pub Bath/Show	£22.00-£30.00 Single	B&B + Eve.Meal
5 Double		£22.00-£30.00 Dbl/Twn	£34.00-£42.00

Beautifully situated overlooking Oban Bay, commanding magnificent views. 2 minutes walk from town centre, promenade, harbour and amenities. Evening meal. Ensuite.

Important: Prices stated are estimates and may be subject to amendments

Oban, Argyll   Map Ref: 1E2

GUEST HOUSE

★★★★

Glenburnie House
Esplanade, Oban, Argyll, PA34 5AQ
Tel: 01631 562089
E-mail: Graeme.Strachan@btinternet.com

Convenient for town centre and all amenities, this family run hotel has magnificient views of the bay and islands.Recently refurbished superior rooms.

2 Single	All En Suite
4 Twin	
8 Double	

B&B per person
from £30.00 Single
from £26.00 Dbl/Twn

Open Apr-Nov

GUEST HOUSE

★★★

Glenrigh Guest House
Corran Esplanade, Oban, Argyll, PA34 5AQ
Tel/Fax: 01631 562991
E-mail: glenrigh@tesco.net

Refurbished large Victorian house with excellent views across Oban Bay. Short walk from town centre and all amenities. Ample private parking.

3 Single	All En Suite
5 Twin	
4 Double	
3 Family	

B&B per person
from £25.00 Single
from £23.00 Dbl/Twn
Room only per person
from £23.00

Open Jan-Dec

GUEST HOUSE

★★★

Glenroy Guest House
Rockfield Road, Oban, Argyll, PA34 5DQ
Tel: 01631 562585
E-mail: boydglen@ukonline.co.uk
Web: www.glenroy-guesthouse.co.uk

Centrally situated family run guest house located only a very short distance from the town centre and all amenities. Owners are life-time locals with extensive local knowledge which they are happy to share with guests.

1 Twin	4 Ensuite fac
5 Double	2 Pub Bath/Show
	2 Limited ensuite

B&B per person
from £20.00 Dbl/Twn

Open Jan-Dec excl
Xmas/New Year

GUEST HOUSE

★★★★

Greencourt Guest House
Benvoulin Lane, Oban, Argyll, PA34 5EF
Tel: 01631 563987 Fax: 01631 571276
E-mail: stay@greencourt-oban.fsnet.co.uk
Web: www.greencourt-oban.fsnet.co.uk

Spacious family run property in quiet situation overlooking outdoor bowling green, a short stroll to town centre and adjacent to leisure centre. Attractive rooms, wholesome breakfasts, private parking. Ideal touring base.

1 Single	5 Ensuite fac
1 Twin	1 Priv.NOT ensuite
4 Double	

B&B per person
£20.00-£26.00 Single
£20.00-£26.00 Dbl/Twn

Open Jan-Dec excl
Xmas/New Year

B&B

★★★

Hawthorn
Benderloch, by Connel, Argyll, PA37 1QS
Tel: 01631 720452

Family bungalow in peaceful rural setting 9 miles (14kms) from Oban and ferry terminals for the islands. 5 minutes walk from the excellent sandy beaches of Tralee Bay. Own restaurant adjacent. Ensuite rooms available.

1 Twin	2 En Suite fac
2 Double	1 Priv.NOT ensuite

B&B per person
from £25.00 Single
from £18.00 Dbl/Twn

Open Jan-Dec
B&B + Eve.Meal
from £28.00

VAT is shown at 17.5%: changes in this rate may affect prices.   **Key to symbols is on back flap.**

Oban, Argyll | Map Ref: 1E2

★★★
B&B

Kathmore Guest House
Soroba Road, Oban, Argyll
Tel: 01631 562104

1 Twin	4 En Suite fac	B&B per person	Open Jan-Dec excl
3 Double	1 Pub Bath/Show	from £18.00 Single	Xmas/New Year
1 Family		from £15.00 Dbl/Twn	

Family run guest house with private parking. Situated within a short walking distance of town centre, shops, hotels and restaurants. Ensuite bedrooms.

★
HOTEL

Kelvin Hotel
Cawdor Place, Shore Street, Oban, Argyll, PA34 4LQ
Tel: 01631 562150 Fax: 01631 570400

6 Single	15 En Suite fac	B&B per person	Open Jan-Dec
5 Twin	3 Pub Bath/Show	£20.00-£33.00 Single	B&B + Eve.Meal
4 Double		£20.00-£31.00 Dbl/Twn	£28.00-£40.00
6 Family			

Close to pier, railway and bus stations. Town centre 5 minutes walk.

★★★★
HOTEL

The Kimberley Hotel
Dalriach Road, Oban, Argyll, PA34 5EQ
Tel: 01631 571115 Fax: 01631 571008
E-mail: reception@kimberley-hotel.com
Web: www.kimberley-hotel.com

5 Single	All En Suite	B&B per person	Open May-Oct
10 Double		£60.00-£70.00 Single	
		£47.50-£65.00 Double	

Victorian building of character set in an elevated position with open outlook over Oban, harbour and islands. Rooms are furnished in the Victorian style with modern comforts. The town centre with rich choice of shops and restaurants is only 5 minutes walk. Truly a choice location.

★★
HOTEL

Kings Knoll Hotel
Dunollie Road, Oban, Argyll, PA34 5JH
Tel: 01631 562536 Fax: 01631 566101
E-mail: kingsknoll@aol.com

2 Single	13 En Suite fac	B&B per person	Open Feb-Dec
3 Twin		from £20.00 Single	B&B + Eve.Meal
7 Double		from £20.00 Dbl/Twn	from £42.00
3 Family		Room only per person	
		from £20.00	

Family run hotel overlooking Oban Bay and close to the town centre and sea front. Theme bar and dining room.

Important: Prices stated are estimates and may be subject to amendments

Oban, Argyll | Map Ref: 1E2

The Manor House
Gallanach Road, Oban, Argyll PA34 4LS
e.mail: me@managed-estates.co.uk

In an enviable position on the foreshore of Oban Bay, The Manor House has long held the reputation for high quality in the comfort of its accommodation and the excellence of its Scottish and French cuisine. One AA Rosette.

All bedrooms have ensuite facilities.
Special weekends and breaks available.
For Reservations or Brochure and Tariff: Tel: 01631 562087 Fax: 01631 563053

HOTEL ★★★★

Manor House Hotel
Gallanach Road, Oban, Argyll, PA34 4LS
Tel: 01631 562087 Fax: 01631 563053
E.mail: me@managed-estates.co.uk

Family run Georgian house on the foreshore on the south side of Oban with extensive views across the Bay, close to the town centre.

5 Twin
6 Double

All En Suite

B&B per person
£30.00-£64.00 Dbl/Twn

Open Feb-Dec
B&B + Eve.Meal
£52.00-£85.00

GUEST HOUSE ★★★★

The Old Manse Guest House
Dalriach Road, Oban, Argyll, PA34 5JE
Tel: 01631 564886 Fax: 01631 570184
E-mail: oldmanse@obanguesthouse.co.uk
Web: www.obanguesthouse.co.uk

Victorian detached Villa set in beautiful gardens, with views of sea and islands. Superior standard of hospitality and comfort. Only minutes walk to town centre. Private parking. Family suite available.

1 Twin
2 Double
1 Family

All En Suite

B&B per person
£20.00-£30.00 Dbl/Twn

Open Mar-Nov

HOTEL ★★

Palace Hotel
George Street, Oban, Argyll, PA34 5SB
Tel: 01631 562294

Personally run hotel in the centre of Oban with front bedrooms and public rooms overlooking harbour to the islands of Kerrera and Mull. A few minutes walk from railway station and all amenities. No evening meal available.

1 Single
3 Twin
5 Double
4 Family

All En Suite

B&B per person
from £20.00 Single
from £20.00 Dbl/Twn
Room only per person
from £17.50

Open Jan-Dec excl
Xmas/New Year

GUEST HOUSE ★★★★

Roseneath Guest House
Dalriach Road, Oban, Argyll, PA34 5EQ
Tel: 01631 562929 Fax: 01631 567218
Web: www.oban.org.uk/accommodation/roseneath/
roseneath-guesthouse.html

Personally run Victorian house in quiet area overlooking town and bay. Near seafront and shops. Private parking. Non-smoking.

2 Twin
6 Double

All En Suite

B&B per person
£19.00-£26.00 Dbl/Twn

Open Jan-Dec excl
Xmas

VAT is shown at 17.5%: changes in this rate may affect prices.

Key to symbols is on back flap.

Oban, Argyll | Map Ref: 1E2

Rowantree Hotel
George Street, Oban, Argyll, PA34 5NX
Tel: 01631 562954 Fax: 01631 565071

6 Twin	All En Suite	B&B per person	Open Jan-Dec
15 Double		£45.50-£50.00 Single	B&B + Eve.Meal
3 Family		£31.00-£35.00 Dbl/Twn	£47.95-£66.95

Privately owned modern hotel situated in centre of town but close to the seafront. Specialising in fresh local seafood and steaks. Car park. Convenient for visiting the Islands of Mull and Iona.

Royal Hotel
Argyll Square, Oban, Argyll, PA34 4BE
Tel: 01631 563021 Fax: 01631 562811

15 Single	All En Suite	B&B per person	Open Jan-Dec
56 Twin		£35.00-£65.00 Single	
18 Double		£35.00-£65.00 Dbl/Twn	
2 Family			

Imposing Victorian town centre hotel near to the water front. Easily accessible for ferry terminal, railway station and major roads.

Sgeir Mhaol Guest House
Soroba Road, Oban, Argyll, PA34 4JF
Tel/Fax: 01631 562650
E-mail: hughes@sgeirmhaol.co.uk
Web: www.sgeirmhaol.co.uk

2 Twin	5 En Suite fac	B&B per person	Open Jan-Dec
4 Double	2 Priv.NOT ensuite	£17.00-£26.00 Single	
1 Family	1 Pub Bath/Show	£18.00-£22.00 Dbl/Twn	

Bungalow style, with ample private car parking and only a short walk from the town centre. All rooms and facilities on the ground floor. Plenty to do and see in the area, Fishing, Golfing, Sailing and Walking.

Sutherland Hotel
Corran Esplanade, Oban, Argyll, PA34 5PN
Tel/Fax: 01631 562539
E-mail: suthotel@aol.com

1 Single	9 En Suite fac	B&B per person	Open Apr-Nov
3 Twin	1 Pub Bath/Show	£18.00-£24.00 Single	B&B + Eve.Meal
7 Double	2 Priv. Bath/Show	£18.00-£24.00 Dbl/Twn	£28.00-£34.00
2 Family		Room only per person	
		£16.00-£22.00	

Traditional Victorian house situated in the centre of Corran Esplanade overlooking Oban Bay with excellent views towards the islands. Conveniently situated close to the seafront with access to all town centre amenities. Good comfortable rooms. Evening meals by arrangement.

Thornloe Guest House
Albert Road, Oban, Argyll, PA34 5JD
Tel/Fax: 01631 562879
E-mail: thornloe@netscapeonline.co.uk

1 Single	7 En Suite fac	B&B per person	Open Mar-Nov
2 Twin	1 Priv.NOT ensuite	from £18.00 Single	
4 Double		from £18.00 Dbl/Twn	
1 Family			

Completely modernised Victorian semi-detached house with garden, in centrally situated residential area with fine views over Oban Bay towards the Isle of Mull. Within easy walking distance from town centre, leisure facilities and other amenities.

Important: Prices stated are estimates and may be subject to amendments

Oban, Argyll | Map Ref: 1E2

Viewbank Guest House
Breadalbane Lane, Oban, Argyll, PA34 5PF
Tel: 01631 562328 Fax: 01631 570222

2 Twin	All En Suite	B&B per person	Open Jan-Dec
1 Double		from £18.00 Dbl/Twn	
2 Family		Room only per person	
		from £16.00	

Viewbank is a spacious Victorian villa recently renovated, set in its own private garden with beautiful views over Oban Bay & Kerrera. All bedrooms ensuite. No smoking house.

Wellpark Hotel
Esplanade, Oban, Argyll, PA34 5AQ
Tel: 01631 562948 Fax: 01631 565808
E-mail: wellpark@dial.pipex.com

5 Single	All En Suite	B&B per person	Open Mar-Oct
4 Twin		from £25.00 Single	
10 Double		from £20.00 Dbl/Twn	
2 Family		Room only per person	
		from £18.00	

Family run establishment in a quiet position on the esplanade. Magnificent views over the bay to Isles of Kerrera and Mull.

by Oban, Argyll | Map Ref: 1E2

Ards House
Connel, by Oban, Argyll, PA37 1PT
Tel: 01631 710255
Web: www.ardshouse.com

1 Single	6 En Suite fac	B&B per person	Open Mar-Dec excl Xmas
3 Twin	1 Priv.NOT ensuite	from £35.00 Single	B&B + Eve.Meal
3 Double		from £35.00 Dbl/Twn	from £54.00

Warm friendly atmosphere in this family run house where husband is a keen cook. Large relaxing lounge, table licence, superb sea and sunset views. Taste of Scotland.

Braeside Guest House
Kilmore, by Oban, Argyll, PA34 4QR
Tel: 01631 770243 Fax: 01631 770343
E-mail: braeside.guesthouse@virgin.net

2 Twin	All En Suite	B&B per person	Open Mar-Nov
3 Double		from £20.00 Single	B&B + Eve.Meal
		from £20.00 Dbl/Twn	from £35.00

Quality licensed Guest House located 3 miles South of Oban. Rural setting with uninterrupted views of Loch Feochan and surrounding hills, private parking and pleasant gardens. All rooms are high standard, ensuite, ground level with full amenities. Fine cuisine using fresh produce. Choice of menu and good wine list. Ideal base for touring, walking, trips to Isles of Mull, Iona, Staffa, etc. No smoking or pets. AA Four Diamond Award.

by Oban, Argyll | Map Ref: 1E2

The Falls of Lora Hotel

Connel Ferry, by Oban, Argyll PA37 1PB
Telephone: 01631 710483   Fax: 01631 710694

Overlooking Loch Etive this fine owner-run Hotel has 30 rooms –
from luxury to inexpensive family! Relax in the super Cocktail Bar
with open log fire and over 100 brands of whisky, there is an extensive
Bistro menu featuring local produce. Oban is only 5 miles –
the "Gateway to the Highlands & Islands".

★★★

HOTEL

Falls of Lora Hotel
Connel Ferry, by Oban, Argyll, PA37 1PB
Tel: 01631 710483 Fax: 01631 710694

6 Single   All En Suite
9 Twin
11 Double
4 Family

B&B per person
from £29.50 Single
from £19.50 Dbl/Twn

Open Feb-mid Dec

Oban 5 miles, only 2 1/2 to 3 hours drive north-west of
Glasgow/Edinburgh. A fine owner-run Victorian hotel with a modern
extension.

BRONZE

★★★

GUEST
HOUSE

Loch Etive House
Connel Village, by Oban, Argyll, PA37 1PH
Tel: 01631 710400 Fax: 01631 710680

2 Twin   4 En Suite fac
2 Double 1 Pub Bath/Show
2 Family

B&B per person
£25.00-£35.00 Single
£20.00-£28.00 Dbl/Twn

Open Apr-Oct

Fully modernised Victorian house, most rooms having ensuite facilities,
quietly situated off the main road. Home cooking and personal attention.
Evening meal by arrangement.

Port of Menteith, Perthshire | Map Ref: 1H3

THE LAKE HOTEL – TROSSACHS

PORT OF MENTEITH, PERTHSHIRE FK8 3RA
Telephone: 01877 385258   Fax: 01877 385671
e.mail: enquiries@lake-of-menteith-hotel.com
Web: www.lake-of-menteith-hotel.com

*Outstanding situation on the shore of the Lake of Menteith. Bordering the Highlands
and within one hour of Edinburgh and Glasgow. All rooms with ensuite facilities.
Our cuisine emulates the restaurant with its spectacular lakeside setting.
2 AA Rosettes. Special weekends and breaks available.*
Reservations and brochure from above address.

★★★

HOTEL

Lake Hotel
Port of Menteith, Perthshire, FK8 3RA
Tel: 01877 385258 Fax: 01877 385671
E.mail: enquiries@lake-of-menteith-hotel.com
Web: www.lake-of-menteith-hotel.com

9 Twin   All En Suite
7 Double

B&B per person
£35.00-£77.00 Dbl/Twn

Open Jan-Dec
B&B + Eve.Meal
£54.00-£98.00

Situated beside the Lake of Menteith with long views to the Isle of
Inchmahome and the hills beyond. Wonderful opportunities for
hillwalking, fishing, golf or just touring the marvellous countryside of the
Trossachs.

Important: Prices stated are estimates and may be subject to amendments

Rhu, Dunbartonshire — Map Ref: 1G4

Rosslea Hall Hotel ★★ HOTEL
Ferry Road, Rhu, by Helensburgh, Dunbartonshire, G84 8NF
Tel: 01436 439955 Fax: 01436 820897

6 Single	34 En Suite fac	B&B per person	Open Jan-Dec
16 Twin		£60.00-£80.00 Single	B&B + Eve.Meal
10 Double		£35.00-£45.00 Dbl/Twn	£45.00-£55.00
2 Family			

Country house hotel with fine views of Gare Loch and the hills. Under an hour's drive from the centre of Glasgow. Ideal for small conferences.

Rowardennan, Stirlingshire — Map Ref: 1G3

Rowardennan Hotel ★★ HOTEL
Rowardennan, by Drymen, Loch Lomond, Stirlingshire, G63 0AR
Tel: 01360 870273 Fax: 01360 870251

1 Single	5 En Suite fac	B&B per person	Open Jan-Dec
6 Twin		from £50.00 Single	
5 Double		from £38.00 Dbl/Twn	
2 Family			

Set in the Queen Elizabeth Forest Park on the West Highland Way. In the lee of Ben Lomond with the loch on the doorstep.

Sandbank, by Dunoon, Argyll — Map Ref: 1F5

The Cot House Hotel ★★ INN
Sandbank, Kilmun, Dunoon, Argyll, PA23 8QS
Tel/Fax: 01369 840260
Web: www.cothousehotel.co.uk

4 Single	All En Suite	B&B per person	Open Jan-Dec excl
3 Twin		from £25.00 Single	Xmas/New Year
4 Double		from £20.00 Dbl/Twn	
2 Family		Room only per person	
		from £18.00	

Personally run Inn in rural setting outside Dunoon. Ideally situated for exploring the Cowal Peninsula. Extensive a la carte menu including local ingredients. Well stocked bar with range of malt whiskies. Cosy log fire.

Clachan Seil, by Oban, Isle of Seil, Argyll — Map Ref: 1E3

Willowburn Hotel ★★★★ SMALL HOTEL
Clachan Seil, by Oban, Argyll, PA34 4TJ
Tel: 01852 300276 Fax: 01852 300597
E-mail: willowburn.hotel@virgin.net
Web: www.willowburn.co.uk

1 Single	7 En Suite fac	Open Mar-Dec
3 Twin		B&B + Eve.Meal
3 Double		£55.00-£60.00

Family-run, on the shore, in 2 acres of garden, approx. 0.5 miles from famous Atlantic Bridge, on Seil Island. Taste of Scotland recommended. Two AA rosettes. Peaceful, homely atmosphere.

Stirling — Map Ref: 2A4

Express By Holiday Inn - Stirling ★★★ HOTEL
Springkerse Business Park, Stirling, FK7 7XH
Tel: 01786 449922 Fax: 01786 449932
Web: www.hiex-stirling.com

38 Twin	All En Suite	Room+Cont.B/fast	Open Jan-Dec
4 Double		from £49.50 Single	
38 Family		from £24.75 Dbl/Twn	

Designed for the business and leisure traveller alike, offering well equipped rooms and a range of business services. Situated on the eastern outskirts of the town with open views towards the Ochil Hills. Complimentary continental breakfast.

VAT is shown at 17.5%: changes in this rate may affect prices.

Key to symbols is on back flap.

Stirling | Map Ref: 2A4

★★★★

GUEST HOUSE

Forth Guest House
23 Forth Place, Riverside, Stirling, FK8 1UD
Tel: 01786 471020 Fax: 01786 447220
Web: www.forthguesthouse.freeserve.co.uk

2 Twin	All En Suite	B&B per person	Open Jan-Dec excl
2 Double		from £25.00 Single	Xmas/New Year
1 Family		from £19.50 Dbl/Twn	

Georgian terraced house within easy walking distance of railway station, town centre and swimming pool. Good location for touring. Private parking.

THE GOLDEN LION MILTON HOTEL
8-10 KING STREET, STIRLING FK8 1BD
Freephone: 0808 100 55 56
Fax: 01786 469 400
Please quote ref HGH01
★★★ Hotel

One of the oldest hotels in Scotland. Lovingly restored, it looks and feels very Scottish. £1m spent on its bedrooms, 2 restaurants and bar with its 18th-century library. Location is second to none, situated in a cobbled precinct, near shops and castle. Private car parking.
Many holiday offers with our other hotels all over Scotland including Oban, Fort William and Inverness. RAC ★★★.
e.mail: sales@miltonhotels.com
Web: www.miltonhotels.com

Milton

★★★

HOTEL

Golden Lion Milton Hotel
8 King Street, Stirling, FK8 1BD
Milton Sales Centre: Freefone 0808 100 55 56
Fax: 01786 469 400
E-mail: sales@miltonhotels.com
Web: www.miltonhotels.com

18 Single	All En Suite	B&B per person	Open Jan-Dec
38 Twin		£65.00-£81.00 Single	
15 Double		£45.00-£55.00 Dbl/Twn	

In the town centre with car park at the rear of the hotel. Stirling Castle, Bannockburn and Wallace Monument a short distance away.

★★

SMALL HOTEL

The Park Lodge Country House Hotel
32 Park Terrace, Stirling, FK8 2JS
Tel: 01786 474862 Fax: 01786 449748
E-mail: parklodge@stirlinghotel.fsnet.co.uk
Web: www.stirlinghotel.fsnet.co.uk

2 Single	All En Suite	B&B per person	Open Jan-Dec
8 Double		£50.00-£60.00 Single	B&B + Eve.Meal
		£42.50-£45.00 Double	£62.00-£84.00
		Room only per person	
		£45.00-£65.00	

Georgian country house with French provincial style interior. Quiet residential area. Easy access to town centre and all amenities.

★★★

GUEST HOUSE

Ravenswood Guest House
94 Causewayhead Road, Causewayhead, Stirling, FK9 5HJ
Tel: 01786 475291

1 Twin	3 En Suite	B&B per person	Open Jan-Dec
2 Double	1 Priv fac	£18.00-£25.00 Single	
1 Family		£18.00-£19.00 Dbl/Twn	
		Room only per person	
		£15.00-£16.00	

Traditional stone, semi-detached villa ideally placed for Wallace Monument, Castle and university. Convenient for town centre amenities.

Important: Prices stated are estimates and may be subject to amendments

Stirling
Map Ref: 2A4

★★★
HOTEL
&

Stirling Management Centre
University of Stirling, Stirling, FK9 4LA
Tel: 01786 451712 Fax: 01786 449940
E-mail: smc.sales@stir.ac.uk
Web: www.stir.ac.uk/theuni/mancen

Purpose built conference centre/hotel in peaceful setting on picturesque campus. University leisure facilities available. Ideal touring base.

44 Single	All En Suite	B&B per person	Open Jan-Dec excl Xmas
4 Twin		£35.00-£75.00 Single	B&B + Eve.Meal
25 Double		£30.00-£50.00 Dbl/Twn	£50.00-£95.00
1 Family			
2 Disabled			

★★★
GUEST HOUSE

Whitegables
112 Causewayhead Road, Stirling, FK9 5HJ
Tel/Fax: 01786 479838
E-mail: whitegables@b-j-graham.freeserve.co.uk

Tudor-style detached house in residential area located midway between Stirling Castle and the Wallace Monument. Easily accessible to motorway links. Private off road car parking available. Non smoking house.

2 Double	All En Suite	B&B per person	Open Jan-Dec excl
2 Family		from £30.00 Single	Xmas/New Year
		from £20.00 Double	
		Room only per person	
		from £20.00	

---

nr Stirling
Map Ref: 2A4

★★★★★
HOTEL

Cromlix House
Kinbuck, by Dunblane, Perthshire, FK15 9JT
Tel: 01786 822125 Fax: 01786 825450
Web: www.cromlixhouse.com

Built in 1874 Cromlix is a unique country house. The authentic ambience of an Edwardian home invites total relaxation. Set in a 2000 Acre Estate, and only 5 minutes off the A9 - an enviable location for golf and touring. 6 bedrooms and 8 huge suites with private sitting rooms are individual in style whilst 7 public and dining rooms are welcoming, original and elegant. Award winning fresh menu daily. Private chapel for weddings.

8 Twin	All En Suite	B&B per person	Open 25Jan-1Jan
6 Double		from £110.00 Single	B&B + Eve.Meal
		from £100.00 Dbl/Twn	from £140.00
		from £140.00 Suites	

Strachur, Argyll
Map Ref: 1F3

★★★
HOTEL

The Creggans Inn
Strachur, Argyll, PA27 8BX
Tel: 01369 860279 Fax: 01369 860637
E-mail: info@creggans-inn.co.uk

The cottages are all traditional stone houses, each with its own character and log fire. Laurel Bank stands proud and commanding looking down Loch Fyne. Gate Lodge is snugly tucked inside the gate keeper's arch with both loch and parkland views. Garden Cottage sits in the middle of Strachur Park, entirely alone but only a short distance from the old road to the Church and Glen Cottage, nestling high in the grazing land beyond the village.

1 Single	All En Suite	B&B per person	Open Jan-Dec
4 Twin		from £49.00 Single	B&B + Eve.Meal
12 Double		from £49.00 Dbl/Twn	from £70.00
2 Family			

Strathyre, Perthshire
Map Ref: 1H3

★★★
GUEST HOUSE
&

Airlie House
Main Street, Strathyre, Stirling, FK18 8NA
Tel: 01877 384622 Fax: 01877 384305

Set off the main road in the charming village of Strathyre, in own large garden. Walking distance of local restaurants. Owners also have award winning restaurant/hotel in Balquhidder. House is recently refurbished with luxurious fittings and cutting edge decor. Each room is furnished to the highest standard, all with double ended baths and power showers. Wood stove in guest's lounge, plenty of privacy. Ideal location for walking/cycling and touring the Trossachs. Off-street parking.

1 Twin	All En Suite	B&B per person	Open Jan-Dec
2 Double		from £32.50 Single	
1 Family		from £32.50 Dbl/Twn	

VAT is shown at 17.5%: changes in this rate may affect prices.

Key to symbols is on back flap.

Strathyre, Perthshire | Map Ref: 1H3

**RESTAURANT
WITH ROOMS**

Creagan House Restaurant with Accommodation
Strathyre, Callander, Perthshire, FK18 8ND
Tel: 01877 384638 Fax: 01877 384319
Web: www.milford.co.uk/go/creaganhouse.html

1 Twin	All En Suite	B&B per person	Open Mar-Jan
3 Double		from £52.50 Single	B&B + Eve.Meal
1 Family		from £42.50 Dbl/Twn	from £62.00

A peaceful little gem of comfort surrounded by beautiful scenery. Five charming bedrooms with many thoughtful extras and a growing collection of antiques, friendly perfection is our aim. The baronial dining hall helps make each evening a special occasion, using meat from Perthshire, fruits and vegetables grown locally, herbs from our garden, all complemented by fine wines. Recently awarded two AA Rossettes and Red Star.

Tarbert, Loch Fyne, Argyll | Map Ref: 1E5

The Columba Hotel
Tarbert, Loch Fyne, Argyll PA29 6UF
Tel: 01880 820808   Fax: 01880 820808
e.mail: columbahotel@FSBDial.co.uk
Web: www.columbahotel.com

★★★ HOTEL
AA ❀
2 RAC dining awards

In a peaceful lochside setting within the fishing village of Tarbert with superb views across Loch Fyne. Rooms are ensuite. Sauna, gym and solarium. Log fires, bars and a restaurant serving only the best of Scottish produce, imaginatively prepared. Ideally placed for touring Kintyre and the Islands of Argyll.

BRONZE

HOTEL

The Columba Hotel
East Pier Road, Tarbert, Loch Fyne, Argyll, PA29 6UF
Tel/Fax: 01880 820808
E-mail: columbahotel@FSBDial.co.uk
Web: www.columbahotel.com

2 Single	All En Suite	B&B per person	Open Jan-Dec excl
		from £34.95 Single	Xmas
		Room only per person	B&B + Eve.Meal
		from £34.95	from £50.95

Tranquilly situated overlooking Loch Fyne within walking distance of Tarbert. Warm welcome, open fires, local produce imaginatively prepared.

BRONZE

Stonefield Castle Hotel
Tarbert, Loch Fyne, Argyll PA29 6YJ
Tel: 01880 820836   Fax: 01880 820929
Web: www.stonefieldcastle.co.uk

★★★★
HOTEL

Breathtaking natural beauty surrounds the castle standing high on the Kintyre peninsula. The awarded restaurant has one of the finest views on the West Coast, while the gardens are renowned for their rare Rhododendrons, and exotic plants and shrubs. Dinner, Bed & Breakfast from £43-£89 per person per night. Taste of Scotland. Two RAC Blue Ribbons. AA ★★★ RAC ★★★

HOTEL

Stonefield Castle Hotel
Loch Fyne, Tarbert, Loch Fyne, Argyll, PA29 6YJ
Tel: 01880 820836 Fax: 01880 820929
Web: www.stonefieldcastle.co.uk

4 Single	32 En Suite fac	Open Jan-Dec
16 Twin	Suites avail	B&B + Eve.Meal
12 Double	1 Priv.NOT ensuite	£45.00-£90.00
1 Family		

Breathtaking natural beauty surrounding the baronial elegance of the Castle with spectacular views over Loch Fyne and awarded restaurant.

Important: Prices stated are estimates and may be subject to amendments

Tarbert, Loch Fyne, Argyll — Map Ref: 1E5

★★★

INN

The Victoria Hotel
Barmore Road, Tarbert, Loch Fyne, Argyll, PA29 6TW
Tel: 01880 820236/820431 Fax: 01880 820638
E-mail: victoria.hotel@lineone.net

1 Single	All En Suite
3 Twin	
1 Double	

B&B per person
from £26.00 Single
from £26.00 Dbl/Twn
Room only per person
from £19.50

Open Jan-Dec excl
Xmas day
B&B + Eve.Meal
from £46.00

Personally run Inn with Bedrooms all recently refurbished to high standard. Most rooms with sea view. New Taste of Scotland Restaurant with splendid views over picturesque Tarbert harbour, close to yacht moorings. Extensive menu featuring the best of fresh local produce.

---

by Tarbet, by Arrochar, Dunbartonshire — Map Ref: 1G3

★★★★

GUEST
HOUSE

Bonniebank House
Tarbet, Loch Lomond, G83 7DJ
Tel: 01301 702300
Web: www.bonniebank.F9.co.uk

2 Double	All En Suite
2 Family	

B&B per person
from £45.00 Single
from £30.00 Double

Open Jan-Dec excl
Xmas/New Year

Bonniebank truly lives up to its name, being situated on the lochside with magnificnet views across the water to Ben Lomond. Friendly Scottish welcome; well appointed rooms. Weather permitting, breakfast on the terrace right by the lochside.

Tighnabruaich, Argyll — Map Ref: 1E5

★★★

INN

Kames Hotel
Kames, Tighnabruaich, Argyll, PA21 2AF
Tel: 01700 811489 Fax: 01700 811283
E-mail: Kameshotel@aol.com

2 Single	All En Suite
1 Twin	
4 Double	
2 Family	

B&B per person
from £35.00 Single
from £30.00 Dbl/Twn
Room only per person
from £20.00

Open Jan-Dec
B&B + Eve.Meal
from £42.50

A friendly welcome and spectacular views over the Kyles of Bute. Well known for good food, real ales, fine malts. Close to golf and fishing. Dogs and children welcome. Mooring available for visiting yachts.

Royal Hotel

Tighnabruaich, Argyll PA21 2BE
Tel: 01700 811239 Fax: 01700 811300
e.mail: royalhotel@btinternet.com Web: www.royalhotel.org.uk
Waterside location. Dine by candlelight tasting imaginative modern Scottish food prepared by chef proprietor. Oyster, langoustine, venison. Individual, tastefully decorated rooms with stunning views. Sample our fine wines and malts in front of log fires. Golf, watersports, bird watching all available locally.

★★★★

HOTEL

Royal Hotel
Shore Road, Tighnabruaich, Argyll, PA21 2BE
Tel: 01700 811239 Fax: 01700 811300
E.mail: royalhotel@btinternet.com
Web: www.royalhotel.org.uk

9 Double	All En Suite
2 Family	

B&B per person
from £67.00 Single
from £37.00 Double

Open Jan-Dec
B&B + Eve.Meal
from £50.00

A warm welcome and traditional Scottish hospitality awaits you at this hotel situated on the waters edge of the Kyles of Bute in one of the most scenic and unspoilt areas of Scotland's west coast. Personally run, chef-owner specialising in local seafood, venison and game. Taste of Scotland member.

VAT is shown at 17.5%: changes in this rate may affect prices.

Key to symbols is on back flap.

Tillicoultry, Clackmannanshire   Map Ref: 2A3

★★★

SMALL
HOTEL

The Harviestoun Country Hotel & Restaurant
Dollar Road, Tillicoultry, Clackmananshire, FK13 6PQ
Tel: 01259 752522 Fax: 01259 752523
Web: www.harviestouncountryhotel.com

2 Twn/Dbl	All En Suite	
9 Double		

B&B per person
from £50.00 Single
from £32.50 Dbl/Twn

Open Jan-Dec

Sympathetically converted listed building beside Ochil Hills – privately
owned and run, courtyard restaurant, coffee house and gifts,
conference/function/weddings, lounge with open fire. Central Scotland
location for business and touring.

Tyndrum, by Crianlarich, Perthshire   Map Ref: 1G2

THE INVERVEY HOTEL
TYNDRUM, PERTHSHIRE FK20 8RY
TEL: 01838 400219 FAX: 01838 400280
Family run hotel situated on the A82/85 at Tyndrum. It snuggles below
some of the finest mountain scenery in Scotland and is ideally situated for
the West Highland Way, hill-walking, climbing and ski-ing.
Large lounge bar, restaurant, conservatory and games room wonderful
meeting places for guests and locals. Open all year.

★★

HOTEL

The Invervey Hotel
Tyndrum, Perthshire, FK20 8RY
Tel: 01838 400219 Fax: 01838 400280
Web: www.inverveyhotel.com

5 Single	18 En Suite	
7 Twin	1 Pub Bath/Show	
6 Double		
3 Family		

B&B per person
from £20.00 Single
from £20.00 Dbl/Twn

Open Jan-Dec
B&B + Eve.Meal
from £36.00

Family hotel on main tourist route, surrounded on all sides by mountain
scenery. An ideal base for fishing, shooting, walking. Climbing and ski-ing
with 1/2 an hour drive.

Sandaig, Isle of Tiree, Argyll   Map Ref: 1A1

★★★

GUEST
HOUSE

The Glassary Guest House and Restaurant
Sandaig, Isle of Tiree, Argyll, PA77 6XQ
Tel/Fax: 01879 220684

2 Single	All En Suite	
1 Twin		
2 Double		

B&B per person
from £28.00 Single
from £28.00 Dbl/Twn

Open Jan-Dec excl
Xmas/New Year

Detached house with adjacent converted byre and conservatory extension
which serves as a licensed restaurant. 7 miles (11 km) from ferry and 4
miles (7 km) from airport. Panoramic view over islands and Atlantic
Ocean.

Plenty of contrasts here: from the white-walled harbourfront houses of the East Neuk fishing villages to the heathery silence of Rannoch moor, from the arts and culture of Dundee to the tranquillity of the Angus Glens. This area makes a good place for a break, with a little of everything within easy reach.

Crail Harbour, East Neuk of Fife

Perth is an important commercial centre for its hinterland both above and below the Highland line. Another Perthshire speciality are the little resort towns such as Dunkeld, Pitlochry or Aberfeldy, with their good range of visitor attractions such as the new Dewar's World of Whisky at Aberfeldy.

The Kingdom of Fife has plenty of character, with St Andrews noted as Scotland's oldest university and also often called 'the home of golf'. The town offers excellent shopping and is within easy reach of attractive East Neuk villages like Crail southwards and also the city of Dundee across the Tay Bridge to the north.

Dundee is the city of Discovery, with Discovery Point one of Scotland's top attractions while its new Science Centre, "Sensation" provides the whole family with hands-on fun. The Angus Glens are special

places, with roads running deep into the hills through Glens Isla, Prosen, Clova or Esk – great country for walkers, birdwatchers and botanists. The coastline of Angus also offers plenty of interest, with spectacular cliffs and coves and small fishing ports such as Arbroath, home of the 'Arbroath smokie' – a fishy treat! Between hills and coast lie attractions such as Glamis Castle, birthplace of HM Queen Elizabeth the Queen Mother, and Edzell Castle with its unique garden.

Glenesk, Angus

Dunkeld and River Tay, Perthshire

SCATTERED ACROSS THE WHOLE area are a
wide range of other attractions, such as
Deep Sea World by North Queensferry
(an aquarium featuring the world's largest
walk-through tunnel), the birthplace cottage
of the playwright JM Barrie in Kirriemuir,
and also Scotland's National Garden at Perth
(opening 2001).

EVENTS
PERTHSHIRE, ANGUS &
DUNDEE AND THE
KINGDOM OF FIFE

18-23 APRIL
Kirkcaldy Links Market
Kirkcaldy Links
The longest street fair in
Europe.
Contact: Mr J Haggart, Fife
Community Services
TEL: 01592 417846

23 JUNE
Ceres Highland Games
Ceres, Fife
The Worlds oldest Highland
Games.
Contact: Ms M Glen
TEL: 01334 828811

7-8 JULY
Game Conservancy Ltd
Scottish Fair
Scone Palace, Nr Perth
Game fair with a wide spread of
associated activities,
competitions, demonstrations
and trade stands.
TEL: 01620 850577

14-15 JULY
Scottish Transport
Extravaganza
Glamis Castle, Angus
Comprehensive display of
vintage vehicles with trade &
craft stalls, entertainment and
amusements.
TEL: 01307 462496

12 AUGUST
Perth Highland Games
Traditional Highland Games
Contact: Mr A Rettie
TEL: 01738 627782
EMAIL: s.g.a@cableinet.co.uk

18-19 AUGUST
Arbroath Sea Fest
Arbroath Harbour
Weekend festival celebrating the
maritime history, culture and
seafood in Arbroath, with events
for all the family.
Contact: Colin Stewart,
Arbroath Sea Fest Company
TEL: 01241 870563
EMAIL: cstewart@bsang.co.uk

15 SEPTEMBER
Battle of Britain
International Air Show
RAF Leuchars, Fife
Scotland's largest airshow
featuring flying displays,
exhibitions & aerobatics display
teams.
Contact: Air Show Office
TEL: 01334 838559
www.airshow.co.uk

22-23 SEPTEMBER
Fife Family History Fair
Various venues, Fife
Genealogy Fair
Contact: Janet Klack, Fife
Central Area Libraries, East
Fergus Place, Kirkcaldy, Fife,
KY1 1XT (by post only)

*14-19 OCTOBER
Pitlochry Festival of Walking
Various venues, Pitlochry
The walking programme will
consist of a selected series of
graded walks, formulated and
led by local guides. The routes
will encompass hills, forests,
lochs and rivers amidst the
magnificent scenery of Highland
Perthshire.
Contact: Pitlochry Tourist
Information Centre.
TEL: 01796 472 215

*24-30 NOVEMBER
St Andrews Week
Various venues, St Andrews
A week of festivities celebrating
St Andrews day, including a
festival of Scottish food and
drink and an arts festival.
Contact: Ms Alison Laughlin,
Project Co-ordinator
TEL: 01334 477872

*provisional dates

PERTHSHIRE	ANGUS AND DUNDEE	KINGDOM OF FIFE
TOURIST BOARD	TOURIST BOARD	TOURIST BOARD
Lower City Mills	21 Castle Street	70 Market Street
West Mill Street	Dundee	St Andrews
Perth	DD1 3AA	KY16 9NU
PH1 5QP		
TEL: **01738 627958/9**	TEL: **01382 527527**	TEL: **01334 472021**
FAX: **01738 630416**	FAX: **01382 527550**	FAX: **01334 478422**
www.perthshire.co.uk	www.angusanddundee.co.uk	www.standrews.com

ANGUS & CITY OF DUNDEE TOURIST BOARD

ARBROATH
Market Place
DD11 1HR
TEL: **(01241) 872609**
Jan-Dec

BRECHIN
Pictavia Centre
TEL: **(01356) 623050**
April-Sept

CARNOUSTIE
1b High Street
TEL: **(01241) 852258**
April-Sept

DUNDEE
7-21 Castle Street
TEL: **(01382) 527527**
Jan-Dec

FORFAR
45 East High Street
TEL: **(01307) 467876**
April-Sept

KIRRIEMUIR
St. Malcom's Wynd
TEL: **(01575) 574097**
April-Sept

MONTROSE
Bridge Street
TEL: **(01674) 672000**
April-Sept

KINGDOM OF FIFE TOURIST BOARD

ANSTRUTHER
Scottish Fisheries Museum
TEL: **(01333) 311073**
Easter-Sept

CRAIL
Museum and Heritage Centre
Marketgate
TEL: **(01333) 450859**
Easter-Sept

DUNFERMLINE
13/15 Maygate
TEL: **(01383) 720999**
April-Oct

FORTH BRIDGES
by North Queensferry
TEL: **(01383) 417759**
Jan-Dec

KIRKCALDY
19 Whytecauseway
TEL: **(01592) 267775**
Jan-Dec

ST ANDREWS
70 Market Street
TEL: **(01334) 472021**
Jan-Dec

PERTHSHIRE TOURIST BOARD

ABERFELDY
The Square
TEL: **(01887) 820276**
Jan-Dec

AUCHTERARDER
90 High Street
TEL: **(01764) 663450**
Jan-Dec

BLAIRGOWRIE
26 Wellmeadow
TEL: **(01250) 872960**
Jan-Dec

CRIEFF
Town Hall
High Street
TEL: **(01764) 652578**
Jan-Dec

DUNKELD
The Cross
TEL: **(01350) 727688**
Jan-Dec

KINROSS
Kinross Service Area
off Junction 6, M90
TEL: **(01577) 863680**
Jan-Dec

PERTH
Lower City Mills
West Mill Street
TEL: **(01738) 450600**
Jan-Dec

PERTH (INVERALMOND)
Caithness Glass
Inveralmond
A9 Western City Bypass
TEL: **(01738) 638481**
Jan-Dec

PITLOCHRY
22 Atholl Road
TEL: **(01796) 472215/472751**
Jan-Dec

Aberdour, Fife — Map Ref: 2C4

★★★ HOTEL

The Aberdour Hotel
38 High Street, Aberdour, Fife, KY3 0SW
Tel: 01383 860325 Fax: 01383 860808
Web: www.aberdourhotel.co.uk

5 Twin	All En Suite	
7 Double		
4 Family		

B&B per person
from £35.00 Single
from £25.00 Dbl/Twn

Open Jan-Dec
B&B + Eve.Meal
from £35.00

Personally run hotel specialising in traditional cooking and real ales on Fife coast in Conservation village 6 miles (10kms) from Forth Bridges. Convenient for touring and golf. Recently converted stables annexe furnished to a high standard.

Aberfeldy, Perthshire — Map Ref: 2A1

★★★★ B&B

Tigh'n Eilean
Taybridge Drive, Aberfeldy, Perthshire, PH15 2BP
Tel/Fax: 01887 820109
Mobile: 07889 472248

1 Single	All En Suite	
1 Twin		
2 Double		

B&B per person
from £20.00 Single
from £20.00 Dbl/Twn

Open Jan-Dec
B&B + Eve.Meal
from £34.00

Elegant Victorian house overlooking the river. Warm and comfortable, home cooking. One room with jacuzzi.

Alyth, Perthshire — Map Ref: 2C1

★★★★ HOTEL

Drumnacree House
St Ninians Road, Alyth, Perthshire, PH11 8AP
Tel/Fax: 01828 632194

2 Double	5 En Suite fac	
1 Family	1 Limited ensuite	
3 Twn/Dbl		

B&B per person
from £43.50 Single
£40.00-£45.00 Dbl/Twn

Open Jan-Dec
B&B + Eve.Meal
£60.00-£65.00

Family run country house hotel, 5 miles (8 kms) from Blairgowrie. Emphasis on comfort and food, using seasonal garden produce.

★★★ HOTEL

Lands of Loyal Hotel
Loyal Road, Alyth, Perthshire, PH11 8JQ
Tel: 01828 633151 Fax: 01828 633313
E-mail: info@landsofloyal.co.uk
Web: www.landsofloyal.com

9 Twin	All En Suite	
5 Double		

B&B per person
£55.00 Single
£44.50 Dbl/Twn

Open Jan-Dec
B&B + Eve.Meal
£65.00-£75.00

Country house with magnificent views of surrounding countryside. Central for many sports: walking, fishing, golf. Delicious food, fresh ingredients.

Anstruther, Fife — Map Ref: 2D3

★★★ HOTEL

The Smugglers Inn
High Street East, Anstruther, Fife, KY10 3DG
Tel: 01333 310506 Fax: 01333 312706

1 Single	All En Suite	
5 Twin		
3 Double		
1 Family		

B&B per person
from £29.50 Single
from £29.50 Dbl/Twn

Open Jan-Dec
B&B + Eve.Meal
from £43.00

Listed 17th century Inn under personal supervision of owners. Interesting menu using fresh local produce. Seafood a speciality. Recently refurbished bedrooms.

VAT is shown at 17.5%: changes in this rate may affect prices.

Key to symbols is on back flap.

Anstruther, Fife

Map Ref: 2D3

★★★★
GUEST
HOUSE

The Spindrift
Pittenweem Road, Anstruther, Fife, KY10 3DT
Tel/Fax: 01333 310573
E-mail: info@thespindrift.co.uk
Web: www.thespindrift.co.uk

Stone built Victorian house with wealth of original features, set in fishing
village. Short walk from town centre. Ideal touring base. Non smoking.
Private parking. Evening meal by arrangement.

2 Twin	All En Suite
5 Double	
1 Family	

B&B per person
from £30.00 Single
from £26.50 Dbl/Twn
Room only per person
from £20.00

Open Jan-Dec
B&B + Eve.Meal
from £40.00

Arbroath, Angus

Map Ref: 2D1

★★★
INN

Colliston Inn
Colliston, by Arbroath, Angus, DD11 3RP
Tel/Fax: 01241 890232

Colliston Inn, a former manse is situated on the A933 west of the historic
Scottish fishing town of Arbroath. The Inn has an interesting varied menu
using local fresh produce to create good honest, up to date traditional
Scottish food. Many highly successful functions have taken place at
Colliston. We pride ourselves in giving a very personal service.
Attending to all organisation etc personally.

1 Twin	2 En Suite fac
1 Double	1 Priv.NOT ensuite
1 Family	

B&B per person
from £30.00 Single
from £25.00 Dbl/Twn

Open Jan-Dec excl
Xmas/New Year

★
HOTEL

Rosely Country House Hotel
Arbroath, Angus, DD11 3RB
Tel/Fax: 01241 876828
Web: www.theroselyhotel.co.uk

Listed Victorian style family run residence. Set in 4 acres of lawns, trees
and shrubs. Close to numerous golf courses and tourist routes. Quiet and
relaxing atmosphere. Clay Pigeon and Game Shooting, plus Fishing
arranged.

4 Single	All En Suite
4 Twin	
4 Double	
2 Family	

B&B per person
from £40.00 Single
from £30.00 Dbl/Twn

Open Jan-Dec excl
Xmas/New Year
B&B + Eve.Meal
from £40.00

★★
GUEST
HOUSE

Scurdy Guest House
33 Marketgate, Arbroath, Angus, DD11 1AU
Tel: 01241 872417 Fax: 01241 874603

Family run licensed Guest House & Restaurant. Close to harbour and town
centre. A warm welcome awaits you. Ideal for touring.

2 Twin	4 En Suite fac
4 Double	1 Pub Bath/Show
3 Family	1 Private fac

B&B per person
£15.00-£25.00 Single
£15.00-£22.00 Dbl/Twn

Open Jan-Dec
B&B + Eve.Meal
£20.00-£30.00

★★★
HOTEL

Viewfield Hotel
1 Viewfield Road, Arbroath, DD11 2BS
Tel: 01241 872446

Comfortable, friendly, family run hotel, 5 minutes from town centre and
harbour. Ideally located for golfing and fishing breaks. Ensuite rooms.

1 Single	All En Suite
1 Twin	
2 Double	
1 Family	

B&B per person
£30.00-£40.00 Single
£25.00-£35.00 Dbl/Twn

Open Jan-Dec

Important: Prices stated are estimates and may be subject to amendments

Auchterarder, Perthshire   **Map Ref: 2B3**

★★★★

SMALL HOTEL

Collearn House Hotel
High Street, Auchterarder, Perthshire, PH3 1DF
Tel: 01764 663553 Fax: 01764 662376

1 Single	All En Suite	B&B per person	Open Jan-Dec excl
1 Double		from £55.00 Single	Xmas/New Year
5 Double/Twin		from £42.50 Dbl/Twn	
1 Family			

Family run country house hotel in extensive gardens, spacious bedrooms, magnificent panelling, stained glass windows. A la carte menu available for lunch and dinner.

★★★★

SMALL HOTEL

Duchally Country Estate
Gleneagles, Auchterarder, Perthshire, PH3 1PN
Tel: 01764 663071 Fax: 01764 662464

13 Rooms	All En Suite fac	B&B per room	Open Jan-Dec
Single		£65.00 Single	
Twin		£110.00 Double	
Double			

Large country house set in 27 acres of parkland. Wide choice of golf courses; range of outdoor activities in area. Accent on comfort. Taste of Scotland.

★★

B&B

The Parsonage
111 High Street, Auchterarder, Perthshire, PH3 1AA
Tel: 01764 662392

2 Twin	1 En Suite fac	B&B per person	Open Jan-Dec
2 Family	2 Pub Bath/Show	£20.00-£25.00 Single	
		£18.00-£20.00 Twin	

Personally run guest house in the centre of Auchterarder. Convenient for golf courses, restaurants and all amenities. Lovely views from all bedrooms.

---

by Auchterarder, Perthshire   **Map Ref: 2B3**

★★★★★

INTERNATIONAL RESORT HOTEL

&

The Gleneagles Hotel
Auchterarder, Perthshire, PH3 1NF
Tel: 01764 662231 Fax: 01764 662134
E-mail: resort.sales@gleneagles.com
Web: www.gleneagles.com

14 Single	222 En Suite fac	B&B per room	Open Jan-Dec
51 Twin	15 Suites avail	£290-00-£410.00 Single	B&B + Eve.Meal
142		from £200.00 Dbl/Twn	£362.00-£470.00
Double			

A traditional hotel in the grand style with a wide range of world class sporting and leisure facilities; situated amidst the beautiful countryside of central Perthshire.

GOLD

Ballingry, nr Loch Leven, Fife   **Map Ref: 2C3**

★★

GUEST HOUSE

Navitie Guest House
by Ballingry, Lochgelly, Fife, KY5 8LR
Tel: 01592 860295 Fax: 01592 869769
Web: http://members.aol.com/navitie

1 Single	All En Suite	B&B per person	Open Jan-Dec
2 Twin		from £25.00 Single	B&B + Eve.Meal
1 Double		from £22.00 Dbl/Twn	from £32.00
3 Family			

Detached 200-year-old house in its own grounds overlooking Ballingry village. Only 4 miles (6kms) from the Edinburgh to Perth motorway. Centrally located only 30/40 minutes drive from Edinburgh, Stirling, Perth and St Andrews. Evening meal by arrangement.

VAT is shown at 17.5%: changes in this rate may affect prices.

Key to symbols is on back flap.

Blair Atholl, Perthshire

Map Ref: 4C12

★★★

GUEST HOUSE

Dalgreine Guest House
off St Andrews Crescent, Bridge of Tilt
Blair Atholl. Perthshire, PH18 5SX
Tel/Fax: 01796 481276

1 Single	3 En Suite fac	B&B per person	Open Jan-Dec
2 Twin	1 Pub Bath/Show	from £17.00 Single	B&B + Eve.Meal
2 Double		from £17.00 Dbl/Twn	from £28.50
1 Family			

Well appointed guest house, convenient for Blair Castle, Pitlochry Festival Theatre and the many local activities and attractions, including golf, pony-trekking, mountain bike hire, hill walks and river walks. Evening meals by arrangement.

★★★

GUEST HOUSE

The Firs
St Andrews Crescent, Blair Atholl, Perthshire, PH18 5TA
Tel: 01796 481256 Fax: 01796 481661
E-mail: geoff.crerar@lineone.net

1 Twin	All En Suite	B&B per person	Open 2Jan-22Dec
2 Double		from £18.50 Dbl/Twn	
1 Family			

Friendly family home with half an acre of garden, in a tranquil setting. Fine touring centre, close to Blair Castle.

Blairgowrie, Perthshire

Map Ref: 2B1

★★★

GUEST HOUSE

The Laurels
Golf Course Road, Rosemount, Blairgowrie, Perthshire, PH10 6LH
Tel/Fax: 01250 874920
E-mail: laurels-blairgowrie@talk21.com

1 Single	4 En Suite fac	B&B per person	Open Feb-mid Nov
3 Twin	1 Pub Bath/Show	from £20.00 Single	B&B + Eve.Meal
2 Double		from £19.50 Db/Twn	from £30.00

Originally a farmhouse dating from 1873, set back from main road, on outskirts of Blairgowrie with own large garden and ample parking. Rosemount Golf Course is a short walk away with a selection of 20 golf courses nearby. Ideal base for touring the beautiful Perthshire countryside. Fishing, shooting, mountaineering, ski-ing, pony trekking all in the local area.

ROSEBANK HOUSE

Balmoral Road, Blairgowrie, Perthshire PH10 7AF
Telephone: 01250 872912
e.mail: colhotel@rosebank35.fsnet.co.uk
Absorb the tranquil atmosphere of this lovely Georgian house set in spacious gardens. Guests return year after year, never tiring of the natural beauty surrounding Blairgowrie and of Rosebank's own enchanting charm and fine food.
Special Breaks available from 3 nights onwards.
Licensed. Private facilities.

★★★

GUEST HOUSE

Rosebank House
Balmoral Road, Blairgowrie, Perthshire, PH10 7AF
Tel: 01250 872912
E.mail: colhotel@rosebank35.fsnet.co.uk

1 Single	5 En Suite fac	B&B per person	Open Jan-Oct
1 Twin	1 Priv.NOT ensuite	£21.00-£24.00 Single	
3 Double	1 Pub Bath/Show	£21.00-£24.00 Dbl/Twn	
2 Family			

Georgian house set in spacious gardens on the road to Braemar, Balmoral and the Highlands. Traditional cooking using only fresh produce.

Important: Prices stated are estimates and may be subject to amendments

by Blairgowrie, Perthshire — Map Ref: 2B1

Kinloch House Hotel
★★★★★ HOTEL

Kinloch, by Blairgowrie, Perthshire, PH10 6SG
Tel: 01250 884237 Fax: 01250 884333
E-mail: info@kinlochhouse.com

4 Sporting	All En Suite		Open Jan-Dec
Singles	Suites avail		B&B + Eve.Meal
5 Double			£95.00-£98.00
9 Twin			

An elegant Scottish country home with galleried hall in beautiful Perthshire countryside. Ideal for golfing, fishing and shooting.

Burntisland, Fife — Map Ref: 2C4

Burntisland Sands Hotel
★★ HOTEL

Lochies Road, off Kinghorn Road, Burntisland, Fife, KY3 9JX
Tel/Fax: 01592 872230

1 Single	3 En Suite fac	B&B per person	Open Jan-Dec
1 Twin	1 Priv.NOT ensuite	from £39.50 Single	
1 Double		from £29.50 Dbl/Twn	
1 Family			

Personally run small hotel with Bistro, Pool room and Function Suite. Children love the fun farm and play area. Close to Sandy South facing beach. Fax facilities. Close to rail and bus links.

Inchview Hotel
★★★ INN

69 Kinghorn Road, Burntisland, Fife, KY3 9EB
Tel: 01592 872239 Fax: 01592 874866
E-mail: inchview@msn.com

2 Single	All En Suite	B&B per person	Open Jan-Dec
3 Twin		£42.50-£52.50 Single	B&B + Eve.Meal
6 Double		£35.00-£38.00 Dbl/Twn	£56.00-£65.00
1 Family			

Family run hotel overlooking Burntisland Links and Pettycur Bay to the Islands of the Forth Estuary. Flambe cooking in restaurant. Good selection of real ales and continental beers in the lounge bar. Convenient road and rail links to Edinburgh.

Kingswood Hotel
★★★ HOTEL

Kinghorn Road, Burntisland, Fife, KY3 9LL
Tel: 01592 872329 Fax: 01592 873123

5 Twin	All En Suite	B&B per person	Open Jan-Dec
4 Double		from £52.00 Single	B&B + Eve.Meal
1 Family		from £33.75 Dbl/Twn	from £47.25

Privately owned, set in 2 acres of garden and woodland with fine views across the Firth of Forth. Comfortable, modern bedrooms. Function and conference facilities.

Carnoustie, Angus — Map Ref: 2D2

Joseph's Hotel & Restaurant
★★★ HOTEL

13 Philip Street, Carnoustie, Angus, DD7 6ED
Tel: 01241 852182 Fax: 01241 855440
E-mail: hotel_josephs@hotmail.com

4 Twin	All En Suite	B&B per person	Open Jan-Dec
1 Family		£29.50-£42.50 Twin	
1 Single			
1 Double			

Detached Victorian house with large south facing garden in town centre. Near championship golf course and sandy beach. Private parking. International chef, meals all day.

VAT is shown at 17.5%: changes in this rate may affect prices.

Key to symbols is on back flap.

Carnoustie, Angus — Map Ref: 2D2

Lochty Bank Guest House
20 High Street, Carnoustie, Angus, DD7 6AQ
Tel/Fax: 01241 854849

★★
GUEST HOUSE

3 Twin	4 En Suite fac	B&B per person	Open Mar-Oct
2 Family	1 Priv.NOT ensuite	from £20.00 Single	
		from £20.00 Twn/Fam	

Family run, semi-detached house with south facing garden and private parking in town centre close to famous championship golf courses and sandy beaches. Tee-off times can be arranged.

TV 📺 🖼 P ☕ 🛏

V

Ceres, Fife — Map Ref: 2C3

Meldrums Hotel
Main Street, Ceres, by Cupar, Fife, KY15 5NA
Tel: 01334 828286 Fax: 01334 828795

★★★
INN

1 Single	All En Suite	B&B per person	Open Jan-Dec
5 Twin		£42.00 Single	
1 Double		£33.00 Dbl/Twn	

Situated in the picturesque village of Ceres, ideal golfing base 6 miles from St Andrews, the home of golf. Family run country Inn offering fine food and ale.

TV 🖼 P ☕ 🥤 ✂ 🍴 🍽 🍷 ⚱

C 🐾 ♿ V

Coupar Angus, Perthshire — Map Ref: 2C1

Red House Hotel
Station Road, Coupar Angus, Perthshire, PH13 9AL
Tel/Fax: 01828 628500
E-mail: stay@red-house-hotel.co.uk

★★★
HOTEL

🚶

6 Twin	All En Suite	B&B per person	Open Jan-Dec excl
6 Double		from £35.00 Single	Xmas/New Year
8 Family		from £35.00 Dbl/Twn	B&B + Eve.Meal
			£50.00

Modern hotel with conservatory restaurant adjacent to A93. Meals served all day. Snooker, saunas, squash and gymnasium. Accommodation has separate entrance.

TV 🍷 📞 🖼 P ☕ 🥤 ✂ 🍽 🏓 🏆 🍷

C ♿ V

Crail, Fife — Map Ref: 2D3

Balcomie Links Hotel
Balcomie Road, Crail, Fife, KY10 3TN
Tel: 01333 450237 Fax: 01333 450540

AWAITING INSPECTION

3 Single	All En Suite	B&B per person	Open Jan-Dec
8 Twin		£25.00-£45.00 Single	B&B + Eve.Meal
3 Double		£25.00-£35.00 Dbl/Twn	£38.00-£50.00
1 Family		Room only per person	
		£20.00-£30.00	

Recently refurbished hotel, close by picturesque harbour village.
Nine miles (14 kms) from St Andrews. Ideal golfing base. Families and groups welcome. Wide choice of dishes available in either the lounge or the non-smoking dining room. Picturesque harbour and shoreline within a few minutes walk.

Croma Hotel
33-35 Nethergate, Crail, Fife, KY10 3TU
Tel: 01333 450239 Fax: 01333 451433
E-mail: cromahotel@crail.fsbusiness.co.uk
Web: www.cromahotel.co.uk

★★
SMALL HOTEL

1 Twin	4 Ensuite fac	B&B per person	Open Apr-Nov
4 Family	2 Pub Bath/Show	from £20.00 Single	B&B + Eve.Meal
		from £20.00 Twin	from £37.00

Long established family run hotel in this picturesque fishing village.
Near to harbour and beaches. Home cooked dinner at weekends.
Fully licensed bar. Golfing parties and children welcome.

TV 📺 🖼 ☕ ✂ 🍽 🍷

C 🐾 ♿ V

Important: Prices stated are estimates and may be subject to amendments

Crail, Fife
Map Ref: 2D3

Denburn House
★★★ GUEST HOUSE

1 Marketgate North, Crail, Fife, KY10 3TQ
Tel: 01333 450253
Web: www.s-h-systems.co.uk/hotels/denburnh.html

1 Single	5 Ensuite fac
3 Twin	1 Priv.NOT ensuite
2 Double	

B&B per person
from £20.00 Single
from £23.00 Dbl/Twn

Open Jan-Dec

18th century town house in small fishing village in the East Neuk of Fife. 15 minutes from St Andrews.

Selcraig Guest House
★★★ GUEST HOUSE

47 Nethergate, Crail, Fife, KY10 3TX
Tel: 01333 450697 Fax: 01333 451113
E-mail: margaretselcraigcrail@compuserve.com
Web: www.smoothhound.co.uk/hotels/selcraig.html

2 Single	4 En Suite fac
2 Twin	2 Priv.NOT ensuite
1 Double	
1 Family	

B&B per person
from £20.00 Single
from £22.50 Dbl/Twn

Open Jan-Dec

200-year-old Listed house in quiet street close to seashore. Convenient for touring the East Neuk of Fife and very close to coastal path walk. Non-smoking. Ample quiet village parking.

Crieff, Perthshire
Map Ref: 2A2

Ardo Howe
★★★ GUEST HOUSE

29/31 Burrell Street, Crieff, Perthshire, PH7 4DT
Tel: 01764 652825
Web: www.ardo-howe.co.uk

1 Single	1 En Suite fac
2 Twin	1 Priv.NOT ensuite
2 Double	2 Pub Bath/Show
1 Family	

B&B per person
from £16.00 Single
from £16.00 Dbl/Twn

Open Jan-Dec excl Xmas/New Year
B&B + Eve.Meal from £24.00

Comfortable, friendly guest house near town centre, providing quality service at reasonable prices.

Crieff Hydro
★★★★ HOTEL

Crieff, Perthshire, PH7 3LQ
Tel: 01764 655555 Fax: 01764 653087
E-mail: enquiries@crieffhydro.com
Web: www.crieffhydro.com

44 Single	225 En Suite fac
60 Twin	Suites avail
30 Double	
88 Family	

B&B per person
£31.00-£71.00 Single
£31.00-£105.00 Dbl/Twn

Open Jan-Dec
B&B + Eve.Meal £35.00-£110.00

Beautifully appointed Victorian resort hotel on edge of Highlands. Maintaining much of its original character. Exceptional for family holidays. Unrivalled leisure faciliites. Excellent food. Personal service.

Drummond Arms Hotel
★★ HOTEL

James Square, Crieff, Perthshire, PH7 3HX
Tel: 01764 652151 Fax: 01764 655222
E-mail: drummondarmshotel@btinternet.com

4 Single	35 En Suite fac
17 Twin	1 Pub Bath/Show
12 Double	
3 Family	

B&B per person
£25.50-£29.50 Single
£25.50-£29.50 Dbl/Twn

Open Jan-Dec
B&B + Eve.Meal £35.50-£40.50

Victorian built hotel, located in the centre of the town, recently refurbished, of historic interest. Ideally located for all local amenities, touring and golfing.

CRIEFF HYDRO

SCOTLAND'S LEADING LEISURE HOTEL

Awarded Independent Hotel of the Year in July 1998, it is the unique combination of superb accommodation and unrivalled leisure facilities which won Crieff Hydro Hotel this prestigious award.

Always with guests needs in mind, choice is a watch word. Each day can be filled with golf, horse riding, off road driving, swimming, films in the digital surround sound cinema, tennis, beauty treatments, aromatherapy and a full activity programme for children and adults. Children are made welcome with soft play rooms and parents can relax with eleven hours of supervised child care each day. In the evening, dining can suit your mood in the grand Dining Room or lively Brasserie.

Set in 900 acres of Perthshire countryside, Crieff Hydro has been sensitively upgraded to meet the demands for quality of today's guests.

www.crieffhydro.com

Call for reservations or brochure: **01764 655555**

Or write to The Manager, Reservations Department,
Crieff Hydro Ltd., Crieff, Perthshire, Scotland PH7 3LQ
Tel 01764 655555 Fax 01764 653087
Email: enquiries@crieffhydro.com

Important: Prices stated are estimates and may be subject to amendments

Crieff, Perthshire — Map Ref: 2A2

GUEST HOUSE ★★★

Gwydyr House Hotel
Comrie Road, Crieff, Perthshire, PH7 4BP
Tel/Fax: 01764 653277
E-mail: george.blackie@iclweb.com

3 Twin	All En Suite	B&B per person	Open Jan-Dec excl Xmas
4 Double		from £30.00 Dbl/Twn	B&B + Eve.Meal
1 Family			from £43.00

Scottish Victorian villa in elevated position overlooking Macrosty Park on the west side of Crieff. Town centre only 5 minutes walk. Sited close to numerous Perthshire golf courses. Enjoy a dram in our cosy lounge bar with superb views across the southern slopes of the Grampians. Relaxing base for an enjoyable break in this picturesque area of Scotland. Hearty Scottish breakfast.

HOTEL ★★

Leven House Hotel
Comrie Road, Crieff, Perthshire, PH7 4BA
Tel: 01764 652529

1 Single	8 En Suite fac	B&B per person	Open Feb-Nov
3 Twin	2 Pub Bath/Show	from £22.00 Single	B&B + Eve.Meal
6 Double		from £22.00 Dbl/Twn	from £37.00

Small family run hotel near town centre serving dinners and Scottish high teas. Ideally situated for touring and golf. Spacious car park.

HOTEL ★★★

Lockes Acre Hotel
Comrie Road, Crieff, Perthshire, PH7 4BP
Tel/Fax: 01764 652526

2 Twin	4 En Suite fac	B&B per person	Open Jan-Dec
4 Double	2 Pub Bath/Show	from £28.00 Single	B&B + Eve.Meal
1 Family		from £27.00 Dbl/Twn	from £42.00

Large Victorian house set in an acre of garden with magnificent views, in the centre of a fine touring area. Modern standards of comfort and service.

Crossford, by Dunfermline, Fife — Map Ref: 2B4

HOTEL ★★★

Pitfirrane Arms Hotel
Main Street, Crossford, by Dunfermline, Fife, KY12 8NJ
Tel: 01383 736132 Fax: 01383 621760

10 Single	All En Suite	B&B per person	Open Jan-Dec
15 Twin		£31.00-£58.00 Single	B&B + Eve.Meal
12 Double		£26.00-£35.00 Dbl/Twn	£47.50-£51.50
1 Family			

Large, family run hotel, on main road from Dunfermline to Kincardine Bridge, but only 2 miles (4kms) from Dunfermline city centre. Large car park. Golfing breaks are our speciality.

VAT is shown at 17.5%: changes in this rate may affect prices.

Key to symbols is on back flap.

Cupar, Fife   Map Ref: 2C3

HOTEL

Eden House Hotel
2 Pitscottie Road, Cupar, Fife, KY15 4HF
Tel: 01334 652510 Fax: 01334 652277
Web: www.eden-group.com

2 Single	All En Suite	B&B per person	Open Jan-Dec excl
5 Twin		£50.00-£57.00 Single	Xmas/New Year
3 Double		£38.00-£53.00 Dbl/Twn	B&B + Eve.Meal
1 Family			£57.00-£63.00

Former Victorian merchants house. Overlooking the Haugh Park in Cupar.
Only 7 miles from St Andrews. A la Carte, 1 Rosette award restaurant and
bar meals. Satellite and cable television available in hotel.

---

by Cupar, Fife   Map Ref: 2C3

**RESTAURANT
WITH
ROOMS**

The Peat Inn
by Cupar, Fife, KY15 5LH
Tel: 01334 840206 Fax: 01334 840530
E-mail: reception@thepeatinn.co.uk

1 Twin	All En Suite	B&B per person	Open Jan-Dec excl
7 Double		from £75.00 Single	Xmas/New Year
		from £72.50 Dbl/Twn	

Situated 6 miles from St Andrews in the village named after the Inn.
Guests stay in The Residence - 8 suites offering peace and comfort. The
cooking has earned international recognition over 26 years.

Dundee, Angus   Map Ref: 2C2

**GUEST
HOUSE**

Anderson's Guest House
285 Perth Road, Dundee, Angus, DD2 1JS
Tel/Fax: 01382 668585

1 Single	6 En Suite fac	B&B per person	Open Jan-Dec excl
1 Twin	1 Priv.NOT ensuite	from £20.00 Single	Xmas/New Year
3 Double		£20.00-£24.00 Dbl/Twn	
2 Family			

Centrally heated, comfortable, refurbished accommodation on main bus
route for city centre, close to University and Ninewells Hospital. En-suite
rooms and river views.

HOTEL

Beach House Hotel
22 Esplanade, Broughty Ferry, Dundee, Angus, DD5 2EN
Tel: 01382 776614 Fax: 01382 480241

5 Single	All En Suite	B&B per person	Open Jan-Dec
2 Twin		from £35.00 Single	B&B + Eve.Meal
5 Double		from £22.50 Dbl/Twn	from £57.00
1 Family		Room only per person	
		£30.00-£38.00	

Small, friendly tourist and commercial hotel, 4 miles (6kms) to centre,
overlooking River Tay to Fife coast. Ideal base for touring and walking.
For the golfer 25 minutes drive to St Andrews Championship course and
10 minutes to Carnoustie.

HOTEL

Dunlaw House Hotel
10 Union Terrace, Dundee, DD3 6JD
Tel/Fax: 01382 221703

1 Single	7 Ensuite fac	B&B per person	Open Jan-Dec
5 Twin	3 Pub Bath/Show	from £27.50 Single	B&B + Eve.Meal
2 Double		from £22.50 Dbl/Twn	from £27.50
2 Family			

Hotel is situated in quiet coservation area of the city, but only 5 minutes
down to the city centre. We are on the South side of the Lawhill, with
views over the River Tay and very close to Dundee Universities and
colleges.

Important: Prices stated are estimates and may be subject to amendments

Map Ref: 2C2

GUEST HOUSE ★★★

Errolbank Guest House
9 Dalgleish Road, Dundee, Angus, DD4 7JN
Tel/Fax: 01382 462118

1 Single	5 En Suite fac	B&B per person	Open Jan-Dec excl Xmas
3 Twin	1 Priv fac	from £26.00 Single	
2 Double		from £22.00 Dbl/Twn	

Victorian villa in quiet residential area. Centrally situated for touring, golf and all local amenities. Ground floor bedroom available. Private parking. Non smoking.

SMALL HOTEL ★★

Grosvenor Hotel
1 Grosvenor Road, 313 Perth Road, Dundee
Tel: 01382 642991 Fax: 01382 644256

1 Single	All En Suite	B&B per person	Open Jan-Nov
2 Twin		£38.50-£42.00 Single	B&B + Eve.Meal
3 Double		£24.00-£30.00 Dbl/Twn	£37.50-£55.00
1 Family		Room only per person	
		£38.00-£45.00	

Victorian terraced house with many original features. Close to city centre, university and Ninewells Hospital. Ideal touring base.

HOTEL ★★★★

Hilton Dundee Hotel
Earl Grey Place, Dundee, Angus, DD1 4DE
Tel: 01382 229271 Fax: 01382 200072

74 Twin	129 En Suite fac	B&B per person	Open Jan-Dec
54 Double	Suites avail	from £65.00 Single	B&B + Eve.Meal
		from £45.00 Dbl/Twn	to £60.00

Modern hotel with leisure facilities situated on the banks of the River Tay with views of the Kingdom of Fife. Easy access by road, rail and air. Conference facilities.

Queens Hotel
160 Nethergate, Dundee DD1 4DU
Tel: 01382 322515 Fax: 01382 202668
Web: www.queenshotel-dundee.com

The Queens Hotel is Dundee's oldest and grandest hotel and has recently been totally refurbished to provide all the modern facilities today's market demand whilst retaining it's Victorian charm. Situated just off the town centre in Dundee's West End cultural quarter. Nosey Parker's Bistro & Lounge is a bright colourful setting to enjoy a meal or relaxing drink.

HOTEL ★★★

Queens Hotel
160 Nethergate, Dundee, DD1 4DU
Tel: 01382 322515 Fax: 01382 202668
Web: www.queenshotel-dundee.com

7 Single	All En Suite	B&B per person	Open Jan-Dec
22 Twin		from £40.00 Single	
13 Double		from £30.00 Dbl/Twn	
10 Family			

Privately owned city centre hotel built in 1878, this hotel still retains its original features. Newly refurbished restaurant and large car park. Close to university.

VAT is shown at 17.5%: changes in this rate may affect prices.

Key to symbols is on back flap.

Dundee, Angus

Map Ref: 2C2

★★

GUEST
HOUSE

Restalrig Guest House
69 Clepington Road, Dundee, Angus, DD4 7BQ
Tel: 01382 455412 Fax: 01382 459864

1 Twin	All En Suite
1 Double	1 Pub Bath/Show
2 Family	

B&B per person
from £23.00 Single
from £18.00 Dbl/Twn

Open Jan-Dec

Close to ring road yet within walking distance of Dundee city centre, this traditional stone built guest house is a good base for both business and touring. Close to the new international indoor sports centre.

St Leonards Guest House
22 Albany Terrace, Dundee, Angus, DD3 6HR
Tel: 01382 227146/224612(guests)

★

GUEST
HOUSE

2 Twin	2 Pub Bath/Show
1 Family	

B&B per person
£18.00-£20.00 Single
£15.00-£17.00 Twin
Room only per person
£10.00-£12.00

Open Jan-Dec

Traditional stone built house in elevated position situated in quiet, residential area of Dundee with view over the river Tay, with easy access to city centre.

Woodlands Hotel
13 Panmure Terrace, Barnhill, Dundee, Angus, DD5 2QL
Tel: 01382 480033 Fax: 01382 480126
Web: www.bettins.co.uk

★★

HOTEL

3 Single	All En Suite
13 Twin	
21 Double	
1 Family	

B&B per person
£37.50-68.00 Single
£32.00-£45.00 Dbl/Twn

Open Jan-Dec

Set in 4 acres of private grounds in quiet residential area. Close to the village of Broughty Ferry. Leisure facilities, satellite TV.

Dunfermline, Fife

Map Ref: 2B4

★★★

HOTEL

Abbey Park Hotel
5 Abbey Park Place, Dunfermline, Fife, KY12 7PT
Tel: 01383 739686 Fax: 01383 722801

2 Single	8 En Suite fac
6 Twin	1 Priv.NOT ensuite
2 Double	2 Pub Bath/Show
1 Family	

B&B per person
from £34.00 Single
from £22.50 Dbl/Twn

Open Jan-Dec

Built around 1825, a Georgian town house set in the shadow of the Abbey, with its own rear gardens, yet close to the town centre. Ample private parking. Good rail and road links to Edinburgh – 15 miles (25km). No evening meals.

★★★

GUEST
HOUSE

Clarke Cottage Guest House
139 Halbeath Road, Dunfermline, Fife, KY11 4LA
Tel: 01383 735935 Fax: 01383 623767
E-mail: clarkecottage@ukonline.co.uk

6 Twin	All En Suite
3 Double	

B&B per person
from £29.00 Single
from £24.00 Dbl/Twn

Open Jan-Dec

Situated 1 mile West of Junction 3 (M90) and only a 2 minute walk to the new Railway Station, this 19th century Victorian house has been tastefully extended to provide comfortable en-suite accommodation with independent access. Ample off-street parking. Ideally situated for visiting Edinburgh and surrounding areas in Fife.

Important: Prices stated are estimates and may be subject to amendments

Dunfermline, Fife   **Map Ref: 2B4**

★★★
HOTEL

Davaar House Hotel
126 Grieve Street, Dunfermline, Fife, KY12 8DW
Tel: 01383 721886 Fax: 01383 623633

2 Single	All En Suite	B&B per person	Open Jan-Dec
3 Twin		from £48.00 Single	B&B + Eve.Meal
4 Double		from £35.00 Dbl/Twn	from £60.00
1 Family		Room only per person	
		from £30.00	

Comfortable, tastefully furnished hotel retaining original Victorian
features. Personally run with friendly individual attention. Taste of
Scotland. Within easy access to M90 and only 14 miles from Edinburgh.

★★★★
SMALL HOTEL

Garvock House Hotel
St John's Drive, Transy, Dunfermline, KY12 7TU
Tel: 01383 621067 Fax: 01383 621168
Web: www.garvock.co.uk

6 Twin	All En Suite	B&B per person	Open Jan-Dec
5 Double		from £65.00 Single	
		from £42.50 Dbl/Twn	

A restored Georgian house set in its own grounds boasting a wealth of
original features. Spacious non-smoking bedrooms with many thoughtful
touches. Privately owned and managed with the aim of giving quality,
value and service.

★★
GUEST HOUSE

Jacobean Hotel
Halbeath Road, Dunfermline, Fife, KY11 4LF
Tel: 01383 732152
E-mail: 113072.2221@compuserve.com

7 Twin	All En Suite	B&B per person	Open Jan-Dec
1 Double		£26.00-£30.00 Single	
		£24.00-£25.00 Dbl/Twn	
		Room only per person	
		from £24.00	

Small family run Guest House situated less than 1/2 mile from Junction 3
on the M90 in a quiet secluded location ground floor accommodation, all
rooms en suite. Ample parking.

★★★★
HOTEL

Keavil House Hotel
Crossford, Dunfermline, Fife, KY12 8QW
Tel: 01383 736258 Fax: 01383 621600
Web: www.keavilhouse.co.uk

4 Single	All En Suite	B&B per person	Open Jan-Dec
19 Twin		£60.00-£90.00 Single	B&B + Eve.Meal
20 Double		£85.00-£140.00 Double	£55.00-£68.50
4 Family			

Historic country house, including extensive leisure facilities, is set in 12
acres of grounds and gardens, making it an ideal location for relaxing.
The Hotel offers 2 highly recommended restaurants – awarded AA Rosette
and member of Taste of Scotland. Within easy access of Edinburgh – only
20 minutes by train.

★★★
HOTEL

Pitbauchlie House Hotel
Aberdour Road, Dunfermline, Fife, KY11 4PB
Tel: 01383 722282 Fax: 01383 620738
Web: www.pitbauchlie.com

6 Single	All En Suite	B&B per person	Open Jan-Dec excl
24 Twin		from £66.00 Single	New Year
18 Double		from £41.50 Dbl/Twn	
2 Family			

Hotel with modern and older style rooms, set in 3 acres of woodland and
1 mile (2kms) from the town centre. Ample parking available. 18 miles
from Edinburgh.

VAT is shown at 17.5%: changes in this rate may affect prices.   *Key to symbols is on back flap.*

Dunfermline, Fife | Map Ref: 2B4

Saline Hotel
West Road, Saline, Dunfermline, Fife, KY12 9UN
Tel: 01383 852798 Fax: 01383 851737

★★ INN

3 Twin	All En Suite	B&B per person from £25.00 Single from £50.00 Twin Room only rate from £45.00	Open Jan-Dec B&B + Eve.Meal from £65.00

Friendly, family run inn situated on the edge of the village 6 miles from Dunfermline and 4 miles from Knockhill racetrack. Relaxing, informal style of service. The bedrooms are in a building adjacent to the inn.

Edzell, Angus | Map Ref: 4F12

Glenesk Hotel
High Street, Edzell, Angus, DD9 7TF
Tel: 01356 648319 Fax: 01356 647333

★★★ HOTEL

7 Single	All En Suite	B&B per person	Open Jan-Dec
11 Twin		£50.00-£60.00 Single	
1 Double		£40.00-£50.00 Dbl/Twn	
5 Family			

Family run hotel with sports complex including an indoor swimming pool. Golf course, with fishing and shooting available locally.

Elie, Fife | Map Ref: 2D3

The Golf Hotel

BANK STREET, ELIE, FIFE KY9 1EF
Telephone: 01333 330209
Fax: 01333 330381
e.mail: golf@StAndrews.co.uk
web: www.golfhotel.co.uk

This Scottish Baronial-style hotel is situated in the picturesque seaside town of Elie, 12 miles from St Andrews *"the home of golf"*, with fine views over the Firth of Forth. **The Golf Hotel** combines the friendliness and charm of a country house with the comfort and facilities of a modern hotel. All the bedrooms have private bathrooms, are centrally heated, have television, radio, tea and coffee-making facilities. The hotel cuisine is based upon local fresh produce – Scottish beef and lamb and the freshest of local fish and shellfish.
Golf tee-times arranged.

The Golf Hotel
Bank Street, Elie, Fife, KY9 1EF
Tel: 01333 330209 Fax: 01333 330381
E-mail: golf@StAndrews.co.uk
Web: www.golfhotel.co.uk

★★★ HOTEL

2 Single	All En Suite	B&B per person	Open Jan-Dec excl
13 Twin		from £45.00 Single	Xmas/New Year
5 Double		from £35.00 Dbl/Twn	
2 Family			

Baronial-style hotel, near sandy beach. Beside 9-hole golf course, sports complex and driving range and the superb 18-hole Elie golf course. 25 courses within 25 miles. On Fife coastal path with access to many excellent walks.

Important: Prices stated are estimates and may be subject to amendments

Forfar, Angus   Map Ref: 2D1

★★★★

SMALL HOTEL

Chapelbank House Hotel & Restaurant
69 East High Street, Forfar, Angus, DD8 2EP
Tel: 01307 463151 Fax: 01307 461922

2 Twin   All En Suite
2 Double

B&B per person
from £55.00 Single
from £41.00 Dbl/Twn

Open Jan-Dec

Elegant town house hotel. Friendly family run, offering first class cuisine, incorporating much quality local produce. Member of Taste of Scotland.

★★★

HOTEL

Royal Hotel
Castle Street, Forfar, Angus, DD8 3AE
Tel/Fax: 01307 462691

4 Single   All En Suite
8 Twin
6 Double
1 Family

B&B per person
from £49.80 Single
from £39.00 Dbl/Twn

Open Jan-Dec excl Xmas

Privately owned hotel in town centre, with leisure facilities, function suite, and restaurant. Large car park, security cameras.

---

by Forfar, Angus   Map Ref: 2D1

★★★

B&B

'Redroofs'
Balgavies, by Forfar, Angus, DD8 2TN
Tel/Fax: 01307 830268

1 Twin   All En Suite
1 Double
1 Family

B&B per person
from £25.00 Single
from £20.00 Dbl/Twn

Open Jan-Dec excl
Xmas/New Year
B&B + Eve.Meal
from £27.50

House in woodland area. Ideal central base for outdoor activities. Children and pets welcome. Private parking. Less than an hours drive to Aberdeen. Plenty of beaches and golf courses nearby. All rooms on ground floor.

Freuchie, Fife   Map Ref: 2C3

★★

INN

Lomond Hills Hotel
Lomond Road, Parliament Square, Freuchie, Fife, KY15 7EY
Tel: 01337 857329/ Fax: 01337 857329

2 Single   All En Suite
8 Twin
11 Double
4 Family

B&B per person
£42.00-£52.00 Single
£63.00-£78.00 Dbl/Twn

Open Jan-Dec
B&B + Eve.Meal
£47.00-£67.00 pp

Set in rolling countryside, hotel with leisure facilities, in the centre of the village which won the 1995 and 1996 'Village in Bloom' award.

Glendevon, Perthshire   Map Ref: 2B3

★★★

SMALL HOTEL

Tormaukin Hotel
Glendevon, Dollar, South Perthshire, FK14 7JY
Tel: 01259 781252 Fax: 01259 781526
E-mail: reservations@tormaukin.co.uk
Web: www.tormaukin.co.uk

1 Single   All En Suite
6 Twin
2 Double
1 Family

B&B per person
from £50.00 Single
from £40.00 Dbl/Twn

Open Jan-Dec excl Xmas
Bar meals avail

Originally a Drovers' Inn, retaining old world warmth. Beamed ceilings, open log fires, good food available as bar meals or in a more formal a la carte restaurant. Ideal centre for the keen golfer and fisherman. Some annexe bedrooms.

VAT is shown at 17.5%: changes in this rate may affect prices.   *Key to symbols is on back flap.*

Glenrothes, Fife — Map Ref: 2C3

HOTEL ★★★

Balgeddie House Hotel
Balgeddie Way, Glenrothes, Fife, KY6 3ET
Tel: 01592 742511 Fax: 01592 621702
E-mail: balgeddie@easynet.co.uk

2 Single	All En Suite	B&B per person	Open Jan-Dec
7 Twin	Suite avail	£60.00-£70.00 Single	B&B + Eve.Meal
10 Double		£55.00-£60.00 Dbl/Twn	£75.00-£90.00

1930's country house style hotel set in 4 acres of parkland. Games room, in quiet location close to town centre.

Glenshee, Perthshire — Map Ref: 4D12

Dalmunzie House Hotel

Tel: 01250 885224
Fax: 01250 885225
e.mail: dalmunzie@aol.com

SPITTAL OF GLENSHEE, BLAIRGOWRIE, PERTHSHIRE PH10 7QG

This family run Country House Hotel "in the hills", situated $1^{1}/_{2}$ miles off the main A93 Perth-Braemar road, offers an ideal base for touring Royal Deeside and the Highlands. A relaxed, informal atmosphere, where roaring log fires, personal service, traditional Scottish cooking with AA Rosette and 16 bedrooms all with private bathrooms are our hallmarks.

Golf, tennis, fishing and shooting are available on our 6,000-acre estate, and in winter months, skiing is on our doorstep – only 5 miles away.

HOTEL ★★★

Dalmunzie House Hotel
Spittal of Glenshee, Blairgowrie, Perthshire, PH10 7QG
Tel: 01250 885224 Fax: 01250 885225
E-mail: dalmunzie@aol.com

7 Twin	All En Suite	B&B per person	Open Jan-Dec
9 Double	1 Pub Bath/Show	£40.00-£61.00 Single	
		£30.00-£55.00 Double	

Referred to as the 'hotel in the hills', a warm and friendly family run hotel with log fires, games room, tennis, shooting and golfing.

Inverkeilor, by Arbroath, Angus — Map Ref: 2E1

B&B ★★★

The Chance Inn
Main Street, Inverkeilor,by Arbroath, Angus, DD11 5RN
Tel/Fax: 01241 830308

1 Single	1 Pub Bath/Show	B&B per person	Open Jan-Dec excl
1 Twin		from £20.00 Single	Xmas/New Year
1 Double		from £20.00 Dbl/Twn	
1 Family		Room only per person	
		from £20.00	

200 year old Coaching Inn serving fine food and real ales in a warm and relaxed atmosphere. Golf, fishing, walking, ideal stop for touring and exploring the East. Everybody welcome. Members of CAMRA.

Important: Prices stated are estimates and may be subject to amendments

Inverkeithing, Fife | Map Ref: 2B4

★★

GUEST HOUSE

Forth Craig Private Hotel
90 Hope Street, Inverkeithing, Fife, KY11 1LL
Tel: 01383 418440

2 Single	All En Suite	B&B per person	Open Jan-Dec
1 Twin		£28.00-£30.00 Single	
2 Double		£22.00-£25.00 Dbl/Twn	

All ensuite rooms in this modern purpose built private hotel overlooking the Firth of Forth. Convenient road access to Edinburgh, St. Andrews & Stirling. Excellent train service to Edinburgh, only 15 minutes travel time.

★★★

B&B

The Roods Guest House
16 Bannerman Avenue, Inverkeithing, Fife, KY11 1NG
Tel/Fax: 01383 415049
E-mail: isobel@theroods.com
Web: www.theroods.com

1 Twin	All En Suite	B&B per person	Open Jan-Dec
1 Double		from £22.00 Single	
		from £22.00 Dbl/Twn	

Quietly secluded family home. Close to rail station and M90. Well-appointed bedrooms offering mini office and direct dial telephones. Evening meal by arrangement.

Killiecrankie, Perthshire | Map Ref: 4C12

The Killiecrankie Hotel

Killiecrankie, By Pitlochry, Perthshire PH16 5LG
Tel: 01796 473220 Fax: 01796 472451
e.mail: enquiries@killiecrankiehotel.co.uk
web: www.killiecrankiehotel.co.uk

The Killiecrankie Hotel enjoys a fine setting in peaceful gardens overlooking the beautiful Pass of Killiecrankie. There are 10 attractive bedrooms, including a ground-floor suite, with views of the surrounding gardens and woodland. Exceptional food (Good Food Guide, 2 AA Rosettes for dinner), and a congenial atmosphere help make guests feel at home. All rooms have bath and/or shower, colour television, radio, telephone and tea trays. The area offers walking to suit everyone, is a photographer/ artist's paradise, a golfer's delight and is well located for touring. Pitlochry and Blair Atholl 3 miles. Closed Jan. (and Mon/Tues in December, February and March). Also special breaks, Christmas and Hogmanay breaks.

AA ★★ (76%) ❀❀ ★★★★ SMALL HOTEL

★★★★

SMALL HOTEL

The Killiecrankie Hotel
Killiecrankie, by Pitlochry, Perthshire, PH16 5LG
Tel: 01796 473220 Fax: 01796 472451
E-mail: enquiries@killiecrankiehotel.co.uk
Web: www.killiecrankiehotel.co.uk

2 Single	All En Suite	Open Feb-Dec
3 Twin		B&B + Dinner
4 Double		£69.00-£89.00
1 Family		

Personally run country hotel with warm and friendly atmosphere set in 4 acres of grounds, overlooking Pass of Killiecrankie.

Kinloch Rannoch, Perthshire — Map Ref: 1H1

★★★

HOTEL

Dunalastair Hotel
Kinloch Rannoch, Perthshire, PH16 5PW
Tel: 01882 632323 Fax: 01882 632371
E-mail: reservations@dunalastair.co.uk
Web: www.dunalastair.co.uk

Traditional Scottish hotel in picturesque village square. Ideal touring base for the central Highlands.

2 Single	22 En Suite fac	B&B per person	Open Jan-Dec
10 Twin		£35.00-£50.00 Single	B&B + Eve.Meal
10 Double		£35.00-£50.00 Dbl/Twn	£35.00-£55.00
3 Family			

Kinross, Perthshire — Map Ref: 2B3

★★★★

HOTEL

The Green Hotel
2 The Muirs, Kinross, Perthshire, KY13 8AS
Tel: 01577 863467 Fax: 01577 863180
E-mail: reservations@green-hotel.com
Web: www.green-hotel.com

Ideally located in central Scotland. This is one of Scotland's fine independently owned country house hotels. 47 spacious bedrooms equipped to the highest standard. The leisure complex has indoor pool, sauna, solarium, exercise facility and squash court. The hotel has 2 'all weather' tennis courts and 2 '18 hole' golf courses.

31 Twin	All En Suite	B&B per person	Open Jan-Dec
12 Double		from £78.00 Single	B&B + Eve.Meal
4 Family		from £67.50 Dbl/Twn	£59.00-£100.00

★★★

RESTAURANT WITH ROOMS

The Grouse & Claret Restaurant
Heatheryford, Kinross, KY13 0NQ
Tel: 01577 864212 Fax: 01577 864920

Restaurant featuring fresh local Scottish produce with a hint of oriental flavours. Separate accommodation, all overlooking the trout lochans to the Ochil Hills beyond. Conveniently situated off junction 6 on the M90 motorway. Edinburgh, St Andrews, Perth, Stirling and Glasgow all within an hour's drive.

3 Double	All En Suite	B&B per person	Open Jan-Dec excl
		from £34.50 Single	middle 2 wks Jan.
		from £29.50 Dbl/Twn	B&B + Eve.Meal
			from £55.00

LOMOND COUNTRY INN & RESTAURANT
Kinnesswood, by Loch Leven, Kinross-shire KY13 9HN
Telephone: 01592 840253   Fax: 01592 840693
e.mail: lomondcountryinn@aol.com   AA ★ ★ ❀

Enjoy good food and real ales in this cosy family run hotel with stunning views overlooking Loch Leven. All rooms have ensuite facilities, colour TV and direct dial telephone. 9-hole golf course adjacent. Only 45 minutes from Edinburgh, 20 minutes from Perth and St Andrews.
B&B from £42.50 single, £34 twin/double per person.

★★

INN

Lomond Country Inn
Main Street, Kinnesswood, Kinross, KY13 9HN
Tel: 01592 840253 Fax: 01592 840693
E-mail: lomondcountryinn@aol.com

Comfortable family run inn in small village. Award winning restaurant with panoramic views across Loch Leven. Interesting menu reflects the use of locally produced foods according to season. Convenient for Scottish Gliding Centre plus over 130 golf courses within one hour's drive of Kinnesswood.

2 Single	All En Suite	B&B per person	Open Jan-Dec
5 Twin		From £42.50 Single	B&B + Eve.Meal
5 Double		From £34.00 Dbl/Twn	from £40.00

Important: Prices stated are estimates and may be subject to amendments

by Kinross, Perthshire   Map Ref: 2B3

Nivingston Country House Hotel

Cleish, near Kinross, Kinross-shire KY13 0LS
Tel: 01577 850216   Fax: 01577 850238
e.mail: info@nivingstonhousehotel.co.uk
Web: www.nivingstonhousehotel.co.uk

★★★
HOTEL

You will find Nivingston Country House Hotel an ideal base from which to explore Tayside, Fife and Edinburgh or for a relaxing golfing or fishing break. You can enjoy superb comfort and food in a traditional environment where you will be spoiled by our attentive and caring team.

★★★
HOTEL

Nivingston Country Hotel & Restaurant
Cleish, Kinross-shire, KY13 0LS
Tel: 01577 850216 Fax: 01577 850238
E-mail: info@nivingstonhousehotel.co.uk
Web: www.nivingstonhousehotel.co.uk

2 Single	All En Suite	B&B per person	Open Jan-Dec
5 Twin		from £85.00 Single	
9 Double		from £52.50 Dbl/Twn	
1 Family		Room only per person	
		from £94.50	

Kirkcaldy, Fife   Map Ref: 2C4

★★
HOTEL

Belvedere Hotel
Coxstool, West Wemyss, by Kirkcaldy, Fife, KY1 4SL
Tel: 01592 654167 Fax: 01592 655279
E-mail: info@thebelvederehotel.com

1 Single	All En Suite	B&B per person	Open Jan-Dec
7 Twin		from £40.00 Single	B&B + Eve.Meal
9 Double		from £25.00 Dbl/Twn	from £42.50
3 Family		Room only per person	
		from £25.00	

Set in the picturesque Fife village of West Wemyss, dynamic view across the Firth of Forth, we pride ourselves on delivering the highest standards of service in relaxed and friendly surroundings. Ample free car parking. 30 minutes from St Andrews, Edinburgh and Perth, 15 minutes to Lundin Links.

★★★
HOTEL

Dunnikier House Hotel
Dunnikier Park, Dunnikier Way, Kirkcaldy, Fife, KY1 3LP
Tel: 01592 268393 Fax: 01592 642340
E-mail: recp@dunnikier-house-hotel.co.uk

5 Single	All En Suite	B&B per person	Open Jan-Dec
7 Twin/Double		from £52.50 Single	B&B + Eve.Meal
2 Double		from £37.50 Dbl/Twn	from £52.50

18th century country house hotel, set in parkland adjacent to golf course. Easy access to A92 and motorway system. Member of Taste of Scotland and AA rosette award.

★★
HOTEL

Parkway Hotel
6 Abbotshall Road, Kirkcaldy, Fife, KY2 5PQ
Tel: 01592 262143 Fax: 01592 200433

2 Single	All En Suite	B&B per person	Open Jan-Dec excl
24 Twin		from £40.00 Single	Xmas/New Year
6 Double		from £27.50 Dbl/Twn	
3 Family			

Privately owned hotel close to town centre, railway station and convenient for all local amenities. Dining available in our informal bistro restaurant. We offer wedding, seminar, conference and banqueting facilities.

VAT is shown at 17.5%: changes in this rate may affect prices. | Key to symbols is on back flap. |

Ladybank, Fife

Map Ref: 2C3

HOTEL

★★★★

Fernie Castle Hotel
Letham, by Cupar, Letham, by Ladybank, Fife, KY15 7RU
Tel: 01337 810381 Fax: 01337 810422
Web: ferniecastle.demon.co.uk

3 Single	All En Suite	B&B per person	Open Jan-Dec
8 Twin		from £45.00 Single	B&B + Eve.Meal
8 Double		from £45.00 Dbl/Twn	from £65.00
1 Family			

16th century castle with 17 acres of mature grounds and small loch.
Dungeon Bar, Wallace Lounge and Auld Alliance Room for formal dining.
Situated in the heart of the Kingdom of Fife with all its golf courses
including St Andrews within easy reach. Ground floor rooms available.

**GUEST
HOUSE**

★★★★

Redlands Country Lodge
Pitlessie Road, Ladybank, Cupar, Fife, KY15 7SH
Tel/Fax: 01337 831091

| 2 Twin | All En Suite | B&B per person | Open Feb-Nov |
| 2 Double | | from £24.00 Dbl/Twn | |

Redlands is an attractive country cottage, with an adjacent Norwegian pine
lodge, set in attractive gardens, with acres of woodland and fields all
around. Good home cooking and baking. Only 14 miles from St Andrews
and an ideal base for golfing and touring.

Leuchars, Fife

Map Ref: 2D2

St Michael's Inn

Leuchars, by St Andrews, Fife KY16 0DU
Tel: 01334 839220 e.mail: grahame@st-michaels-inn.co.uk
Fax: 01334 838299 Web: www.st-michaels-inn.co.uk

This 18th-century inn has 8 well-appointed bedrooms with self-control heating,
colour television, complimentary tea/coffee. Ideally situated for golfing breaks.
There is an abundance of sightseeing in the area with good walks and beaches.
10 minutes from St Andrews, rail link is one mile, airport five miles.

INN

★★★

St Michaels Inn
St Michaels, Leuchars, by St Andrews, Fife, KY16 0DU
Tel: 01334 839220 Fax: 01334 838299
E.mail: grahame@st-michaels-inn.co.uk
Web: www.st-michaels-inn.co.uk

1 Single	All En Suite	B&B per person	Open Jan-Dec
2 Twin		from £37.50 Single	
3 Double		from £35.00 Dbl/Twn	
2 Family			

Totally refurbished 200 year old former coaching Inn. Ideally located for
golfing and St Andrews. Convenient for touring the Central Belt. Good
reputation for traditional bar food, cooked to order.

---

by Leuchars, Fife

Map Ref: 2D2

**GUEST
HOUSE**

★★★★

Vicarsford Lodge
St Michaels, by St Andrews, Fife, KY16 0DT
Tel/Fax: 01334 838906

3 Twin	3 En Suite fac	B&B per person	Open Jan-Dec
2 Double	2 Priv.NOT ensuite	£35.00 Dbl/Twn	B&B + Eve.Meal
			£50.00-£60.00

Country house accommodation with en-suite rooms. Set in open farmland
offering warmth and comfort in a peaceful setting. In the heart of golfing
country with St. Andrews only 7 miles away, and two courses practically on
the doorstep. Ideal for small groups. Dinner available by arrangement.

Important: Prices stated are estimates and may be subject to amendments

Loch Earn, Perthshire | Map Ref: 1H2

Achray House Hotel ★★★ Small Hotel

Loch Earn, St Fillans, Perthshire PH6 2NF
Telephone: 01764 685231 Fax: 01764 685320
e.mail: achrayhotelsltd@btinternet.com Web: www.achray-house.co.uk

AA ★★

Stunning lochside position in St Fillans – an area of outstanding natural beauty. Well-established, family run hotel, known for its wide selection of good food, service and a caring attitude that brings people back year after year. The perfect base for sightseeing, golf, walking, field and watersports.

SMALL HOTEL

Achray House Hotel
Loch Earn, St Fillans, Perthshire, PH6 2NF
Tel: 01764 685231 Fax: 01764 685320
E.mail: achrayhotelsltd@btinternet.com
Web: www.achray-house.co.uk

Small, personally run hotel with extensive bar and restaurant menu. Picturesque village with magnificent views over Loch Earn.

3 Twin	8 En Suite fac	B&B per person	Open Feb-Jan
5 Double	1 Priv.NOT ensuite	from £32.00 Single	B&B + Eve.Meal
1 Family		from £20.00 Dbl/Twn	from £32.00

The Four Seasons Hotel

St Fillans, Perthshire PH6 2NF
Tel: 01764 685333 Fax: 01764 685444
e.mail: info@thefourseasonshotel.co.uk
Web: www.thefourseasonshotel.co.uk

The finest lochside location in The Southern Highlands
with views down Loch Earn.
Meall Reamhar Restaurant and Tarken Rum
offer imaginative cuisine using the best fresh local produce whilst considering both the adventurous and the traditional diner. Well placed in Scotland to enjoy many day trips including the scenic West Coast, Stirling Castle, Edinburgh, Blair Atholl and the Trossachs to name a few. For the energetic there are 26 golf courses within an hour, scenic walks, Munros to climb, fishing and shooting.
Spectacular views with food to match, a warm welcome and friendly service. 3 RAC dining awards.
What more could you wish for.
AA ★★★ ⚛⚛ RAC ★★★

SMALL HOTEL

The Four Seasons Hotel
St Fillans, Perthshire, PH6 2NF
Tel: 01764 685333 Fax: 01764 685444
E.mail: info@thefourseasonshotel.co.uk
Web: www.thefourseasonshotel.co.uk

The finest lochside location in the Southern Highlands with views over Loch Earn. To dine... you can choose between the Meall Reamhar Restaurant or the more informal Tarken Rum. In both we serve contemporary Scottish Cuisine, ranging from the imaginative to the traditional. Chef uses only the best ingredients from Scotland's natural larder which in many cases are supplied locally to produce a truly memorable meal.

5 Twin	All En Suite	B&B per person	Open Mar-Jan
7 Double		from £35.00 Single	
6 Family		from £35.00 Dbl/Twn	

VAT is shown at 17.5%: changes in this rate may affect prices. | *Key to symbols is on back flap.*

Loch Rannoch, Perthshire
Map Ref: 1H1

★★★

GUEST
HOUSE

Talladh-A-Bheithe Lodge
North Lochside Road, at Loch Rannoch, nr Pitlochry
Perthshire, PH17 2QW
Tel/Fax: 01882 633203
E-mail: ludwig@schottlandfreunde.mainz-online.de
Web: http://schottlandfreunde.mainz-online.de

Former shooting lodge overlooking Loch Rannoch. International cuisine.
Emphasis on German home baking.

3 Single	12 En Suite fac
6 Twin	2 Priv.NOT ensuite
4 Double	2 Pub Bath/Show
3 Family	

B&B per person
from £29.00 Single
from £24.00 Dbl/Twn
Room only per person
from £17.00

Open May-Oct
B&B + Eve.Meal
from £39.50

Lower Largo, Fife
Map Ref: 2D3

CRUSOE HOTEL
Main Street, Lower Largo KY8 6BT
Tel: 01333 320759   Fax: 01333 320865
e.mail: relax@crusoehotel.co.uk   Web: www.crusoehotel.co.uk

Family run hotel on the harbour front of historical Lower Largo.
Variety of golf courses close by including St Andrews only 20 minutes drive.
Good selection of home cooked bar food with extensive a la carte dinner
menu complemented by a reasonably priced wine list. All served with a smile!

★★★

HOTEL

Crusoe Hotel
2 Main Street, Lower Largo, Fife, KY8 6BT
Tel: 01333 320759 Fax: 01333 320865
E-mail: relax@crusoehotel.co.uk
Web: www.crusoehotel.co.uk

The Crusoe enjoys an excellent seafront situation with it's own harbour
and beach in the picturesque village of Lower Largo, the birthplace of
Alexander Selkirk who inspired the Robinson Crusoe Story. A wide
selection of bar meals are available with an extensive a' la carte menu
available in the restaurant, all served with a smile. A first class centre for
a family or golfing break with numerous attractions and courses nearby.

2 Single	All En Suite
5 Twin	
9 Double	

B&B per person
from £35.00 Single
from £27.50 Dbl/Twn

Open Jan-Dec
B&B + Eve.Meal
from £42.50

Lundin Links, Fife
Map Ref: 2C3

★★★★

HOTEL

Old Manor Country House Hotel
Leven Road, Lundin Links, Fife, KY8 6AJ
Tel: 01333 320368 Fax: 01333 320911
E-mail: enquiries@oldmanorhotel.co.uk
Web: www.oldmanorhotel.co.uk

Late 19c house with excellent views across Lundin Links golf course, Largo
Bay and the Firth of Forth. Function room for conferences/banqueting.
Taste of Scotland and Scotch Beef Club. Membership of Scotland's Hotels of
Distinction.

1 Single	All En Suite
10 Twin	
10 Double	
2 Family	

B&B per person
from £50.00 Single
from £30.00 Dbl/Twn

Open Jan-Dec
B&B + Eve.Meal
from £45.00

Markinch, Fife
Map Ref: 2C3

★★★★

HOTEL

Balbirnie House
Markinch, Fife, KY7 6NE
Tel: 01592 610066 Fax: 01592 610529
Web: www.balbirnie.co.uk

Balbirnie is a quite unique multi-award winning Country House Hotel
which combines understated luxury with superb service and outstanding
value. Many feature breaks available throughout the year.

1 Single	All En Suite
29	
Dbl/Twn	

B&B per person
from £125.00 Single
from £80.00 Dbl/Twn

Open Jan-Dec
B&B + Eve.Meal
from £89.50

Important: Prices stated are estimates and may be subject to amendments

Markinch, Fife — Map Ref: 2C3

HOTEL ★★★

Laurel Bank Hotel
Balbirnie Street, Markinch, Fife, KY7 6DB
Tel/Fax: 01592 611205
Web: www.laurelbankhotel.fsnet.co.uk

2 Single	All En Suite	B&B per person	Open Jan-Dec
4 Twin		from £32.00 Single	B&B + Eve.Meal
3 Double		from £21.00 Dbl/Twn	from £32.50
2 Family			

Friendly family run hotel, 1 mile from Glenrothes and convenient for the business traveller visiting the many commercial centres. Fax and office services available. Good home cooking.

Methven, by Perth, Perthshire — Map Ref: 2B2

INN ★

Methven Arms Hotel
35-37 Main Street, Methven, by Perth, Perthshire, PH1 3PT
Tel: 01738 840232

1 Twin	1 Pub Bath/Show	B&B per person	Open Jan-Dec
1 Double		£16.00-£18.00 Single	B&B + Eve.Meal
1 Family		from £16.00 Dbl/Twn	from £25.00

Village Inn on main Perth to Crieff road. Some off street parking. Seven day licence. Lunches available, all home cooking and local produce where possible.

Monifieth, by Dundee, Angus — Map Ref: 2D2

HOTEL ★★★

Monifieth House Hotel
Albert Street, Monifieth, Angus, DD5 4JX
Tel: 01382 532630

2 Twin	4 En Suite fac	B&B per person	Open Jan-Dec
2 Double	1 Priv.NOT ensuite	£38.00-£40.00 Single	B&B + Eve.Meal
1 Family		£25.00-£30.00 Dbl/Twn	£37.00-£42.00

Family run, elegant Victorian Hotel in extensive grounds. Friendly atmosphere. Views over Firth of Tay. 4 miles (6kms) East of Dundee city centre.

Montrose, Angus — Map Ref: 4F12

HOTEL ★★★

Carlton Hotel & Restaurant
139 High Street, Montrose, Angus, DD10 8QN
Tel/Fax: 01674 677237
E-mail: graeme@peelhouse139.freeserve.co.uk

2 Single	7 En Suite fac	B&B per person	Open Jan-Dec
2 Twin	1 Priv.NOT ensuite	from £25.00 Single	
3 Double		from £25.00 Dbl/Twn	
1 Family			

Personally run refurbished restaurant with rooms, in the centre of town. Most rooms with private bathrooms. Varied a la carte menu. Private car park.

HOTEL ★★

George Hotel Montrose
22 George Street, Montrose, Angus, DD10 8EW
Tel: 01674 675050 Fax: 01674 671153
E-mail: thegeorge@talk21.com

10 Single	All En Suite	B&B per person	Open Jan-Dec
4 Twin		from £30.00 Single	
9 Double		from £25.00 Dbl/Twn	
1 Family			

A privately owned stone-built hotel located in the centre of Montrose providing a central base for exploring this interesting part of Eastern Scotland with its championship golf courses sandy beaches and beautiful glens. There are some bedrooms on the third floor and no lift available.

Montrose, Angus

Map Ref: 4F12

The Limes Guest House

GUEST HOUSE
★★★

15 King Street, Montrose, Angus, DD10 8NL
Tel/Fax: 01674 677236
E-mail: thelimes@easynet.co.uk
Web: http://easyweb.easynet.co.uk/thelimes/

Family run, centrally situated in quiet, residential part of town. A few
minutes walk from the centre, railway station, beach and two golf courses.
Private parking.

2 Single	4 En-suite fac	B&B per person	Open Jan-Dec
4 Twin	2 Priv.NOT ensuite	from £21.00 Single	
4 Double	3 Pub Bath/Show	from £18.00 Dbl/Twn	
2 Family	4 Limited ensuite	Room only per person	
		from £16.00	

The Links Hotel

HOTEL
★★★★

Mid Links, Montrose, Angus, DD10 8RL
Tel: 01674 671000 Fax: 01674 672698
E-mail: linkshotel@merproleisure.demon.co.uk

Friendly hotel in quiet location yet close to town centre, golf course and
beach.

6 Single	All En Suite	B&B per person	Open Jan-Dec
13 Twin		from £49.00 Single	B&B + Eve.Meal
6 Double		from £36.00 Dbl/Twn	from £59.00

Montrose Park Hotel & Golf Lodges

HOTEL
★★★

Mid Links, Montrose, DD10 8RJ
Tel: 01674 663400 Fax: 01674 677091
E-mail: recep@montrosepark.co.uk
Web: www.montrosepark.co.uk

Family hotel with attractive mature gardens situated in residential area at
Mid Links, close to town centre. Conference and function suites (200
people).

12 Single	All En Suite	B&B per person	Open Jan-Dec
22 Twin			
16 Double			
8 Family			

Perth

Map Ref: 2B2

Abercrombie

GUEST HOUSE
★★★★

85 Glasgow Road, Perth, PH2 0PQ
Tel: 01738 444728 Fax: 01738 444728

Family run, Victorian town house, a few minutes from town centre. Ample
parking. Ideal for all outdoor activities.

2 Single	3 En Suite fac	B&B per person	Open Jan-Dec
1 Twin	1 Priv.NOT ensuite	£19.00-£30.00 Single	
1 Double		£20.00-£30.00 Dbl/Twn	

Ackinnoull Guest House

GUEST HOUSE
★★★★

5 Pitcullen Crescent, Perth, PH2 7HT
Tel: 01738 634165

Beautifully decorated Victorian semi-villa on the outskirts of town. Private
parking on premises. 'Perth in Bloom' winners, as picturesque outside as
in. Special rates for bookings of 3 days or more.

1 Twin	All En Suite	B&B per person	Open Jan-Dec
2 Double		from £20.00 Single	
1 Family		from £18.00 Dbl/Twn	

Important: Prices stated are estimates and may be subject to amendments

Perth | Map Ref: 2B2

Almond Villa Guest House
51 Dunkeld Road, Perth, PH1 5RP
Tel: 01738 629356 Fax: 01738 446606
E-mail: almondvilla@compuserve.com

GUEST HOUSE ★★★★

1 Single	4 En Suite fac	B&B per person	Open Jan-Dec
2 Twin	1 Priv.NOT En Suite	from £23.00 Single	B&B + Eve.Meal
1 Double		from £23.00 Double	from £35.00
1 Family		Room only per person	
		£23.00	

Semi-detached Victorian villa, close to town centre, Gannochy Trust Sports Complex, the North Inch and River Tay. Non smoking house.

Ardfern Guest House
15 Pitcullen Crescent, Perth, PH2 7HT
Tel: 01738 637031

GUEST HOUSE ★★★★

1 Twin	2 En Suite fac	B&B per person	Open Jan-Dec excl
1 Double	1 Priv Bathroom	20s20x	Xmas/New Year
1 Family		from £18.00 Dbl/Twn	

Victorian semi-villa on outskirts of city within easy access to all amenities. Non-smoking throughout. Off road parking. Many original features of the house sympathetically restored and retained.

Arisaig Guest House
4 Pitcullen Crescent, Perth, PH2 7HT
Tel/Fax: 01738 628240
E-mail: reservations@arisaig.demon.co.uk

GUEST HOUSE ★★★★

1 Single	All En Suite	B&B per person	Open Jan-Dec
1 Twin		from £22.50 Single	
2 Double		from £21.00 Dbl/Twn	
1 Family			

Comfortable family run guest house, with off street parking. Close to city's many facilities. Local touring base. Ground floor bedroom.

Beechgrove Guest House
Dundee Road, Perth, PH2 7AQ
Tel/Fax: 01738 636147
E-mail: beechgroveg.h@sol.co.uk
Web: www.beechgrove.uk.com

GUEST HOUSE ★★★★

1 Single	All En Suite	B&B per person	Open Jan-Dec
2 Twin		from £25.00 Single	
2 Double		from £25.00 Dbl/Twn	
1 Family			

Listed building, former manse (Rectory) set in extensive grounds. Peaceful, yet only a few minutes walk from the city centre. Non-smoking establishment.

Castleview Guest House
166 Glasgow Road, Perth, PH2 0LY
Tel: 01738 626415 Fax: 01738 451573

GUEST HOUSE ★★

1 Twin	All En Suite	B&B per person	Open Feb-Dec excl Xmas
1 Double		from £42.00 Dbl/Twn	
1 Family			

Close to Cherrybank Heather Collection yet only minutes from all amenities. Victorian house with private parking. Open views to frontage. 1 mile from by-pass.

Perth   Map Ref: 2B2

★★★

INN

🚶

Cherrybank Inn
210 Glasgow Road, Perth, PH2 0NA
Tel: 01738 624349

1 Single	All En Suite	B&B per person	Open Jan-Dec
6 Twin		to £28.00 Single	
1 Double		to £20.00 Dbl/Twn	

Cherrybank Inn is situated on the outskirts of Perth, 2 miles off the motorway, offering accommodation in twin bedded ensuite rooms. Bar meals available. Continental breakfast only served in rooms and full breakfast available.

📺 ⚲ 🖰 🅿 ☕ 🍴 🛏 🍷 🕮

🅲 ⬛ 🆅

★★★

GUEST HOUSE

Clunie Guest House
12 Pitcullen Crescent, Perth, PH2 7HT
Tel/Fax: 01738 623625
E-mail: ann@clunieperth.freeserve.co.uk

1 Single	All En Suite	B&B per person	Open Jan-Dec
1 Twin		£19.00-£25.00 Single	B&B + Eve.Meal
2 Double		£19.00-£23.00 Dbl/Twn	£30.00-£34.00
3 Family			

A warm welcome awaits you at Clunie Guest House which is situated on the A94 Coupar Angus road. There is easy access to the city centre with all its amenities including a variety of eating establishments. Alternatively, an evening meal can be provided if it is booked in advance.

📺 🖰 🅿 ☕ 🍳 ✂ ✗ 🛏 🕮

🅲 🐕 ⬛ 🆆 🆅

★★★★

GUEST HOUSE

Dunallan Guest House
10 Pitcullen Crescent, Perth, PH2 7HT
Tel/Fax: 01738 622551

3 Single	All En Suite	B&B per person	Open Jan-Dec
2 Twin		£22.00 Single	B&B + Eve.Meal
2 Double		£21.00 Dbl/Twn	from £34.00
		Room only per person	
		£18.00	

Family run, conveniently located on A94 tourist route, within easy reach of town centre. All rooms with TV. All rooms en-suite. Ground floor bedroom with level access to house from private car park.

📺 🖰 🅿 ☕ 🍳 ✂ ✗ 🛏 🕮

🅲 ⬛ 🆆 🆅

★★★★

HOTEL

♿

Huntingtower Hotel
Crieff Road, Perth, PH1 3JT
Tel: 01738 583771 Fax: 01738 583777
E-mail: reception.huntingtower@talk21.com
Web: www.huntingtowerhotel.com

3 Single	All En Suite	B&B per person	Open Jan-Dec
24 Twin	Suite avail	from £89.50 Single	B&B + Eve.Meal
6 Double		from £55.00 Dbl/Twn	£109.00 Single
1 Family			£74.50 Dbl/Twn

Country house hotel situated in its own grounds 2 miles West of Perth City centre. A fine reputation for Scottish and continental cuisine in a choice of restaurants. With facilities for conference and banquetting.

📺 ⚲ 📞 🖰 🅿 ☕ 🍴 👥 🏠 🍷

🅲 🐕 ⬛ 🆅

Iona Guest House
2 Pitcullen Crescent, Perth, PH2 7HT
Tel/Fax: 01738 627261

★★★

GUEST HOUSE

2 Single	4 En Suite fac	B&B per person	Open Jan-Dec
1 Twin	1 Priv.NOT ensuite	from £21.00 Single	
1 Double		from £19.00 Dbl/Twn	
1 Family			

In residential area, 10 minutes walk from Perth centre and river Tay. Ideal base for touring Perthshire and Scottish Highlands. Excellent golf courses, fishing and hill walking nearby.

📺 🖰 🅿 ☕ ✂ 🛏 🕮

🅲 ⬛ 🆅

Important: Prices stated are estimates and may be subject to amendments

Perth		Map Ref: 2B2		

★★★
HOTEL

Jarvis Perth Hotel
West Mill Street, Perth, PH1 5QP
Tel: 01738 628281 Fax: 01738 643423

2 Single	All En Suite	B&B per person	Open Jan-Dec
48 Twin		from £35.00 Single	
24 Double		from £25.00 Dbl/Twn	
2 Family			

Attractive stone building with millrace feature, situated in the town centre. Choice of restaurants. Excellent conference facilities available.

★★★★
GUEST HOUSE

Kinnaird Guest House
5 Marshall Place, Perth, PH2 8AH
Tel: 01738 628021/630685 Fax: 01738 444056

1 Single	All En Suite	B&B per person
3 Twin		from £28.00 Single
3 Double		from £23.00 Dbl/Twn

Georgian house, centrally situated overlooking park. Short walk to town centre and convenient for railway and bus stations. Personally run attentive owners.

★★★
HOTEL

Lovat Hotel
Glasgow Road, Perth, PH2 0LT
Tel: 01738 636555 Fax: 01738 643123
E-mail: e-mail@lovat.co.uk
Web: www.scotlandhotels.co.uk

9 Single	All En Suite	B&B per person	Open Jan-Dec
13 Twin		from £45.00 Single	B&B + Eve.Meal
7 Double		from £30.00 Dbl/Twn	from £39.00
1 Family			

Excellent location close to city centre with private free parking with facilities that include good quality bedrooms, function/conference rooms, conservatory and large bistro bar. Speciality dining and fine Scottish cuisine available.

★★★★
HOTEL

Murrayshall House Hotel
Scone, Perth, PH2 7PH
Tel: 01738 551171 Fax: 01738 552595

27 Single	All En Suite	B&B per person	Open Jan-Dec
4 Double	Suites avail	£50.00-£90.00 Single	B&B + Eve.Meal
10 Family		£50.00-£75.00 Dbl/Twn	£46.00-£75.00

Edwardian country house with two golf courses and golf training facilities set amidst 300 acres of parkland.

VAT is shown at 17.5%: changes in this rate may affect prices.

Key to symbols is on back flap.

200

PERTH

Perth

E

**PERTHSHIRE, ANGUS AND DUNDEE
AND THE KINGDOM OF FIFE**

Map Ref: 2B2

The New County Hotel

22-30 County Place, Perth PH2 8EE
Tel: 01738 623355 Fax: 01738 628969
e.mail: info@countyhotel.co.uk

*Friendly, privately owned, city centre hotel 5 minutes walk from
bus/train stations, cinema, theatre and leisure pool. All bedrooms
ensuite. Ideal base for exploring Perthshire and the Scottish Highlands.
Enjoy a relaxing drink before dining in our elegant bistro. Numerous
golf courses, excellent fishing and hill-walking in close proximity.*

★★

HOTEL

The New County Hotel
22-30 County Place, Perth, PH2 8EE
Tel: 01738 623355 Fax: 01738 628969
E.mail: info@countyhotel.co.uk
Web: www.newcountyhotel.com

Friendly, privately owned, city centre hotel, recently refurbished, own car
park. All bedrooms en-suite. Renowned for its food. Ideal base for
exploring Perthshire and the Scottish Highlands. Numerous golf courses,
excellent fishing and hill-walking in close proximity.

2 Single	23 rooms all ensuite	B&B per person sharing	Open all year
9 Twin		£30.00	
8 Double		B&B £40.00 Single	
4 Family		D,B&B per person sharing	
		£40.00	
		D,B&B £50.00 Single	

★★★★
**SMALL
HOTEL**

PARKLANDS HOTEL

2 St Leonard's Bank, Perth PH2 8EB
Telephone: 01738 622451 Fax: 01738 622046
e.mail: parklands.perth@virgin.net

*Overlooking South Inch Park the beautifully decorated rooms within this classical
town house offer the amenities you would expect in a hotel of this quality.
Our Colourists Bistro offers informal dining whilst the Acanthus Restaurant offers
excellent cusine imaginatively presented by our award winning chef in elegant
surroundings.*

★★★★

**SMALL
HOTEL**

Parklands Hotel
2 St Leonards Bank, Perth, PH2 8EB
Tel: 01738 622451 Fax: 01738 622046
E-mail: parklands.perth@virgin.net

Overlooking South Inch Park the beautifully decorated rooms within this
classical town house offer the amenities you would expect in a hotel of this
quality. Our colourists bistro offers informal dining whilst the Acanthus
restaurant offers excellent cuisine imaginatively presented by our award
winning chef in elegant surroundings.

6 Twin	All En Suite	B&B per person	Open Jan-Dec
8 Double		£69.00-£85.00 Single	
		£40.00-£58.00 Dbl/Twn	

★★★★

**GUEST
HOUSE**

Park Lane Guest House
17 Marshall Place, Perth, PH2 8AG
Tel: 01738 637218 Fax: 01738 643519
E-mail: stay@parklane-uk.com

Georgian house overlooking park next to city centre. All ensuite rooms,
private car park. Walking distance to golf course, restaurants and all
amenities, including bus and railway stations.

1 Single	All En Suite	B&B per person	Open Jan-Nov excl
2 Twin		from £23.00 Single	New Year
2 Double		from £23.00 Dbl/Twn	
1 Family			

Important: Prices stated are estimates and may be subject to amendments

Perth

Map Ref: 2B2

Queens Hotel
★★★

HOTEL

♿

Leonard Street, Perth, PH2 8HB
Tel: 01738 442222 Fax: 01738 638496
E-mail: e-mail@queensperth.co.uk
Web: www.scotlandhotels.co.uk

Privately owned and family run hotel ideally situated in city centre with ample free car-parking. High quality bedrooms, function and conference facilities. Leisure club including pool, jacuzzi, sauna, steam bath and gym.

| 51 rooms | All En Suite | B&B per person
from £47.00 Single
from £33.00 Dbl/Twn | Open Jan-Dec
B&B + Eve.Meal
from £45.00 |

Rhodes Villa
★★★

B&B

75 Dunkeld Road, Perth, PH1 5RP
Tel: 01738 628466

Personal attention and a friendly welcome. Close to amenities with private parking. En-route to the north. Ideally situated for touring. Just a nice stroll away from city centre.

| 1 Twin
1 Double
1 Family | All En Suite | B&B per person
from £20.00 Dbl/Twn | Open Jan-Dec |

Salutation Hotel
34 South Street, Perth PH2 8PH
Tel: 01738 630066   Fax: 01738 633598

The Salutation is one of Scotland's oldest established hotels (1699). It is reputed Bonnie Prince Charlie made his headquarters here during the '45.
The Salutation has recently been modernised. All 84 bedrooms are ensuite with colour television, tea/coffee making facilities and direct dial telephones.
The Salutation is the place to stay if you are visiting Perth on business or on holiday – The Adam Restaurant with its feature window has a reputation for fine food and efficient friendly service.

Salutation Hotel
★★

HOTEL

34 South Street, Perth, PH2 8PH
Tel: 01738 630066 Fax: 01738 633598

Town centre hotel with refurbished bedrooms conveniently situated for shops and theatre. Leisure centre within 0.5 miles (1km).

| 17 Single
48 Twin
17 Double
2 Family | All En Suite | B&B per person
£65.00-£67.00 Single
£34.00-£43.00 Dbl/Twn | Open Jan-Dec
B&B + Eve.Meal
£55.00-£72.00 |

VAT is shown at 17.5%: changes in this rate may affect prices.

Key to symbols is on back flap.

Perth — Map Ref: 2B2

Royal George Hotel
★ HOTEL

Tay Street, Perth, PH1 5LD
Tel: 01738 624455 Fax: 01738 630345

8 Single	All En Suite	B&B per person
11 Twin		from £65.00 Single
20 Double		from £42.50 Dbl/Twn

Open Jan-Dec

Dating from 18c, located in centre of historic Perth, with sun lounge overlooking River Tay. Meeting and conference facilities.

Sunbank House Hotel
★★★★ HOTEL

50 Dundee Road, Perth, PH2 7BA
Tel: 01738 624882 Fax: 01738 442515

2 Twin	All En Suite	B&B per person
6 Double		£54.00-£65.00 Single
2 Family		£29.00-£36.00 Dbl/Twn

Open Jan-Dec
B&B + Eve.Meal
£49.00-£55.00

Beautiful early Victorian house situated in its own grounds in the suburbs of Perth enjoying scenic views of the city and River Tay yet a short walk from the city centre. Perfectly placed for shopping, theatre going, golf, fishing and business. Non smoking bedrooms. Superior rooms with bath & shower. Choice of table d'hote or a la carte menus.

Two-o-Eight Hotel
★★ INN

208 Crieff Road, Perth, PH1 2PE
Tel/Fax: 01738 628936
E-mail: 208@easynet.co.uk
Web: www.vacations-scotland.co.uk/208hotel.html

6 Twin	6 En Suite fac	B&B per person
2 Family	2 Priv.NOT ensuite	from £18.80 Single
	1 Pub Bath/Show	from £18.80 Twin

Open Jan-Dec
B&B + Eve.Meal
from £24.80

Modern detached public house with bedrooms above. On a bus route to city centre. Ample car parking. Owner a golf enthusiast : packages arranged.

Westview Bed & Breakfast
★★★★ B&B

49 Dunkeld Road, Perth, PH1 5RP
Tel/Fax: 01738 627787

1 Twin	All En Suite	B&B per person
2 Double	1 Pub Bath/Show	from £20.00 Dbl/Twn

Open Jan-Dec
B&B + Eve.Meal
from £28.00

Town house in easy walking distance of town centre, on A9 with private parking. All rooms with colour TV, twin let as single.

---

by Perth — Map Ref: 2B2

Ballathie House Hotel
★★★★ HOTEL

Kinclaven, Stanley, Perth, Perthshire, PH1 4QN
Tel: 01250 883268 Fax: 01250 883396
E-mail: email@ballathiehousehotel.com
Web: www.ballathiehousehotel.com

7 Single	All En Suite	B&B per person
18 Twin	Suite avail	£75.00-£80.00 Single
16 Double		£75.00-£100.00 Db/Twn
2 Family		

Open Jan-Dec
B&B + Eve.Meal
£95.00-£125.00

Victorian Country House within its own grounds overlooking the River Tay. 12 miles from historic city of Perth.

Important: Prices stated are estimates and may be subject to amendments

Pitlochry, Perthshire   Map Ref: 2A1

HOTEL

Acarsaid Hotel
8 Atholl Road, Pitlochry, Perthshire, PH16 5BX
Tel: 01796 472389 Fax: 01796 473952
E-mail: acarsaid@msn.com

3 Single	All En Suite	B&B per person	Open Mar-Jan
8 Twin	2 Pub Bath/Show	£29.00-£37.00 Single	B&B + Eve.Meal
8 Double		£29.00-£37.00 Dbl/Twn	£39.00-£55.00

Former Victorian House converted to comfortable small hotel retaining much of the charm and character of a period villa. Family run with personal attention from Sandy & Ina. Ideal location close to town centre and access to Festival Theatre.

GUEST HOUSE

Annslea Guest House
164 Atholl Road, Pitlochry, Perthshire, PH16 5AR
Tel: 01796 472430 Fax: 01224 495020
E-mail: annslea@artech.co.uk
Web: www.pitlochryguesthouse.com

2 Twin	4 En Suite fac	B&B per person	Open Apr-Nov
4 Double	2 Pub Bath/Show	from £20.00 Dbl/Twn	

Victorian house situated within easy walking of town centre. Large garden and private parking. Ideally located for restaurants, Festival Theatre and all other amenities. Some accommodation in annexe cottage in garden and grounds.

HOTEL

Balrobin Hotel
Higher Oakfield, Pitlochry, Perthshire, PH16 5HT
Tel: 01796 472901 Fax: 01796 474200
E-mail: info@balrobin.co.uk   Web: www.balrobin.co.uk

1 Single	All En Suite	B&B per person	Open Mar-Oct
3 Twin		£25.00-£40.00 Single	B&B + Eve.Meal
10 Double		£25.00-£37.00 Dbl/Twn	£36.00-£49.00
1 Family			

Situated in residential yet central part of town with most bedrooms (12-4 on ground floor) with superb panoramic views.Traditional home cooked food from a varied choice menu changing daily accompanied by a selection of fine wines. Residents only bar. Our central location affords easy access to 60% of Scotland making it a perfect base for long & short stays. Special short break & advance booking rates. To find us follow the brown tourist signs.

GUEST HOUSE

Bendarroch Guest House
Strathtay, Pitlochry, Perthshire, PH9 0PG
Tel: 01887 840420 Fax: 01887 840438
Web: www.bendarroch-house.demon.co.uk

1 Single	All En Suite	B&B per person	Open Jan-Dec
3 Twin		from £28.00 Single	B&B + Eve.Meal
1 Family		from £25.00 Dbl/Twn	from £37.00

Fully refurbished Victorian house set in landscaped grounds, panoramic views with the River Tay running past the estate. Situated between Aberfeldy and Pitlochry. Golfing, fishing and canoeing only 2 minutes away, other sports available in the vicinity. Dinner, freshly cooked daily using local produce. Coffee and liqueurs found in the conservatory lounge.

SMALL HOTEL

Birchwood Hotel
2 East Moulin Road, Pitlochry, Perthshire, PH16 5DW
Tel: 01796 472477 Fax: 01796 473951
E-mail: viv@birchwoodhotel.co.uk

3 Single	All En Suite	B&B per person	Open Mar-Dec
5 Twin		from £31.00 Single	B&B + Eve.Meal
3 Double		from £31.00 Dbl/Twn	from £51.00
1 Family			

Fine Victorian country house in secluded, wooded grounds, conveniently close to town and Festival Theatre. The cracking log fire complements the warmth of welcome and individual attention from Viv and John. The dining is memorable.

VAT is shown at 17.5%: changes in this rate may affect prices.   **Key to symbols is on back flap.**

Pitlochry, Perthshire   Map Ref: 2A1

GUEST HOUSE

Carra Beag Guest House
16 Toberargan Road, Pitlochry, Perthshire, PH16 5HG
Tel/Fax: 01796 472835
E-mail: visitus@carrabeag.oik.co.uk

2 Single	9 En Suite fac	
3 Twin	1 Pub Bath/Show	
3 Double		
2 Family		

B&B per person
from £15.00 Single
from £15.00 Dbl/Twn

Open Feb-Dec incl
New Year

Whatever your pursuits a friendly enjoyable stay is assured at Carra Beag. Enjoy magnificent uninterrupted views of the surrounding hills or stroll through our garden directly to Pitlochry's main street. We offer full facilities for walkers and cyclists. Private car park, and value for money.

HOTEL

Craigvrack Hotel
38 West Moulin Road, Pitlochry, Perthshire, PH16 5EQ
Tel: 01796 472399 Fax: 01796 473990
E-mail: irene@craigvrack-hotel.demon.co.uk
Web: www.craigvrack-hotel.demon.co.uk

7 Twin	All En Suite
7 Double	
2 Family	

B&B per person
from £29.00 Single
from £29.00 Dbl/Twn

Open Jan-Dec
B&B + Eve.Meal
from £36.00

A family run Hotel offering a warm, friendly and relaxed atmosphere. The Craigvrack enjoys an enviable position with stunning, panoramic views of the surrounding hills and mountains and offers International award winning cuisine, from Masterchef Gerard Pequegnot. Theatre goers can enjoy meals from 5.45pm. OPEN ALL YEAR. Brand new 'Bar' and 'Willow Restaurant'. New conference facilities. Pets welcome by arrangement.

GUEST HOUSE

Dalshian House
Old Perth Road, Pitlochry, Perthshire, PH16 5JS
Tel: 01796 472173

1 Twin	All En Suite
4 Double	
2 Family	

B&B per person
from £18.50 Single
from £18.50 Dbl/Twn

Open Mar-Oct
B&B + Eve.Meal
from £29.00

A warm welcome awaits you at this listed property situated on outskirts of Pitlochry. Set in picturesque parkland. An 18th century farmhouse retaining its original style but with all bedrooms en-suite and well equipped.

SMALL HOTEL

Donavourd Country House Hotel
Pitlochry, Perthshire, PH16 5JS
Tel: 01796 472100
E-mail: nemckechnie@hotmail.com

1 Twin	All En Suite
8 Double	

B&B per person
from £25.00 Single
from £25.00 Dbl/Twn

Open 15Mar-3Jan
B&B + Eve.Meal
from £35.00

Traditional country house hotel with 8 acres of ground situated in a peaceful elevated location 1 mile south of Pitlochry. Some rooms with four poster beds. Imaginative Scottish cuisine using fresh local ingredients.

HOTEL

Dundarach Hotel
Perth Road, Pitlochry, Perthshire, PH16 5DJ
Tel: 01796 472862 Fax: 01796 473024

4 Single	All En Suite
13 Twin	
8 Double	
2 Family	

B&B per person
£25.00-£54.00 Single
£25.00-£40.00 Dbl/Twn

Open 9 Feb-14 Jan

This hotel on the edge of the village is architecturally interesting, inside and out and stands in its own secluded garden but still close to town centre. A warm friendly welcome is assured by the resident owners the Smail family. The hotel offers both traditional and new bedrooms. All are well equipped. The airy, well seated public rooms are attractively decorated in warm colours and give many fine views over the surrounding valley.

Important: Prices stated are estimates and may be subject to amendments

Pitlochry, Perthshire | Map Ref: 2A1

SMALL HOTEL
★★

Fasganeoin Hotel
Perth Road, Pitlochry, Perthshire, PH16 5DJ
Tel: 01796 472387 Fax: 01796 474285
E-mail: sabrina@fasganeoin.freeserve.co.uk

2 Single	6 En Suite fac	B&B per person	Open Apr-Oct
2 Twin	3 Pub Bath/Show	from £23.00 Single
4 Double		from £26.00 Dbl/Twn
1 Family		

Traditional family run hotel, with spacious and secluded garden, over 100 years old, situated on the edge of town, close to the theatre. Enjoy morning coffee, an old fashioned "set afternoon tea" or high tea in pleasant surroundings. Home baking and tasty theatre suppers.

HOTEL
★★★★
🚶

The Green Park Hotel
Clunie Bridge Road, Pitlochry, Perthshire, PH16 5JY
Tel: 01796 473248 Fax: 01796 473520
E-mail: bookings@thegreenpark.co.uk
Web: www.thegreenpark.co.uk

6 Single	All En Suite	Open Jan-Dec
15 Twin		
16 Double		
2 Family		

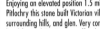

Family run country house hotel enjoying spectacular views over Loch Faskally. Within strolling distance of the shops and a pleasant walk from the Festival theatre, the hotel has become a well known landmark of the town. The hotel has a Red Rossette for food, and is a Taste of Scotland member.

GUEST HOUSE
★★★★

Kinnaird House
Kirkmichael Road, Pitlochry, Perthshire, PH16 5JL
Tel/Fax: 01796 472843
Web: www.kinnaird-house.co.uk

1 Single	4 En Suite fac	B&B per person	Open Jan-Dec
1 Twin	1 Pub Bath/Show	£20.00-£26.00 Single
4 Double		£20.00-£28.00 Dbl/Twn

Enjoying an elevated position 1.5 miles above the delightful small town of Pitlochry this stone built Victorian villa has magnificent views of the surrounding hills, and glen. Very comfortable accommodation, a super breakfast and Mrs Burrows offers hospitality to match.

KNOCKENDARROCH HOUSE

Higher Oakfield, Pitlochry, Perthshire PH16 5HT
Telephone: 01796 473473 Fax: 01796 474068
e.mail: info@knockendarroch.co.uk
web: www.knockendarroch.co.uk

★★★★
SMALL HOTEL

The warmest of welcomes, with first-class food, wines and personal service complement this elegant Victorian mansion. Surrounded by mature oaks and beeches with glorious views over Pitlochry and the Tummel Valley, yet within walking distance of the town centre. Stay at Knockendarroch once and we're confident you'll want to return. AA ★★ 75% Rosettes.

SMALL HOTEL
★★★★

Knockendarroch House Hotel
Higher Oakfield, Pitlochry, Perthshire, PH16 5HT
Tel: 01796 473473 Fax: 01796 474068
E-mail: info@knockendarroch.co.uk
Web: www.knockendarroch.co.uk

6 Twin	All En Suite	Open Mar-Nov
6 Double		B&B + Eve.Meal
		from £48.00

An oasis of tranquillity in the heart of the town. Knockendarroch a gracious Victorian mansion, with glorious views over Pitlochry and Tummel valley. Set in it's own grounds surrounded by mature oaks, Knockendarroch with resident proprietors Jane & Tony Ross, combines a relaxed atmosphere, high standards in food, wines and personal attention. Lots to do locally and a perfect base for sightseeing and touring. Non-smoking hotel.

VAT is shown at 17.5%: changes in this rate may affect prices. |  *Key to symbols is on back flap.*

Pitlochry, Perthshire

Map Ref: 2A1

GUEST HOUSE

★★★

Number 10

10 Atholl Road, Pitlochry, Perthshire, PH16 5BX
Tel: 01796 472346
E-mail: num10pit@tinyonline.co.uk

The relaxed warm atmosphere, and friendly hospitality of experienced hosts Fran and Alan will make you want to return regularly to this cosy retreat. The hotel has comfortable bedrooms, a snug bar, quiet lounge and a dining room serving only fresh food based on Scottish produce. In easy walking distance of the town centre, with a lovely ten minute walk over the river to Pitlochry Theatre.

2 Single	9 En Suite fac	B&B per person	Open Jan-Dec excl
3 Twin	1 Pub Bath/Show	£20.00-£30.00 Single	Xmas/New Year
4 Double		£20.00-£30.00 Dbl/Twn	
2 Family		Room only per person	
		£15.00-£25.00	

PINE TREES HOTEL

Strathview Terrace, Pitlochry PH16 5QR

Telephone: 01796 472121 Fax: 01796 472460
Freephone Reservations: 0800 3281450
e.mail: info@pinetreeshotel.co.uk Web: www.pinetreeshotel.co.uk

Pitlochry's premier country house hotel, discreetly hidden in private woodlands just a short stroll from the town centre. All 20 bedrooms have been superbly refurbished in January 2000. Enjoy the quiet ambience of our beautifully appointed public areas and superb cuisine in our 2 rosetted restaurant.

HOTEL

★★★★

The Pine Trees Hotel

Strathview Terrace, Pitlochry, Perthshire, PH16 5QR
Tel: 01796 472121 Fax: 01796 472460
Freephone Reservations: 0800 3281450
E-mail: info@pinetreeshotel.co.uk
Web: www.pinetreeshotel.co.uk

Personally run Victorian country house in elevated position, with 10 acres of garden and woodland yet close to town centre, neighbouring golf course and all amenities. Two rosettes for food.

2 Single	All En Suite	B&B per person	Open Jan-Dec
1 Suite		£35.00-£64.00 Single	B&B + Eve.Meal
10 Double		£35.00-£49.00 Dbl/Twn	£50.00-£88.00
7 Twin			

SMALL HOTEL

★★★

The Poplars Hotel

27 Lower Oakfield, Pitlochry, Perthshire, PH16 5DS
Tel: 01796 472129 Fax: 01796 472554
E-mail: enquiries@poplars-hotel.co.uk
Web: www.poplars-hotel.co.uk

An imposing Victorian house with a rather unique atmosphere, beautifully situated in a very quiet yet convenient near town-centre location. Tastefully modernised to retain its traditional ambience. True Scottish hospitality personally and caringly provided by experienced Scottish owners Kathleen and Ian, whose local area and activity knowledge can greatly enhance your stay. Glenturret tourism award winner 'Most Enjoyable Hotel in Perthshire 1999.

4 Twin	All En Suite	B&B per person	Open Jan-Dec
4 Double		from £36.00 Single	B&B + Eve.Meal
3 Family		from £28.00 Dbl/Twn	from £43.00

INN

★★★

Port-na-Craig Inn

Port-na-Craig, Pitlochry, Perthshire, PH16 5ND
Tel: 01796 472777 Fax: 01796 472931
E-mail: portnacraig@talk21.com

Nestling on the spectacular banks of the River Tummel in one of the oldest buildings in Pitlochry dating back over 300 years, the Portnacraig Inn and Restaurant has been lovingly restored. Directly below the Pitlochry Festival Theatre and only 200 yards from the famous salmon ladder. Taste of Scotland. 5 minute walk from town centre.

1 Double	All En Suite	B&B per person	Open Feb-Dec
1 Family		from £30.00 Single	B&B + Eve.Meal
		from £22.00 Double	from £40.00
		Room only per person	
		from £18.00	

Important: Prices stated are estimates and may be subject to amendments

Pitlochry, Perthshire | Map Ref: 2A1

★★★

GUEST
HOUSE

Rosehill
47 Atholl Road, Pitlochry, Perthshire, PH16 5BX
Tel/Fax: 01796 472958

| 5 Double | 6 En Suite fac | B&B per person | Open Apr-Oct |
| 2 Family | 1 Pub Bath/Show | £18.00-£21.00 Double | |

Very neat guest house at the centre of this popular Highland town. Peaceful situation just off the high street in easy walking distance of shops, bars and restaurants. Off-road parking. Colourful small garden – Five times winner of Pitlochry in Bloom.

TV 🛏️ 🖥️ P ☕ 🍴 📞

★★★

HOTEL

Rosemount Hotel
12 Higher Oakfield, Pitlochry, Perthshire, PH16 5HT
Tel: 01796 472302/472262 Fax: 01796 474216
E-mail: anne@scottishhotels.co.uk
Web: http://www.scottishhotels.co.uk

2 Single	21 En Suite fac	B&B per person	Open Jan-Dec
8 Twin	1 Priv.NOT ensuite	£22.00-£33.00 Single	B&B + Eve.Meal
8 Double		£22.00-£33.00 Dbl/Twn	£39.00-£50.00
4 Family			

Personally run fully licenced hotel with friendly atmosphere, situated in elevated position overlooking Tummel Valley.

TV 🛏️ 🖥️ P ☕ 🍴 🍽️ 🍷

C 🐕 📠 W V

★★★

HOTEL

Scotland's Hotel
40 Bonnethill Road, Pitlochry, PH16 5BT
Tel: 01796 472292 Fax: 01796 473284
E-mail: stay@scotlandshotel.co.uk
Web: www.scotlandshotel.co.uk

8 Single	75 En Suite fac	B&B per person	Open Jan-Dec
23 Twin		from £28.00 Single	B&B + Eve.Meal
30 Double		from £20.00 Dbl/Twn	from £35.00
10 Family			

Traditionally run Scottish Hotel with garden and views of the countryside, close to the centre of Pitlochry. Health and Leisure Club.

TV 📞 🛏️ P ☕ 🍴 🍽️ 🎱 🎿 🏊 ✂️ 🍷

C 🐕 📠 V

★★★★

GUEST
HOUSE

Torrdarach Hotel
Golf Course Road, Pitlochry, Perthshire, PH16 5AU
Tel: 01796 472136

1 Single	6 En Suite fac	B&B per person	Open Mar-Jan
2 Twin	1 Priv.NOT ensuite	£18.00-£26.00 Single	
4 Double		£18.00-£26.00 Dbl/Twn	

Torrdarach is a splendid country house set in its own beautiful garden close to the golf course with excellent views over the Tummel Valley and Pitlochry. Privately owned and run by Beryl and David. Torrdarach offers quality and comfort in a warm and relaxing atmosphere.

TV 🛏️ 🖥️ P ☕ 🍴 ✗ 🍷 📞

📠 V

★★★

GUEST
HOUSE

The Well House
11 Toberargan Road, Pitlochry, Perthshire, PH16 5HG
Tel: 01796 472239
E-mail: enquiries@wellhouseandarrochar.co.uk
Web: www.wellhouseandarrochar.co.uk

1 Twin	All En Suite	B&B per person	Open Mar-Nov
4 Double		£18.50-£24.50 Dbl/Twn	B&B + Eve.Meal
1 Family			£29.00-£35.00

Personally run, centrally situated in residential area. Easy access to shops, amenities and theatre.

TV 🛏️ P ☕ 🍴 🍽️ 🍷

C 🐕 📠 V

VAT is shown at 17.5%: changes in this rate may affect prices.

Key to symbols is on back flap.

Pitlochry, Perthshire | Map Ref: 2A1

Westlands of Pitlochry ★★ AA

THE TASTE
OF SCOTLAND

160 Atholl Road, Pitlochry, PH16 5AR
Telephone: 01796 472266 Fax: 01796 473994
e.mail: info@westlandshotel.co.uk Web: www.westlandshotel.co.uk

Beautifully situated and enjoying wonderful views, Westlands has been carefully extended and refurbished throughout. All rooms ensuite with TV/radio, tea/ coffee tray, telephone, hairdryer and central heating. Outstanding bistro restaurant/bar food. Special rates for Spring, Winter and Theatre Breaks.
For full details contact Andrew and Sue Mathieson (resident proprietors).

★★★

HOTEL

Westlands of Pitlochry
160 Atholl Road, Pitlochry, Perthshire, PH16 5AR
Tel: 01796 472266 Fax: 01796 473994
E-mail: info@westlandshotel.co.uk
Web: www.westlandshotel.co.uk

1 Single	All En Suite	B&B per person	Open Jan-Dec excl
6 Twin		from £33.75 Single	Xmas/New Year
6 Double		from £28.75 Dbl/Twn	
2 Family			

Recently refurbished, the hotel is pleasantly situated on the edge of town. The new Garden Room Restaurant uses fresh produce. Taste of Scotland.

St Andrews, Fife | Map Ref: 2D2

THE ALBANY HOTEL

56-58 NORTH STREET, ST ANDREWS, FIFE KY16 9AH
TEL: 01334 477737 FAX: 01334 477742
E.MAIL: enqu@standrewsalbany.co.uk WEB: www.standrewsalbany.co.uk

Peacefully situated in the heart of St Andrews beside the cathedral, castle and university, close to shops, restaurants, theatre and all golf courses. Our traditional, elegant, Georgian terraced house built in 1795 is tastefully converted for use as a small informal licensed hotel specialising in very comfortable accommodation for groups and individuals at a most competitive price.

★★★

HOTEL

The Albany Hotel
56/58 North Street, St Andrews, KY16 9AH
Tel: 01334 477737 Fax: 01334 477742
E.mail: enqu@standrewsalbany.co.uk
Web: www.standrewsalbany.co.uk

6 Single	All En Suite	B&B per person	Open Jan-Dec
8 Twin		from £75.00 Single	
3 Double		from £55.00 Dbl/Twn	
4 Family			

Peacefully situated in the heart of St Andrews. Close to shop, restaurants, golf courses and historic amenity. This elegant Georgian town house has been cleverly and simpathetically converted for use as a hotel. With only 21 rooms, each one tastefully decorated, the Albany Hotel is able to maintain high standards in accommodation at a very competitive price.

★★★

GUEST
HOUSE

Amberside Guest House
4 Murray Park, St Andrews, Fife, KY16 9AW
Tel/Fax: 01334 474644
E-mail: amberside@talk21.com

1 Single	Priv.facilities	B&B per person	Open Jan-Dec
2 Twin	Ensuite	from £20.00 Single	
1 Double	Ensuite	from £20.00 Dbl/Twn	
1 Family	Ensuite	Room only per person	
		from £17.00	

A warm welcome awaits at this Victorian town home with traditional, wide breakfast choice. Splendid central location. Non smoking. Let us help to arrange your vacation time and interests, eg golf, horse riding, sightseeing etc.

Important: Prices stated are estimates and may be subject to amendments

St Andrews, Fife   Map Ref: 2D2

Annandale Guest House
23 Murray Park, St Andrews, Fife, KY16 9AW
Tel: 01334 475310/0800 9804690 Fax: 01334 475310
E-mail: brian@dcs.st-and.ac.uk

2 Twin	All En Suite	B&B per person	Open Jan-Dec
2 Double		from £21.00 Dbl/Twn	
1 Family			

A family run guest house in centre of town, just off the beach and foreshore. Convenient to Old Course for golfers and St Andrews Aquarium for families. Central to university, shops, restaurants and historical areas.

Arran House
5 Murray Park, St Andrews, Fife, KY16 9AW
Tel: 01334 474724 Fax: 01334 477364
Web: www.smoothhound.co.uk/hotels/arran

1 Single	3 En Suite fac	B&B per person	Open Jan-Dec
1 Twin	1 Pub Bath/Show	from £25.00 Single	
1 Double	1 Priv.NOT ensuite	from £25.00 Dbl/Twn	
1 Family			

Comfortably appointed Victorian terraced home located within the centre of historic St. Andrews town. Cinema, restaurants and other amenities nearby. Within easy access of golf courses, cathedral and castle. Excellent base for enjoying this University town, or exploring the East Neuk of Fife.

Aslar Guest House
120 North Street, St Andrews, Fife, KY16 9AF
Tel: 01334 473460 Fax: 01334 477540
E-mail: enquiries@aslar.com
Web: www.aslar.com

1 Single	All En Suite	B&B per person	Open Jan-Dec
2 Twin		from £28.00 Single	
2 Double		from £28.00 Dbl/Twn	
		Room only	
		from £50.00	

Victorian family run terraced house furnished to a high standard with period features. Centrally situated for shops, golf courses, restaurants and cultural pursuits.

Burness House
Murray Park, St Andrews, Fife, KY16 9AW
Tel/Fax: 01334 474314
E-mail: burness.house@virgin.net
Web: www.burnesshouse.co.uk

1 Twin	All En Suite	B&B per person	Open Jan-Dec
2 Double		from £28.00 Single	
2 Family		from £20.00 Dbl/Twn	

Comfortable family run guest house located near the centre of St Andrews with easy access to historic monuments and golf courses. Expect a very warm welcome.

Five Pilmour Place
5 Pilmour Place, St Andrews, Fife, KY16 9HZ
Tel: 01334 474001 Fax: 01334 473881

1 Twin	All En Suite	B&B per person	Open Jan-Dec
1 Double		£28.00-£60.00 Single	
2 Family		£18.00-£30.00 Dbl/Twn	

Personally run Georgian terraced guest house with its own walled garden, 2 minutes from golf course, town centre with its many restaurants and speciality shops, beach and University.

VAT is shown at 17.5%: changes in this rate may affect prices.   *Key to symbols is on back flap.*

St Andrews, Fife   Map Ref: 2D2

★★

CAMPUS
ACCOMMODATION

Hamilton Hall, Univ. of St Andrews
The Scores, St Andrews, Fife, KY16 9BD
Tel: 01334 462000 Fax: 01334 462500
E-mail: holidays@st-andrews.ac.uk
Web: www.st-andrews.ac.uk

20 Single	45 Pub Bath/Show	B&B per person	Open Jun-Sep
25 Twin		from £25.70 Single	B&B + Eve.Meal
			from £34.95

A spacious Victorian building with fine architectural features which is
situated opposite the Old Course and the sea. Five minutes walk from a
range of pubs and restaurants. Ten minutes from the major historic
attractions of St Andrews. Easy access from the bus station.

★★★

HOTEL

Hazelbank Hotel
28 The Scores, St Andrews, Fife, KY16 9AS
Tel/Fax: 01334 472466

2 Single	All En Suite	B&B per person	Open Jan-Dec excl
8 Twin		from £45.00 Single	Xmas/New Year
8 Double		from £30.00 Dbl/Twn	B&B + Eve.Meal
3 Family			from £45.00

Refurbished elegant Victorian townhouse. Overlooking St Andrews Bay and
golf courses. A drive and a wedge from the 18th on the Old Course. 3
minutes walk to University and historic town centre.

★★★

GUEST
HOUSE

Montague House
21 Murray Park, St Andrews, Fife, KY16 9AW
Tel: 01334 479287 Fax: 01334 475827
E-mail: montague@easynet.co.uk

1 Single	All En Suite	B&B per person	Open Jan-Dec
1 Twin		from £25.00 Single	
2 Double		from £25.00 Dbl/Twn	
3 Family			

Completely refurbished Victorian terraced house with themed rooms, some
with hand painted murals, convenient for the town centre, cinema, shops,
restaurants and bars. Golf courses, historic buildings, University, seashore
all within a few minutes walk.

★★★

HOTEL

New Hall, University of St Andrews
North Haugh, St Andrews, Fife, KY16 9XW
Tel: 01334 462000 Fax: 01334 462500
E-mail: holidays@st-andrews.ac.uk
Web: www.st-andrews.ac.uk

48 Double	All En Suite	B&B per person	Open Jun-Sep
24 Family		from £38.95 Single	B&B + Eve.Meal
		from £30.75 Double	from £40.10

Modern accommodation in parkland setting for conferences and groups, as
well as short breaks for individuals and families. Breakfast, lunch and
dinner are served in the restaurant. The bar provides informal meals
throughout the day. There is ample car parking. New Hall is within
walking distance of the old town, the golf courses and the beach.

★★★★★

INTERNATIONAL
RESORT HOTEL

The Old Course Hotel Golf Resort & Spa
St Andrews, Fife, KY16 9SP
Tel: 01334 474371 Fax: 01334 477668
E-mail: info@oldcoursehotel.co.uk

146 Twin/	All En Suite	B&B per person	Open Jan-Dec
Double	Suites avail	From £180.00-£425.00 Single	B&B + Eve.Meal
		From £195.00-£520.00 Dbl/Twn	£218.50-£463.50

Overlooking the famous 17th Fairway, the Old Course Hotel Golf Resort
and Spa blends the elegant with the strikingly modern. Enjoy superb
cuisine and international atmosphere in the cocktail bar and grill
restaurant whilst admiring the views across St Andrews Bay. The hotel also
boasts its own championship 18 hole course, the Dukes Course.

Important: Prices stated are estimates and may be subject to amendments

St Andrews, Fife | Map Ref: 2D2

GUEST HOUSE
★★★

Pinewood Country House
Tayport Road, St Michaels, by St Andrews, Fife, KY16 0DU
Tel: 01334 839860 Fax: 01334 839868
E-mail: accommodation@pinewoodhouse.com
Web: www.pinewoodhouse.com

2 Twin	4 En Suite fac	B&B per person	Open Jan-Dec excl
3 Double	1 Priv.NOT ensuite	from £22.00 Dbl/Twn	Xmas/New Year
			B&B + Eve.Meal
			from £34.00

A country guest house near Tentsmuir Forest, close to three golf courses and just ten minutes drive from St Andrews. Recently refurbished and offers a homely and relaxing atmosphere with good food using fresh, local produce. Scotlands Best Award.

HOTEL
★★★★★

Rufflets Country House
Strathkinness Low Road, St Andrews, Fife, KY16 9TX
Tel: 01334 472594 Fax: 01334 478703
Web: www.rufflets.co.uk

4 Single	All En Suite	B&B per person	Open 12Jan 2001 -
11 Twin		from £95.00 Single	3 Jan 2002
5 Double		from £90.00 Dbl/Twn	B&B + Eve.Meal
1 Suite			from £110.00

Country house with relaxing ambience, set in 10 acres of beautiful gardens providing fresh seasonal produce served in the restaurant. 1.5 miles (3kms) from golf courses and coast.

HOTEL
★★★

The Russell Hotel
26 The Scores, St Andrews, Fife, KY16 9AS
Tel: 01334 473447 Fax: 01334 478279

7 Twin	All En Suite	B&B per person	Open Jan-Dec excl
2 Double		from £45.00 Single	Xmas/New Year
1 Family		from £34.00 Dbl/Twn	B&B + Eve.Meal
			from £49.00

Overlooking St Andrews Bay and 300 yards from 'The Old Course' and town centre. A la carte restaurant. Real ales. Family run with friendly atmosphere.

VAT is shown at 17.5%: changes in this rate may affect prices. | *Key to symbols is on back flap.*

212

ST ANDREWS, FIFE

E

PERTHSHIRE, ANGUS AND DUNDEE
AND THE KINGDOM OF FIFE

St Andrews, Fife

Map Ref: 2D2

St Andrews Golf Hotel

40 The Scores, St Andrews KY16 9AS
Tel: 01334 472611 Fax: 01334 472188
e.mail: thegolfhotel@standrews.co.uk

This beautifully restored Victorian house sits on
the cliffs overlooking St Andrews Bay and Links,
200 metres from the 1st tee of the'Old Course'.
The hotel is owned and operated by the Hughes
family. The 22 individually styled ensuite
bedrooms are rich in fabrics and textures. Enjoy
the elegant lounges and the oak-panelled,
candlelit restaurant with its stunning sea view.
Here chef Colin Masson creates mouthwatering
dishes from the best of local produce
complemented by a wine list of rare quality. More
casual dining is found in Ma Bells Bistro Bar,
serving food all day and grills in the evening. Golf
is central to our business and we specialise in
tailoring holidays to your particular needs.

★★★★

HOTEL

St Andrews Golf Hotel
40 The Scores, St Andrews, Fife, KY16 9AS
Tel: 01334 472611 Fax: 01334 472188
E-mail: thegolfhotel@standrews.co.uk
Web: www.standrews-golf.co.uk

Privately owned hotel, situated 200 yards from the Old Course,
overlooking St Andrews Bay. Imaginative use of local ingredients.

1 Single	All En Suite	B&B per person	Open Jan-Dec
6 Twin		£92-£102.00 Single	
6 Double		£77.50-£100.00	
9 Family		Dbl/Twn	

★★★

HOTEL

Scores Hotel
76 The Score, St Andrews, Fife, KY16 9BB
Tel: 01334 472451 Fax: 01334 473947

Traditional hotel overlooking the Bay. Opposite the 1st tee of the Old
Course. Close to town centre. Renowned restaurant. Special low season
breaks Oct-Apr.

7 Single	All En Suite	B&B per person	Open Jan-Dec
7 Twin		from £73.00 Single	
10 Double		fr £46.50 Dbl/Twn Std	
6 Family		fr £56.50 Dbl/Twn Prm	

★★★

GUEST
HOUSE

West Park House
5 St Marys Place, St Andrews, Fife, KY16 9UY
Tel: 01334 475933 Fax: 01334 476634
E-mail: rosemary@westparksta.freeserve.co.uk

Beautiful Listed Georgian house c1830 in heart of historic town.
Close to Old Course and all amenities.

1 Twin	3 En Suite fac	B&B per person	Open Jan-Dec excl
2 Double	1 Priv.NOT ensuite	from £30.00 Single	Xmas/New Year
1 Family		from £23.00 Dbl/Twn	

Important: Prices stated are estimates and may be subject to amendments

St Andrews, Fife

Map Ref: 2D2

GUEST HOUSE

Yorkston House
68&70 Argyle Street, St Andrews, Fife, KY16 9BU
Tel/Fax: 01334 472019

2 Single	6 En Suite fac	B&B per person	Open Feb-Nov
4 Twin	2 Pub Bath/Show	from £22.00 Single	
3 Double		from £21.00 Dbl/Twn	
1 Family			

Privately owned guest house with several spacious family rooms situated close to west port and town with easy access to golf course, shops, restaurants and cafe bars.

---

by St Andrews, Fife

Map Ref: 2D2

INN

The Inn at Lathones
by Largoward, St Andrews, Fife, KY9 1JE
Tel: 01334 840494 Fax: 01334 840694
E-mail: Lathones@theinn.co.uk

2 Single	All En Suite	B&B per person	Open Jan-Dec
5 Twin		from £60.00 Single	B&B + Eve.Meal
5 Double		from £50.00 Dbl/Twn	from £144.00
2 Family			

Charming 400 year old Coaching Inn, just 5 miles from St Andrews. Sympathetically restored and enlarged. Offering modern comfort, great food and friendly people to look after your every need. Award winning chef, using freshest of local Scottish produce.

---

nr St Andrews, Fife

Map Ref: 2D2

HOTEL

Drumoig Hotel & Golf Course
St Andrews, Fife, KY16 0BE
Tel: 01382 541800 Fax: 01382 542211
Web: www.drumoigleisure.com

18 Twin	All En Suite	B&B per person	Open Jan-Dec
6 Double		from £57.50 Single	B&B + Eve.Meal
5 Suites		from £40.00 Dbl/Twn	from £75.00

Set in 400 acres of charming countryside. A 15 minute drive from St Andrews or 10 minutes to Dundee. Surrounding area offers many activities and cultural places of interest. The restaurant and bar overlooks a well manicured 18-hole championship golf course, with patio terrace from which to enjoy the view.

VAT is shown at 17.5%: changes in this rate may affect prices.

Key to symbols is on back flap.

BETWEEN THE GRANITE OF THE HIGH CAIRNGORMS AND A DRAMATIC UNSPOILT COASTLINE, LIE HILLS, MOORS AND WOODED FARMLANDS, RIVER VALLEYS AND CHARACTERFUL TOWNS, AS WELL AS ABERDEEN, SCOTLAND'S THIRD CITY, NOTED FOR ITS UNIQUE SILVER GRANITE ARCHITECTURE AND ITS FLORAL DISPLAYS.

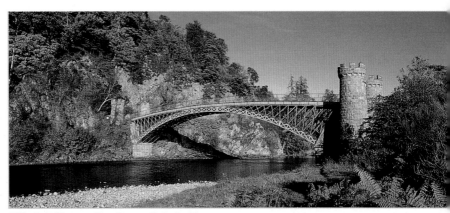

Telford's Bridge over River Spey at Craigellachie

ABERDEEN OFFERS PLENTY for visitors: museums, art gallery, great shopping plus an expanding range of leisure attractions along its extensive promenade. The city is also the gateway to Royal Deeside, noted not just for Balmoral Castle and royal family connections, but beautiful scenery with plenty of walking, climbing and castles to visit nearby, plus Royal Lochnagar Distillery.

MALT WHISKY IS MOST strongly associated with Moray and its unique Malt Whisky Trail, offering a wide choice of distilleries to visit many of which are located along the beautiful birchwood setting of the River Spey. The third major river in this area, the River Don, is associated with the Castle Trail, where some of the finest castles in Scotland are linked in a signposted trail, which range from the medieval fortress of Kildrummy to the Adam revival grandeur of Haddo House.

THE COASTLINE OFFERS yet more delights, not just in the coastal links golf courses, endless beaches and spectacular cliffs and coves, but also in a further range of visitor attractions, including the unique Museum of Scottish Lighthouses at Fraserburgh, the site of Scotland's first lighthouse, and also the equally unique displays at Macduff Marine Aquarium, where a natural kelp reef – seen through one of the largest viewing windows in any British aquarium – shelters a community of fish and other sea creatures usually only seen by divers.

Cardhu Distillery, Knockando, Aberlour

Grathes Castle, Banchory

GRAMPIAN IS CERTAINLY full of surprises –
including the chance to see Britain's largest
resident colony of bottle-nose dolphins, which
turn up close to land anywhere on the coast
between Findhorn and Banff.

EVENTS
GRAMPIAN HIGHLANDS, ABERDEEN AND THE NORTH EAST COAST

4-7 APRIL
Sprit of Speyside Whisky Festival
Various venues, Speyside
Enjoy tastings, distillery visits, music and other themed activities during the celebration of whisky in it's spiritual home.
Contact: Elgin Tourist Information Centre
TEL: **01343 542666**
www.spiritofspeyside.com

7-8 JULY
Scottish Traditional Boat Festival
Portsoy, Banffshire
Traditional boats, craft and trade demonstrations, live music, street theatre, and food fayre.
TEL: **01261 842951**
www.sixvillages.org.uk/boatfest

1-11 AUGUST
Aberdeen International Youth Festival
Various venues, North East
An international multi-arts festival featuring some if the world's finest orchestras, bands, choirs, dance and theatre groups.
Contact: Ms N Wallis
TEL: **020 8946 2995**
TICKET LINE: **01224 641122**

3-6 AUGUST
Speyfest
Various venues, Fochabers
Pan-Celtic festival of traditional music and crafts.
Contact: Mr P Devine
TEL: **01343 820951**
www.speyfest.com

1 SEPTEMBER
Braemar Highland Gathering
The Princess Royal and Duke of Fife Memorial Park, Braemar
The first gathering in Braemar was nine hundred years ago making it the longest running gathering. The event is very popular and tickets need to be booked in advance. Attractions include heavy and track events, piping & highland dancing. The patron of the gathering is Her Majesty the Queen.
Contact: WM Meston
TEL: **01399 755377**

8-17 SEPTEMBER
Techfest
Various venues, Aberdeenshire
Aberdeen and the North East of Scotland's festival of technology and science, involving industry, schools and the community in an effort to promote science and technology.
TEL: **01224 274195**

*12-20 OCTOBER
Aberdeen Alternative Festival
Various venues, Aberdeen
Arts festival featuring music, drama, comedy, dance & children's events.
Contact: Aberdeen Alternative Festival
TEL: **01224 635822**
www.abfest.dial.pipex.com

31 DECEMBER
Stonehaven Fireball Festival
High Street, Stonehaven
Traditional fireball festival parade through the streets of Stonehaven.
Contact: Leisure & Recreation Department, South Aberdeenshire Council
TEL: **01569 762001**

*provisional dates

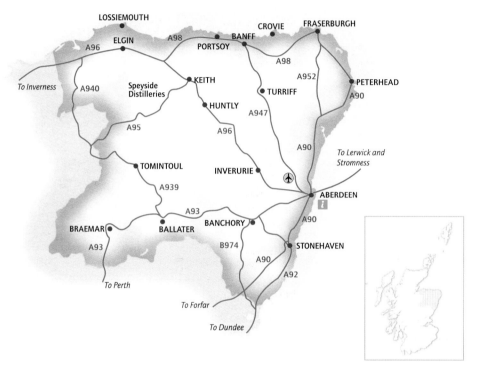

ABERDEEN AND GRAMPIAN TOURIST BOARD

27 Albyn Place

Aberdeen

AB10 1YL

TEL: **01224 632727**

FAX: **01224 581367**

www.agtb.org

ABERDEEN AND
GRAMPIAN
TOURIST BOARD

ABERDEEN
St Nicholas House
Broad Street
TEL: **(01224) 632727**
Jan-Dec

ALFORD
Railway Museum
Station Yard
TEL: **(019755) 62052**
Easter-Sept

BALLATER
Station Square
TEL: **(013397) 55306**
Easter-end Oct

BANCHORY
Bridge Street
TEL: **(01330) 822000**
Easter-Oct

BANFF
Collie Lodge
TEL: **(01261) 812419**
Easter-Sept

BRAEMAR
The Mews
Mar Road
TEL: **(013397) 41600**
April-Oct

CRATHIE
Car Park
Balmoral Castle
TEL: **(013397) 42414**
Easter-Oct

DUFFTOWN
Clock Tower
The Square
TEL: **(01340) 820501**
Easter-Oct

ELGIN
17 High Street
TEL: **(01343) 542666/543388**
Jan-Dec

FORRES
116 High Street
TEL: **(01309) 672938**
Easter-Oct

FRASERBURGH
Saltoun Square
TEL: **(01346) 518315**
Easter-Sept

HUNTLY
The Square
TEL: **(01466) 792255**
Easter-Oct

INVERURIE
18 High Street
TEL: **(01467) 625800**
Jan-Dec

STONEHAVEN
66 Allardice Street
TEL: **(01569) 762806**
Easter-Oct

TOMINTOUL
The Square
TEL: **(01807) 580285**
Easter-Oct

| Aberdeen | | | | Map Ref: 4G10 | | | |

GUEST HOUSE
★★★

Abbian Guest House
148 Crown Street, Aberdeen, AB11 6HS
Tel/Fax: 01224 575826

1 Single	7 En Suite fac	B&B per person
1 Twin		£28.00-£35.00 Single
3 Double		£22.00-£25.00 Dbl/Twn
2 Family		

Open Jan-Dec

Victorian mid-terraced family run house, in central location convenient for bus, rail, sea ferry and city centre entertainments. Completely modernised, fantastic power showers.

SMALL HOTEL
★★★★

Aberdeen Craiglynn Hotel
36 Fonthill Road, Aberdeen, AB11 6UJ
Tel: 01224 584050 Fax: 01224 212225
E-mail: info@craiglynn.co.uk
Web: www.craiglynn.co.uk

5 Single	7 En Suite fac	B&B per person
1 Twin	2 Priv Bath/Show	from £30.00 Single
2 Double		from £27.50 Dbl/Twn
1 Family		

Open Jan-Dec excl Xmas

A small family run hotel renowned for its Victorian elegance with modern comforts. Ideally situated for business or leisure. Taste of Scotland member. Car park. Residential licence.

HOTEL
★★★★
&

Aberdeen Patio Hotel
Beach Boulevard, Aberdeen, AB24 5EF
Tel: 01224 633339/380000 Fax: 01224 638833
E-mail: patioab@globalnet.co.uk
Web: www.patiohotels.com

29 Twin	All En Suite	B&B per person
93 Double		from £39.50 Single
2 Family		from £52.00 Dbl/Twn

Open Jan-Dec

Modern hotel 1/2 mile from city centre and close to Aberdeen seafront. Choice of restaurants. Leisure club, swimming pool and conference facilities. 34 Premier Clubrooms furnished in traditional style.

GUEST HOUSE
★★

Albany Guest House
18 Whinhill Road, Aberdeen, AB11 7XH
Tel/Fax: 01224 571703
E-mail: albanyguesthouse@btinternet.com

1 Single	5 En Suite fac	B&B per person
5 Twin	1 Priv.NOT ensuite	from £23.00 Single
4 Double		from £21.00 Dbl/Twn
5 Family		

Open Jan-Dec

Victorian granite built semi-detached villa in easy walking distance to town centre. Quiet residential area on main bus route. Unrestricted street parking.

GUEST HOUSE
★★★★

Allan Guest House
56 Polmuir Road, Aberdeen, AB11 7RT
Tel: 01224 584484 Fax: 01224 595988
E-mail: stbagh@camtay.co.uk
Web: www.camtay.co.uk

2 Single	5 En Suite fac	B&B per person	Open Jan-Dec
1 Twin	1 Pub Bath/Show	from £25.00 Single	B&B + Eve.Meal
2 Double		from £24.00 Dbl/Twn	from £34.50
2 Family			

A Victorian terraced house situated on a bus route to the city centre. A free parking area close to Duthie Park and Winter Gardens. Sociable owners who are keen to offer comfortable accomodation and warm hospitality. Home cooked suppers available on request, with a wide choice available at breakfast. Special diets can be catered for.

Important: Prices stated are estimates and may be subject to amendments

Aberdeen

Map Ref: 4G10

The Angel Islington Guest House
191 Bon Accord Street, Aberdeen, AB11 6UA
Tel/Fax: 01224 587043

2 Single | 7 En Suite fac
3 Twin | 2 Pub Bath/Show
2 Double
2 Family

B&B per person
from £20.00 Single
from £17.00 Dbl/Twn

Open Jan-Dec

GUEST HOUSE
★★

Semi-detached granite built Victorian house in residential area on south side of city. Shops, railway station and Duthie Park within 10 minutes walk.

Antrim Guest House
157 Crown Street, Aberdeen, AB11 6HT
Tel/Fax: 01224 590987

2 Single | 3 Pub Bath/Show
2 Twin
1 Double
1 Family

B&B per person
from £20.00 Single
from £16.00 Dbl/Twn

Open Jan-Dec

GUEST HOUSE
★

Situated close to city centre, railway and bus stations. Private parking.

Arden Guest House
61 Dee Street, Aberdeen, AB11 6EE
Tel: 01224 580700 Fax: 01224 585396
E-mail: ann@ardenguesthouse.co.uk
Web: www.ardenguesthouse.co.uk

3 Single | 7 En Suite fac
4 Twin | 1 Priv.NOT ensuite
3 Double | 2 Pub Bath/Show

B&B per person
from £25.00 Single
from £20.00 Dbl/Twn

Open Jan-Dec

GUEST HOUSE
★★★

Small, friendly guest house, ideally situated in city centre, close to bus, rail and ferry terminals.

Ardoe House Hotel
South Deeside Road, Blairs, Aberdeen, AB12 5YP
Tel: 01224 867355 Fax: 01224 861283

4 Single | 112 En Suite fac
31 Twin | Suites avail
77 Double

B&B per person
£69.50-£150.00 Single
£49.50-£83.00 Dbl/Twn
Room only per person
£60.00-£150.00

Open Jan-Dec
B&B + Eve.Meal
£95.00-£170.00

HOTEL
★★★★

A Baronial mansion built in 1878, enclosed by trees and rich foliage. Ardoe House stands on high ground commanding a magnificent view of the river Dee and open country. Menus are imaginitive and varied and the Chef gives great attention to the flavour and presentation of each dish.

Arkaig Guest House
43 Powis Terrace, Aberdeen, AB25 3PP
Tel: 01224 638872 Fax: 01224 622189
E-mail: arkaig@netcomuk.co.uk
Web: www.arkaig.co.uk

4 Single | 7 En Suite fac
2 Twin | 1 Pub Bath/Show
2 Double
1 Family

B&B per person
from £21.00 Single
from £21.00 Dbl/Twn

Open Jan-Dec
B&B + Eve.Meal
from £30.00

GUEST HOUSE
★★★

Traditional granite house, city centre 1/2 mile (1km). Convenient to places of interest, station, harbour, airport, both universities and hospital.

VAT is shown at 17.5%: changes in this rate may affect prices.

Key to symbols is on back flap.

Aberdeen	Map Ref: 4G10

HOTEL ★★★★

Atholl Hotel
54 Kings Gate, Aberdeen, AB15 4YN
Tel: 01224 323505 Fax: 01224 321555
E-mail: info@atholl-aberdeen.co.uk
Web: www.atholl-aberdeen.co.uk

11 Single	35 En Suite fac	B&B per person	Open Jan-Dec
10 Twin		£71.00-£81.00 Single	
14 Double		to £45.00 Dbl/Twn	
1 Family			

Privately owned and managed hotel in the West End of Aberdeen, this distinctive building provides comfortable and well appointed accommodation, along with high standards of service, in a friendly and relaxed atmosphere. Extensive menu, bar, conference and function facilities available. Excellent base for exploring the city, and the countryside beyond.

GUEST HOUSE ★★

Balvenie Guest House
9 St Swithin Street, Aberdeen, AB10 6XB
Tel: 01224 322559 Fax: 01224 322773
E-mail: balveniegh@aol.com

2 Single	2 Pub Bath/Show	B&B per person	Open Jan-Dec
2 Twin		£18.00-£22.00 Single	
1 Double		£16.00-£18.00 Dbl/Twn	

Late Victorian granite built house in residential area in West End, close to city centre. Parking. Convenient for local and airport buses.

The Beeches Guest House
112 Victoria Street, Dyce, Aberdeen,
Aberdeenshire, AB21 7AU
Tel/Fax: 01224 722249

3 Single	7 En Suite fac	B&B per person	Open Jan-Dec
4 Twin	1 Pub Bath/Show	from £20.00 Single	
2 Double		from £20.00 Dbl/Twn	

GUEST HOUSE ★★

Family run Guest House. Rooms mainly en-suite. 5 ground floor rooms. Near airport and railway station (Dyce). On bus route to Aberdeen and North. Disabled room (en-suite) with separate enterance and parking space. Non-smoking throughout.

GUEST HOUSE ★★★

Belhaven Private Hotel
152 Bon-Accord Street, Aberdeen, AB11 6TX
Tel/Fax: 01224 588384

3 Single	4 En Suite fac	B&B per person	Open Jan-Dec
1 Twin	4 Pub Bath/Show	£22.00-£32.00 Single	
3 Double		£17.00-£22.00 Dbl/Twn	
1 Family			

Late Victorian granite house in residential area, close to city centre and local park. Rail and bus station nearby. Small private sauna with adjoining Jacuzzi and shower available for guests use.

HOTEL ★★★

The Brentwood Hotel
101 Crown Street, Aberdeen, AB11 6HH
Tel: 01224 595440 Fax: 01224 571593
E-mail: reservation@brentwood-hotel.demon.co.uk

18 Single	All En Suite	B&B per person	Open Jan-Dec excl
3 Twin		£35.00-£70.00 Single	Xmas/New Year
37 Double		£25.00-£40.00 Dbl/Twn	B&B + Eve.Meal
7 Family			£40.00-£50.00

Centrally situated personally run hotel, recently refurbished and within minutes of the city centre. 'Carriages' Brasserie and Bar with A la carte menu.

Aberdeen

Map Ref: 4G10

GUEST HOUSE ★★★

Butler's Islander Guest House
122 Crown Street, Aberdeen, AB11 6HJ
Tel: 01224 212411 Fax: 01224 212411/586448
E-mail: islander@butlerigh.demon.co.uk
Web: www.butlerigh.demon.co.uk/index.htm

A Georgian terraced house in a central situation close to the city centre with all its amenities. A family run establishment with owners keen to maintain high standards throughout. Bus and railways stations nearby.

1 Single	3 En Suite fac	B&B per person	Open Jan-Dec
3 Twin	2 Pub Bath/Show	from £25.00 Single	
3 Double		from £18.00 Dbl/Twn	
		Room only	
		from £20.00 Single	
		from £13.50 Double	

GUEST HOUSE ★★

Campbells Guest House
444 King Street, Aberdeen, AB24 3BS
Tel: 01224 625444 Fax: 01224 624556
E-mail: cam444@zetnet.co.uk

Semi detached house, own car park and on main bus route. City centre 1 mile (2kms). Close to golf links, sandy beach, leisure centre and University. Residents bar/lounge with cable TV. Popular base for golfing parties and close to AECC. About 1 mile to beach and leisure attractions.

1 Single	4 En Suite fac	B&B per person	Open Jan-Dec
3 Twin	1 Pub Bath/Show	from £25.00 Single	
2 Family		from £20.00 Twin	

HOTEL ★★

The Clubhouse Hotel
239 Great Western Road, Aberdeen, AB10 6PS
Tel: 01224 574484 Fax: 01224 585070

Small hotel situated in the West End of the city. Steakhouse serving a wide range of quality beef dishes, plus a selection of other choices; good sized bar, with a sporting theme. Excellent base for the business traveller, or for the visitor coming to explore the city and sorrounding countryside.

10 Twin	All En Suite	B&B per person	Open Jan-Dec excl
1 Double		from £28.00 Single	Xmas/New Year
2 Family		from £20.00 Dbl/Twn	

HOTEL ★★★★

Copthorne Hotel Aberdeen
122 Huntly Street, Aberdeen, AB10 1SU
Tel: 01224 630404 Fax: 01224 640573
E-mail: reservations.aberdeen@mill-cop.com
Web: www.stay.with-us.com

Traditional granite built city centre hotel with tastefully modernised interior.

15 Twin	All En Suite	B&B per person	Open Jan-Dec
74 Double		from £40.00 Single	B&B + Eve.Meal
		from £25.00 Dbl/Twn	from £43.00
		Room only per person	
		from £20.00	

HOTEL ★★★

Corner House Hotel
385 Great Western Road, Aberdeen, AB10 6NY
Tel/Fax: 01224 313063
E-mail: cornerhouse.hotel@virgin.net
Web: www.cornerhousehotel.co.uk

Situated west of the city centre, with easy access to Royal Deeside, this friendly family-run hotel has comfortable and well appointed bedrooms. There is a relaxing residents' lounge and a bright dining room where breakfast and evening meals are served. Private car parking.

6 Single	All En Suite	B&B per person	Open Jan-Dec excl
3 Twin		from £38.00 Single	Xmas/New Year
6 Double		from £25.00 Dbl/Twn	B&B + Eve.Meal
2 Family			from £35.00

Aberdeen | Map Ref: 4G10

CAMPUS ACCOMMODATION ★★

Craibstone Estate
Scottish Agricultural College, Bucksburn, Aberdeen, AB21 9YA
Tel: 01224 711195 Fax: 01224 711298
Web: www.craibstone.com

Halls of Residence, set in extensive country park on outskirts of Aberdeen, with easy access to all amenities.

38 Single	64 En Suite fac	B&B per person	Open mid
20 Twin	13 Pub Bath/Show	from £20.00 Single	March-mid April,
1 Double	4 Priv.NOT ensuite	from £26.00 Twin	July-Sept
			B&B + Eve.Meal
			from £27.00

HOTEL ★★★

&

The Craighaar Hotel
Waterton Road, Bankhead, Aberdeen, AB21 9HS
Tel: 01224 712275 Fax: 01224 716362
E-mail: info@craighaar.co.uk

Quality hotel 5 minutes from Airport and 10 minutes to city centre. First class cuisine. 55 modern ensuite bedrooms/suites all with direct dial telephone, tea/coffee making facilities, satellite TV and trouser press.

3 Single	All En Suite	B&B per person	Open Jan-Dec excl
8 Twin		from £45.00 Single	Xmas/New Year
38 Double		from £26.00 Dbl/Twn	
6 Suites			

GUEST HOUSE ★★★

Crynoch Guest House
164 Bon-Accord Street, Aberdeen, AB11 6TX
Tel: 01224 582743
E-mail: crynoch@talk21.com

Family run Victorian guest house in quiet residential street close to city centre, shops and all amenities.

3 Single	4 En Suite fac	B&B per person	Open Jan-Dec
1 Twin	2 Pub Bath/Show	£20.00-£24.00 Single	
3 Double		£20.00-£24.00 Dbl/Twn	
1 Family			

HOTEL ★★★

Cults Hotel
328 North Deeside Road, Cults, Aberdeen, AB15 9SB
Tel: 01224 867632 Fax: 01224 867699

One of Aberdeen's oldest hotels refurbished to modern standards. Warm relaxing atmosphere.

1 Twin	All En Suite	B&B per person	Open Jan-Dec
8 Double		£39.00-£49.00 Single	
1 Family		£24.00-£32.50 Dbl/Twn	

GUEST HOUSE ★★

Dunromin Guest House
75 Constutition Street, Aberdeen, AB24 5ET
Tel/Fax: 01224 647995

Terraced house in side street, close to RGU and 5 minutes walk to city centre. 10 minutes from bus and rail stations.

1 Single	1 Pub Bath/Show	B&B per person	Open Jan-late Dec
2 Twin		from £20.00 Single	
1 Double		from £19.00 Dbl/Twn	
1 Family			

Important: Prices stated are estimates and may be subject to amendments

Aberdeen				Map Ref: 4G10		

HOTEL

★★★

Dyce Skean Dhu
Farburn Terrace, Dyce, Aberdeen, AB21 7DW
Tel: 01224 723101 Fax: 01224 722965
Web: www.thistlehotels.com

Modern motel, 1 mile (2kms) from airport. Conference and function facilities ,sports complex with squash court, solarium, gym and sauna.

140 Twin   All En Suite
79
Dbl/Fam

B&B per person
from £25.00 Single
from £25.00 Dbl/Twn
Room only per person
from £18.00

Open Jan-Dec
B&B + Eve.Meal
from £40.00

GUEST HOUSE

★

Four Bees Guest House
356 Holburn Street, Aberdeen, AB10 7GX
Tel: 01224 585110

Traditional granite house with long garden, set back from the road. Convenient for city centre and all amenities. On main bus routes.

2 Twin   1 En Suite fac
1 Double   3 Pub Bath/Show
3 Family

B&B per person
from £16.00 Single
from £16.00 Dbl/Twn

Open Jan-Dec

GUEST HOUSE

★★★

Furain Guest House
92 North Deeside Road, Peterculter, Aberdeen, AB14 0QN
Tel: 01224 732189 Fax: 01224 739070

Late Victorian house built of red granite. Family run. Convenient for town, Royal Deeside and the Castle Trail. Private car parking. Dinner available on Wedensday, Friday and Saturday.

1 Single   All En Suite
3 Twin
2 Double
2 Family

B&B per person
from £30.00 Single
from £20.00 Dbl/Twn
Room only per person
from £28.00

Open Jan-Dec excl
Xmas/New Year
B&B + Eve.Meal
from £35.00

HOTEL

★★★

Jarvis Aberdeen City Hotel
Market Street, Aberdeen, AB11 5EL
Tel: 01224 582255 Fax: 01224 582966

Aberdeen's oldest hotel situated in city centre close to harbour and railway station with all day brasserie.

35 Single   All En Suite
15 Twin
48 Double

B&B per person
£47.00-£95.00 Single
£45.00-£55.00 Dbl/Twn
Room only per person
£50.00-£95.00

Open Jan-Dec

HOTEL

★★★

Jarvis Aberdeen Hotel
448 Great Western Road, Aberdeen, AB10 2NP
Tel: 01224 318724 Fax: 01224 312716
Web: www.jarvis.co.uk

Modern hotel close to town centre. Informal atmosphere. A la carte menu, carvery and bar meals. Ample car parking. Functon suites.

13 Single   All En Suite
9 twin
31 Double

B&B per person
from £45.00 Single
from £25.00 Dbl/Twn
Room only per person
from £39.00

Open Jan-Dec
B&B + Eve.Meal
from £35,00

VAT is shown at 17.5%: changes in this rate may affect prices.

Key to symbols is on back flap.

Aberdeen				Map Ref: 4G10

GUEST HOUSE ★★★

Lillian Cottage Guest House
442 King Street, Aberdeen, AB24 3BS
Tel: 01224 636947

1 Single · 1 En Suite fac · B&B per person · Open Jan-Dec
2 Twin · 2 Pub Bath/Show · £23.00-£30.00 Single
2 Double · £19.00-£21.00 Dbl/Twn

Comfortable Guest House, near to city centre, beach and leisure complex. Robert Gordon's Aberdeen Universities and Exhibition Centre nearby. Secure private parking.

B&B ★★★

'Manorville'
252 Great Western Road, Aberdeen, AB10 6PJ
Tel/Fax: 01224 594190
E-mail: manorvilleabz@aol.com

1 Twin · All En Suite · B&B per person · Open Jan-Dec
1 Double · from £25.00 Single
1 Family · from £20.00 Dbl/Twn

Granite dwelling house in close proximity to town centre. On main bus route to Deeside. All rooms ensuite. AA 3 diamonds.

THE MARCLIFFE AT PITFODELS
North Deeside Road, Aberdeen AB15 9YA
Telephone: 01224 861000 Fax: 01224 868860
e.mail: enquiries@marcliffe.com

Independent luxury hotel opened in 1993 in eight acres of wooded grounds in Aberdeen's West End – en route to Royal Deeside. Forty-two rooms and suites, two restaurants, atrium, bar, conservatory. Golf at Royal Aberdeen. Salmon fishing. Galleries, museums, distilleries. A member of Small Luxury Hotels of the World.

★★★★★ HOTEL

HOTEL ★★★★★
&

The Marcliffe at Pitfodels
North Deeside Road, Cults, Aberdeen, AB15 9YA
Tel: 01224 861000 Fax: 01224 868860
E-mail: stewart@marcliffe.com
Web: www.marcliffe.com

2 Single · All En Suite · B&B per person · Open Jan-Dec excl
12 Twin · from £95.00 Single · Xmas/New Year
28 Double · from £105.00 Dbl/Twn · B&B + Eve.Meal · from £125.00

The Marcliffe at Pitfodels is the country house hotel in the city, providing all modern business facilities in 8 acres of wooded grounds.

HOTEL ★★★

Norwood Hall Hotel
Garthdee Road, Cults, Aberdeen, AB15 9FX
Tel: 01224 868951 Fax: 01224 869868
Web: www.norwood-hall.co.uk

2 F.poster · All En Suite · B&B per person · Open Jan-Dec
2 Suites · from £40.00 Single · B&B + Eve.Meal
2 Family · from £30.00 Dbl/Twn · from £45.00
1 Twin
14 Double

21 Bedroom Victorian Mansion within 7 acres of Wooded Gardens. Situated 3 miles of City Centre en route to Royal Deeside. Choice of dining in Tapestry Restaurant or Georgian Bar. A favourite choice for conferences, weddings and family gatherings.

Important: Prices stated are estimates and may be subject to amendments

Aberdeen	Map Ref: 4G10

HOTEL ★★★

Old Mill Inn
South Deeside Road, Maryculter, Aberdeenshire, AB12 5FX
Tel: 01224 733212 Fax: 01224 732884
Web: www.oldmillinn.co.uk

1 Single
2 Twin
3 Double
1 Family

All En Suite

B&B per person
from £45.00 Single
from £27.50 Dbl/Twn

Open Jan-Dec

Delightful, family run, country Inn, 5 miles (8kms) from Aberdeen on the edge of the River Dee. All bedrooms with ensuite facilities.

HOTEL ★★★★

The Palm Court Hotel
81 Seafield Road, Aberdeen, AB15 7YU
Tel: 01224 310351 Fax: 01224 312707
E-mail: info@palmcourt.co.uk

3 Single
1 Twin
19 Double
1 Family

All En Suite

B&B per person
from £30.00 Single
from £40.00 Dbl/Twn

Open Jan-Dec excl
Xmas/New Year
B&B + Eve.Meal
from £37.50

Popular hotel with themed bar and restaurant situated in quiet residential area in West End of city. Convenient for city bypass, airport 5 miles (8kms).

HOTEL ★★★

The Prince Regent Hotel
20/22 Waverley Place, Aberdeen, AB10 1XP
Tel: 01224 645071 Fax: 01224 648157

8 Single
2 Twin
12 Double

All En Suite

B&B per person
from £65.00 Single
from £75.00 Dbl/Twn

Open Jan-Dec excl
Xmas/New Year

Recently refurbished traditional hotel situated in Aberdeen's West End, with easy access to city centre. Ample on site parking.

HOTEL ★★★

The Queens Hotel
51-53 Queen's Road, Aberdeen, AB15 4YP
Tel: 01224 209999 Fax: 01224 209009
Web: www.vagabond-hotels.com

6 Single
5 Twin
15 Double
1 Family

All En Suite

B&B per person
from £40.00 Single
from £25.00 Dbl/Twn

Open Jan-Dec

Occupying an enviable location in the heart of the West End of Aberdeen, this family run city centre hotel offers modern comforts in the traditional style. All bedrooms have ensuite bath and shower and there is ample parking. A range of function suites and conference facilities.

B&B ★★

Regency Rooms
89 Crown Street, Aberdeen, AB11 6HH
Tel: 01224 211600 Fax: 01224 211884

5 Single
3 Twin
1 Double

All En Suite
1 Pub Bath/Show

B&B per room
£30.00 Single Ens
£35.00 Twn/Dbl Ens

Open Jan-Dec

Beautifully appointed rooms with first class facilities. City centre location. Complimentary continental breakfast tray.

VAT is shown at 17.5%: changes in this rate may affect prices.

Key to symbols is on back flap.

Aberdeen		Map Ref: 4G10

Thistle Aberdeen Airport
Aberdeen Airport, Argyll Road, Aberdeen, AB21 0AF
Tel: 01224 725252 Fax: 01224 723745
Web: www.thistlehotels.com

Modern and conveniently located for airport; free courtesy coach.
Banqueting and conference facilities for 500 persons. Swimming pool.

8 Twin   All En Suite
136
Double
3 Family

B&B per person
from £47.00 Single
from £47.00 Dbl/Twn
Room only per person
from £40.00

Open Jan-Dec
B&B + Eve.Meal
from £59.00

Thistle Aberdeen Altens
Souterhead Road, Altens, Aberdeen, AB12 3LF
Tel: 01224 877000 Fax: 01224 896961
Web: www.thistlehotels.com

Modern hotel sited on edge of city with easy access from A90. Bedrooms
thoughtfully designed for your comfort. A la carte restaurant. New leisure
club.

102 Twin   All En Suite   B&B per person
111   from £64.00 Single
Double   from £44.00 Dbl/Twn
3 Family

Open Jan-Dec
D,B&B per person
from £76.00 Single
from £56.00 Dbl/Twn

Thistle Aberdeen Caledonian
14 Union Terrace, Aberdeen, AB10 1WE
Tel: 01224 640233 Fax: 01224 641627
Web: www,thistlehotels.com

City centre hotel in traditional style offering a choice of bars and
restaurants.

20 Single   All En Suite
15 Twin
41 Double
1 Family

B&B per person
from £45.00 Single
from £30.00 Dbl/Twn
Room only per person
from £40.00

Open Jan-Dec
B&B + Eve.Meal
from £60.00 Single

University of Aberdeen
King's College, Aberdeen, AB24 3FX
Tel: 01224 273444 Fax: 01224 276246
E-mail: mary.duncan@abdn.ac.uk

Modern accommodation on university campus all ensuite with access to all
facilities.

43 Single   All En Suite
22 Twin

B&B per person
from £27.50 Single
from £19.75 Twin

Open Jan-Dec excl
Xmas/New Year
B&B + Eve.Meal
from £37.00

University of Aberdeen Conference Office
Kings College, Aberdeen, AB24 3FX
Tel: 01224 273444 (res) Fax: 01224 276246
E-mail: mary.duncan@abdn.ac.uk

Student accommodation in heart of Aberdeen University's old town
campus.

362 Single   76 En Suite fac
22 Twin   Ensuite
43 Single   Ensuite
             45 Pub Bath/Show

B&B per person
£15.00-£27.50 Single
£39.50 Twin

Open 26Mar-12Apr
11Jun-18Sep
from £9.50-£15.50

Important: Prices stated are estimates and may be subject to amendments

Aberdeen
Map Ref: 4G10

★★★
HOTEL

Westhill Hotel
Westhill, Aberdeenshire, AB32 6TT
Tel: 01224 740388 Fax: 01224 744354
Web: www.westhillhotel.co.uk

Modern style hotel in suburbs of Aberdeen, 6 miles (11kms) from city centre. Banqueting and conference facilities. Live entertainment at weekends. New fitness centre.

8 Single	All En Suite	B&B per person
20 Twin		from £40.00 Single
22 Double		from £25.00 Dbl/Twn
		Room only per person
		from £20.00

Open Jan-Dec
B&B + Eve.Meal
from £39.00

★★★
HOTEL

The White Horse Inn
Old Road, Balmedie, Aberdeenshire, AB23 8XR
Tel/Fax: 01358 742404
Web: www.whitehorseinn.co.uk

Modern hotel, 7 miles (10kms) north of Aberdeen on main A90 Aberdeen – Ellon road. Nearby sandy beach and local golf courses. Function suite for 120. Golf packages can be arranged. Large car park adjacent to bedrooms.

17 Double	All En Suite	B&B per person
3 Family		from £30.00 Single
		from £20.00 Double
		Room only per person
		from £15.00

Open Jan-Dec

---

by Aberdeen
Map Ref: 4G10

★★★
HOTEL

Maryculter House Hotel
South Deeside Road, Maryculter, Aberdeenshire, AB12 5GB
Tel: 01224 732124 Fax: 01224 733510
E-mail: info@maryculterhousehotel.co.uk

Dating from 13th century. On the south bank of the River Dee. 7 miles (11k ms) from Aberdeen. Banqueting and conference facilities.

12 Twin	All En Suite	B&B per person
11 Double		from £65.00 Single
		from £45.00 Dbl/Twn
		Room only
		from £75.00

Open Jan-Dec
B&B + Eve.Meal
from £65.00

Ballater, Aberdeenshire
Map Ref: 4E11

★★
HOTEL

Alexandra Hotel
12 Bridge Square, Ballater, Aberdeenshire, AB35 5QJ
Tel: 013397 55376 Fax: 013397 55466

Family run hotel in Deeside village. 7 miles (11km) from Ballmoral and 30 minutes drive from Glenshee ski slopes. Scottish and French cusine served. Non residents very welcome and popular local bar for serving bar lunches and supers.

1 Single	All En Suite	B&B per person
3 Twin		from £24.00 Single
2 Double		from £24.00 Dbl/Twn
1 Family		

Open Jan-Dec
B&B + Eve.Meal
from £42.00

★★★
HOTEL

Auld Kirk Hotel
Braemar Road, Ballater, Aberdeenshire, AB35 5RQ
Tel: 013397 55762 Fax: 013397 55707
E-mail: auld_kirkhotel@compuserve.com

Hotel converted from old church, still retaining many original features. Located in scenic splendour and easy walking distance from Ballater.

3 Twin	All En Suite	B&B per person
3 Double		from £30.00 Single
		from £24.00 Dbl/Twn
		Room only per person
		from £24.00

Open Jan-Dec

VAT is shown at 17.5%: changes in this rate may affect prices.

Key to symbols is on back flap.

Ballater, Aberdeenshire

Map Ref: 4E11

Balgonie Country House

Braemar Place, Ballater AB35 5NQ
Telephone: 013397 55482   Fax: 013397 55482
This charming Edwardian country house is set in three acres of
tranquil gardens, overlooking Ballater Golf Course towards the
hills beyond. Our attentive service to each guest ensures a
relaxing and enjoyable stay. An idyllic base from which to
explore an area of outstanding beauty.

HOTEL

Balgonie Country House Hotel
Braemar Place, Ballater, Aberdeenshire, AB35 5NQ
Tel/Fax: 013397 55482

3 Twin   All En Suite
6 Double

B&B per person
from £69.50 Single
from £59.50 Dbl/Twn

Open Feb-Dec
B&B + Eve.Meal
from £89.50

In heart of Royal Deeside, secluded Edwardian country house set in 4
acres overlooking golf course. Fine Scottish cuisine and attentive service.

**GUEST
HOUSE**

Celicall Guest House
3 Braemar Road, Ballater, Aberdeenshire, AB35 5RL
Tel: 013397 55699

2 Twin   All En Suite
2 Double

B&B per person
from £17.00 Dbl/Twn

Open Apr-Oct

Completely refurbished comfortable accomodation, all en-suite and with
private parking. At centre of this Royal Deeside village with shops and
Restaurants all within strolling distance.

HOTEL

Darroch Learg Hotel
Braemar Road, Ballater, Aberdeenshire, AB35 5UX
Tel: 013397 55443 Fax: 013397 55252
E-mail: info@darrochlearg.co.uk

1 Single   All En Suite
17
Dbl/Twn

B&B per person
from £45.00 Single
from £45.00 Dbl/Twn

Open Feb-Dec excl
Xmas
B&B + Eve.Meal
from £75.00

Country house charm and sophisticated food yet only minutes from
picturesque Ballater. Stunning views south across Royal Deeside from
wooded grounds. The restaurant is also popular with non residents.

HOTEL

Deeside Hotel
Braemar Road, Ballater, Aberdeenshire, AB35 5RQ
Tel: 013397 55420 Fax: 013397 55357
Web: www.royal-deeside.org.uk/deeside.htm

4 Twin   All En Suite
4 Double
1 Family

B&B per person
from £25.00 Single
from £22.00 Dbl/Twn

Open Feb-Dec
B&B + Eve.Meal
from £35.00

Comfortable family hotel in a quiet location serving good freshly prepared
food in an informal atmosphere. Our menu changes daily to reflect the
availability of fresh local produce. Real Ale and interesting malt whiskies
are available in our cosy bar. Two ground floor bedroooms, large garden
and conservatory. Ample off road parking.

Important: Prices stated are estimates and may be subject to amendments

Ballater, Aberdeenshire		Map Ref: 4E11		

B&B ★★

Dee Valley Guest House
26 Viewfield Road, Ballater, Aberdeen-shire, AB35 5RD
Tel/Fax: 013397 55408

1 Twin	1 En Suite	B&B per person	Open Easter – end Oct
1 Double		from £22.00 Single	
2 Family		from £17.00 Dbl/Twn	

Detached house in quiet residential area, close to village centre, bus station and golf course. Ideal for the older / infirm guest with a stair-lift to all bedrooms. Excellent base for touring.

HOTEL ★★★★

Glen Lui Hotel
Invercauld Road, Ballater, Royal Deeside, AB35 5RP
Tel: 013397 55402 Fax: 013397 55545

2 Single	All En Suite	B&B per person	Open Jan-Dec
10 Twin		from £29.00 Single	B&B + Eve.Meal
5 Double		from £34.00 Dbl/Twn	from £45.00
2 Family			

A small friendly Country House Hotel situated in a quiet corner of this picturesque Highland village with views over the golf course to the dark mountains beyond. Separate pine terrace accommodation available in the garden grounds, particularly suited to the more independant traveller. A wide range of outdoor activities available in this spectacular region.

GOLD

RESTAURANT WITH ROOMS ★★★★

The Green Inn Restaurant with Rooms
9 Victoria Road, Ballater, Aberdeenshire, AB35 5QQ
Tel/Fax: 013397 55701

2 Twin	All En Suite	Open Jan-Dec excl
1 Double		New Year
		B&B + Eve.Meal
		from £59.50

'A Restaurant with Rooms' overlooking the village green. With ample free on street parking. The Inn has a 'Taste of Scotland' menu specialising in freshly prepared local produce.

HOTEL ★★★★

Hilton Craigendarroch
Braemar Road, Ballater, Aberdeenshire, AB35 5XA
Tel: 013397 55858 Fax: 013397 55447

14 Twin	All En Suite	B&B per person	Open Jan-Dec
25 Double	Suites avail	from £100.00 Single	
6 Family		from £70.00 Dbl/Twn	

Country house elegance in an unparalleled setting, with a relaxing leisure club and timeshare lodges. Restaurant enjoys a fine reputation.

GUEST HOUSE ★★★★

Moorside Guest House
Braemar Road, Ballater, Aberdeenshire, AB35 5RL
Tel/Fax: 013397 55492
E-mail: moorside.house@virgin.net

2 Twin	All En Suite	B&B per person	Open Apr-Oct
4 Double		from £20.00 Dbl/Twn	
3 Family			

Friendly, personally run guest house in beautiful village in heart of Royal Deeside. All rooms ensuite, TVs, hairdryers and courtesy trays. Excellent breakfasts with homemade bread and preserves. Large garden and car park. Excellent restaurants nearby.

VAT is shown at 17.5%: changes in this rate may affect prices.

Key to symbols is on back flap.

by Ballater, Aberdeenshire   Map Ref: 4E11

Loch Kinord Hotel

Ballater Road, Dinnet, Royal Deeside, Aberdeenshire AB34 5JY
Tel: 013398 85229 Fax: 013398 87007
e.mail: info@loch-kinord-hotel.com Web: www.loch-kinord-hotel.com

Set in the heart of Royal Deeside, this Victorian Hotel offers an ideal location to explore the many tourist and sporting activities. Whisky distilleries, Highland Games, castles, golf, fishing, shooting, skiing, walking etc. Afterwards enjoy good food and a fine selection of malt whisky in front of real log fires.

★★★

HOTEL

Loch Kinord Hotel
Ballater Road, Dinnet, Aberdeenshire, AB34 5JY
Tel: 013398 85229 Fax: 013398 87007
E.mail: info@loch-kinord-hotel.com
Web: www.loch-kinord-hotel.com

Under the enthusiastic new ownership of Jenny and Andrew Cox the hotel has undergone some refurbishment. Situated in the centre of this small village it makes a great base for exploring Royal Deeside, skiing, walking, and playing golf. Non-residents very welcome and popular in the area for excellent food.

1 Single	9 En Suite fac	B&B per person	Open Jan-Dec
1 Twin	6 Pub Bath/Show	from £30.00 Single	B&B + Eve.Meal
10 Double		from £20.00 Dbl/Twn	from £45.00
3 Family			

Banchory, Aberdeenshire   Map Ref: 4F11

★★★

HOTEL

Banchory Lodge Hotel
Dee Street, Banchory, Kincardineshire, AB31 3HS
Tel: 01330 822625 Fax: 01330 825019

Privately owned Georgian country house hotel, set amidst Highland scenery with River Dee running through its extensive grounds.

4 Twin	All En Suite	B&B per person	Open Jan-Dec
11 Double		from £65.00 Single	B&B + Eve.Meal
7 family		from £90.00 Dbl/Twn	from £80.00

★★

HOTEL

The Burnett Arms Hotel
25 High Street, Banchory, Kincardineshire, AB31 5TD
Tel: 01330 824944 Fax: 01330 825553
E-mail: theburnett@totalise.co.uk

Former 19c coaching inn situated at the centre of a small, attractive gateway town to Royal Deeside. An ideal base for touring numerous local attractions.

4 Single	All En Suite	B&B per person	Open Jan-Dec
6 Twin		£40.00-£56.00 Single	B&B + Eve.Meal
6 Double		£28.00-£38.00 Dbl/Twn	£35.00-£45.00

Important: Prices stated are estimates and may be subject to amendments

Banchory, Aberdeenshire   Map Ref: 4F11

★★★★
HOTEL

Raemoir House Hotel
Raemoir, Banchory, Aberdeen AB31 4ED
Tel: 01330 824884 Fax: 01330 822171
e.mail: raemoirhse@aol.com Web: www.raemoir.com

Beautiful and timeless, a Scottish Baronial Manor set in 3,500 acres of
parkland and forest in Royal Deeside. Filled with a fine collection of
antiques, Raemoir is famed and has prestigious awards
for its hospitality and food. A host of activities available including
romantic castles and whisky trails.

★★★★
HOTEL

Raemoir House Hotel
Raemoir, Banchory, Kincardineshire, AB31 4ED
Tel: 01330 824884 Fax: 01330 822171
E-mail: raemoirhse@aol.com
Web: www.raemoir.com

Dating from 16c, country house on a 3,500 acre estate. We offer salmon
fishing, tennis, shooting and 9 hole mini-golf. Self catering apartments
available.

5 Single	All En Suite	B&B per person	Open Jan-Dec
7 Twin		from £50.00 Single	B&B + Eve.Meal
8 Double		from £40.00 Dbl/Twn	from £65.00

★★★★
HOTEL

Tor-Na-Coille Hotel
Inchmarlo Road, Banchory, Aberdeenshire AB31 4AB
Tel: 01330 822242 Fax: 01330 824012
E-mail: tornacoille@btinternet.com

Privately owned country house hotel, close to Banchory town centre with
recreational facilities. Conference and private dining facilities. 2 squash
courts. Seasonal breaks available.

1 Single	All En Suite	B&B per person	Open Jan-Dec excl Xmas
11 Twin		from £55.00 Single	
11 Double		from £55.00 Dbl/Twn	
2 Family			

Banff   Map Ref: 4F7

BANFF LINKS HOTEL
SWORDANES, BANFF AB45 2JJ
Tel: 01261 812414 Fax: 01261 812463

A warm and friendly welcome awaits at this family run hotel.
All rooms ensuite with magnificent sea views. Highly acclaimed
restaurant specialising in fresh local seafood. Ideal base for golf,
walking, fishing, water sports, castle and whisky trails. Special
offer breaks.

★★
HOTEL

Banff Links Hotel
Swordanes, Banff, AB45 2JJ
Tel: 01261 812414 Fax: 01261 812463

Family run hotel on Links with sandy beach and most rooms ensuite with
sea views. Ideal for fishing, golfing and outdoor activities.

2 Single	All En Suite	B&B per person	Open Jan-Dec
2 Twin	1 Pub Bath/Show	£30.00-£39.00 Single	B&B + Eve.Meal
4 Double		£20.00-£30.00 Dbl/Twn	£30.00-£45.00
1 Family			

Banff   Map Ref: 4F7

BANFF SPRINGS HOTEL
Golden Knowes Road, Banff AB45 2JE
Tel: 01261 812881   Fax: 01261 815546
Web: www.banffspringshotel.co.uk

Overlooking the golden sands of the Moray Firth awaits a beautiful and
unexploited part of Scotland and a truly special family run hotel. A warm welcome
from genuinely caring staff. Restaurant and brasserie with Taste of Scotland
Award. Ideal for golfing, fishing, art galleries, aquarium, castle and whisky trail.

★★★

HOTEL

Banff Springs Hotel
Golden Knowes Road, Banff, AB45 2JE
Tel: 01261 812881 Fax: 01261 815546
Web: www.banffspringshotel.co.uk

5 Single   All En Suite   Open Jan-Dec
23 Twin
3 Double

A warm welcome awaits you in this family run hotel overlooking the
golden sands of the Moray Firth, a beautiful and unexploited part of
Scotland. Thirty one en-suite bedrooms. Restaurant and Lounge, with the
prestigious 'Taste of Scotland' award. Ideal venue for golfing, fishing, art
galleries, aquarium, antiques, equestrian centres, castles and whisky trails.

★★

**GUEST
HOUSE**

Carmelite House Hotel
Low Street, Banff, AB45 1AY
Tel/Fax: 01261 812152
E-mail: CarmeliteHoHo@aol.com

3 Single   3 Limited ensuite   B&B per person   Open Jan-Dec
1 Twin   from £23.00 Single   B&B + Eve.Meal
1 Double   from £18.00 Dbl/Twn   from £25.00
4 Family

Family run Georgian town house in central location. Convenient for golf
and all amenities. Evening meals available. Cosy residents bar.
Private parking.

★★★

HOTEL

Fife Lodge Hotel
Sandyhill Road, Banff, AB45 1BE
Tel: 01261 812436 Fax: 01261 812636
E-mail: fifelodge@aol.com

1 Single   All En Suite   B&B per person   Open Jan-Dec excl
2 Twin   from £35.00 Single   Xmas/New Year
3 Double   from £27.00 Dbl/Twn   B&B + Eve.Meal
1 Family   from £45.00

Family run hotel in 2 acres, overlooking River Deveron and golf course.
Children's garden area. Function suite available for 280. Many places of
interest locally including Duff House, Sculpture Garden and MacDuff
Aquarium.

Braemar, Aberdeenshire   Map Ref: 4D11

★★

HOTEL

Braemar Lodge Hotel
Glenshee Road, Braemar, Aberdeenshire, AB35 5YQ
Tel/Fax: 013397 41627
Web: www.braemarlodge.co.uk

2 Single   All En Suite   B&B per person   Open Jan-Dec
1 Twin   from £20.00 Single
2 Double   from £20.00 Dbl/Twn
2 Family

Former hunting lodge with 2 acre garden, log fires in public rooms in
winter. 9 miles (14kms) from Balmoral and Glenshee ski area. Non
residents very welcome and a popular local venue for evening meals.

Important: Prices stated are estimates and may be subject to amendments

Braemar, Aberdeenshire — Map Ref: 4D11

★★★★

**GUEST
HOUSE**

Callater Lodge

9 Glenshee Road, Braemar, Aberdeenshire, AB35 5YQ
Tel: 013397 41275 Fax: 013397 41345
E-mail: maria@hotel-braemar.co.uk
Web: www.hotel-braemar.co.uk

A warm welcome awaits you at this pleasant Victorian house in its own spacious grounds. Ideal centre for touring and walking. Village centre nearby. 8 miles to Balmoral Castle and Glenshee Ski Centre. All home cooking using fresh local produce. Evening meal by arrangement.

1 Single	6 En Suite fac
3 Twin	1 Pub Bath/Show
3 Double	

B&B per person
from £25.00 Single
from £25.00 Dbl/Twn

Open Jan-Dec
B&B + Eve.Meal
from £39.50

★★★

**GUEST
HOUSE**

Schiehallion House

10 Glenshee Road, Braemar, Aberdeenshire, AB35 5YQ
Tel: 013397 41679

Comfortable, tastefully decorated, Victorian house with attractive garden at gateway to Royal Deeside. Offering personal service and log fires. One ground floor annexe room. All nationalities welcome.

1 Single	5 En Suite fac
3 Twin	1 Pub Bath/Show
3 Double	
2 Family	

B&B per person
from £20.00 Single
from £18.00 Dbl/Twn

Open Jan-Oct excl
New Year

Buckie, Banffshire — Map Ref: 4E7

★

HOTEL

The Marine Hotel

Marine Place, Buckie, Banffshire, AB56 1UT
Tel: 01542 832249 Fax: 01542 834443

A modern hotel on the harbour front of this busy coastal town. Sauna, jacuzzi and fitness room add to the many facilities available. Popular venue for bar meals and functions.

4 Single	All En Suite
1 Twin	
3 Double	
2 Family	

Room only £29.95
Breakfast from £3.50 pp

Open Jan-Dec

★★★

HOTEL

The Old Coach House Hotel

High Street, Buckie, Banffshire, AB56 1AR
Tel: 01542 836266 Fax; 01542 836361
E-mail: enquiries@oldcoachhouse.co.uk

Former coaching Inn in the heart of Buckie. Recently refurbished offering fresh local produce and a friendly and personal service.

10 Single	All En Suite
9 Double	2 Pub Bath/Show
2 Family	

B&B per person
from £28.00 Single
from £24.00 Double

Open Jan-Dec
B&B + Eve.Meal
from £44.00

Cullen, Banffshire   Map Ref: 4E7

SEAFIELD HOTEL

19 SEAFIELD STREET, CULLEN, BUCKIE, BANFFSHIRE AB56 2SG
TEL: 01542 840791 FAX: 01542 840736

The Seafield Hotel, owned by Alison and Herbert Cox, is situated in the historic town of Cullen. It provides excellent accommodation and service for those requiring peace and quiet. Enjoy a classic menu specialising in local produce, and sample from a selection of over 130 malt whiskies while relaxing in the open fire lounge.

★★★
HOTEL

The Seafield Hotel
Cullen, Banffshire, AB56 2SG
Tel: 01542 840791 Fax: 01542 840736
Web: www.theseafieldarms.co.uk

21 Rooms All En Suite	B&B per person from £48.00 Single from £35.00 Double	Open Jan-Dec

A warm friendly welcome at this family run hotel in the centre of a small town on the Moray coast. Ideal location for golfing, walking and exploring the whisky trail. Midway between Inverness and Aberdeen.

Dufftown, Banffshire   Map Ref: 4E9

★★★
GUEST
HOUSE

Tannochbrae Guest House & Restaurant
22 Fife Street, Dufftown, Keith, Banffshire, AB55 4AL
Tel: 01340 820541
E-mail: tannochbrae@dufftown.co.uk
Web: www.dufftown.co.uk

1 Single	5 En Suite fac	B&B per person	Open Jan-Dec
1 Twin	1 Priv.NOT ensuite	£17.50-£24.00 Single	B&B + Eve.Meal
1 Double		£17.50-£24.00 Dbl/Twn	from £25.00
2 Family			

Personally run restaurant and guesthouse. Ideal for Speyside Way and famous whisky trail. Scottish chef specialises in local fare. Always a warm welcome from Rachel and Graham.

Elgin, Moray   Map Ref: 4D8

★★★★
GUEST
HOUSE

Ardgye House
Elgin, Moray, IV30 3UP
Tel/Fax: 01343 850618
E-mail: ardgyehouse@hotmail.com
Web: www.scottishholidays.net

1 Single	7 En Suite fac	B&B per person
2 Twin	3 Priv.NOT ensuite	up to £20.00 Single
3 Double		up to £20.00 Dbl/Twn
4 Family		

Gracious Edwardian mansion in own extensive grounds easily accessible from A96. 3 miles (5kms) from Elgin. Private facilities available.

★★★
HOTEL

Laichmoray Hotel
Maisonview Road, Elgin. Morayshire, IV30 1QR
Tel: 01343 540045 Fax: 01343 540055
Web: www.laichmorayhotel.co.uk

12 Single All En Suite	B&B per person	Open Jan-Dec excl
10 Twin	from £38.00 Single	Xmas/New Year
12 Double	from £30.00 Dbl/Twn	
4 Family		

Family-run hotel with large car park, close to Railway Station and town centre. Whisky Theme Bar and new conservatory/family room. Serving quality lunch, high tea, supper and dinner. Conference & function facilities also available.

Important: Prices stated are estimates and may be subject to amendments

Elgin, Moray	Map Ref: 4D8

The Lodge Guesthouse
20 Duff Avenue, Elgin, Moray, IV30 1QS
Tel: 01343 549981 Fax: 01343 540527
E-mail: marilynspence5@hotmail.com

4 Single	All En Suite	B&B per person	Open Jan-Dec
2 Single		from £22.00 Single	
1 Double		from £20.00 Dbl/Twn	
1 Family			

A late Victorian listed villa in extensive grounds with private parking, located in a quiet avenue but only a short stroll from the town centre.

Mansefield House Hotel
Mayne Road, Elgin, Moray, IV30 1NY
Tel: 01343 540883 Fax: 01343 552491
E-mail: reception@mansfieldhousehotel.com
Web: www.mansfieldhousehotel.com

5 Single	All En Suite	B&B per person	Open Jan-Dec
3 Twin		from £55.00 Single	B&B + Eve.Meal
10 Double		from £40.00 Dbl/Twn	from £60.00
3 Family			

Completely refurbished former manse with a la carte restaurant conveniently situated near centre of Elgin. 4 poster rooms available. Ideal base for both business and leisure. Member of Taste of Scotland.

The Mansion House Hotel & Country Club
Stirrat's Ltd, The Haugh, Elgin, Moray, IV30 1AW
Tel: 01343 548811 Fax: 01343 547916
E-mail: reception@mhelgin.co.uk

6 Twin	All En Suite	B&B per person	Open Jan-Dec
16 Double		£70.00-£95.00 Single	
		£60.00-£75.00 Dbl/Twn	

19c Scots baronial mansion with a castellated tower set in a quiet situation overlooking the River Lossie. Tastefully restored and decorated. Centrally situated for the castle and whisky trails and within easy reach of numerous excellent golf courses.

Southbank Guest House
36 Academy Street, Elgin, Moray, IV30 1LP
Tel/Fax: 01343 547132

2 Single	10 En Suite fac	B&B per person	Open Jan-Dec
4 Twin	1 Priv.NOT ensuite	£23.00-£26.00 Single	
3 Double		£19.00-£22.00 Dbl/Twn	
2 Family			

Family run, Georgian detached house in quiet residential street. 5 minutes walk from railway station and town centre. Close to Castle and Whisky Trails, walking, watersports.

Sunninghill Hotel
Hay Street, Elgin, Moray, IV30 1NH
Tel: 01343 547799 Fax: 01343 547872
E-mail: wross94063@aol.com

3 Single	All En Suite	B&B per person	Open Jan-Dec
12 Twin		from £35.00 Single	
1 Double		from £27.50 Dbl/Twn	
3 Family			

Victorian house, modern extension with annexe accommodation. Near centre of historic Cathedral town. Many golf courses. Sandy beaches 5 miles (8kms).

Ellon, Aberdeenshire Map Ref: 4G9

HOTEL

★★

Station Hotel
Station Brae, Ellon, Aberdeenshire, AB41 9BD
Tel: 01358 720209 Fax: 01358 722855
E-mail: stathotel@aol.com

Friendly and welcoming family run hotel in the town of Ellon, some 15
miles north of Aberdeen. Restaurant, bar lunches and evening meals;
bus parties for high tea, a speciality, also function facilities available.
Excellent base for exploring the north east: golf, fishing, Castle and
Whisky Trails, historic harbours and coastal villages.

1 Single	All En Suite	B&B per person	Open Jan-Dec
1 Twin		£20.00-£35.00 Single	B&B + Eve.Meal
3 Double		£35.00-£45.00 Dbl/Twn	£25.00-£50.00
3 Family		£50.00-££60.00 Family	
		Room only per person	
		£17.50-£25.00	

Forres, Moray Map Ref: 4C8

HOTEL

★★★★

Knockomie Hotel
Grantown Road, Forres, Moray, IV36 0SG
Tel: 01309 673146 Fax: 01309 673290
Web: www.knockomie.co.uk

A 'B' listed country house c1914, built in an arts and crafts style.
Extended and created to a high standard, retaining much warmth and
character.

6 Twin	All En Suite	B&B per person	Open Jan-Dec
8 Double		£74.00-£115.00 Sgl	B&B + Eve.Meal
1 Family		£57.50-£75.00 Dbl/Twn	from £86.00

SILVER

Ramnee Hotel and Restaurant
Victoria Road, Forres, Moray IV36 3BN
Telephone: 01309 672410   Fax: 01309 673392
e.mail: ramneehotel@btconnect.com

THE TASTE
OF SCOTLAND

A "country house in town" graciously set in manicured gardens a few
minutes' walk from the centre of Forres – "floral capital of Moray".
Ramnee has been consistently commended for true Highland hospitality
and superb cuisine and offers elegant ensuite accommodation.
Ideal for Whisky and Castle Trails, golf, shooting, fishing.

HOTEL

★★★★

Ramnee Hotel
Victoria Road, Forres, Moray, IV36 3BN
Tel: 01309 672410 Fax: 01309 673393
E-mail: ramneehotel@btconnect.com

Close to the centre of Forres and golf course, imposing Edwardian mansion
house refurbished to high standard. Excellent cuisine, hospitality and
service.

2 Single	All En Suite	B&B per person	Open Jan-Dec
7 Twin		£55.00-£80.00 Single	B&B + Eve.Meal
9 Double		£37.50-£60.00 Dbl/Twn	£57.50-£75.00
2 Family			

Fraserburgh, Aberdeenshire Map Ref: 4G7

HOTEL

★★

Saltoun Arms Hotel
Saltoun Square, Fraserburgh, Aberdeenshire, AB43 9DA
Tel: 01346 518282 Fax: 01346 515882

Stonebuilt hotel, family run, situated in town centre close to harbour.
Private car park.

3 Single	All En Suite	B&B per person	Open Jan-Dec excl
5 Twin		£38.00-£50.00 Single	Xmas/New Year
4 Double		£27.50-£45.00 Dbl/Twn	
2 Family			

Important: Prices stated are estimates and may be subject to amendments

---

Garmouth, Moray | Map Ref: 4E7

★★

SMALL
HOTEL

The Garmouth Hotel
South Road, Garmouth, Fochabers, Moray, IV32 7LU
Tel: 01343 870226 Fax: 01343 870632

1 Single	All En Suite	B&B per person	Open Jan-Dec excl
3 Twin		from £30.00 Single	Xmas/New Year
1 Double		from £22.50 Dbl/Twn	B&B + Eve.Meal
2 Family			from £30.00

Family run hotel in listed village at mouth of River Spey. Ideal for walking the Speyside Way, fishing, golfing and riding. 2 annexe bedrooms.

Huntly, Aberdeenshire | Map Ref: 4F9

Castle Hotel

Huntly, Aberdeenshire AB54 4SH
Telephone: 01466 792696   Fax: 01466 792641
e.mail: castlehot@enterprise.net Web: www.castlehotel.uk.com
17th-century former home of the Dukes of Gordon situated in its own grounds above the River Deveron. Comfortable well-appointed ensuite accommodation. Good Scottish food served in our dining room and bar. An ideal base for touring, hillwalking, castle and whisky trails.
Golf courses abound in the area.

★★★

HOTEL

Castle Hotel
Huntly, Aberdeenshire, AB54 4SH
Tel: 01466 792696 Fax: 01466 792641
E.mail: castlehot@enterprise.net
Web: www.castlehotel.uk.com

10 Twin	All En Suite	B&B per person	Open Jan-Dec
5 Double		£45.00-£55.00 Single	
4 Family		£32.50-£42.50 Double	

Formerly the ancient family home of the Gordons. Standing in own grounds overlooking Huntly. Open fires in dining room and lounge. Local fishing.

★★

HOTEL

Huntly Hotel
18 The Square, Huntly, Aberdeenshire, AB54 8BR
Tel/Fax: 01466 792703

3 Single	7 En Suite fac	B&B per person	Open Jan-Dec
2 Twin	3 Priv.NOT ensuite	£25.00-£35.00 Single	
5 Double	1 Pub Bath/Show	£22.50-£25.00 Dbl/Twn	

Traditional Victorian granite built privately owned hotel situated in the town square of market town, ideally situated for touring castle and whisky trails and Nordic Ski Centre. Local golf courses and fishing on Rivers Deveron and Bogie.

---

by Huntly, Aberdeenshire | Map Ref: 4F9

★★★

SMALL
HOTEL

Forbes Arms Hotel
Milltown of Rothiemay, Huntly, Aberdeenshire, AB54 7LT
Tel: 01466 711248 Fax: 01466 711328
E-mail: halkett@forbesarms.co.uk
Web: www.regionline.com/grampian/forbesarms

1 Single	All En Suite	B&B per person	Open Jan-Dec
4 Twin		from £35.00 Single	
1 Double		from £25.00 Dbl/Twn	
		Room only per person	
		from £17.50	

Small coaching Inn on banks of River Deveron. Salmon and sea trout fishing. 40 miles (64kms) west of Aberdeen. Some annexe accommodation.

VAT is shown at 17.5%: changes in this rate may affect prices. | *Key to symbols is on back flap.*

Inverurie, Aberdeenshire — Map Ref: 4G9

SMALL HOTEL ★★

Ardennan House Hotel
Port Elphinstone, Inverurie, Aberdeenshire, AB51 3XD
Tel: 01467 621502 Fax: 01467 625818
E-mail: reception@ardennan.co.uk

2 Single	5 Ensuite fac	B&B per person	Open Jan-Dec
2 Twin	1 Private fac	from £40.00 Single	
2 Double		from £30.00 Dbl/Twn	

Family run hotel on outskirts of Inverurie. Central for touring Aberdeenshire and Castle Trail. Good home cooking using fresh local produce. 15 minutes drive from Aberdeen airport.

HOTEL ★★★

Pittodrie House Hotel
Chapel of Garioch, Inverurie. Aberdeenshire, AB51 5HS
Tel: 01467 681444 Fax: 01467 681648
E-mail: info@pittodrie.macdonaldhotels.co.uk

10 Twin	25 En Suite fac	B&B per person	Open Jan-Dec
17 Double	2 Priv.NOT ensuite	from £90.00 Single	B&B + Eve.Meal
		from £70.00 Dbl/Twn	from £60.00

Country house dating from 1480 on large estate. Mixed arable, forestry and hill land with interesting walks. Open fires, billiards, squash, clay pigeon shooting and 4x4 off road driving.

HOTEL ★★★★

Strathburn Hotel
Burghmuir Drive, Inverurie, Aberdeenshire, AB51 4GY
Tel: 01467 624422 Fax: 01467 625133
Web: www.strathburn-hotel.co.uk

6 Single	All En Suite	B&B per person	Open Jan-Dec excl
4 Twin		from £50.00 Single	Xmas/New Year
14 Double		from £35.00 Dbl/Twn	B&B + Eve.Meal
1 Family			from £65.00

Modern hotel and restaurant with friendly atmosphere, overlooking Strathburn Park in Inverurie. Personally run.

Kildrummy, Aberdeenshire — Map Ref: 4E10

HOTEL ★★★★

Kildrummy Castle Hotel
Kildrummy, Alford, Aberdeenshire, AB33 8RA
Tel: 01975 571288 Fax: 019755 71345
E-mail: bookings@kildrummycastlehotel.co.uk
Web: www.kildrummycastlehotel.co.uk

1 Single	All En Suite	B&B per person	Open 10Feb-2Jan
6 Twin		from £80.00 Single	B&B + Eve.Meal
7 Double		from £67.50 Dbl/Twn	from £69.00
2 Family			

Traditional Scottish mansion house set amidst acres of gardens and woodland overlooking the original 13th century castle ruins. Tastefully furnished and decorated retaining original features. A la carte restaurant using finest local ingredients.

Laurencekirk, Kincardineshire — Map Ref: 4F12

INN ★★★

Marykirk Hotel
Main Street, Marykirk, Laurencekirk, Aberdeenshire AB30 1UT
Tel: 01674 840239

3 Twin	All En Suite	B&B per person	Open Jan-Dec excl
1 Family		from £30.00 Single	Xmas/New Year
		from £30.00 Twin	
		Room only per person	
		from £25.00	

Important: Prices stated are estimates and may be subject to amendments

Macduff, Aberdeenshire — Map Ref: 4F7

The Highland Haven
Shore Street, Macduff, Aberdeenshire, AB44 1UB
Tel: 01261 832408 Fax: 01261 833652

5 Single	All En Suite	B&B per person	Open Jan-Dec
15 Twin		from £30.00 Single	
13 Double		from £22.50 Dbl/Twn	
7 Family			

Well appointed family run 40 bedroom hotel overlooking the Moray Firth. All bedrooms ensuite with satellite tv. etc. The hotel has Whirlpool Spa Bath, Sauna, Turkish Steam Room. Golf, river and loch fishing, sea angling, Duff House (stately house and art gallery), Deep sea Aquarium, Aden Country Park, castle, coastal and whisky trails, near by.

Methlick, Aberdeenshire — Map Ref: 4G9

Gight House Hotel
Methlick, Aberdeenshire, AB41 7BP
Web: www.gight-house@freeuk.com

1 Twin	All En Suite	B&B per person	Open Jan-Dec
2 Double		from £27.50 Single	
		from £22.50 Dbl/Twn	

A small country inn on the edge of the village of Methlick. Characterful bar with a warm and friendly atmosphere, and a good local reputation for real ales and home cooked meals served in the bar and dining conservatory. Gardens containing a putting green and children's play area. Fishing, shooting, golfing and walking are all available nearby, as are several historic castles and gardens.

Newburgh, Aberdeenshire — Map Ref: 4H9

Udny Arms Hotel
Main Street, Newburgh, Aberdeenshire, AB41 6BL
Tel: 01358 789444 Fax: 01358 789012
E-mail: enquiry@udny.demon.co.uk

7 Single	All En Suite	B&B per person	Open Jan-Dec
6 Twin		from £45.00 Single	B&B + Eve.Meal
12 Double		from £41.00 Dbl/Twn	from £48.00
1 Family			

Modernised Victorian hotel, featuring antique furniture, overlooking River Ythan Estuary. Overlooks local golf course and Forvie nature reserve. Home of the famous Sticky Toffee Pudding. Award winning restaurant. Visit us at our website www.udny.co.uk

Oldmeldrum, Aberdeenshire — Map Ref: 4G9

The Redgarth
Kirk Brae, Oldmeldrum, AB51 0DJ
Tel: 01651 872353
E-mail: redgarth1@aol.com

1 Twin	All En Suite	B&B per person	Open Jan-Dec excl
2 Double	3 Pub Bath/Show	from £40.00 Single	Xmas/New Year
		from £25.00 Dbl/Twn	

Detached, granite-built house with large gardens & car park, with fine views towards Bennachie. Non-smoking bedrooms. Home-cooking, including vegetarian choice. Selection of ales (cask conditioned).

Peterhead, Aberdeenshire — Map Ref: 4H8

Carrick Guest House
16 Merchant Street, Peterhead, Aberdeenshire, AB42 1DU
Tel/Fax: 01779 470610
E-mail: carrickhouse@ukonline.co.uk

1 Single	All En Suite fac	B&B per person	Open Jan-Dec excl
3 Twin		from £20.00 Single	Xmas/New Year
2 Family		from £20.00 Twn/Fam	

Comfortable accommodation, centrally situated for all amenities. Two minutes walk from main shopping centre, harbour and beach. Convenient for maritime museum, lighthouse museum and several nearby golf courses.

Peterhead, Aberdeenshire — Map Ref: 4H8

★★★

GUEST HOUSE

&

Invernettie Guest House
South Road, Peterhead, Aberdeenshire, AB42 0YX
Tel: 01779 473530
E-mail: invernettie@talk21.com
Web: www.btinternet.com/~invernettie/

Friendly family run guest house within walking distance of Peterhead.
Ideally located for golf, fishing, and sailing at the marina. Close to the
Maritime Heritage Centre. Evening meal by arrangement.

5 Single	5 En Suite fac	B&B per person	Open Jan-Dec
1 Twin	2 Priv.NOT ensuite	£20.00-£25.00 Single	B&B + Eve.Meal
1 Family	2 Pub Bath/Show	£20.00-£22.50 Twin	£27.50-£32.50

★★★

HOTEL

The Palace Hotel
Prince Street, Peterhead, Aberdeenshire, AB42 1PL
Tel: 01779 474821 Fax: 01779 476119
E-mail: info@palacehotel.co.uk
Web: www.palacehotel.co.uk

Friendly and welcoming privately owned hotel, centrally situated in
Peterhead, but with ample private parking. Dining options include the
Brasserie and the more informal Diner; choice of bars, with live music
some nights. Excellent base for both business and leisure traveller. Much to
see and do in the area, including golf, watersports , fishing, pony trekking,
or exploring the facinating coastline.

3 Single	All En Suite	B&B per person	Open Jan-Dec
3 Twin	Suite avail	£60.00 Single	
62 Double		£25.00-£30.00 Dbl/Twn	
1 Family			

★★★★

HOTEL

Waterside Inn
Fraserburgh Road, Peterhead, Aberdeenshire, AB42 3BN
Tel: 01779 471121 Fax: 01779 470670

Modern 69 bedroomed hotel with leisure club and swimming pool.
All culinary needs met by award-winning team of chefs. Excellent
reputation for hospitality.

22 Twin	All En Suite	B&B per person	Open Jan-Dec
66 Double		from £69.50 Single	
21 Family		from £47.00 Dbl/Twn	
		Room only per person	
		from £55.00	

Portsoy, Banffshire — Map Ref: 4F7

★★

HOTEL

The Boyne Hotel
2 North High Street, Portsoy, Banffshire, AB45 2PA
Tel/Fax: 01261 842242
E-mail: enquiries@boynehotel.co.uk
Web: www.boynehotel.co.uk

Refurbished 18c building on Square in seaside town, close to harbour and
sandy seaside. Home cooking. Under personal supervision.

4 Single	All En Suite	B&B per person	Open Jan-Dec
4 Twin		£20.00-£25.00 Single	B&B + Eve.Meal
4 Double		£20.00-£25.00 Dbl/Twn	£25.00-£30.00
		Room only per person	
		£15.00-£20.00	

Rothienorman, Aberdeenshire — Map Ref: 4F9

★★★

INN

Rothie Inn
Main Street, Rothienorman, Aberdeenshire, AB51 8UD
Tel/Fax: 01651 821206
E-mail: rothieinn@accom90.freeserve.co.uk

Family run 19c stone built inn in village, with own garden. 10 miles
(16kms) north of Inverurie, situated on Castle Trail. Home cooking in
refurbished lounge/restaurant. Cosy ensuite bedrooms recently upgraded.

1 Twin	All En Suite	B&B per person	Open Jan-Dec excl
1 Double		from £30.00 Single	Xmas/New Year
1 Family		£20.00-£25.00 Dbl/Twn	

Important: Prices stated are estimates and may be subject to amendments

Stonehaven, Kincardineshire   Map Ref: 4G11

Arduthie House
GUEST HOUSE ★★★★

Ann Street, Stonehaven, Kincardineshire, AB39 2DA
Tel: 01569 762381 Fax: 01569 766366
E-mail: arduthie@talk21.com

1 Single   5 En Suite fac   B&B per person   Open Jan-Dec
2 Twin   from £18.00 Single   Evening Meal
2 Double   from £24.00 Dbl/Twn   from £12.00
1 Family

Centrally located elegant detached Victorian house with attractive garden. Spacious guests lounge, sun lounge and 4 poster bedroom available. Evening meals by arrangement.

County Hotel & Leisure Club
HOTEL ★★

Arduthie Road, Stonehaven, Kincardineshire, AB39 2EH
Tel: 01569 764386 Fax: 01569 762214

2 Single   All En Suite   B&B per person   Open Jan-Dec
4 Twin   £40.00-£46.00 Single
7 Double   £25.00-£30.00 Dbl/Twn
1 Family

A warm welcome awaits at this personally run family hotel. Opposite railway station, close to A90, a few miles south of Aberdeen. 14 ensuite bedrooms, a choice of bars and eating areas serving local foods, featuring a wide range of freshly cooked daily specials. Squash courts, gym and saunas with extensive conference and banqueting facilities makes the hotel equally suited to the business traveller and families alike.

Heugh Hotel
HOTEL ★★★

Westfield Road, Stonehaven, Kincardineshire, AB39 2EE
Tel: 01569 762379 Fax: 01569 766637

3 Single   All En Suite   B&B per person   Open Jan-Dec excl
2 Twin   from £52.00 Single   Xmas/New Year
1 Double   from £30.00 Dbl/Twn

Granite baronial mansion, built at the turn of the century, with extensive original oak panelling; standing in its own grounds a short distance from the centre of Stonehaven. A family run hotel, with a friendly and relaxed atmosphere, providing an excellent base for exploring the east coast, Royal Deeside and beyond.

Station Hotel
INN ★

Arduthie Road, Stonehaven, Kincardineshire, AB39 2NE
Tel: 01569 762277

4 Single   5 En Suite fac   B&B per person   Open Jan-Dec
7 Twin   £24.00-£35.00 Single   B&B + Eve.Meal
3 Double   £36.00-£46.00 Dbl/Twn   £30.00-£58.00

Recently refurbished this well placed Station Hotel only 50 metres from the train offers some ensuite bedrooms and tea and coffee making facilities. A large lounge bar with separate public bar. Only a short distance to town centre, harbour and beach.

Tarland, Aberdeenshire   Map Ref: 4E10

Aberdeen Arms Hotel
INN ★★

Tarland, Aberdeenshire, AB34 4TX
Tel/Fax: 013398 81225
E-mail: JoanneReddy@aol.com

1 Single   2 En Suite fac   B&B per person   Open Jan-Dec excl
1 Twin   3 Pub Bath/Show   £27.00 Ensuite   Xmas/Boxing day.
2 Double   £17.00 Others
1 Family

Small family run Deeside village hotel. Delightful farmland with rolling hills. Golf course, tennis court and horse riding nearby. Major gliding centre with airfield nearby.

VAT is shown at 17.5%: changes in this rate may affect prices.   Key to symbols is on back flap.

S CENIC VARIETY IS THE KEYNOTE IN THIS AREA — FROM THE SOARING CRAGGY
HEIGHTS OF GLENCOE TO THE WIDE-SKIES AND GLITTERING LOCHANS OF THE
FLOW COUNTRY OF CAITHNESS IN THE NORTH. EAST-WEST CONTRASTS ARE JUST AS
SPECTACULAR. THIS AREA TAKES IN BOTH THE SUNNY, SANDY SHORES OF THE INNER
MORAY FIRTH AROUND NAIRN, WITH ITS COASTAL LINKS GOLF COURSES, AND THE
DAZZLING WHITE BEACHES AROUND MORAR IN THE WEST, WITH THE SMALL ISLES
FILLING THE HORIZON.

Trotternish Peninsula, Isle of Skye

WITH THE TORRIDON MOUNTAINS, Kintail and
the peaks of Sutherland all adding to the
spectacle, this area has more than simply
scenic grandeur. There are substantial towns
with everything for the visitor. Inverness,
sometimes called 'the capital of the Highlands'
is a natural gateway to the northlands. At the
western end of the Great Glen is Fort
William, in the shadow of Britain's highest
mountain, Ben Nevis. This town is another
busy location, a natural route centre and
meeting place with a whole range of facilities
and attractions. The eastern seaboard also has
plenty of interesting towns: picturesque

Cromarty, with the air of an old-time Scottish
burgh, Dornoch with its cathedral and famous
championship golf course. Tain with
Glenmorangie Distillery on its outskirts.
Helmsdale with its evocation of Highland life
in the Timespan Heritage Centre and Art
Gallery. Further north, Wick and Thurso are
major centres.

Dunrobin Castle, Golspie

Plockton

THE ISLE OF SKYE is famed for the spectacle of the Cuillin Hills with their craggy ridges offering a serious climbing challenge. However, there are plenty of less active pursuits. Armadale Castle and the Museum of the Isles, Dunvegan Castle and the Aros Experience all tell the fascinating story of the island.

HOTELS & GUEST HOUSES

EVENTS
THE HIGHLANDS AND SKYE

27-28 JANUARY
Sled Dog Rally
Aviemore, Highlands
Sled dog racing and timed trials
taking place over two days
attracting many teams.
Contact: John & Penny Evans
TEL: **01604 686281**

14 FEBRUARY-3 MARCH
Inverness Music Festival
Various venues, Inverness
Annual music festival and gala.
Contact: Mr R Grant, Inverness
Music Festival
TEL: 01463 716616

5-7 MAY
Feis Rois
Wester Ross, Highlands
Feis Rios is a 3-day traditional
music, song and dance tuition
festival that is now a celebrated
national event.
Contact: Rita Hunter, Feis Rois
Inbhich
TEL: **01349 862600**
EMAIL:
rita@feisrois.freeserve.co.uk

25 MAY-9 JUNE
The Highland Festival
Various venues over the
Highlands.
Music, theatre, dance, visual art
and street events to celebrate
Highland culture.
Contact: Balnain House
TEL: **01463 711112**
EMAIL:
info@highlandfestival.org.uk
www.highlandfestival.demon.co.uk

8 AUGUST
Skye Highland Games
Portree, Isle of Skye
Traditional Highland games plus
a three day piping competition
commencing on Monday 6th
August.
Contact: Allan Stewart
TEL: **01478 612540**

4-7 OCTOBER
Highland Food Festival
Various venues, Highlands
Exhibitions, cookery
demonstrations, wine and food
tastings, competitions, music
and entertainment.
Contact: Pauline Munro
TEL: **01463 713504**

13-28 OCTOBER
Highland Archaeology Week
Various venues, Highlands and
Skye
Many events throughout the
Highlands with an archaeology
theme including walks, talks,
children's activities, exhibitions,
concerts and films.
Contact: Archaeology Unit,
Highland Council
TEL: **01463 702502**
EMAIL:
archaeology@highland.gov.uk

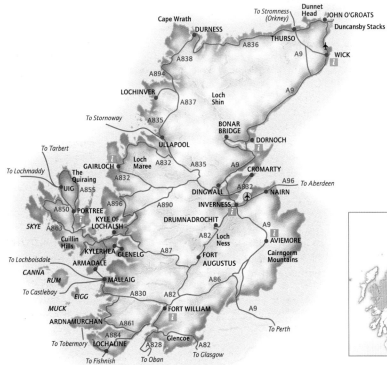

THE HIGHLANDS OF SCOTLAND TOURIST BOARD
Peffery House
Strathpeffer
Ross-shire
IV14 9HA

TEL: **0870 5143070**
FAX: **01997 421168**
www.highlandfreedom.com

THE OFFICIAL WHERE TO STAY G

THE HIGHLANDS OF SCOTLAND TOURIST BOARD

AVIEMORE
Grampian Road
Inverness-shire
TEL: **(01479) 810363**
Jan-Dec

BALLACHULISH
Argyll
TEL: **(01855) 811296**
April-Oc

BETTYHILL
Clachan
Sutherland
TEL: **(01641) 521342**
April-Sept

BROADFORD
Isle of Skye
TEL: **(01471) 822361**
April-Oct

DAVIOT WOOD
A9 by Inverness
TEL: **(01463) 772203**
April-Oct

DORNOCH
The Square
Sutherland
TEL: **(01862) 810400**
Jan-Dec

DUNVEGAN
2 Lochside
Isle of Skye
TEL: **(01470) 521581**
April-Sept

DURNESS
Sango
Sutherland
TEL: **(01971) 511259**
April-Oct

FORT AUGUSTUS
Car Park
Inverness-shire
TEL: **(01320) 366367**
April-Oct

FORT WILLIAM
Cameron Square
Inverness-shire
TEL: **(01397) 703781**
Jan-Dec

GAIRLOCH
Auchtercairn
Ross-shire
TEL: **(01445) 712130**
Jan-Dec

GLENSHIEL
Kintail
Kyle of Lochalsh
Ross-shire
TEL: **(01599) 511264**
April-Oct

GRANTOWN ON SPEY
High Street
Morayshire
TEL: **(01479) 872773**
April-Oct

HELMSDALE
Timespan
Sutherland
TEL: **(01431) 821640**
April-Sept

INVERNESS
Castle Wynd
TEL: **(01463) 234353**
Jan-Dec

JOHN O'GROATS
County Road
Caithness
TEL: **(01955) 611373**
April-Oct

KILCHOAN
Pier Road
Argyll
TEL: **(01972) 510222**
Easter-Oct

KINGUSSIE
King Street
Inverness-shire
TEL: **(01540) 661297**
May-Sept

KYLE OF LOCHALSH
Car Park
Inverness-shire
TEL: **(01599) 534276**
April-Oct

LAIRG
Sutherland
TEL: **(01549) 402160**
April-Oct

LOCHCARRON
Main Street
Ross-shire
TEL: **(01520) 722357**
April-Oct

LOCHINVER
Main Street
Sutherland
TEL: **(01571) 844330**
April-Oct

MALLAIG
Inverness-shire
TEL: **(01687) 462170**
April-Oct

NAIRN
62 King Street
Nairnshire
TEL: **(01667) 452753**
April-Oct

NORTH KESSOCK
Ross-shire
TEL: **(01463) 731505**
Jan-Dec

PORTREE
Bayfield House
Bayfield Road
Isle of Skye
TEL: **(01478) 612137**
Jan-Dec

RALIA
A9 North
by Newtonmore
Inverness-shire
TEL: **(01540) 673253**
April-Oct

SPEAN BRIDGE
Inverness-shire
TEL: **(01397) 712576**
April-Oct

STRATHPEFFER
The Square
Ross-shire
TEL: **(01997) 421415**
April-Nov

STRONTIAN
Argyll
TEL: **(01967) 402131**
April-Oct

THURSO
Riverside
TEL: **(01847) 892371**
April-Oct

UIG
Ferry Terminal
Isle of Skye
TEL: **(01470) 542404**
April-Oct

ULLAPOOL
Argyle Street
Ross-shire
TEL: **(01854) 612135**
April-Nov

WICK
Whitechapel Road
Caithness
TEL: **(01955) 602596**
Jan-Dec

Achiltibuie, Ross-shire — Map Ref: 3G6

★★★★ HOTEL

Summer Isles Hotel
Achiltibuie, Ross-shire, IV26 2YG
Tel: 01854 622282 Fax: 01854 622251
E-mail: summerisleshotel@aol.com

4 Twin	All En Suite	B&B per person	Open Easter-Oct
7 Double		from £50.00 Dbl/Twn	B&B + Eve.Meal
2 Family			from £90.00

Personally run hotel, set amidst magnificent scenery. Annexe accommodation available. Emphasis on cuisine using fresh local ingredients and home baking.

Achnasheen, Ross-shire — Map Ref: 3H8

★★★ HOTEL

Ledgowan Lodge Hotel
Achnasheen, Ross-shire, IV22 2EJ
Tel: 01445 720252 Fax: 01445 720240
Web: www.ledgowanlodge.co.uk

2 Single	All En Suite	B&B per person	Open Apr-Oct
6 Twin		from £34.00 Single	B&B + Eve.Meal
2 Double		from £31.00 Dbl/Twn	from £49.00
		Room only per person	
		from £25.00	

A personally run former hunting lodge, c1904, retaining much of its original charm and character. All bedrooms have private facilities.

Alness, Ross-shire — Map Ref: 4B7

★ INN

Morven House Hotel
70 Novar Road, Alness, Ross-shire, IV17 0RG
Tel/Fax: 01349 882323
E-mail: morvenhotel@gevalvetech.com

1 Single	All En Suite	B&B per person	Open Jan-Dec excl
3 Twin		£30.00-£35.00 Single	Xmas/New Year
1 Double		£22.50-£25.00 Dbl/Twn	B&B + Eve.Meal
		Room only per person	£32.50-£40.00
		from £20.00	

Family run Inn with ample parking. Lounge bar serving bar meals daily. Entertainment most Friday and Saturday nights. Ideal for business travel or touring North Highlands. All rooms have ensuite facilities and telephones. 15 miles from Inverness.

Applecross, Ross-shire — Map Ref: 3F9

AWAITING INSPECTION

Applecross Inn
Shore Street, Applecross, Strathcarron, Wester Ross, IV54 8LR
Tel: 01520 744262 Fax: 01520 744400

2 Single	3 Ensuite fac	B&B per person	Open Jan-Dec excl
3 Double	2 Pub Bath/Show	from £25.00 Single	Xmas/New Year
1 Family		from £25.00 Double	B&B + Eve.Meal
1 Twin		£30.00 Ensuite	from £45.00

Ardelve, by Dornie, Ross-shire — Map Ref: 3F9

★★★★ GUEST HOUSE

Conchra House
Conchra, Ardelve,by Kyle, Ross-shire, IV40 8DZ
Tel: 01599 555233 Fax: 01599 555433
E-mail: enquiries@conchra.co.uk
Web: www.conchra.co.uk

1 Single	5 En Suite fac	B&B per person	Open Jan-Dec excl
2 Twin	1 Priv.NOT ensuite	from £30.00 Single	Xmas/New Year
3 Double		from £25.00 Dbl/Twn	

Former seat and ancestral home of the Macrae's of Conchra dating from 1760. In secluded and tranquil lochside setting. Warm West Highland hospitality. In comfortable country house, family environment, personally run by proprietors.

Important: Prices stated are estimates and may be subject to amendments

Ardgour, by Fort William, Inverness-shire

Map Ref: 3G12

★★★★

INN

The Inn at Ardgour
Ardgour, by Fort William, Inverness-shire, PH33 7AA
Tel: 01855 841225 Fax: 01855 841214
E-mail: ardgour@ecosse.net
Web: sites.netscape.net/ardgour

Britain's Best Inn of 1999 is famed for its warm Highland welcome.
Bedrooms with mountain-framed sea views, open fires, real ale, Graham's
(a Maltmaster award winner) malt whisky collection in the bar and Alison's
home-cooked Scottish food in the restaurant help make the Highland's
best inn. Ideal touring base for the West Highlands, it even sells Hebridean
ferry tickets and runs tutored whisky tastings in the summer.

4 Twin	All En Suite	B&B per person	Open Feb-Dec
4 Double		from £35.00 Single	B&B + Eve.Meal
2 Family		from £30.00 Dbl/Twn	from £45.00
		Room only per person	
		from £25.00	

Ardnamurchan, Argyll

Map Ref: 3E12

★★★★★

GUEST HOUSE

Feorag House
Glenborrodale, Acharacle, Argyll, PH36 4JP
Tel: 01972 500248 Fax: 01972 500285
E-mail: admin@feorag.demon.co.uk
Web: www.feorag.demon.co.uk

Delightful country house on the shores of Loch Sunart. Peace and
tranquility, warm and friendly atmosphere with imaginative cuisine.
Ideal central location for exploring Ardnamurchan. Unlicensed, but you
are welcome to bring your own wine.

1 Twin	All En Suite	B&B per person	Open Jan-Dec
2 Double		from £47.50 Single	B&B + Eve.Meal
		from £35.00 Dbl/Twn	from £55.00

Arisaig, Inverness-shire

Map Ref: 3F11

★★★

HOTEL

The Arisaig Hotel
Arisaig, Inverness-shire, PH39 4NH
Tel: 01687 450210 Fax: 01687 450310
E-mail: arisaighotel@dial.pipex.com
Web: www.arisaighotel.co.uk

Family run traditional Highland hotel with excellent sea views.
Accent on cuisine, using fresh local ingredients.

2 Single	All En Suite	B&B per person	Open Jan-Dec excl Xmas
3 Twin	1 Pub Bath/Show	£32.00-£36.00 Single	B&B + Eve.Meal
6 Double		£32.00-£36.00 Dbl/Twn	from £48.00
2 Family			

Kilmartin Guest House
Kinloid, Arisaig, Inverness-shire, PH39 4NS
Tel: 01687 450366 Fax: 01687 450611

★★★

B&B

B & B on working farm (0.5 miles) 1 km from Arisaig attractively sited on
an elevated position commanding magnificent views overlooking the
village to the sea and the islands of Skye, Rhum and Eigg. 5 mins car
journey to wonderful white sands. Evening meals available. Golf course 3
miles.

1 Twin	All En Suite	B&B per person	Open Easter-Sep
2 Double		from £24.00 Single	B&B + Eve.Meal
		from £24.00 Dbl/Twn	from £40.00
		Room only per person	
		from £24.00	

Old Library Lodge
Arisaig, Inverness-shire, PH39 4NH
Tel: 01687 450651 Fax: 01687 450219
E-mail: reception@oldlibrary.co.uk
Web: www.oldlibrary.co.uk

★★★

RESTAURANT WITH ROOMS

Small 'Restaurant with Rooms' with excellent fresh, natural Scottish
cooking. The kind of 'find' people are always looking for. Essential to
book at night.

1 Twin	All En Suite	B&B per person	Open Apr-Oct
5 Double		from £40.00 Single	B&B + Eve.Meal
		from £34.00 Dbl/Twn	from £58.00

VAT is shown at 17.5%: changes in this rate may affect prices.

Key to symbols is on back flap.

Assynt, Sutherland — Map Ref: 3H5

Inchnadamph Hotel
Assynt, Sutherland, IV27 4HN
Tel: 01571 822202 Fax: 01571 822203
E-mail: inchnadamphhotel@assynt99.freeserve.co.uk

★★★
HOTEL

9 Single	19 En Suite fac
5 Twin	2 Pub Bath/Toilet
6 Double	
4 Family	

B&B per person
from £26.00 Single
from £26.00 Dbl/Twn

Open Mar-Dec excl
Xmas/New Year

Family run hotel in remote setting overlooking Loch Assynt. Fishing free to guests and boats available. Study area for geologists and botanists.

Auldearn, by Nairn, Inverness-shire — Map Ref: 4C8

Boath House
Auldearn, Nairn, IV12 5TE
Tel: 01667 454896 Fax: 01667 455469
Web: www.boath-house.com

★★★★
HOTEL

| 1 Twin | All En Suite |
| 6 Double | |

B&B per person
from £57.50 Single
from £85.00 Dbl/Twn
Room only per person
from £85.00

Open Jan-Dec excl Xmas
B&B + Eve.Meal
from £92.50

Grade A listed Georgian mansion set in 20 acres of lawns, woodland and streams. Award winning restaurant overlooking the lake. Facilities include fishing, gymnasium, Beauty and Hairdressing salon and leisure area with sauna and Jacuzzi. Wonderful beaches, golf course, and some of Scotland's best loved castles all within minutes of this beautiful and historic house.

Aultbea, Ross-shire — Map Ref: 3F6

Aultbea Hotel
Aultbea, Ross-shire, IV22 2HX
Tel: 01445 731201 Fax: 01445 731214
E-mail: aultbeahotel@btconnect.com

★★
HOTEL

1 Single	All En Suite
1 Twin	
5 Double	
1 Family	

B&B per person
from £32.50 Single
from £32.50 Dbl/Twn

Open Jan-Dec

Comfortable hotel situated on the shore of Loch Ewe with magnificent views. Fishing available. Inverewe Gardens, 5 miles (9kms). Food served in our Waterside Bistro, lounge bar & Zetland Restaurant.

Cartmel Guesthouse
Birchburn Road, Aultbea, Ross-shire, IV22 2HZ
Tel: 01445 731375

★★★
GUEST
HOUSE

| 2 Twin | 2 En Suite fac |
| 2 Double | 1 Pub Bath/Show |

B&B per person
£24.00-£28.00 Single
£19.00-£23.00 Dbl/Twn

Open Mar-Oct
B&B + Eve.Meal
£31.50-£35.50

Comfortable bungalow guest house set in 1.5 acres of mature garden. Personally run. Evening meals by prior arrangement and vegetarians very welcome. Regret no smoking.

Aultbea, Ross-shire | Map Ref: 3F6

Mellondale Guest House

47 Mellon Charles, Aultbea, Ross-shire IV22 2JL
Telephone: 01445 731326 Fax: 01445 731326

Enjoy the personal touch at Mellondale. From the warm
welcome to the home cooking in a peaceful setting
overlooking Lochewe, Mellondale is the perfect place to
relax and take in the spectacular scenery. Ideal for walking,
climbing and birdwatching. Inverewe Gardens 9 miles.

★★★★

**GUEST
HOUSE**

Mellondale Guest House
47 Mellon Charles, Aultbea, Ross-shire, IV22 2JL
Tel/Fax: 01445 731326

Comfortable family guest house set in 4 acres, with open views of Loch
Ewe. 9 miles (14.4 Kms) from Inverewe Gardens. Ideal walking centre.

2 Twin	All En Suite	B&B per person	Open Mar-Nov
2 Double	2 Pub Bath/Show	from £21.00 Single	B&B + Eve.Meal
		from £21.00 Dbl/Twn	from £34.00

Aviemore, Inverness-shire | Map Ref: 4C10

★★★

HOTEL

Aviemore Highlands Hotel
Aviemore Centre, Aviemore, Inverness-shire, PH22 1PJ
Tel: 01479 810771 Fax: 01479 811473

Modern, purpose built, within the Aviemore Mountain Resort.

53 Twin	All En Suite	B&B per person	Open Jan-Dec
10 Double		£25.00-£90.00 Single	B&B + Eve.Meal
40 Family		£40.00-£110.00 Dbl/Twn	from £45.00
		Room only per person	
		£20.00-£85.00	

Aviemore Inn
Aviemore, Inverness-shire, PH22 1PH
Tel (Hotel): 01479 810261 Fax (Hotel): 01479 814777
Tel (Reservations): 01479 811811
Fax (Reservations): 01479) 811309
Web: www.hilton.com

**AWAITING
INSPECTION**

62 Twin	All En Suite	B&B per person	Open Jan-Dec
		£35.00-£75.00 Single	B&B + Eve.Meal
		£30.00-£55.00 Twin	£39.00-£55.00

★★

**GUEST
HOUSE**

Cairngorm Guest House
Main Road, Aviemore, Inverness-shire, PH22 1RP
Tel/Fax: 01479 810630
Web: www.aviemore.co.uk/cairngormguesthouse

Detached stone house, within 5 minutes walk of the centre and bus and
rail stations. Private parking.

3 Twin	All En Suite	B&B per person	Open Jan-Dec
5 Double		£20.00-£40.00 Single	
1 Family		£18.00-£25.00 Dbl/Twn	

VAT is shown at 17.5%: changes in this rate may affect prices. | *Key to symbols is on back flap.*

Aviemore, Inverness-shire   Map Ref: 4C10

Cairngorm Hotel
Grampian Road, Aviemore, Inverness-shire, PH22 1PE
Tel: 01479 810233 Fax: 01479 810791
Web: www.cairngorm.com

6 Single	All En Suite	B&B per person	Open Jan-Dec
8 Twin		from £25.00 Single	
14 Double		from £25.00 Dbl/Twn	
4 Family		Room only per person	
		from £25.00	

Independent hotel providing 3 star accommodation with that friendly, caring service only a privately run hotel can offer.

★★★
HOTEL

Corrour House Hotel
Rothiemuchus, by Aviemore, Inverness-shire, PH22 1QH
Tel: 01479 810220 Fax: 01479 811500
Web: www.corrourhouse.co.uk

1 Single	All En Suite	B&B per person	Open Jan-Nov
2 Twin		from £30.00 Single	B&B + Eve.Meal
3 Double		from £60.00 Dbl/Twn	from £50.00
2 Family			

Friendly family run, country house hotel, standing in four acres of garden and woodland, with views of Rothiemurchus and Cairngorm mountains.

★★★★
SMALL
HOTEL

Freedom Inn
Aviemore, Inverness-shire, PH22 1PF
Tel: 01479 810781 Fax: 01479 811167
Web: www.aviemore.org

60 Twin	All En Suite	B&B per person	Open Jan-Dec
34 Double		from £30.00 Single	B&B + Eve.Meal
		from £30.00 Dbl/Twn	from £40.00
		Room only per person	
		from £25.00	

In the centre of Aviemore, this modern hotel is equipped so that every room has self catering facilities.

★★
HOTEL

Hilton Aviemore
Aviemore, Inverness-shire, PH22 1PF
Tel (Hotel): 01479 810681 Fax (Hotel): 01479 810534
Tel (Reservations): 01479 811811
Fax (Reservations): 01479 811309
Web: www.hilton.com

6 Single	All En Suite	B&B per person	Open Jan-Dec
56 Twin		£55.00-£110.00 Single	B&B + Eve.Meal
7 Double		£35.00-£65.00 Dbl/Twn	£39.00-£75.00
20 Family			

Modern spacious Spey Valley hotel with magnificient views. Mainly fresh produce used. Pleasant and attentive staff. A la carte restaurant.

★★★★
HOTEL

Hilton Coylumbridge
Coylumbridge, Aviemore, Inverness-shire, PH22 1QN
Tel: 01479 811811 Fax: 01479 811309
Web: www.hilton.com

4 Single	All En Suite	B&B per person	Open Jan-Dec
19 Twin		£55.00-£110.00 Single	B&B + Eve.Meal
65 Double		£35.00-£65.00 Dbl/Twn	£39.00-£65.00
87 Family			

The family hotel in the Highlands, Hilton Coylumbridge enjoys a peaceful woodland setting, surrounded by the beautiful Cairngorm countryside and the Spey Valley. a year-round holiday centre with nightly entertainment, the hotel's magnificent leisure facilities include the Fun House – with children's soft play, Mini Golf and 10-pin bowling.

★★★★
HOTEL

Important: Prices stated are estimates and may be subject to amendments

Aviemore, Inverness-shire   Map Ref: 4C10

★★

INN

Mackenzies Inn
125 Grampian Road, Aviemore, Inverness-shire,
PH22 1RL
Tel: 01479 810672 Fax: 01479 810595
E-mail: mackhotel@aol.com

'Mackenzies' is the ideal base to sample all that the Highlands and the
Strathspey valley have to offer, with friendly and helpful staff to make
your stay one you'l never forget.

4 Single	All En Suite	B&B per person	Open Jan-Dec excl Xmas
4 Double		from £18.00 Dbl/Twn	B&B + Eve.Meal
			from £33.00

★★

GUEST
HOUSE

Ravenscraig Guest House
Grampian Road, Aviemore, Inverness-shire, PH22 1RP
Tel: 01479 810278 Fax: 01479 812742
E-mail: ravenscrg@aol.com

Ravenscraig is centrally located in the village and an ideal base for touring
the Highlands. Popular with birdwatchers, golfers, walkers & cyclists are
our quiet ground floor annex rooms with their own front doors allowing
easy access as well as privacy. We also offer family rooms, a comfortable
guest lounge with a small library, drying facilities, ski/golf locker, plentiful
parking and legendary breakfasts!

1 Single	All En Suite	B&B per person	Open Jan-Dec
4 Twin		from £18.00 Single	
5 Double		from £18.00 Dbl/Twn	
2 Family			

★★★

SMALL
HOTEL

The Rowan Tree Country Hotel
Loch Alvie, by Aviemore, Inverness-shire, PH22 1QB
Tel/Fax: 01479 810207
E-mail: enquiries@rowantreehotel.com

The hotel is set amid stunning scenery overlooking peaceful Loch Alvie and
offers a calm, relaxing haven, ideally located for the area's many activities.
Our 12 characterful, well equipped, bedrooms, cosy lounges with open fires,
home cooked 4 course dinners and selection of superb wines all combine
with our warm welcome to ensure that you enjoy your stay to the full.

2 Single	10 En Suite fac	B&B per person	Open Jan-Dec
3 Twin	1 Pub Bath/Show	from £26.50 Single	B&B + Eve.Meal
5 Double		from £26.50 Dbl/Twn	from £42.00
2 Family			

Ballachulish, Argyll   Map Ref: 1F1

★★★★

HOTEL

The Ballachulish Hotel
Ballachulish, nr Fort William, Argyll, PH49 4JY
Tel: 01855 821582 Fax: 01855 821463
Web: www.freedomglen.co.uk

Glide through dramatic Glencoe and the mountains divide to reveal this
breathtaking lochside setting. Fulfill your dream of the historic Highland
Hotel. Savour fine Scottish cuisine, relax to the welcoming log fires in the
elegant lounge. Complimentary use of nearby indoor heated pool and
leisure centre.

8 Single	All En Suite	B&B per person	Open Jan-Dec
23 Twin		£33.00-£55.00 Single	B&B + Eve.Meal
19 Double		£33.00-£55.00 Dbl/Twn	£49.00-£80.50
4 Family			

★★★

GUEST
HOUSE

Craiglinnhe House
Lettermore, Ballachulish, Argyll, PH49 4JD
Tel/Fax: 01855 811270
web: www.milford.co.uk/go/craiglinnhe.html

Lochside victorian villa a mid spectacular mountain scenery offering period
charm with modern comfort warm friendly atmosphere good food and
wine ideal base for exploring the western highlands.

3 Twin	All En Suite	B&B per person	Open Feb-Dec
3 Double		from £22.00 Dbl/Twn	B&B + Eve.Meal
			from £37.00

Enjoy Your Freedom

Choose from two remarkable Highland Hotels. Each has stunning loch views, offers a genuine welcome and displays a great blend of style and atmosphere. These hotels make wonderful bases for a memorable holiday.

Ballachulish · HOTEL ·

"an irresistible mix of history and style with modern comforts."

Glide through the dramatic pass of Glencoe and the mountains divide to reveal this breathtaking lochside setting. Fulfil your dream of the **perfect historic Highland Hotel** by staying here amongst the turrets.

Savour **fine Scottish cuisine** in the Leaping Salmon restaurant. Relax to the welcoming crackle of log fires in the elegant Lounge or the cosy Old Library. Unwind in the sunny Cocktail Bar or the lively Ferry Inn.

Enjoy complimentary use of the nearby **indoor heated swimming pool and leisure centre.**

Typical summer rate for Dinner, Bed and Breakfast – £69.50 per person per night.

The Isles of Glencoe Hotel & Leisure Centre

"a really friendly place to go with a great, relaxed family atmosphere. The pool and leisure centre make it perfect!"

Almost afloat, nestling on the side of the loch, this breathtaking new hotel offers everything for which you dream on holiday; spacious loch and mountain-view bedrooms and a relaxed, convivial ambience.

The **sparkling waters** of the heated pool entice to the delights of the Leisure Centre: jacuzzi, sauna, steam room, exercise room and solarium. Enjoy the casual surroundings of the magnificent **lochside conservatory restaurant** or the lively and informal Bistro Bar.

Typical summer rate for Dinner, Bed and Breakfast – £72.50 per person per night.

Late availability 3 night Breaks from only £99 per person for 3 nights Bed and Breakfast. Dinner only £15 per person per night! Call us, see our website or use faxback for latest availability.

For further information call 01855 821582

Web: www.freedom.co.uk   Faxback: 01855 821580

The Freedom of the Glen Family of Hotels, Onich, Nr Fort William, The Scottish Highlands PH33 6RY
Telephone: 01855 821582 Facsimile: 01855 821463 e.mail: reservations@freedomglen.co.uk

Important: Prices stated are estimates and may be subject to amendments

Ballachulish, Argyll   Map Ref: 1F1

Fern Villa Guest House
LOAN FERN, BALLACHULISH, ARGYLL PH49 4JE
Telephone: 01855 811393 Fax: 01855 811727
e.mail: GH@fernvilla.com
Non-smoking. All rooms ensuite. Guest lounge. A warm welcome awaits you in this fine Highland house as you prepare to enjoy the spectacular West Highlands. Close to many exhibitions and historic sites. Perfect base for walking, climbing. Home-made food and fine wines. Natural cooking of Scotland. AA ♦♦♦♦ accommodation.

★★★

GUEST HOUSE

Fern Villa Guest House	2 Twin	All En Suite	B&B per person	Open Jan-Dec
Loanfern, Ballachulish, Argyll, PH49 4JE	3 Double		from £20.00 Dbl/Twn	B&B + Eve.Meal
Tel: 01855 811393 Fax: 01855 811727				from £33.00
E-mail: GH@fernvilla.com				
Web: www.fernvilla.com				

A warm welcome awaits you in this fine Victorian granite built house in the lochside village amidst spectacular scenery. One mile from Glencoe, convenient for Fort William. Home baking and Natural Cook of Scotland features on our dinner menu. Table licence. The perfect base for walking, climbing or touring in the West Highlands. Private parking.

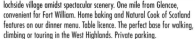

★★★★

GUEST HOUSE

Lyn-Leven Guest House	1 Single	All En Suite	B&B per person	Open Jan-Dec excl Xmas
Ballachulish, Argyll, PH39 4JP	2 Twin		from £25.00 Single	B&B + Eve.Meal
Tel: 01855 811392 Fax: 01855 811600	3 Double		from £21.00 Dbl/Twn	from £30.00
	2 Family			

A very warm Highland welcome awaits you at the RAC small hotel of the year 1996. Situated within attractive, well cared for gardens overlooking Loch Leven in the heart of some of Scotlands most spectacular scenery. Traditional home cooking. Ample parking. Glencoe only 1 mile. Ideal base for skiing, walking, climbing and fishing.

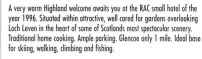

★★★

GUEST HOUSE

Strathassynt Guest House	2 Twin	All En Suite	B&B per person	Open Jan-Dec
Loan Fern, Ballachulish, Argyll, PH49 4JB	3 Double		from £20.00 Single	B&B + Eve.Meal
Tel: 01855 811261 Fax: 0870 0569202	1 Family		from £18.00 Dbl/Twn	from £27.00
Web: www.strathassynt.com				

Comfortable family run licenced guest house in a small village amidst superb loch & mountain scenery. Excellent facilities for walkers and cyclists including skiing, canoeing and bike hire. Home baking and cooking using fresh local produce. Family room available. French/German spoken. Evening meal by prior arrangement.

Beauly, Inverness-shire   Map Ref: 4A8

★

INN

Caledonian Hotel	1 Single	All En Suite	B&B per person	Open Jan-Dec
The Square, High Street, Beauly, Inverness-shire, IV4 7BY	2 Twin		from £26.00 Single	B&B + Eve.Meal
Tel/Fax: 01463 782278	2 Double		from £24.00 Dbl/Twn	from £30.00
	4 Family		Room only per person	
			from £22.00	

Small, personally run hotel in town square 12 miles (19kms) from Inverness. Convenient for touring the Black Isle and Loch Ness. Open fire in bar.

VAT is shown at 17.5%: changes in this rate may affect prices.

Key to symbols is on back flap.

Beauly, Inverness-shire — Map Ref: 4A8

★★★★

HOTEL

&

Priory Hotel

The Square, Beauly, Inverness-shire, IV4 8BX
Tel: 01463 782309 Fax: 01463 782531
E-mail: reservations@priory-hotel.com

2 Single	All En Suite
15 Twin	
9 Double	
3 Family	
6 Exec Singles	

B&B per person
from £39.50 Single
from £26.00 Dbl/Twn

Open Jan-Dec
B&B + Eve.Meal
from £39.50

Situated in the attractive village square of Beauly, this privately run hotel offers excellent facilities, coupled with friendly, efficient informal service. Enjoy the flexibility of early check-in's, late check out's, food available all day and best of all - breakfast available till lunchtime.

Boat of Garten, Inverness-shire — Map Ref: 4C10

★★★

**GUEST
HOUSE**

Avingormack Guest House

Boat of Garten, Inverness-shire, PH24 3BT
Tel: 01479 831614 Fax: 01479 831344
E-mail: avin.gormack@ukgateway.net

1 Twin	2 En Suite fac
2 Double	2 Pub Bath/Show
1 Family	

B&B per person
from £19.00 Dbl/Twn

Open Jan-Dec
B&B + Eve.Meal
from £34.00

Converted crofthouse with panoramic mountain views in rural location. Award winning traditional and vegetarian food.

★★★★

HOTEL

The Boat Hotel

Deshar Road, Boat of Garten, Inverness-shire, PH24 2BH
Tel: 01479 831258 Fax: 01479 831414
Web: www.boathotel.co.uk

4 Single	All En Suite
19 Twin	
8 Double	
1 Family	

B&B per person
£25.00-£45.00 Single
£25.00-£45.00 Dbl/Twn

Open Jan-Dec
B&B + Eve.Meal
£45.00-£65.00

Privately owned Victorian hotel recently refurbished to a very high standard, overlooking the 18 hole championship golf course. Award winning 'Taste of Scotland' cuisine in 'The Capercaillie' restaurant. Individual in style with friendly personalised service. Golf and fishing packages arranged.

★★★★★

**GUEST
HOUSE**

Glenavon House

Kinchurdy Road, Boat of Garten, Inverness-shire, PH24 3BP
Tel/Fax: 01479 831213

1 Single	All En Suite
4 Twn/Dbl	

B&B per person
£30.00-£32.50 Single
£30.00-£32.50 Dbl/Twn

Open Apr-Oct
B&B + Eve.Meal
£52.50-£55.00

Recently renovated Victorian mansion with the highest standard of personal care and cuisine. Ideal for small sporting house parties, or just relaxing in perfect central Highland location.

★★★

**GUEST
HOUSE**

Granlea Guest House

Deshar Road, Boat of Garten, Inverness-shire, PH24 3BN
Tel/Fax: 01479 831601
E-mail: dixons@granlea.freeserve.co.uk
Web: www.granlea.freeserve.co.uk

1 Twin	2 En Suite fac
2 Double	1 Pub Bath/Show
1 Family	

B&B per person
from £19.00 Single
from £19.00 Dbl/Twn

Open Jan-Dec excl
Xmas/New Year
B&B + Eve.Meal
from £32.00

Stone built Edwardian house, in village centre, close to Osprey reserve and golf course. Ideal touring base.

Important: Prices stated are estimates and may be subject to amendments

Boat of Garten, Inverness-shire   Map Ref: 4C10

SMALL HOTEL
★★★★

Heathbank Hotel
Boat of Garten, Inverness-shire, PH24 3BD
Tel: 01479 831234 Fax: 01479 831234

2 Twin	All En Suite
5 Double	

B&B per person
£28.00-£40.00 Dbl/Twn

Open Jan-Dec
B&B + Eve.Meal
£48.00-£64.95

Late Victorian house situated in the 'Osprey' village of Boat of Garten; run as a small, homely hotel by the owners David and Janet Lawton. Freshly prepared dinners served in the Rennie Mackintosh inspired dining room; a selection of wines and spirits is available. 7 individually designed bedrooms, some with 4 poster beds. Non-smoking house, open all year. Bird-watching, golf, fishing and more all available nearby.

Brora, Sutherland   Map Ref: 4C6

HOTEL
★★★

Links Hotel
Golf Road, Brora, Sutherland, KW9 6QS
Tel: 01408 621252
E-mail: highlandescape@btinternet.com
Web: www.highlandescape.com

4 Single	All En Suite
13 Twin	
5 Double	
2 Family	

B&B per person
from £65.00 Single
from £49.00 Dbl/Twn

Open Apr-Oct
B&B + Eve.Meal
from £69.00

Open outlook over the golf course to the sea beyond. Access to sandy beach. The hotel has a relaxed atmosphere and good food in its award winning Panorama Restaurant. It makes an excellent base for golfing or fishing holidays, or for touring the northern Highlands. Leisure facilities, including indoor swimming pool, are situated at our sister hotel 200 metres away and are available to guests.

HOTEL
★★★★

Royal Marine Hotel
Brora, Sutherland, KW9 6QS
Tel: 01408 621252 Fax: 01408 621181
E-mail: highlandescape@btinternet.com
Web: www.highlandescape.com

1 Single	All En Suite
15 Twin	
5 Double	
1 Family	

B&B per person
from £65.00 Single
from £48.00 Dbl/Twn

Open Jan-Dec
B&B + Eve.Meal
from £69.00

Traditional country house hotel, offering excellent facilities and acces to golfing, fishing and countryside. Newly completed leisure complex with restaurant, indoor pool, sauna, steam room, jacuzzi and curling rink. Taste of Scotland/AA Rosette restaurant.

Cannich, Inverness-shire   Map Ref: 3H9

HOTEL
★★★★

Mullardoch House Hotel
Glen Cannich, Cannich, by Beauly, Inverness-shire, IV4 7LX
Tel/Fax: 01456 415460
E-mail: andy@mullhouse1.demon.co.uk
Web: www.mullhouse1.demon.co.uk

2 Twin	All En Suite
4 Double	1 Pub Bath/Show
1 Family	

B&B per person
from £59.00 Single
from £47.00 Dbl/Twn

Open Jan-Dec
B&B + Eve.Meal
from £65.00

Former shooting lodge offering comfort and tranquility, in remote highland glen overlooking Loch Sealbanach. With views to the Affric Mountains. Within 1 hour's drive of Inverness.

Carrbridge, Inverness-shire   Map Ref: 4C9

HOTEL
★★★

The Cairn Hotel
Main Road, Carrbridge, Inverness-shire, PH23 3AS
Tel: 01479 841212 Fax: 01479 841362

2 Single	4 En Suite fac
1 Twin	1 Pub Bath/Show
2 Double	
2 Family	

B&B per person
from £19.00 Single
from £19.00 Dbl/Twn

Open Jan-Dec

Family run hotel with cosy bar and friendly atmosphere, situated in the centre of small Highland village. A good base for touring and skiing.

Dalrachney Lodge Hotel
CARRBRIDGE, INVERNESS-SHIRE PH23 3AT
Telephone: 01479 841252   Fax: 01479 841383
e.mail: stay@dalrachney.co.uk Web: www.dalrachney.co.uk

Situated in 16 acres with magnificent views of Cairngorms. This AA ★★★ former hunting lodge, just off the A9, makes an ideal base for your Highland holiday. Tastefully refurbished **Dalrachney** offers spacious very well-appointed rooms. Emphasis on good food complemented by fine selection of wines, malts and liqueurs. Easy access to many attractions.

HOTEL

Dalrachney Lodge Hotel	1 Single	10 En Suite fac	B&B per person	Open Jan-Dec
Carrbridge, Inverness-shire, PH23 3AT	4 Twin	1 Priv.NOT ensuite	from £25.00 Single	B&B + Eve.Meal
Tel: 01479 841252 Fax: 01479 841383	4 Double		from £25.00 Dbl/Twn	from £40.00
E-mail: stay@dalrachney.co.uk	2 Family			
Web: www.dalrachney.co.uk				

Victorian former hunting lodge, with many antique and period furnishings, set in 16 acres of peaceful surroundings. Cuisine using local produce.

HOTEL

Fairwinds Hotel & Chalets	1 Single	En suite fac	B&B per person	Open Jan-Dec
Carrbridge, Inverness-shire, PH23 3AA	2 Twin		£29.00-£34.00 Single	B&B + Eve.Meal
Tel/Fax: 01479 841240	2 Double		£28.00-£34.00 Double	£44.00-£50.00
E-mail: fairwindsinfo@tesco.net				
Web: www.scotlandhotels.uk.com				

Small, comfortable privately owned Hotel set in 7 acres of tranquil grounds. Conservatory Restaurant, small bar and attractive public area. Ideal base for touring the Highlands.

GUEST HOUSE

The Pines Country House	1 Twin	All En Suite	B&B per person	Open Jan-Dec
Duthil, Carrbridge, Inverness-shire, PH23 3ND	1 Double	1 Pub Bath/Show	from £21.50 Single	B&B + Eve.Meal
Tel: 01479 841220 Fax: 01479 841220*51	1 Family		from £19.00 Dbl/Twn	from £29.00
E-mail: lynn@thepines-duthil.fsnet.co.uk				
Web: www.thepines-duthil.fsnet.co.uk				

Set in 2 acres of mature woodland, 2 miles (3kms) from village. Offering personal service and homely atmosphere. Ideal for all activities.

Important: Prices stated are estimates and may be subject to amendments

Contin, Ross-shire | Map Ref: 4A8

Coul House Hotel
by Strathpeffer, Ross-shire IV14 9EY
Tel: 01997 421487 Fax: 01997 421945
Web: www.milford.co.uk/go/coulhouse.html

Our views are breathtaking. The ancient "Mackenzies of Coul" picked a wonderful situation for their lovely home. Today, Ann and Martyn will give you a warm Highland welcome. You'll enjoy the "Taste of Scotland" food of Chefs Taylor and Maclean, log fires, summer evening piper and "Hamish", the hotel's loveable labrador. From Coul House it's so easy to cruise on Loch Ness, visit Cawdor Castle, sail to the Summer Isles . . . sample numerous distilleries (Glen Ord is only 5 miles), or visit the Wildlife Park, Culloden Battlefield . . . for golfers, there's a 5-course holiday including championship Royal Dornoch . . . for anglers, we can arrange salmon and trout fishing . . . there's pony trekking too.
Ring or write for our colour brochure.

HOTEL

★★★★

Coul House Hotel
Contin, by Strathpeffer, Ross-shire, IV14 9EY
Tel: 01997 421487 Fax: 01997 421945
Web: www.milford.co.uk/go/coulhouse.html

Personally run, secluded country house with fine views over surrounding countryside. 4-Poster room and suite available. Taste of Scotland.

3 Single	All En Suite	B&B per person	Open Jan-Dec
7 Twin		£53.00-£70.00 Single	B&B + Eve.Meal
7 Double		£38.00-£55.00 Dbl/Twn	£53.50-£80.00
3 Family			

📺 🔌 📞 ♨ 🅿 💪 🎣 🍴 🛏 💷 🏆

Ⓒ 🐕 £ Ⓦ Ⓥ

Dornie, by Kyle of Lochalsh, Ross-shire | Map Ref: 3G9

★★★

HOTEL

The Dornie Hotel
7/10 Francis Street, Dornie, Rossshire, IV40 8DT
Tel: 01599 555205 Fax: 01599 555429
E-mail: dornie@madasafish.com

Family run hotel overlooking Loch Long and the Hills of Skye. Restaurant specialising in local seafood.

2 Single	6 En Suite fac	B&B per person	Open Jan-Dec
3 Twin	6 Pub Bath/Show	from £25.00 Single	
4 Double		from £25.00 Dbl/Twn	
3 Family			

📺 🅿 💪 ✂ 🍴 🏆

Ⓒ 🐕 £

VAT is shown at 17.5%: changes in this rate may affect prices.

Key to symbols is on back flap.

BURGHFIELD HOUSE HOTEL

DORNOCH • SUTHERLAND • IV25 3HN

Tel: 01862 810212   Fax: 01862 810404

e.mail: burghfield@cali.co.uk

Web: www.burghfieldhouse.com

Under new management this family and comfortable golfing resort hotel is one of Scotlands "Hidden Gems". Superb food, friendly service and beautiful gardens overlooking the cathedral and the Links bring our guests back time after time. Special seasonal prices and golf packages available. Golf, fishing, touring, birdwatching are just a few of the things to do. Dinner, bed and breakfast from £49.00-£76.50.

HOTEL

Burghfield House Hotel
Dornoch, Sutherland, IV25 3HN
Tel: 01862 810212 Fax: 01862 810404
E-mail: burghfield@cali.co.uk
Web: www.burghfieldhouse.com

Set in 5 acres of well maintained gardens and overlooking Dornoch and the Firth beyond. Flowers and open fires. Home from home for the golf lover. Excellent base for exploring the Northern Highlands. Annexe accommodation available.

14 Twin	All En Suite	B&B per person	Open Mar-Nov
9 Double	1 Priv.NOT ensuite	from £45.00 Single	B&B + Eve.Meal
5 Family		from £32.00 Dbl/Twn	from £49.00

HOTEL

Dornoch Castle Hotel
Castle Street, Dornoch, Sutherland, IV25 3SD
Tel: 01862 810216 Fax: 01862 810981
Web: www.dornochcastlehotel.com

Dating in part from 16c with a modern bedroom wing; restaurant with interesting wine list. Situated in the centre of this historic Royal Burgh, opposite the Cathedral, with some views of the Dornoch Firth. Close to the Royal Dornoch Golf Course.

3 Single	All En Suite	B&B per person	Open Jan-Dec
7 Twin		from £25.00 Single	B&B + Eve.Meal
6 Double		from £25.00 Dbl/Twn	from £48.00
2 Family			

HOTEL

The Eagle Hotel and Bank House
Castle Street, Dornoch, Sutherland, IV25 3SR
Tel: 01862 810008 Fax: 01862 811355
Web: www.eagle-dornoch.co.uk

Paul and Irene welcome you to the Eagle Hotel. Personal attention guaranteed. 'Every customer is a new friend'. Meals - all day, every day. Friendly pub atmosphere. Families welcome.

4 Twin	All En Suite	B&B per person	Open Jan-Dec
4 Double		from £24.00 Dbl/Twn	B&B + Eve.Meal
4 Family			from £34.00

Important: Prices stated are estimates and may be subject to amendments

Dornoch, Sutherland		Map Ref: 4B6

B&B ★★★★★

Highfield House
Evelix Road, Dornoch, Sutherland, IV25 3HR
Tel: 01862 810909 Fax: 01862 811605
E-mail: enquiries@highfieldhouse.co.uk
Web: www.highfieldhouse.co.uk

A modern house at edge of this picturesque golfing town - a warm welcome assured in this very comfortable family home.

1 Twin All En Suite   B&B per person from £35.00 Single from £26.00 Dbl/Twn   Open Jan-Dec
2 Double

GUEST HOUSE ★★★★

Inistore Guest House
Castle Street, Dornoch, Sutherland, IV25 3SN
Tel: 01862 811263
Web: www.inistore.co.uk

Traditional Victorian town house in the centre of the historic cathedral town of Dornoch. Relaxing and comfortable atmosphere, personal attention; a great place to make home as you explore the area, play golf, enjoy the sandy beaches or just relax.

1 Twin 1 En Suite fac   B&B per person   Open mid Mar -
2 Double 1 Priv.NOT ensuite from £27.50 Single mid Feb
1 Family from £27.50 Dbl/Twn

HOTEL ★★

Mallin House Hotel
Church Street, Dornoch, Sutherland, IV25 3LP
Tel: 01862 810335 Fax: 01862 810810
E-mail: mallin.house.hotel@zetnet.co.uk
Web: www.users.zetnet.co.uk/mallin-house

Friendly family run hotel, situated close to the centre of the charming and historic town of Dornoch. A choice of menus available. Carefully prepared by the chef/patron and his wife. Excellent sandy beaches close by. Ideal base for golfing, fishing, shooting and birdwatching or for exploring the varied scenic splendours of Sutherland.

3 Single All En Suite   B&B per person   Open Jan-Dec excl
3 Twin from £32.00 Single New Year's Day
3 Double from £27.00 Dbl/Twn B&B + Eve.Meal
1 Family from £35.00

HOTEL ★★★★

Royal Golf Hotel
Grange Road, Dornoch, Sutherland, IV25 3LG
Tel: 01862 810283 Fax: 01862 810923
E-mail: rooms@morton-hotels.com

Previously a family mansion, the hotel overlooks the golf course and the Dornoch Firth. 5 minutes walk to town. Taste of Scotland. Special breaks can be arranged.

5 Single All En Suite   B&B per person   Open Mar-Dec
18 Twin Suites avail from £85.00 Single
2 Double from £51.00 Dbl/Twn

SILVER

INN ★★

The Trenthan Hotel
The Poles, Dornoch, Sutherland, IV25 3HZ
Tel: 01862 810551 Fax: 01862 811426

18c coaching inn on main Inverness – Wick road, under 3 miles (5kms) from Dornoch. Good base for the golf courses of East Sutherland. Ideal stopover on road to Orkney. Extensive bar menu available, wide selection of malt whiskies. Beauty salon.

1 Single 2 Pub Bath/Show B&B per person   Open Jan-Dec excl
3 Twin from £20.00 Single Xmas/New Year
1 Double from £17.50 Dbl/Twn B&B + Eve.Meal
1 Family Room only per person from £36.00
 from £17.00

VAT is shown at 17.5%: changes in this rate may affect prices.

Key to symbols is on back flap.

| Drumnadrochit, Inverness-shire | | Map Ref: 4A9 | | |

GUEST HOUSE

Mrs F Meredith, Clunebeg Lodge
Highland Sport Fishing Ltd, Drumnadrochit,
Inverness-shire, IV3 6UU
Tel: 01456 450387 Fax: 01456 450854
E-mail: clunebeglodge@tinyworld.co.uk

6 Twin

All En Suite
2 Pub Bath/Show

B&B per person
£20.00-£28.00 Twin

Open Jan-Dec

Comfortable modern lodge on quiet livestock farm set in woodland regeneration area overlooking Drumnadrochit. Fishing, riding, boat trips nearby.

Polmaily House Hotel

LOCH NESS, DRUMNADROCHIT, INVERNESS-SHIRE IV63 6XT
Telephone: 01456 450343   e.mail: polmaily@BTinternet.com
Fax: 01456 450813   Web: www.smoothhound.co.uk/hotels/polmaily.html

Polmaily leads the way in child friendly country house hotels, set in 18 acres of grounds close to Loch Ness. Our unrivalled reputation of meeting the expectations of all members of the family means while parents enjoy the luxuries, their children's dreams come true – heated indoor pool, ponies, yacht on Loch Ness and organised children's activities. B&B from £38-£64 per person per night.

★★★

SMALL HOTEL

Polmaily House Hotel
Drumnadrochit, Inverness-shire, IV63 6XT
Tel: 01456 450343 Fax: 01456 450813
E-mail: polmaily@BTinternet.com
Web: www.smoothhound.co.uk/hotels/polmaily.html

1 Twin
2 Double
6 Family

All En Suite

B&B per person
from £38.00 Single
from £38.00 Dbl/Twn
per room

Open Jan-Dec
B&B + Eve.Meal
from £50.00

A country house in extensive grounds with a restaurant using fresh local ingredients. Leisure facilities with a wide range of organised activities for children. Fishing, sailing and horse riding activities can also be arranged for children. Indoor pool included. The grounds include large outdoor play area, rabbits, guinea pigs to pet and indoor play areas for wet weather.

★★

B&B

Riverbank
West Lewiston, Drumnadrochit, Inverness-shire, IV63 6UW
Tel: 01456 450274
E-mail: jennydru@breathemail.net

1 Single
1 Twin
2 Double

1 En Suite fac
3 Priv.NOT ensuite

B&B per person
from £15.00 Single
from £17.00 Dbl/Twn

Open Jan-Dec

Modern chalet style house with ground floor accommodation peacefully situated. Ample parking. Riverside and woodland walks nearby.

| Dulnain Bridge, by Grantown-on-Spey, Inverness-shire | | Map Ref: 4C9 | | |

★★★★

SMALL HOTEL

Auchendean Lodge Hotel
Dulnain Bridge, by Grantown-on-Spey,
Inverness-shire, PH26 3LU
Tel/Fax: 01479 851347
E-mail: hotel@auchendean.com
Web: www.auchendean.com

2 Single
1 Twin
3 Double
1 Family

All En Suite
1 Pub Bathroom

B&B per person
from £34.50 Single
from £33.50 Dbl/Twn
Room only per person
from £33.50

Open Jan-Dec
B&B + Eve.Meal
from £58.50

Edwardian former shooting lodge, retaining character and style, with panoramic views of the Cairngorm mountains, the River Spey and Abernethy forest. Extensive wine list; interesting cuisine, using home grown and locally sourced vegetables and produce, including wild mushrooms. A friendly welcome and an informal relaxing atmosphere.

Important: Prices stated are estimates and may be subject to amendments

Dulnain Bridge, by Grantown-on-Spey, Inverness-shire — Map Ref: 4C9

Skye of Curr Hotel
Dulnain Bridge, Inverness-shire, PH26 3PA
Tel: 01479 851345 Fax: 01479 821173
E-mail: aileen@skyehotel.freeserve.co.uk

★★★
HOTEL

1 Single	7 Ensuite fac
3 Twin	2 Priv.NOT ensuite
2 Double	
3 Family	

B&B per person
from £35.00 Single
from £35.00 Dbl/Twn

Open Jan-Dec
B&B + Eve.Meal
from £48.00

Magnificent country house, built at the turn of the century and tastefully converted to a hotel some years ago. Set in 2.5 acres of mature wooded grounds supporting a wide variety of wildlife, overlooking the Cairngorms and Cromdale Hills.

Dunbeath, Caithness — Map Ref: 4D4

Dunbeath Hotel
Dunbeath, Caithness, KW6 4EG
Tel: 01593 731208 Fax: 01593 731242
E-mail: dunbeathhotel@i12.com

★★★
SMALL
HOTEL

3 Twin	All En Suite
3 Double	

B&B per person
from £42.00 Single
from £34.00 Dbl/Twn

Open Jan-Dec excl
Xmas/New Year
B&B + Eve.Meal
from £56.00

Victorian coaching inn with sound reputation for good food. Close to the sea and the Strath of Dunbeath.

Dundonnell, Ross-shire — Map Ref: 3G7

Dundonnell Hotel
Dundonnell, Little Loch Broom, Ross-shire, IV23 2QR
Tel: 01854 633204 Fax: 01854 633366

★★★★
HOTEL

2 Single	All En Suite
13 Twin	
11 Double	
2 Family	

B&B per person
£37.50-£69.50 Single
£37.50-£59.50 Dbl/Twn

Open Feb-Dec
B&B + Eve.Meal
£49.50-£82.50

Family run hotel with emphasis on personal service. Interesting cuisine with use of fresh local produce. Situated at end of Little Loch Broom.

Durness, Sutherland — Map Ref: 4A3

Smoo Cave Hotel
Lerin, Durness, Sutherland IV27 4QB
Tel/Fax: 01971 511227 e.mail: smoo.hotel@virgin.net
The most north westerly hotel in mainland Scotland, where you will find a warm and friendly welcome, with comfortable accommodation and the very best of food. Excellent base for enjoying a golf, fishing, walking or touring holiday with wonderful sandy beaches and of course the famous Smoo Caves and Cape Wrath.

Smoo Cave Hotel
Durness, Sutherland, IV27 4QB
Tel/Fax: 01971 511227
E-mail: smoo.hotel@virgin.net

★
INN

1 Twin	2 En Suite fac
1 Double	
1 Family	

B&B per person
from £16.50 Dbl/Twn

Open Jan-Dec

Accommodation provided in this local inn with open fires. Close to the Smoo Cave, which is open to visitors to walk and look at the cave. Ground floor room available.

VAT is shown at 17.5%: changes in this rate may affect prices.

Key to symbols is on back flap.

Evanton, Ross-shire | Map Ref: 4B7

★★★ HOTEL

Novar Arms Hotel
Evanton, Ross-shire, IV16 9UN
Tel: 01349 830210 Fax: 01349 830739
E-mail: novar@globalnet.co.uk

1 Single	All En Suite	B&B per person	Open Jan-Dec
9 Twin		from £35.00 Single	B&B + Eve.Meal
4 Double		from £25.00 Dbl/Twn	from £37.50
3 Family			

Former coaching inn, built in the 1850's, situated in the centre of the village of Evanton. 20 miles north of Loch Ness and 45 miles from the West Coast. Ask us about fishing, dolphin watching, golf, hill walking. Menus concentrate on fresh Scottish produce. 'The answers yes - what's the question'?

BRONZE

Feshie Bridge, by Kincraig, Inverness-shire | Map Ref: 4B11

★★★ GUEST HOUSE

March House
Feshiebridge, Kincraig, Inverness-shire, PH21 1NG
Tel/Fax: 01540 651388
Web: www.kincraig.com/march.htm

2 Twin	All En Suite	B&B per person	Open Jan-Oct excl
2 Double		from £22.00 Single	New Year
1 Family		from £22.00 Dbl/Twn	B&B + Eve.Meal
			from £38.00

Surrounded by spectacular scenery and wildlife, March House offers a truly unique location, fresh homemade meals and a very peaceful relaxing family atmosphere. Set in a glade of mature caledonian pines. Taste of Scotland.

Fort Augustus, Inverness-shire | Map Ref: 4A10

★★ HOTEL

Caledonian Hotel
Fort Augustus, Inverness-shire, PH32 4BQ
Tel: 01320 366256 Fax: 0870 284 1287
E-mail: caledonian.hotel@lochness-scotland.co.uk

1 Single	7 En Suite fac	B&B per person	Open Easter-Sep
3 Twin	2 Pub Bath/Show	from £30.00 Single	B&B + Eve.Meal
4 Double		from £25.00 Dbl/Twn	from £40.00
3 Family			

Warm welcome at this family run hotel overlooking Benedictine Abbey. 32 miles (53 kms) from Inverness and Fort William.

★★★ HOTEL

Inchnacardoch Lodge Hotel
Loch Ness, by Fort Augustus, Inverness-shire, PH32 4BL
Tel: 01320 366258 Fax: 01320 366248
E-mail: lochness97@aol.com

3 Twin	All En Suite	B&B per person	Open Jan-Dec
7 Double		from £45.00 Single	
5 Family		from £35.00 Dbl/Twn	

Country house hotel on north side of Fort Augustus with fine views of Loch Ness and surrounding hills. Ideal base for touring and outdoor activities.

by Fort Augustus, Inverness-shire | Map Ref: 4A10

★★★★ SMALL HOTEL

Knockie Lodge Hotel
Whitebridge, by Fort Augustus, Inverness-shire, IV2 6UP
Tel: 01456 486276 Fax: 01456 486389
E-mail: info@knockielodge.co.uk

2 Single	All En Suite	B&B per person	Open May-Oct
4 Twin		from £75.00 Single	
4 Double		from £60.00 Dbl/Twn	

The ideal hideaway, refreshingly relaxed in style yet with a genuine warmth of hospitality and comfort amidst superb scenery.

Important: Prices stated are estimates and may be subject to amendments

Fort William, Inverness-shire   Map Ref: 3H12

ALEXANDRA MILTON HOTEL

The Parade,
Fort William
PH33 6AZ

The Alexandra is part of the very fabric of Fort William. Right in the centre of town and with private parking. You have a choice of 2 good restaurants and also a choice of room styles, included is the free use of our Milton Hotel's new Leisure Club. (See entry).

AA★★★

Freephone: 0808 100 55 56
Fax: 01786 469 400
Please quote ref HGH01

e.mail: sales@miltonhotels.com
Web: www.miltonhotels.com

It's a great place to stay.

Milton
Hotels & Leisure Clubs

★★

HOTEL

Alexandra Milton Hotel
The Parade, Fort William, PH33 6AZ
Milton Sales Centre: Freefone 0808 100 55 56
Fax: 01786 469 400
E-mail: sales@miltonhotels.com
Web: www.miltonhotels.com

Large traditional hotel fully modernised, situated in town centre. Some rooms with views of the surrounding hills and lochside.

22 Single	All En Suite	B&B per person	Open Jan-Dec
52 Twin		£61.00-£81.00 Single	
10 Double		£40.50-£55.50 Dbl/Twn	
13 Family			

★★★

GUEST HOUSE

Ben View Guest House
Belford Road, Fort William, Inverness-shire,
PH33 6ER
Tel: 01397 702966

Family run guest house conveniently situated for bus and train stations, town centre and leisure centre. All rooms with ensuite or private bathrooms. Tastefully decorated lounges for guests use. Ample private parking available.

2 Single	8 En Suite fac	B&B per person	Open Mar-Oct
1 Twin	3 Priv.NOT ensuite	from £16.00 Single	
7 Double		from £23.00 Dbl/Twn	
1 Family			

★★★

GUEST HOUSE

Berkeley House
Belford Road, Fort William, PH33 6BT
Tel: 01397 701185

Comfortable family home situated conveniently for all town centre amenities. 5 minutes walk to the swimming pool, leisure centre, train and bus stations.

1 Twin	All En Suite	B&B per person	Open Jan-Dec excl
3 Double		from £20.00 Single	Xmas/New Year
		from £18.00 Dbl/Twn	

Clan MacDuff Hotel

Achintore Road, Fort William, Inverness-shire PH33 6RW
Telephone: 01397 702341   Fax: 01397 706174
e.mail: susan@clanmacduff.co.uk   web: www.clanmacduff.co.uk

Situated overlooking Loch Linnhe, with outstanding views of magnificent Highland scenery. Well-appointed bedrooms with colour television, hospitality tray etc. Large choice dinner menu. Delicious bar suppers. Fine selection of malt whiskies. Large car-park. This friendly family-run hotel is dedicated to providing good quality and value hospitality.

★★

HOTEL

Clan MacDuff Hotel

Achintore, Fort William, Inverness-shire, PH33 6RW
Tel: 01397 702341 Fax: 01397 706174
E-mail: susan@clanmacduff.co.uk
Web: www.clanmacduff.co.uk

This family run hotel overlooks Loch Linnhe, 2 miles south of Fort William. The Hotel is situated in its own grounds with large car park. Enjoy the highland scenery from the conservatory or patio. All public rooms have magnificent views of the Loch and the mountains beyond. Dinner is a traditional menu with varied choice. We offer the comfort and freedom of a hotel at economic prices. Brochure on request.

2 Single	40 En Suite fac	B&B per person	Open Apr-Oct
17 Twin	2 Pub Bath/Show	from £25.00 Single	B&B + Eve.Meal
20 Double		from £20.00 Dbl/Twn	from £34.00
2 Family			

Craig Nevis Guest House

Belford Road, Fort William, Inverness-shire, PH33 6BU
Tel: 01397 702023

★★

GUEST HOUSE

Personally run guest house. Offering comfortable reasonably priced accommodation short distance from town centre, swimming pool and all amenities. 2 mins walk from railway station. Off-street parking. 3 rooms in adjacent bungalow.

3 Twin	Ensuite	B&B per person	Open Jan-Dec
3 Double	Ensuite	£14.00-£18.00 Single	
2 Single	Standard	£14.00-£18.00 Dbl/Twn	

Croit Anna Hotel

Situated three miles south of Fort William on the shores of Loch Linnhe, has all rooms with private facilities, colour TV/Sky TV and hospitality trays. We have the ideal location for touring the magnificent West Highlands of Scotland. B&B from as little as £25.00 per person.

Send for full brochure: Croit Anna Hotel,   ★★★ HOTEL
Achintore Road, Fort William PH33 6RR
Tel: 01397 702268 e.mail: croitanna@compuserve.com
Fax: 01397 704099 Web: www.croitanna.co.uk

★★★

HOTEL

Croit Anna Hotel

Achintore Road, Fort William, Inverness-shire, PH33 6RR
Tel: 01397 702268 Fax: 01397 704099
E-mail: croitanna@compuserve.com
Web: www.croitanna.co.uk

Situated on the shores of Loch Linnhe, overlooking the hills of Morven. Quality En-Suite accommodation with SKY TV and Hospitality tray. Menus feature the best of fresh Scottish fare. Traditional Hospitality from a Family run Hotel with regular entertainment.

12 Single	All En Suite	B&B per person	Open Mar-mid Nov
50 Twin		from £30.00 Single	B&B + Eve.Meal
4 Double		from £25.00 Double	from £40.00
2 Family		Room only	
		from £41.50	

Important: Prices stated are estimates and may be subject to amendments

Fort William, Inverness-shire   Map Ref: 3H12

CRUACHAN HOTEL

Achintore Road, Fort William PH33 6RQ

Tel: 01397 702022 Fax: 01397 702239

Family run hotel with warm friendly atmosphere. 200 yards from Fort William on main A82. Large car park next to main road. Magnificent views from our sun terrace. Ideal base for touring the Highlands and islands. Scottish entertainment most nights.

★★

HOTEL

Cruachan Hotel
Achintore Road, Fort William, Inverness-shire, PH33 6RQ
Tel: 01397 702022 Fax: 01397 702239
E-mail: reservations@cruachan-hotel.co.uk
Web: www.cruachan-hotel.co.uk

Victorian villa, modern wing attached, standing in own grounds overlooking Loch Linnhe and only 400 yards from Fort William's main shopping street.

7 Single	All En Suite	B&B per person	Open Feb-Nov
25 Twin		from £25.00 Single	
20 Double		from £22.00 Dbl/Twn	
5 Family			

Distillery Guest House

Nevis Bridge, North Road, Fort William PH33 6LR

Telephone: 01397 700103   Fax: 01397 702980

e.mail: disthouse@aol.com

Web: www.fort-william.net/distillery-house

Situated at the entrance to Glen Nevis just 5 minutes from the Town Centre. *Distillery House* has been upgraded to high standards. Set in the extensive grounds of the *Glenlochy Distillery* with views over the River Nevis, all bedrooms are ensuite. New Self-Catering Apartments now available. *Bed & Breakfast from £22 per person.*

★★★★

GUEST HOUSE

Distillery House
Nevis Bridge, Fort William, Inverness-shire, PH33 6LR
Tel: 01397 700103 Fax: 01397 702980
E-mail: disthouse@aol.com
Web: www.fort-william.net/distillery-house

Distillery house at old Glenlochy Distillery in Fort William beside A82, road to the Isles. Situated at the entrance to Glen Nevis just 5 minutes from the town centre. Distillery House has been upgraded to high standards. Set in the extensive grounds of the Glenlochy Distillery with views over the River Nevis. All bedrooms are ensuite with TV, telephone and hospitality tray.

1 Single	All En Suite	B&B per person	Open Jan-Dec
2 Twin		from £25.00 Single	
3 Double		from £22.00 Dbl/Twn	
1 Family			

Glenlochy Guest House

Nevis Bridge, Fort William, Inverness-shire PH33 6PF
Telephone: 01397 702909

Situated in its own spacious grounds within walking distance of town centre and Ben Nevis. At entrance to Glen Nevis. Recommended by *"Which Best B&B Guide"*. Special rates for 3 or more nights. Large private car park. 8 of 10 bedrooms are ensuite. Phone for reservations or colour brochure. B&B from £18.

★★★

GUEST HOUSE

Glenlochy Guest House and Apartments
Nevis Bridge, North Road, Fort William,
Inverness-shire, PH33 6PF
Tel: 01397 702909

3 Twin	8 En Suite fac	B&B per person	Open Jan-Dec
5 Double	2 Pub Bath/Show	from £20.00 Single	
2 Family		from £18.00 Dbl/Twn	

Detached house with garden situated at Nevis Bridge, midway between Ben Nevis and the town centre. 0.5 miles (1km) to railway station. 2 annexe rooms.

Grand Hotel ★★ HOTEL

FORT WILLIAM,
INVERNESS-SHIRE PH33 6DX
Tel/Fax: 01397 702928
e.mail: enquiries@grandhotel-scotland.co.uk Web: www.grandhotel-scotland.co.uk

This popular town centre hotel enjoys an excellent local reputation with its clientele for friendly service and award winning cuisine. The hotel is an ideal base to tour the scenic West Highlands. Experience the Highlands whilst relaxing in comfortable surroundings. Special 2 and 3 night rates available. Visit our website.

★★

HOTEL

Grand Hotel
Gordon Square, Fort William, Inverness-shire, PH33 6DX
Tel/Fax: 01397 702928
E-mail: enquiries@grandhotel-scotland.co.uk
Web: www.grandhotel-scotland.co.uk

3 Single	All En Suite	B&B per person	Open Feb-Dec excl Xmas
10 Twin		from £25.00 Single	B&B + Eve.Meal
9 Double		from £22.00 Twin	from £38.00
4 Family			

Conveniently located in the town centre, our family run hotel offers good food and accommodation at competitive prices. Excellent base from which to explore the scenic West Highlands by car or by foot. Children welcome. Baby listening service as well as highchairs and cots. Our chef is happy to assist with all your dietary requests.

Fort William, Inverness-shire   Map Ref: 3H12

GUISACHAN HOUSE

Alma Road, Fort William, Inverness-shire PH33 6HA
Telephone: 01397 703797 Fax: 01397 703797
e.mail: info@stablerooms.fsnet.co.uk
Web: www.fort-william.net/guisachan-house

★★★
GUEST HOUSE

Beautifully situated overlooking Loch Linnhe and Ardgour Hills, within 5 mins walking distance of town centre, rail and bus stations. All rooms have private facilities, TV, tea-making. There is a comfortable lounge where you can enjoy a drink from our well-stocked bar. Private parking.

★★★
GUEST HOUSE

Guisachan House
Alma Road, Fort William, Inverness-shire, PH33 6HA
Tel/Fax: 01397 703797
E-mail: info@stablerooms.fsnet.co.uk
Web: www.fort-william.net/guisachan-house

2 Single	14 En Suite fac	B&B per person	Open Jan-Dec excl
4 Twin	1 Priv.NOT ensuite	from £18.00 Single	Xmas/New Year
8 Double		from £18.00 Dbl/Twn	
1 Family			

Family run establishment situated in its own grounds within easy walking distance of town centre, rail and bus stations. There is a comfortable lounge and well-stocked private bar. Open all year round.

IMPERIAL HOTEL

FRASER SQUARE, FORT WILLIAM PH33 6DW
Telephone: 01397 702040 Fax: 01397 706277

Quality town-centre hotel with some fine views over Loch Linnhe and surrounding countryside. Good food and modern luxurious rooms offer the discerning traveller and businessman an ideal base in Fort William. Fully licensed, A La Carte menu, buffet, servery, conference facilities, executive rooms.

★★
HOTEL

Imperial Hotel
Fraser Square, Fort William, Inverness-shire, PH33 6DW
Tel: 01397 702040 Fax: 01397 706277

6 Single	All En Suite fac	B&B per person	Open Jan-Dec
13 Twin		from £45.00 Single	B&B + Eve.Meal
13 Double		from £29.00 Dbl/Twn	from £44.00
3 Family			

Town centre hotel with some fine views over Loch Linnhe and surrounding countryside. Good food and modern rooms offer the discerning traveller and businessman, an ideal base in Fort William. Fully licensed, a la carte menu, buffet, servery, conference facilities.

Innseagan House Hotel

Achintore Road, Fort William PH33 6RW
Tel: 01397 702452   Fax: 01397 702606
e.mail: frontdesk@innseagan-holidays.com
Web: www.innseagan-holidays.com

"The Lochside Hotel where standards matter"

Innseagan House Hotel is situated in its own grounds on the shores of Loch Linnhe yet only 1½ miles from the centre of Fort William. Spectacular views of loch and mountains are seen from our public rooms and most bedrooms. Innseagan is personally managed by the proprietors, ably assisted by their excellent staff. Bedrooms have private facilities, TV, teasmaid, radios etc. Large car parks. We pride ourselves on our high standards of service, comfort and cleanliness.

Sorry no coach parties.
Send now for full colour brochure.

HOTEL

Innseagan House Hotel
Achintore Road, Fort William, Inverness-shire, PH33 6RW
Tel: 01397 702452 Fax: 01397 702606
E-mail: frontdesk@innseagan-holidays.com
Web: www.innseagan-holidays.com

This Victorian house, situated in its own grounds has been tastefully extended and fully modernised. It now offers all the facilities and comfort of a modern hotel whilst maintaining the character of the original building. Only 1.5 miles from Fort William and overlooking Loch Linnhe to the mountains. Cleanliness and efficiency are the watchwords of the management and staff.

2 Single	All En Suite	B&B per person	Open Apr-Oct
9 Twin		from £30.00 Single	B&B + Eve.Meal
13 Double		from £23.00 Dbl/Twn	from £33.00

GUEST HOUSE

Lochan Cottage Guest House
Lochyside, Fort William, Inverness-shire, PH33 7NX
Tel/Fax: 01397 702695
E-mail: lochanco@supanet.com

Lochan Cottage Guest House is situated in 1 acre of gardens with panoramic views over Ben Nevis, the highest mountain in Great Britian, and Aonach Mor. Traditional Scottish, vegetarian or continental breakfast. Home cooked 3 course evening meal available using fresh ingredients. Vegetarians catered for. Relax over a bottle of wine in our comfortable conservatory dining room or enjoy a fine Scottish malt in our cosy lounge.

1 Twin	All En Suite	B&B per person	Open Jan-Dec
5 Double		from £22.00 Dbl/Twn	B&B + Eve.Meal
			from £34.00

GUEST HOUSE

Mansefield House
Corpach, Fort William, Inverness-shire, PH33 7LT
Tel/Fax: 01397 772262
E-mail: mansefield@aol.com

This traditional Scottish Guest House is situated on the 'Road to the Isles' and set in mature gardens with views of the surrounding mountains. We specialise in relaxation, comfort and home cuisine. Being small and select the ambience is special and attention personal and friendly.

1 Twin	All En Suite	B&B per person	Open Jan-Dec excl
2 Double		from £20.00 Dbl/Twn	Xmas
2 Family			B&B + Eve.Meal
			from £30.50

Important: Prices stated are estimates and may be subject to amendments

MILTON HOTEL AND LEISURE CLUB

North Road, Fort William PH33 6TG
Freephone: 0808 100 55 56   Fax: 01786 469 400
e.mail: sales@miltonhotels.com
Web: www.miltonhotels.com   *Milton*
Hotels & Leisure Clubs

As soon as you arrive, you'll know you've made the right choice. Now they've invested £1.3m in improvements, it makes all the difference. You'll have free use of the new Leisure Club with its pool, jacuzzi, gym and sauna. It's the only hotel in town with this facility. There's a super new bar and lounge with a roaring open fire and very comfy and up-to-date bedrooms. The beautiful restaurant has views out towards towering Ben Nevis.

Many leisure break packages available from walking to skiing; family deals, where children stay free, to car touring options with our other hotels in Oban, Inverness and Stirling.
Please quote reference HGH01 when booking.

★★
HOTEL

Milton Hotel & Leisure Club
North Road, Fort William, PH33 6TG
Milton Sales Centre: Freefone 0808 100 55 56
Fax: 01786 469 400
E-mail: sales@miltonhotels.com
Web: www.miltonhotels.com

On the A82 facing Ben Nevis, this hotel with its own grounds and leisure club with new beauty salon is about 1ml (2km) from the town centre.

23 Single	All En Suite	B&B per person Open Jan-Dec
76 Twin		£74.00-£104.00 Single
15 Double		£49.50-£69.50 Dbl/Twn
7 Family		

The Moorings Hotel

BANAVIE, FORT WILLIAM PH33 7LY
Telephone: 01397 772797 Fax: 01397 772441
Web: www.moorings-fortwilliam.co.uk
Relaxing countryside hotel, 5 minutes from Fort William, beside the Caledonian Canal with views of Ben Nevis. Excellent Restaurant with AA Rosette and RAC Merit Awards. Bar meals are served in the Mariners Bar and the Upper Lounge. 21 en-suite bedrooms, friendly, personal service – an ideal base for your Highland holiday. AA ❀ AA/RAC ★★★.

★★★★
HOTEL

The Moorings Hotel
Banavie, by Fort William, Inverness-shire, PH33 7LY
Tel: 01397 772797 Fax: 01397 772441
E-mail: reservations@moorings-fortwilliam.co.uk
Web: www.moorings-fortwilliam.co.uk

Privately owned hotel situated beside the Caledonian Canal and Neptune's Staircase. Many rooms have views of the Ben Nevis mountain range and canal locks. Restaurant and Mariners bar serving interesting and well presented meals using local produce where available.

2 Single	All En Suite	B&B per person Open Jan-Dec
5 Twin		from £50.00 Single
12 Double		from £35.00 Dbl/Twn
2 Family		

VAT is shown at 17.5%: changes in this rate may affect prices.   *Key to symbols is on back flap.*

West End Hotel
Achintore Road, Fort William PH33 6ED
Telephone: 01397 702614   Fax: 01397 706279
e.mail: welcome@westend-hotel.co.uk
Web: www.westend-hotel.co.uk

Family run hotel overlooking Loch Linnhe on main road into town, 3 minutes walk from shops. All rooms ensuite with colour television, telephone and tea-making facilities. Table d'hôte menu/bar meals. Entertainment 3/4 nights during summer season. Enjoys breathtaking views of Loch Linnhe and the Ardgour mountains.

★★★

HOTEL

West End Hotel
Achintore Road, Fort William, Inverness-shire, PH33 6ED
Tel: 01397 702614 Fax: 01397 706279
E-mail: welcome@westend-hotel.co.uk
Web: www.westend-hotel.co.uk

Family run hotel in the centre of Fort William overlooking Loch Linnhe. Ideal base for touring the West Highlands.

7 Single	51 En Suite fac	B&B per person	Open Jan-Dec
21 Twin		£25.00-£40.00 Single	
17 Double		£20.00-£35.00 Dbl/Twn	
5 Family			

---

by Fort William, Inverness-shire   Map Ref: 3H12

★★★★

HOTEL

Corriegour Lodge Hotel
Loch Lochy, by Spean Bridge, Inverness-shire, PH34 4EB
Tel: 01397 712685 Fax: 01397 712696
Web: www.corriegour-lodge-hotel.com

Corriegour Lodge Hotel, a former hunting lodge, is set in nine acres of mature woodland and garden with open views over Loch Lochy. Seventeen miles North of Fort William on the road to Skye, many of Scotland's attractions are in easy reach. Local activities include walking, cycling, climbing, pony trekking or fishing from the hotel jetty. The Loch Restaurant is a distinct member of Taste of Scotland.

2 Single	All En Suite	B&B per person	Open Feb-Nov
2 Twin		from £43.00 Single	and New Year
4 Double		from £43.00 Dbl/Twn	B&B + Eve.Meal
1 Family			from £63.00

★★★★

**RESTAURANT
WITH ROOMS**

Old Pines Restaurant with Rooms
Spean Bridge, by Fort William, PH34 4EG
Tel: 01397 712324 Fax: 01397 712433
E-mail: billandSuKie@oldpines.co.uk
Web: www.oldpines.co.uk

Masterchef Proprietor and Restaurant of the Year 2000 award in Good Food Guide. Taste of Scotland Macallan Award Winner 1998. A rare combination of relaxed informality and seriously good food. Good Food Guide. Restaurant of the Year.

1 Single	All En Suite	Open Jan-Dec excl
2 Twin	1 Pub Bath	Xmas/Dinner B&B
3 Double		£60.00-£75.00
2 Family		

Important: Prices stated are estimates and may be subject to amendments

Foyers, Inverness-shire   Map Ref: 4A10

Foyers Bay House

Foyers, Loch Ness, Inverness IV2 6YB
Tel: 01456 486624 Fax: 01456 486337
e.mail: panciroli@foyersbay.freeserve.co.uk Web: www.foyersbay.freeserve.co.uk
Splendid Victorian villa overlooking Loch Ness. Lovely grounds adjoining
famous falls of Foyers. Conservatory cafe-restaurant with breathtaking views
of Loch Ness. Ideal base for touring the many historical and tourist attractions
in this beautiful region. Also six self-catering units within grounds.

★★★

**GUEST
HOUSE**

Foyers Bay House
Lower Foyers, Inverness-shire, IV2 6YB
Tel: 01456 486624 Fax: 01456 486337
E-mail: panciroli@foyersbay.freeserve.co.uk
Web: www.foyersbay.freeserve.co.uk

2 Twin	All En Suite	B&B per person	Open Jan-Dec
3 Double		from £29.00 Single	B&B + Eve.Meal
		from £24.00 Dbl/Twn	from £33.00

Set in its own 4 acres of wooded pine slopes, rhododendrons and apple
orchard, Foyers Bay House offers 5 rooms all with ensuite facilities. Just
500 yards from the famous Falls of Foyers and situated just by Loch Ness,
home of the famous monster.

Gairloch, Ross-shire   Map Ref: 3F7

★★

HOTEL

Millcroft Hotel
Gairloch, Ross-shire, IV21 2BT
Tel: 01445 712376 Fax: 01445 712091
Web: www.millcroft-hotel.co.uk

1 Single	All En Suite	B&B per person	Open Jan-Dec
2 Twin		from £22.00 Single	B&B + Eve.Meal
2 Double		from £22.00 Dbl/Twn	from £36.00
4 Family			

Elevated position, close to shops, overlooking loch to mountains and
islands. Family run with good reputation for food using fresh local
produce.

★★

**GUEST
HOUSE**

The Mountain Restaurant & Lodge
Strath Square, Gairloch, Ross-shire, IV21 2BX
Tel: 01445 712316

1 Twin	All En Suite	B&B per person	Open Apr-Oct and
2 Double		from £27.00 Single	Xmas/New Year
		from £19.95 Dbl/Twn	

In Gairloch's main square. Unique themed restaurant and lodge. Views
across bay to mountains. 4 poster bed and ocean views. Mountaineering
memorabilia donated by Chris Bonnington and others. Candlelit dinners
during H/S. Daytime speciality coffee shop featuring cappucino and
espresso drinks and over 60 different teas and coffees. Mountain style
home baking, snacks and lunches. All in an informal atmosphere.
Lochside sun terrace. Nature shop/bookstore.

MYRTLE BANK HOTEL

Low Road, Gairloch, Ross-shire IV21 2BS
Telephone: 01445 712004   Fax: 01445 712214
e.mail: MyrtleBank@email.msn.com   Web: www.hotelgairloch.com

Newly extended and refurbished, this family run hotel offers an ideal base for touring Wester Ross. Our widely recommended 'Taste of Scotland' restaurant serves local seafood and enjoys panoramic views to the Isle of Skye. Golf, sailing, sandy beaches and the world-famous Inverewe Garden are all nearby.

★★★

HOTEL

Myrtle Bank Hotel
Low Road, Gairloch, Ross-shire, IV21 2BS
Tel: 01445 712004 Fax: 01445 712214
E-mail: MyrtleBank@email.msn.com
Web: www.hotelgairloch.com

This family run hotel, recently refurbished and extended is situated on waterfront with views over Gairloch towards Isle of Skye. Restaurant and bar meals available, using fresh local produce.

		B&B per person	Open Jan-Dec
1 Single	All En Suite	£35.00-£45.00 Single	B&B + Eve.Meal
5 Twin		£35.00-£45.00 Dbl/Twn	£55.00-£65.00
4 Double			
2 Family			

THE OLD INN

GAIRLOCH, ROSS-SHIRE IV21 2BD
TEL: 01445 712006 FAX: 01445 712445
WEB: www.theoldinn.co.uk

Coaching Inn overlooking the harbour. Specialising in local seafood, game, spit roasts and real ales. Comfortable ensuite rooms, ideal base for walking, fishing, birdwatching, beaches, Inverewe Gardens and Torridon. Highland safaris and wildlife tours, pony trekking and golf close by. Off-season rates. Taste of Scotland accredited.

★★

INN

The Old Inn
Gairloch, Ross-shire, IV21 2BD
Tel: 01445 712006 Fax: 01445 712445
Web: www.theoldinn.co.uk

18c coaching Inn in picturesque setting near sea-loch and hills. All rooms ensuite with colour TV. Specialities include Real Ale and the menu includes special dishes using the best of freshly caught seafood prepared on the premises, spit roast Ross-shire lamb and wild boar.

		B&B per person	Open Jan-Dec
1 Single	All En Suite	from £27.50 Single	
4 Twin		from £25.00 Dbl/Twn	
6 Double			
3 Family			

★★★

GUEST HOUSE

Whindley Guest House
Auchtercairn Brae, Gairloch, Ross-shire, IV21 2BN
Tel/Fax: 01445 712340

Modern bungalow with large garden in elevated position, with fine views overlooking Gairloch Bay, and across to Skye. Beach and golf course nearby. Evening meals by arrangement. Non smoking house.

		B&B per person	Open Jan-Dec excl
1 Twin	All En Suite	from £25.00 Single	Xmas/New Year
1 Double		from £19.00 Dbl/Twn	B&B + Eve.Meal
1 Family			from £33.00

Important: Prices stated are estimates and may be subject to amendments

Garve, Ross-shire — Map Ref: 4A8

HOTEL

Inchbae Lodge Hotel
nr Garve, Ross-shire, IV23 2PH
Tel: 01997 455269 Fax: 01997 455207
Web: www.netesprit.com/inchbae

On River Blackwater, family run former hunting lodge, with open fires. Emphasis on quality cuisine, fresh produce. Trout fishing. Some annexe accommodation.

★★★

1 Single	All En Suite	B&B per person
6 Twin		from £25.00 Single
3 Double		from £20.00 Dbl/Twn
5 Family		Room only
		from £30.00

Open Jan-Dec excl Xmas/New Year
B&B + Eve.Meal from £35.00

BRONZE

Glencoe, Argyll — Map Ref: 1F1

CLACHAIG INN
Glencoe, Argyll PH49 4HX
Tel: 01855 811252 Fax: 01855 811679
e.mail: inn@glencoe-scotland.co.uk
web: www.glencoe-scotland.co.uk

Set in the heart of this awe-inspiring glen with glorious mountain views. A magnificent Highland setting ideal for your holiday to relax, unwind and adjust to a slower pace. Clachaig also makes a perfect base for touring and sightseeing the beautiful West Coast or local walking and bird watching. Mountain sports and fishing, sea, loch and river available locally. Comfortable accommodation in ensuite rooms with TV. Imaginative freshly prepared food. Outstanding range of cask ales and malt whiskies. Recent winners "Best Pub in Scotland". Self Catering chalets available.
B&B from £20-£35 with D,B&B from £32.

INN

Clachaig Inn - Glencoe
Glencoe, Argyll, PH49 4HX
Tel: 01855 811252 Fax: 01855 811679
E-mail: inn@glencoe-scotland.co.uk
Web: www.glencoe-scotland.co.uk

Set in the heart of Glencoe with magnificent views, a unique atmosphere and a warm family welcome. Comfortable accommodation and interesting menus specialising in local produce and a large selection of cask conditioned ales. Your ideal holiday base. Some annexe accommodation. Some non-smoking bedrooms.

★★

2 Single	16 En Suite fac	B&B per person
7 Twin	1 Pub Bath/Show	£25.00-£35.00 Single
5 Double		£20.00-£35.00 Dbl/Twn
5 Family		

Open Jan-Dec
B&B + Eve.Meal £32.00-£45.00

B&B

Dorrington Lodge
Tighphuirst, Glencoe, Argyll, PH47 4HN
Tel: 01855 811653 Fax: 01855 811995
E-mail: hiltons@clara.co.uk

Comfortable, modern house just off main road, with excellent views over Loch Leven. Home cooked meals using quality local produce. Restricted smoking.

★★

1 Twin	All En Suite	B&B per person
2 Double		from £17.50 Dbl/Twn

Open Apr-Oct
B&B + Eve.Meal from £28.00

Glencoe, Argyll   Map Ref: 1F1

★★★

GUEST HOUSE

Dunire Guest House
Glencoe, Argyll, PA39 4HS
Tel/Fax: 01855 811305

| 2 Twin | All En Suite | B&B per person | Open 28 Dec-Nov |
| 3 Double | | from £16.00 Dbl/Twn | excl Xmas |

Modern bungalow in centre of Glencoe Village. Ideal base for touring, climbing and hill walking, infact all outdoor pursuits. All bedrooms tastefully furnished with TV's, radio's and tea-making facilities. Cosy guests lounge. Ample private parking. Drying facilities for walkers.

GLENCOE · SCOTLAND · PH49 4HW
Tel: 01855 811245 Fax: 01855 811687
e.mail: glencoehotel@hotmail.com
web: http://www.GlencoeHotel-Scotland.com

Experience the romance and drama of Scotland's West Highlands where the mountains meet the sea and an air of mystery still shrouds the remote glens. The Glencoe Hotel is the natural choice for holiday satisfaction where we will tempt you with the quality of our cuisine and the extensive selection of Scotch Whiskies in our cosy cocktail bar. All rooms have private facilities. An ideal base for both the outdoor enthusiast and the adventurous motorist and traveller. Full colour brochure and current tariff available on request. Open All Year.

Special **GLENCOE STOPOVER** Holiday

Any five consecutive nights, Full Breakfast and Table d'Hote Dinner, complimentary 'Dram' on arrival and complimentary Wine with Dinner on last evening.

From **£145** per person

★★

HOTEL

The Glencoe Hotel
Glencoe, West Highlands, PH49 4HW
Tel: 01855 811245 Fax: 01855 811687
E-mail: glencoehotel@hotmail.com
Web: www.GlencoeHotel-Scotland.com

2 Single	All En Suite	B&B per person	Open Jan-Dec excl Xmas
3 Twin		from £36.00 Single	
7 Double		from £24.00 Dbl/Twn	
3 Family		Room only per person	
		from £20.00	

In the same family for over 60 years this hotel offers a warm and friendly atmosphere with superb views over Loch Leven and beyond.

★★★

SMALL HOTEL

The Holly Tree Hotel
Kentallen, by Appin, Argyll, PA38 4BY
Tel: 01631 740292 Fax: 01631 740345
E-mail: mail@hollytreehotel.co.uk
Web: www.hollytreehotel.co.uk

5 Twin	B&B per person	Open Feb-Dec
5 Double	from £25.00 Single	B&B + Eve.Meal
	from £25.00 Dbl/Twn	from £45.00

Family run lochside hotel built around former railway station. Excellent views of Loch Linnhe. Accent on food, using fresh produce. Member of Taste of Scotland.

Glencoe, Argyll
Map Ref: 1F1

HOTEL

Isles of Glencoe Hotel & Leisure Centre
Ballachulish, nr Fort William, Argyll, PH49 4HL
Tel: 01855 821582 Fax: 01855 821463
Web: www.freedomglen.co.uk

7 Single	All En Suite	B&B per person	Open Jan-Dec
21 Twin		£33.00-£59.00 Single	B&B + Eve.Meal
15 Double		£33.00-£59.00 Dbl/Twn	£49.00-£85.50
16 Family			

Almost afloat, nestling on the lochside, this friendly, family hotel offers everything for which you dream on holiday; spacious loch and mountain-view bedrooms and a relaxed, convivial ambience. Luxuriate in the Leisure Centre – heated pool, sauna, steam room, jacuzzi, exercise room and solarium. Enjoy the casual lochside conservatory restaurant. Special breaks from just £99.00 pppn B&B.

GUEST
HOUSE

Scorrybreac Guest House
Glencoe, Argyll, PH49 4HT
Tel/Fax: 01855 811354
E-mail: john@scorrybeac.freeserve.co.uk

3 Twin	5 En Suite fac	B&B per person	Open 27Dec-Oct
3 Double	1 Priv.NOT ensuite	£18.00-£40.00 Single	
		£16.00-£22.00 Dbl/Twn	

Scorrybreac is a comfortable single storey guest house in beautiful woodland surroundings, overlooking Loch Leven, in a quiet secluded location on the edge of village, near local forest walks. Ideal base for exploring Glencoe and Ben Nevis area or for a shorter stay on a more extended tour of the Highlands. Colourful garden. Ample parking.

Glenfinnan, near Fort William, Inverness-shire
Map Ref: 3G12

HOTEL

The Prince's House
Glenfinnan, near Fort William, Inverness-shire PH37 4LT
Tel: 01397 722246 Fax: 01397 722307
Web: www.glenfinnan.co.uk

1 Single	All En Suite	B&B per person	Open Mar-Nov
2 Twin		from £40.00 Single	B&B + Eve.Meal
5 Double		from £35.00 Dbl/Twn	from £49.00
1 Family			

Set in historic 'Bonnie Prince Charlie' country on the romantic Road to the Isles this former coaching inn has been tastefully modernised to provide all the facilities of modern day. We pride ourselves on giving individual attention and quality food in a relaxed atmosphere. Awarded an AA red rosette. Taste of Scotland member.

SILVER

Glenshiel, by Kyle of Lochalsh, Ross-shire
Map Ref: 3G10

HOTEL

Kintail Lodge Hotel
Glenshiel, by Kyle of Lochalsh, Ross-shire, IV40 8HL
Tel: 01599 511275 Fax: 01599 511226
E-mail: Kintaillodgehotel@btinternet.com

3 Single	All En Suite	B&B per person	Open Jan-Dec excl
4 Twin		£30.00-£40.00 Single	24,25,31 Dec
5 Double		£30.00-£40.00 Dbl/Twn	B&B + Eve.Meal
			from £50.00

Early Victorian former shooting lodge on shores of Loch Duich at the foot of Five Sisters of Kintail. Ideal touring and hill walking centre. Public bar open all year round for bar meals.

Glen Urquhart, Inverness-shire
Map Ref: 4A9

SMALL
HOTEL

Glenurquhart House Hotel
Glen Urquhart, by Drumnadrochit, Loch Ness,
Inverness-shire, IV3 6TJ
Tel: 01456 476234 Fax: 01456 476286

2 Single	6 En Suite fac	B&B per person	Open Mar-Dec
2 Twin	1 Pub Bath/Show	from £20.00 Single	B&B + Eve.Meal
2 Double		from £25.00 Dbl/Twn	from £35.00
2 Family			

Situated in a scenic location overlooking Loch Meiklie. Attractions nearby include Loch Ness, Glen Affric for hill-walking, loch and river fishing, and pony trekking. Restaurant using freshly prepared produce. At the end of your day relax in our comfortable lounge by the log fires.

Golspie, Sutherland | Map Ref: 4B6

Deo Greine
Backies, Golspie, Sutherland, KW10 6SE
Tel: 01408 633106

B&B

| 1 Twin | 2 En Suite fac | B&B per person | Open Apr-end Sep |
| 2 Double | 1 Priv.NOT ensuite | from £19.00 Single | |

Crofting farmhouse, situated in hills behind Golspie, in an elevated position overlooking surrounding countryside & Dornoch Firth.

Golf Links Hotel
Church Street, Golspie, Sutherland, KW10 6TT
Tel: 01408 633408 Fax: 01408 634184
E-mail: golflinkshotel@btconnect.com
Web: www.golflinkshotel.co.uk

HOTEL

5 Twin	All En Suite	B&B per person	Open Jan-Dec
3 Double		£25.00-£30.00 Single	B&B + Eve.Meal
1 Family		£25.00 Dbl/Twn	£34.00-£45.00
		Room only per person	
		£25.00	

Personally run, this former manse is well sited for golf enthusiasts and ideal for business or pleasure.

Grantown-on-Spey, Moray | Map Ref: 4C9

Ardconnel House

Woodlands Terrace, Grantown-on-Spey, Moray PH26 3JU
Tel/Fax: 01479 872104   e.mail: enquiry@ardconnel.com
Web: www.ardconnel.com
An elegant and comfortable Victorian house furnished with antiques and pine.
All bedrooms are ensuite offering colour TV, hairdryer and hospitality tray. Excellent
"Taste of Scotland" dinner prepared by french owner/chef. Licensed. Ideal base for fishing,
golfing, walking, the whisky trail and visiting Royal Deeside and castles. **AA ♦♦♦♦♦**

Ardconnel House
Woodlands Terrace, Grantown-on-Spey, Moray, PH26 3JU
Tel/Fax: 01479 872104
E-mail: enquiry@ardconnel.com
Web: www.ardconnel.com

GUEST
HOUSE

1 Single	All En Suite	B&B per person	Open Easter-Oct
2 Twin		from £28.00 Single	B&B + Eve.Meal
3 Double		from £28.00 Dbl/Twn	from £46.00

Splendid Victorian villa with private car parking. All rooms ensuite. No smoking throughout. Taste of Scotland selected member. Warm welcome assured. Peaceful friendly ambience. French and German spoken.

Crann-Tara Guest House
High Street, Grantown-on-Spey, Moray, PH26 3EN
Tel: 01479 872197

B&B

1 Single	2 Pub Bath/Show	B&B per person	Open Jan-Dec excl
1 Twin		from £17.00 Single	Xmas
3 Family		from £17.00 Twin	B&B + Eve.Meal
		Room only per person	from £27.00
		from £15.00	

19c town house, recently modernised and personally run. Near River Spey, with rod storage and drying room. Cycle hire and repair. Off-street car parking. Dinner available.

Important: Prices stated are estimates and may be subject to amendments

Grantown-on-Spey, Moray   Map Ref: 4C9

Culdearn House

Woodlands Terrace, Grantown-on-Spey,
Moray PH26 3JU
Telephone: 01479 872106 Fax: 01479 873641
e.mail: culdearn@globalnet.co.uk
Web: www.culdearn.com

Elegant Country House offering a warm welcome from the
Scottish hosts Isobel and Alasdair Little who provide freshly
prepared food and modestly priced wines. All guest rooms
have ensuite private facilities with colour TV, radio, hairdryer
and welcome tray. Culdearn House has been modernised and
decorated with sympathy to offer a high standard of comfort.
Ideal location for fishing, golf, riding, walking, bird-watching
and visiting castles and historic sites. Log fires in season. 3
and 7 day breaks available.

AA ★★ AA Red Rosette   GOLD
RAC Hotel of the Year 1996. RAC ★★
Taste of Scotland selected member.
Please contact Isobel and
Alasdair Little for reservations.

★★★★

HOTEL

Culdearn House Hotel

Woodlands Terrace, Grantown-on-Spey, Moray-shire, PH26 3JU
Tel: 01479 872106 Fax: 01479 873641
E.mail: culdearn@globalnet.co.uk
Web: www.culdearn.com

1 Single	All En Suite	Open Mar-Oct
3 Twin		B&B + Eve.Meal
5 Double		£49.00-£75.00 pppn

Elegant Victorian house, retaining many original features and caringly
restored to include all modern comforts. Warm and friendly atmosphere.
All rooms ensuite facilities. Taste of Scotland member. Award winning
kitchen. Interesting wine list and unique collection of malt whisky.

    GOLD

★★★★

GUEST HOUSE

Dunallan House

Woodside Avenue, Grantown-on-Spey, PH26 3PA
Tel/Fax: 01479 872140
Web: www.dunallan.mcmail.com

1 Single	6 En Suite fac	B&B per person	Open Jan-Dec
3 Twin	1 Priv.NOT ensuite	from £30.00 Single	B&B + Eve.Meal
3 Double		from £22.00 Dbl/Twn	from £30.00

Dunallan is a splendid example of Victorian elegance oozing with the
charm of a bygone era. Original period fireplaces are in the residents
lounge and dining room, giving extra warmth to cheer you on those cooler
evenings. Home cooking, featuring fresh local produce.

V

★★★★

GUEST HOUSE

Garden Park Guest House

Woodside Avenue, Grantown-on-Spey, Moray, PH26 3JN
Tel: 01479 873235

3 Twin	All En Suite	B&B per person	Open Mar-Oct
2 Double		from £22.00 Single	B&B + Eve.Meal
		from £22.00 Dbl/Twn	from £32.00

Victorian, stone built house set in own colourful garden, quietly located a
short walk from the centre of Grantown on Spey. Guests' lounge with log-
burning stove; home cooked meals made with fresh produce served in the
dining room with its individual tables. A short selection of wines is
available. Five ensuite rooms, one of which is on the ground floor.
Dispense bar. French spoken.

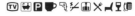

Grantown-on-Spey, Moray

Map Ref: 4C9

Garth Hotel

★★★

HOTEL

Castle Road, Grantown-on-Spey, Moray, PH26 3HN
Tel: 01479 872836 Fax: 01479 872116
E-mail: garth@cairngormhotel.com

1 Single	All En Suite	B&B per person	Open Jan-Dec
8 Twin		from £39.50 Single	
8 Double		from £29.50 Dbl/Twn	

17C building retains Olde Worlde charm. Fishing available. Cairngorm and Lecht ski slopes equidistant from hotel.

Kinross Guest House

★★★★

GUEST HOUSE

Woodside Avenue, Grantown-on-Spey, Moray, PH26 3JR
Tel: 01479 872042 Fax: 01479 873504
Web: www.kinrosshouse.freeserve.co.uk

2 Single	5 Ensuite fac	B&B per person	Open Jan-Dec
2 Twin	2 Priv.NOT ensuite	from £20.00 Single	B&B + Eve.Meal
2 Double		from £20.00 Dbl/Twn	from £34.00
2 Family			

Attractive Victorian villa in peaceful area. Welcoming and relaxed atmosphere with open fires. Traditional home-cooking using fresh local produce. Fine selection of Speyside malts. Fitness suite and sauna. Free use of mountain bikes. No-smoking house.

Muckrach Lodge Hotel & Restaurant

Dulnain Bridge, Grantown-on-Spey, Morayshire PH26 3LY
Tel: 01479 851257 Fax: 01479 851325
e.mail: info@muckrach.co.uk Web: www.muckrach.co.uk

Victorian Lodge in the heart of The Highlands. Cairngorms and Strathspey provides an unspoilt environment for recreation and rare wildlife, or tour Royal Deeside, Loch Ness, Skye and The Malt Whisky Trail. Lovely rooms, hospitable service, fine dining and a distinguished cellar turn a pleasant stay into a memorable experience.

Muckrach Lodge Hotel & Restaurant

★★★★

HOTEL

Dulnain Bridge, Grantown on Spey, Inverness-shire, PH26 3LY
Tel: 01479 851257 Fax: 01479 851325
E-mail: info@muckrach.co.uk
Web: www.muckrach.co.uk

2 Single	12 En Suite fac	B&B per person	Open Jan-Dec excl Xmas
3 Twin	1 Priv.NOT ensuite	from £25.00 Single	
6 Double		from £25.00 Dbl/Twn	
2 Family			

Muckrach overlooks the Cairngorms and Strathspey – an unsurpassed environment for recreation and rare wildlife, or touring Royal Deeside, Loch Ness, Castle and Malt Whisky Trails. Lovely country house, elegant rooms, friendly welcome and fine dining turn a pleasant stay into a memorable experience.

Parkburn Guest House

★★★

GUEST HOUSE

High Street, Grantown-on-Spey, Moray, PH26 3EN
Tel: 01479 873116

2 Single	3 En Suite fac	B&B per person	Open Jan-Dec
2 Twin	1 Limited ensuite	from £20.00 Single	
1 Double	1 Pub Bath/Show	from £20.00 Dbl/Twn	

Semi detached Victorian villa standing back from main road with ample parking available. Fishing and fishing tuition can be arranged.

Important: Prices stated are estimates and may be subject to amendments

Grantown-on-Spey, Moray | Map Ref: 4C9

The Pines

18 Woodside Avenue, Grantown-on-Spey PH26 3JR
Telephone/Fax: 01479 872092
e.mail: enquiry@pinesgrantown.freeserve.co.uk
web: http://www.pinesgrantown.freeserve.co.uk

Spacious Victorian house in tranquil gardens backing onto pine woods with delightful walks to River Spey. Licensed. Good fresh cooking using local produce. Elegant lounge, dining room, many fine paintings, antiques. Comfortable bedrooms with colour TV, refreshment tray, hairdryer, etc. All ensuite or private facilities. Friendly service. Activities include fishing, golfing, birdwatching, walking.

★★★★

SMALL HOTEL

The Pines
Woodside Avenue, Grantown-on-Spey, Moray, PH26 3JR
Tel/Fax: 01479 872092
E-mail: enquiry@pinesgrantown.freeserve.co.uk
Web: www.pinesgrantown.freeserve.co.uk

Beautiful 19th century country house, totally re-furbished and restored to the highest standards. All rooms en-suite or private. Two lounges and small library. Choice of dining room or conservatory. Taste of Scotland members. Large, secluded garden in woodland setting. Rare birds, deer and red squirrel.

1 Single	7 En Suite fac	B&B per person	Open Apr-Oct
3 Twin	1 Priv.NOT ensuite	from £30.00 Single	B&B + Eve.Meal
4 Double		from £27.00 Dbl/Twn	from £45.00

★★★

GUEST HOUSE

Rosegrove Guest House
Skye of Curr, Grantown-on-Spey, Inverness-shire, PH26 3PA
Tel/Fax: 01479 851335
E-mail: rosegroveguesthouse@tesco.net

Modern house, personally run. Home cooking. A short distance from Dulnain Bridge.

1 Single	3 En Suite fac	B&B per person	Open Jan-Dec
2 Twin	1 Pub Bath/Show	£18.00-£20.00 Single	
2 Double		£18.00-£20.00 Dbl/Twn	
1 Family			

★★★★

GUEST HOUSE

Rossmor Guest House
Woodlands Terrace, Grantown-on-Spey, Moray, PH26 3JU
Tel/Fax: 01479 872201
E-mail: dennis.day@virgin.net
http://freespace.virgin.net/dennis.day/rossmor.html

Spacious Victorian detached house with original features and large garden. A warm welcome. Parking. Panoramic views. No smoking throughout.

2 Twin	All En Suite	B&B per person	Open Mar-Nov
4 Double		from £25.00 Single	
		from £21.00 Dbl/Twn	

Helmsdale, Sutherland | Map Ref: 4C5

Navidale House Hotel

Helmsdale, Sutherland KW8 6JS
Tel: 01431 821258 Fax: 01431 821531

Navidale is set within its own private grounds of garden and woodland in a clifftop location commanding magnificent views across the Moray Firth. The hotel has been fully refurbished over the past two years and offers the comfort and amenities expected of a 3-star country house hotel. Ideal as a base for fishing, golf, bird-watching, hill-walking and touring the Northern Highlands. The restaurant has a reputation for fresh local produce, particularly fish, seafood and game, and is included in the Taste of Scotland Scheme. A place to relax and enjoy good food – a warm welcome awaits the discerning traveller.

HOTEL

Navidale House Hotel			
Helmsdale, Sutherland, KW8 6JS	3 Single	All En Suite	B&B per person
Tel: 01431 821258 Fax: 01431 821531	6 Twin		from £35.00 Single
	6 Double		from £45.00 Dbl/Twn
	1 Family		

B&B per person	Open Feb-end Oct
from £35.00 Single	B&B + Eve.Meal
from £45.00 Dbl/Twn	from £60.00

Former hunting lodge set amidst grounds and gardens overlooking the Moray Firth. Menus feature seafood, game, fresh local produce and are prepared by the chef/patron.

Invergarry, Inverness-shire | Map Ref: 3H11

GUEST HOUSE

Forest Lodge			
South Laggan, by Spean Bridge, Inverness-shire, PH34 4EA	2 Twin	6 En Suite fac	B&B per person
Tel: 01809 501219 Fax: 01809 501476	3 Double	1 Priv.NOT ensuite	£17.00-£21.00 Dbl/Twn
E-mail: info@flgh.co.uk	2 Family		

Open Jan-Dec excl
Xmas/New Year
B&B + Eve.Meal
£29.00-£33.00

Staying in the Great Glen for one night or more? Situated where the Caledonian Canal joins Loch Lochy and Oich. We offer pleasant, ensuite accommodation and home cooking in our relaxed and friendly home. Open all year for touring, walking or just to relax. Please call for a brochure.

Glengarry Castle Hotel

Invergarry, Inverness-shire PH35 4HW
Tel: 01809 501254   Fax: 01809 501207
e.mail: castle@glengarry.net
Web: www.glengarry.net

Country House Hotel privately owned and personally run by the MacCallum family for over 40 years. Situated in the heart of the Great Glen, this is a perfect centre for touring both the West Coast and Inverness/Loch Ness area. Magnificently situated in 60 acres of wooded grounds overlooking Loch Oich.

Recently refurbished, 4 rooms with 4-poster beds, all rooms have ensuite bathrooms, TV, radio and telephone. Private tennis court, trout and pike fishing in Loch Oich. Children and dogs welcome.

For brochure please contact Mr D MacCallum.

HOTEL
★★★★

Glengarry Castle Hotel
Invergarry, Inverness-shire, PH35 4HW
Tel: 01809 501254 Fax: 01809 501207
E-mail: castle@glengarry.net
Web: www.glengarry.net

Privately owned country mansion, some rooms with four-poster beds.
Extensive wooded grounds to loch with impressive hill and forest views.

3 Single	25 En Suite fac	B&B per person	Open 31 Mar-6 Nov
11 Twin	1 Priv.NOT ensuite	£47.00-£52.00 Single	B&B + Eve.Meal
10 Double	2 Pub Bath/Show	£39.00-£65.00 Dbl/Twn	from £62.00
2 Family			

INVERGARRY HOTEL

INVERGARRY, INVERNESS-SHIRE PH35 4HJ
Telephone: 01809 501206   Fax: 01809 501400
e.mail: hotel@invergarry.net   Web: www.invergarry.net

Great food, based on local produce – salmon, seafood, lamb, venison, beef, etc. Lots of nearby activities – tennis, watersports, rafting, walks, cycle routes, fishing, pony-trekking, etc. Children and pets welcome. Full details, sample menus and detailed tariff are available on our internet site at **www.invergarry.net**.

HOTEL
★★★

Invergarry Hotel
Invergarry, Inverness-shire, PH35 4HJ
Tel: 01809 501206 Fax: 01809 501400
E-mail: hotel@invergarry.net
Web: www.invergarry.net

Our family owned and managed hotel is the ideal touring base. See Skye, Ben Nevis, Loch Ness and much much more or just relax in front of an open fire with your favourite tipple and good book. The choice is yours. Real ales and a lot of malt whiskys.

1 Single	All En Suite	B&B per person	Open Jan-Dec
3 Twin	1 Pub Bath/Show	from £32.00 Single	
5 Double		from £26.00 Dbl/Twn	
1 Family			

Invergordon, Ross-shire | Map Ref: 4B7

GUEST HOUSE
★★★

Craigaron Guest House
17 Saltburn, Invergordon, IV18 0JX
Tel: 01349 853640 Fax: 01349 853619
E-mail: jobrown@craigaron.freeserve.co.uk

19th century converted fisherman's cottage overlooking the sea.
Five minute drive from town centre. 20+ golf courses within an hours
drive. Dolphins and other sea and birdlife. Many visiting cruise liners
including the QE2.

1 Single   2 Ensuite fac
4 Twin

B&B per person
from £17.00 Single
from £17.00 Twin
Room only per person
from £14.00

Open Jan-Dec excl
Xmas/New Year

Invermoriston, Inverness-shire | Map Ref: 4A10

HOTEL
★★★★

Glenmoriston Arms Hotel & Restaurant
Glenmoriston, Inverness-shire, IV63 7YA
Tel: 01320 351206 Fax: 01320 351308
Web: www.lochness-glenmoriston.co.uk
E-mail: scott@lochness-glenmoriston.co.uk

18c hotel in Highland village, offering a wide range of fine malt whiskies.
Fishing available. Easy access for touring Skye, Torridon and Loch Ness
area.

3 Twin   All En Suite
4 Double
1 4.Poster

B&B per person
from £55.00 Single
from £35.00 Dbl/Twn

Open Mar-Dec

Inverness | Map Ref: 4B8

GUEST HOUSE
★★★

Aberfeldy Lodge Guest House
11 Southside Road, Inverness, IV2 3BG
Tel: 01463 231120 Fax: 01463 234741
E-mail: class@algh.freeserve.co.uk

Comfortable Guest House close to city centre. All rooms ensuite. Hearty
breakfast, vegetarians catered for and children welcome. Private car park.

2 Twin   All En Suite
3 Double
4 Family

B&B per person
from £25.00 Single
from £19.00 Double

Open Jan-Dec

GUEST HOUSE
★★★★

Ach Aluinn Guest House
27 Fairfield Road, Inverness, IV3 5QD
Tel/Fax: 01463 230127

Newly refurbished, detached Victorian house with private parking in quiet
residential road. 5 minutes walk from town centre, restaurants, Eden Court
Theatre and Railway Station. All rooms ensuite, with bath and shower.
Lock-up facilities for motor and pedal cycles.

1 Double   5 En Suite fac
2 Twin
2 Family

B&B per person
£20.00-£30.00

Open Jan-Dec

GUEST HOUSE
★★★

Ardmuir House Hotel
16 Ness Bank, Inverness, IV2 4SF
Tel/Fax: 01463 231151
E-mail: hotel@ardmuir.com
Web: www.ardmuir.com

Family run hotel on the bank of the River Ness close to town centre and
Ness Islands. Conveniently situated for exploring the Highlands.

1 Single   All En Suite
2 Twin
5 Double
2 Family

B&B per person
from £34.50 Single
from £28.50 Dbl/Twn

Open Jan-Dec excl
Xmas/New Year

Important: Prices stated are estimates and may be subject to amendments

Ballifeary House
10 Ballifeary Road, Inverness IV3 5PJ
Telephone: 01463 235572 Fax: 01463 717583
e.mail: ballifhotel@btinternet.com
web: www.ballifearyhousehotel.co.uk
Lovely small hotel with excellent reputation, awarded the top grades for quality by
both Scottish Tourist Board and AA. Ideally situated in own landscaped gardens and
just 10 minutes' picturesque walk to town. All rooms ensuite bathrooms. Excellent
Scottish breakfasts. Table licence. Car park.
NO SMOKING THROUGHOUT.
Brochure/Reservations: Margaret Luscombe.

★★★★★

**GUEST
HOUSE**

Ballifeary House
10 Ballifeary Road, Inverness, IV3 5PJ
Tel: 01463 235572 Fax: 01463 717583
E-mail: ballifhotel@btinternet.com
Web: www.ballifearyhousehotel.co.uk

Attractive detached Victorian villa situated in quiet residential area, and
just a short walk to the Eden Court Theatre, River Ness and many excellent
restaurants. The house is tastefully decorated and furnished throughout
and has a very relaxed and friendly atmosphere. Lovely sitting room with
wealth of tourist information. Large car park in the grounds. Establishment
not suitable for families as minimum age is 15 years.

2 Twin	All En Suite	B&B per person	Open Apr-Oct
3 Double		from £45.00 Single	
		from £35.00 Dbl/Twn	

★★★

HOTEL

Brae Ness Hotel
Ness Bank, Inverness, IV2 4SF
Tel: 01463 712266 Fax: 01463 231732
E-mail: braenesshotel@aol.com
Web: www.braenesshotel.co.uk

Family run hotel on River Ness close to town centre. Home cooking using
fresh local produce a speciality. No smoking in dining room and most
bedrooms.

1 Single	9 En Suite fac	B&B per person	Open Apr-Oct
4 Twin	1 Priv.NOT ensuite	from £35.00 Single	B&B + Eve.Meal
3 Double		from £29.00 Dbl/Twn	from £48.00
2 Family			

Craigmonie Hotel & Leisure Sportif
ANNFIELD ROAD, INVERNESS IV2 3HX
Telephone: 01463 231649   Fax: 01463 233720
e.mail: info@craigmonie.com   Web: www.craigmonie.com
Comfortable Town House style hotel, informal relaxed atmosphere, ensuite accommodation, including
poolside suites and 4-poster deluxe double bedrooms. Full leisure facilities including heated pool,
choice of fine dining in the Chardonnay restaurant, or al fresco Conservatory Wine Bar. Every taste and
dining style is catered for. Room and breakfast, single from £76, twin/double from £96.

STB ★★★★ AA ★★★

★★★★

HOTEL

Craigmonie Hotel
Annfield Road, Inverness, IV2 3HX
Tel: 01463 231649 Fax: 01463 233720
E-mail: info@craigmonie.com
Web: www.craigmonie.com

Privately owned family run hotel. Originally 19c town house with modern
bedroom extension.

4 Single	All En Suite	B&B per person	Open Jan-Dec
14 Twin	Suites avail	£70.00-£78.00 Single	
14 Double	7 Pub Bath/Show	£48.00-£58.00 Dbl/Twn	
3 Family			

VAT is shown at 17.5%: changes in this rate may affect prices. | Key to symbols is on back flap.

Inverness

Map Ref: 4B8

★★★

SMALL HOTEL

Crown Court Hotel
25 Southside Road, Inverness, IV2 3BG
Tel: 01463 234816 Fax: 01463 714900
E-mail: reception@crowncourt.co.uk

Lying in a quiet residential area close to Inverness town centre, the Crown Court Hotel has the ambience of a country house hotel in the town.

1 Single   All En Suite
3 Twin
5 Double

B&B per person
from £59.00 Single
from £39.50 Dbl/Twn

Open Jan-Dec

CULDUTHEL LODGE
14 Culduthel Road, Inverness IV2 4AG
Tel: 01463 240089   Fax: 01463 240089
e.mail: culduth@globalnet.co.uk
Web: www.culduthel.com

Overlooking the River Ness stands Culduthel Lodge, an elegant Georgian residence of architectural interest. Caringly restored, furnished and decorated with great attention to detail and comfort, we offer a warm and relaxed atmosphere. In fine weather, aperitifs are enjoyed on the garden terrace. In cooler months the drawing room beckons with crackling log fires. The dining room provides an inviting setting in which to enjoy a daily changing menu of imaginative cooking with good wines. Our guest rooms provide more than one would expect: television, CD/Radio cassette player, hospitality tray, telephone, flowers, fruit, sherry, umbrella, luxury toiletries, hairdryer and complimentary newspaper.

★★★★

HOTEL

Culduthel Lodge
14 Culduthel Road, Inverness, IV2 4AG
Tel/Fax: 01463 240089
E-mail: culduth@globalnet.co.uk
Web: www.culduthel.com

Impressive Georgian residence of 1837 with elegant reception rooms and well appointed guest rooms. Superb, unobtrusive individual service in stylish surroundings. Ample car-parking in landscaped gardens. Short walk to town centre.

1 Single   All En Suite
2 Twin
8 Double
1 Family

B&B per person
from £45.00 Single
from £44.00 Dbl/Twn

Open Jan-Dec excl Xmas
B&B + Eve.Meal
from £64.00

Important: Prices stated are estimates and may be subject to amendments

Dunain Park Hotel
Inverness IV3 8JN
Tel: 01463 230512   Fax: 01463 224532
e.mail: dunainparkhotel@btinternet.com
web: www.dunainparkhotel.co.uk

Family owned and run and situated on the A82 one mile from Inverness, secluded in six-acres gardens and woodlands offering high standards of comfort and service. Award-winning restaurant where cuisine is Scottish with a French influence. Fresh local produce according to season. Good wine list and vast range of malt whiskies. Home baking. Open fires. Indoor heated swimming pool and sauna. Accommodation includes six suites with twin or double bedroom and lounge; Four-Poster, Half-Tester and Standard bedrooms. All have ensuite Italian marble lined bathrooms with bath and shower. Two cottages. Ideal centre for touring, golfing and walking. **Good Hotel Guide Scottish Country House Hotel of the Year 2000.**

HOTEL

Dunain Park Hotel
Inverness, IV3 8JN
Tel: 01463 230512 Fax: 01463 224532
E-mail: dunainparkhotel@btinternet.com
Web: www.dunainparkhotel.co.uk

Georgian country house hotel in 6 acres of gardens and grounds including 2 acre kitchen garden. Elegant public rooms. Scottish and French cuisine.

4 Twin / 7 Double / 2 Family — All En Suite — B&B per person from £79.00 Dbl/Twn — Open Jan-Dec, B&B + Eve.Meal from £104.00

SILVER

GUEST HOUSE

Eden House
8 Ballifeary Road, Inverness, IV3 5PJ
Tel/Fax: 01463 230278
E-mail: edenhouse@btinternet.com

Small family run establishment in quiet residential area, close to town centre, a few minutes walk to Eden Court Theatre, Ness Riverside walks and sports facilities.

2 Twin / 2 Double / 1 Family — All En Suite — B&B per person from £40.00 Single, from £30.00 Dbl/Twn — Open Apr-Oct

GUEST HOUSE

Fairways Guest House
72 Telford Road, Inverness, IV3 8HN
Tel/Fax: 01463 224934
E-mail: fairwaysgh@hotmail.com
Web: www.scottishholidays.net/fairways

Friendly welcome in our family run modernised guest house in quiet residential area. Close to town centre and all amenities. Children and pets welcome.

4 Twin / 2 Double — 2 Ensuite fac / 2 Pub Bath/Show — B&B per person from £20.00 Single, from £18.00 Dbl/Twn — Open Jan-Dec excl Xmas/New Year

VAT is shown at 17.5%: changes in this rate may affect prices.   *Key to symbols is on back flap.*

| Inverness | | | Map Ref: 4B8 | | | |

GUEST HOUSE ★★★★

Felstead Guest House
18 Ness Bank, Inverness, IV2 4SF
Tel/Fax: 01463 231634
Web: www.jafsoft.com/felstead/felstead.html

2 Single	5 En Suite fac	B&B per person	Open Jan-Dec excl
2 Double	1 Priv.NOT ensuite	from £25.00 Single	Xmas/New Year
3	1 Pub Bath/Show	from £26.00 Double	
Dbl/Twn/			
Fam			

Overlooking the River Ness, 5 mins walk from the town centre, Felstead, an elegant Georgian house, offers a high standard of comfort and service with a homely, relaxing and friendly touch by its owners.

📺 🎮 🎯 🅿 ☕ 🍷 ✳ 🔌 🛏 🎒

C 🈁 W V

Glendruidh House Hotel

Tel: 01463 226499   Fax: 01463 710745
e.mail: wts@cozzee-nessie-bed.co.uk
Web: www.cozzee-nessie-bed.co.uk/intro.html
Glendruidh House specialises in good old-fashioned hospitality. Situated amongst extensive grounds adjacent to Loch Ness golf course. Savour the superb traditional cuisine prepared from the very best fresh local produce. Relax in the circular drawing room or enjoy a dram in the sumptuous bar. **Individual oasis well worth finding!**

SMALL HOTEL ★★★★

Glendruidh House Hotel
by Castle Heather, Old Edinburgh Road South, Inverness, IV2 6AR
Tel: 01463 226499 Fax: 01463 710745
E-mail: wts@cozzee-nessie-bed.co.uk
Web: www.cozzee-nessie-bed.co.uk/intro.html

1 DblSuite	All En Suite	B&B per person	Open Jan-Dec
1 Twin		£56.00-£67.00 Suite	B&B + Eve.Meal
2 Double		£36.00-£49.00 Dbl/Twn	£60.00-£78.00
1 Triple			

Mainly 19th century house set amoungst large grounds consisting of woods and rolling lawns. Unique circular drawing room and elegant dining room serving excellent traditional cuisine prepared from the very best local produce. With a superb wine list and an excellent selection of malt whiskies you can be sure of a very pleasant stay. A wonderful base for many activity holidays, touring or just taking things easy. No smoking throughout.

📺 📞 🎯 🅿 ☕ 🍷 ✳ 🍴 🏆 🍷

🈁 W V

Glen Mhor Hotel & Restaurants

9-12 Ness Bank, Inverness IV2 4SG
Tel: 01463 234308 Fax: 01463 713170
Web: www.glen-mhor.com
Beautifully and quietly situated on River Ness near stations, parks, sports facilities, theatre and shops. All bedrooms ensuite. Plenty of car parking. Great Scottish and international cuisine in 2 restaurants. Resident beautician. Golf, fishing, shooting by arrangement. Ideal base for activity holidays and touring Loch Ness, coastal beaches and the Highlands.

HOTEL ★★★
🧍

Glen Mhor Hotel & Restaurants
10 Ness Bank, Inverness, IV2 4SG
Tel: 01463 234308 Fax: 01463 713170
E-mail: www.glen-mhor.com

6 Single	29 En Suite fac	B&B per person	Open Jan-Dec
12 Twin	Suite avail	£55.00-£69.00 Single	B&B + Eve.Meal
6 Double		£37.50-£75.00 Dbl/Twn	from £57.50
2 Family			

Traditional stone built house in quiet residential area, overlooking River Ness. Only 5 minutes walk to town centre and Eden Court Theatre on opposite side of river. Adjacent cottage/annexe accommodation. Choice of restaurant and Nicos Bistro.

📺 📞 🎯 🅿 ☕ 🍷 ✂ 🍴 🎨 🏆 🛏 🍷

C 🈁 W V

Important: Prices stated are estimates and may be subject to amendments

Inverness   Map Ref: 4B8

★★★★

HOTEL

Inverness Marriott Hotel

Culcabock Road, Inverness, IV2 3LP
Tel: 01463 237166 Fax: 01463 225208
E-mail: inverness@swallow-hotels.co.uk
Web: www.marriot.com/marriott/invkm

4 Single	82 En Suite fac	B&B per person	Open Jan-Dec
38 Twin	Suite avail	from £78.00 Single	B&B + Eve.Meal
28 Double			from £102.00
11 Family			

Original manor house dating back to the 18th century set in 4 acres of
woodland gardens. Leisure club with indoor swimming pool, jacuzzi,
sauna, steam room, exercise room, hairdresser, beauty treatments and
pitch and putt. 1 mile (2kms) from town centre, 7 miles (11kms) from
airport.

★★★

HOTEL

Jarvis Caledonian Hotel

Church Street, Inverness, IV1 1DX
Tel: 01463 235181 Fax: 01463 711206
E-mail: jcaledonianinverness.roomsales@jarvis.co.uk

24 Single	All En Suite	B&B per person	Open Jan-Dec
55 Twin	Suites avail	from £75.00 Single	B&B + Eve.Meal
12 Double		from £47.50 Dbl/Twn	from £37.50
15 Family			

Modern hotel in town centre, recently totally refurbished to a high
standard. 400 yards from railway station.

★★★

GUEST
HOUSE

Larchfield House

15 Ness Bank, Inverness, IV2 4SF
Tel: 01463 233874 Fax: 01463 711600
E-mail: info@larchfield-house.co.uk
Web: www.larchfield-house.co.uk

2 Single	All En Suite	B&B per person	Open Jan-Dec excl
1 Twin		from £30.00 Single	Xmas/New Year
2 Double		from £25.00 Dbl/Twn	
1 Family			

Peacefully situated on the banks of the River Ness and yet within five
minutes pleasant walk to the town centre, rail and coach terminals.
Larchfield House offers quality accommodation at a reasonable price. All
rooms are fully ensuite and prices include a traditional cooked breakfast.
All produce is sourced locally.

★★★★

HOTEL

Lochardil House Hotel

Stratherrick Road, Inverness, IV2 4LF
Tel: 01463 235995 Fax: 01463 713394
E-mail: lochardil@ukonline.co.uk

3 Single	All En Suite	B&B per person	Open Jan-Dec excl
2 Twin		from £75.00 Single	Xmas/New Year
7 Double		from £52.50 Dbl/Twn	

18c castellated country house in 5 acres of private gardens with extensive
parking. Under 2 miles (3kms) from centre. Former home of the
Macdonalds. Popular venue for large and small meetings and conferences.
Day delegate rates. Conservatory restaurant. Serving lunch and dinner
and open to non-residents

VAT is shown at 17.5%: changes in this rate may affect prices. | *Key to symbols is on back flap.* |

★★★

HOTEL

Loch Ness House Hotel
Glenurquhart Road, Inverness, IV3 6JL
Tel: 01463 231248 Fax: 01463 239327
E-mail: lnhhchris@aol.com

1 Single	All En Suite
6 Twin	
8 Double	
7 Family	

B&B per person
from £50.00 Single
from £30.00 Dbl/Twn

Open Jan-Dec
B&B + Eve.Meal
from £65.00

Privately owned, overlooking the Torvean Golf Course and Caledonian Canal. 20 minutes walk to town centre. Restaurant specialising in seafood and Scottish dishes.

★

HOTEL

MacDougall Clansman Hotel
103 Church Street, Inverness, IV1 1ES
Tel/Fax: 01463 713702

3 Single	14 En Suite fac
4 Twin	1 Priv.NOT ensuite
3 Double	
5 Family	

B&B per person
from £25.00 Single
from £24.00 Dbl/Twn

Open Jan-Dec excl
Xmas/New Year
B&B + High.Tea
from £30.00

Family-run hotel in convenient town centre location, close to Rail & Bus stations, Tourist Information Centre and all shops. On street parking and limited private parking available. French, German and Spanish spoken. Non-smoking rooms available.

★★★

GUEST
HOUSE

Malvern Guest House
54 Kenneth Street, Inverness, IV3 5PZ
Tel/Fax: 01463 242251
E-mail: malvern.guesthouse@virgin.net

1 Twin	All En Suite
2 Double	
3 Family	

B&B per person
from £20.00 Dbl/Twn

Open Jan-Dec

Victorian detached house in central location in Inverness. Off-street parking. All rooms are ensuite.

★★★

HOTEL

Maple Court Hotel
12 Ness Walk, Inverness, IV3 5SQ
Tel: 01463 230330 Fax: 01463 237700
Web: www.macleodhotels.co.uk

4 Twin	All En Suite
4 Double	
2 Family	

B&B per person
from £35.00 Single
from £25.00 Dbl/Twn

Open Jan-Dec
B&B + Eve.Meal
from £40.00

Small hotel in a riverside setting close to town centre situated in mature gardens with private parking. Seafood restaurant. Conference and seminar facilities.

★★

GUEST
HOUSE

Mardon Bed & Breakfast
37 Kenneth Street, Inverness, IV3 5DH
Tel: 01463 231005

1 Single	3 Ensuite fac
2 Twin	
3 Double	
1 Family	

B&B per person
from £16.00 Single
from £16.00 Dbl/Twn

Open Jan-Dec

Detached town house within close proximity to town centre and Loch Ness. Friendly atmosphere, special diets catered for. Ground floor room. Limited private parking.

Important: Prices stated are estimates and may be subject to amendments

Inverness | Map Ref: 4B8

Moray Park Hotel

HOTEL

Moray Park Hotel
Island Bank Road, Inverness, IV2 4SX
Tel/Fax: 01463 233528

2 Twin	6 En Suite fac	B&B per person	Open Jan-Dec excl
3 Double	1 Pub Bath/Show	from £22.00 Single	Christmas
1 Family		from £22.00 Dbl/Twn	B&B + Eve.Meal
			from £35.00

Run by owners and pleasantly situated with open outlook over gardens and river, yet close to town centre and all its amenities. Off-road parking. Several european languages spoken.

MOYNESS HOUSE
6 BRUCE GARDENS, INVERNESS IV3 5EN
Telephone/Fax: 01463 233836
e.mail: stay@moyness.co.uk   Web: www.moyness.co.uk

This fine Victorian villa has been sympathetically restored with elegant decoration and furnishings enhancing the many beautiful original features. The delightful bedrooms (all en-suite) offer modern comfort and period charm. All are no smoking. Pretty garden and ample parking. Located in quiet area near town centre, theatre and lovely riverside.

Brochure from Jenny and Richard Jones or book on 01463 233836.

GUEST HOUSE

Moyness House
6 Bruce Gardens, Inverness, IV3 5EN
Tel/Fax: 01463 233836
E-mail: stay@moyness.co.uk
Web: www.moyness.co.uk

1 Single	All En Suite	B&B per person	Open Jan-Dec
2 Twin		from £31.00 Single	
4 Double		from £31.00 Dbl/Twn	

Gracious Victorian villa with attractive walled garden. Family run, in quiet area. Short walk to town centre, river, Eden Court Theatre and many sporting amenities.

Ness Bank Guest House
7 Ness Bank, Inverness, IV2 4SF
Tel/Fax: 01463 232939
E-mail: nessbankgh@btinternet.com
Web: http://nessbankguesthouse.co.uk

1 Single	2 En Suite fac	B&B per person	Open Feb-Nov
1 Twin	1 Priv.	from £26.00 Single	
2 Double	1 Pub Bath/Show	from £20.00 Dbl/Twn	
1 Family	1 Pub toilet		

GUEST HOUSE

A warm welcome awaits you in out Victorian riverside Guest House overlooking River Ness and Cathedral. Quiet location but only 5 minutes walk from town centre, shops, restaurants, railway and bus stations. Close to Eden Court Theatre, pleasant gardens, Ness Islands and riverside walks. Strictly non-smoking throughout.

GUEST HOUSE

Oakfield Guest House
1 Darnaway Road, Kingsmills, Inverness, IV2 3LF
Tel/Fax: 01463 237926
E-mail: oak@btinternet.com

1 Single	6 En Suite fac	B&B per person	Open 6Jan-23Dec
2 Twin		from £18.00 Single	
3 Double		from £18.00 Dbl/Twn	

Detached house with private parking in peaceful residential area within easy walking distance of restaurants, shops and all amenities. Credit cards accepted. Ideal for touring the Highlands Loch Ness and the Moray Coast.

Inverness | Map Ref: 4B8

★★ GUEST HOUSE

Old Royal Guest House
10 Union Street, Inverness, IV1 1PL
Tel: 01463 230551 Fax: 01463 711916
Web: www.old-royal.co.uk

2 Single
3 Twin
3 Double
2 Family

5 En Suite fac
2 Pub Bath/Show

B&B per person
from £22.00 Single
from £20.00 Dbl/Twn

Open Jan-Dec

Four storey terraced guest house in the heart of the town centre and approximately 100yds from the railway station. Friendly personal attention of owners.

PALACE MILTON HOTEL & LEISURE CLUB
NESS WALK
INVERNESS
Freephone:
0808 100 55 56
Fax: (01786) 469400
Please quote ref HGH01

The Palace's situation is second to none – right in front of the River Ness, directly opposite the castle and only a few minutes walk from the main shopping centre. You'll find the £1 million investment has made quite a difference to the Palace Milton Hotel. Brand new Leisure Club with 50-foot swimming pool, fully equipped cardio-vascular gym and beauty salon.

Milton
Hotels & Leisure Clubs

e.mail: sales@miltonhotels.com
Web: www.miltonhotels.com
Also hotels in Oban, Fort William and Stirling.

★★★ HOTEL

Palace Milton Hotel & Leisure Club
Ness Walk, Inverness, IV3 5NE
Milton Sales Centre: Freefone 0808 100 55 56
Fax: 01786 469 400
E-mail: sales@miltonhotels.com
Web: www.miltonhotels.com

9 Single
49 Twin
20 Double
13 Family

All En Suite

B&B per person
£75.00-£95.00 Single
£49.50-£69.50 Dbl/Twn

Open Jan-Dec

Modernised Victorian hotel on banks of the River Ness opposite the castle. Many rooms recently refurbished. Milton Leisure Club features 50ft swimming pool. Close to town centre and Eden Court theatre.

★★★ GUEST HOUSE

Pine Guest House
60 Telford Road, Inverness, IV3 5LE
Tel/Fax: 01463 233032

4 Single
3 Family

5 Ensuite fac
2 Limited ensuite

B&B per person
from £22.00 Single
from £22.00 Double

Open Jan-Dec

Detached town house, 15 minutes easy walk from centre of Inverness and on main bus route. Private parking available.

★★★ GUEST HOUSE

Roseneath Guest House
39 Greig Street, Inverness, IV3 5PX
Tel/Fax: 01463 220201
E-mail: roseneath@lineone.net
Web: www.scottish-holiday.com

1 Twin
2 Double
3 Family

All En Suite

B&B per person
£20.00-£35.00 Single
£17.00-£24,00 Dbl/Twn

Open Jan-Dec

Family run guest house, quiet but short distance from the town centre. Off street parking; 5 minutes walk from Eden Court Theatre.

Important: Prices stated are estimates and may be subject to amendments

Inverness

Inverness

Map Ref: 4B8

Inverness

★★★

GUEST HOUSE

Rotherwood Guest House
7 Midmills Road, Inverness, IV2 3NZ
Tel: 01463 225732

1 Twin	All En Suite	B&B per person	Open Jan-Dec
2 Double		from £25.00 Single	
		from £20.00 Dbl/Twn	

Traditional red sandstone house with a warm relaxing environment. In a quiet residential area yet only a few minutes walk from town centre and station. All rooms ensuite. Non-smoking house. 30 minutes by car to the famous Loch Ness.

THE ROYAL HIGHLAND HOTEL
STATION SQUARE, ACADEMY STREET, INVERNESS IV1 1LG
TEL: 01463 231926 FAX: 01463 710705
WEB: www.royalhighlandhotel.co.uk

Welcome to one of Scotland's best loved hotels. Situated in the heart of Inverness, ideal for most itineraries. The cosy cocktail bar is the ideal place to relax and enjoy high quality dishes from the imaginative menu which utilises the finest of local produce.

★★★

HOTEL

Royal Highland Hotel
Station Square, 18 Academy Street, Inverness, IV1 1LG
Tel: 01463 231926 Fax: 01463 710705
E-mail: info@royalhighlandhotel.co.uk
Web: www.royalhighlandhotel.co.uk

17 Single	All En Suite	B&B per person	B&B + Eve.Meal
41 Twin		from £45.00 Single	from £51.50
10 Double		from £39.50 Dbl/Twn	
2 Family			

Elegant hotel with modern facilities offering Highland hospitality. Centrally situated for shops and local attractions. Ideal base for touring Loch Ness and the Northern Highlands.

★★★

HOTEL

Thistle Inverness
Millburn Road, Inverness, IV2 3TR
Tel: 01463 239666 Fax: 01463 711145
Web: www.thistlehotels.com

22 Single	All En Suite	B&B per room	Open Jan-Dec
47 Twin		from £50 Single	B&B + Eve.Meal
37 Double		from £64 Dbl/Twn	per room
2 Family		Room only from £49.49	from £66 Single
			from £96 Dbl/Twn

Modern, conveniently situated to main thoroughfares of town. Cromarty Brasserie.

★★★

GUEST HOUSE

Whin Park Guest House
17 Ardross Street, Inverness, IV3 5NS
Tel/Fax: 01463 232549
E-mail: whinparkhotel@talk21.com

1 Single	All En Suite	B&B per person	Open Jan-Dec excl Xmas
2 Twin		£23.00-£28.00 Single	
4 Double		£19.00-£25.99 Dbl/Twn	
3 Family			

Family run stone built house in quiet location close to town centre, Eden Court Theatre. Some private parking.

VAT is shown at 17.5%: changes in this rate may affect prices.

Key to symbols is on back flap.

Inverness

Map Ref: 4B8

★★★

HOTEL

Windsor Town House Hotel
22 Ness Bank, Inverness, IV2 4SF
Tel: 01463 715535 Fax: 01463 713262
Web: www.windsor-inverness.co.uk

2 Single	All En Suite	B&B per person	Open Jan-Dec
2 Twin		from £60.00 Single	
4 Double		from £35.00 Dbl/Twn	
2 Family			

Traditional, comfortable Scottish hotel with breakfast conservatory in attractive area on the banks of River Ness. Ony minutes from town centre. New riverside suite. Private parking.

by Inverness

Map Ref: 4B8

★★★★

SMALL
HOTEL

Kinkell House Hotel
Easter Kinkell, by Conon Bridge, Ross-shire, IV7 8HY
Tel: 01349 861270 Fax: 01349 865902
E-mail: kinkell@aol.com
Web: www.kinkell-house.co.uk

3 Twin	All En Suite	B&B per person	Open Jan-Dec
4 Double		from £39.50 Single	B&B + Eve.Meal
2 Family		from £35.00 Dbl/Twn	from £55.00

Secluded, restored farmhouse with excellent views over Cromarty Firth. Superior rooms, quality food and wine. Taste of Scotland. Ground floor bedroom available.

John o'Groats, Caithness

Map Ref: 4E2

★★

GUEST
HOUSE

Caber-feidh Guest House
John O'Groats, Caithness, KW1 4YR
Tel: 01955 611219

2 Single	7 En Suite fac	B&B per person	Open Jan-Dec excl
4 Twin	3 Pub Bath/Show	from £18.00 Single	Xmas/New Year
4 Double		from £17.00 Dbl/Twn	B&B + Eve.Meal
4 Family			from £24.00

Centrally situated in John O' Groats and 2 miles (3kms) from Duncansby Head. It is well situated for exploring the north east, including the north coast of Sutherland, the inland Flow Country, and more. Day trips to Orkney are a popular choice.

AWAITING
INSPECTION

John o'Groats House Hotel
John o'Groats, Caithness, KW1 4YR
Tel: 01955 611203 Fax: 01955 611408
Web: www.jogroats.co.uk

4 Single	All En Suite	B&B per person	Open Jan-Dec
15 Twin		from £35.00 Single	B&B + Eve.Meal
10 Double		from £30.00 Dbl/Twn	from £55.00
6 Family		Room only per person	
		from £30.00	

★

HOTEL

Seaview Hotel
John o'Groats, Caithness, KW1 4YR
Tel/Fax: 01955 611220

1 Single	5 En Suite fac	B&B per person	Open Jan-Dec excl
4 Twin	4 Priv.NOT ensuite	from £20.00 Single	Xmas/New Year
7 Double	2 Pub Bath/Show	from £14.50 Dbl/Twn	B&B + Eve.Meal
4 Family		Room only per person	from £25.00
		from £14.00	

Comfortable range of accommodation. 5 mins walk or 2 mins drive from Orkney Passenger Ferry. Secure facilities for bikes/cycles. Off-road parking. John 'O' Groats Visitor/Craft Centre, Stacks of Duncansby, cliff walks and puffins, fine views of the sea and nearby Orkney.

John o'Groats, Caithness   **Map Ref: 4E2**

★★

INN

Sinclair Bay Hotel
Main Street, Keiss by Wick, Caithness, KW1 4UY
Tel: 01955 631233 Fax: 01955 631492
E-mail: sinclairbayhotel@yahoo.com

1 Single	Ensuite fac	B&B per person	Open Jan-Dec excl
1 Twin	Pub Bath/Show	from £15.00 Single	Xmas/New Year
3 Double		from £15.00 Dbl/Twn	
2 Family			

Kentallen, by Appin, Argyll   **Map Ref: 1F1**

★★★★

SMALL HOTEL

Ardsheal House
Kentallen of Appin, Kentallen,by Appin, Argyll, PA38 4BX
Tel: 01631 740227 Fax: 01631 74342
E-mail: info@ardsheal.co.uk
Web: www.ardsheal.co.uk

1 Single	All En Suite	B&B per person	Open Feb-Nov
1 Twin		from £45.00 Single	B&B + Eve.Meal
4 Double		from £45.00 Dbl/Twn	from £70.00

Historic Manor House, dating from the 18th Century. A former home of the Stewarts of Appin, situated in 800 quiet secluded acres, including 11 acres of garden and parkland, with walks down to the shoreline. A comfortable family home, with a welcoming and relaxing atmosphere.

Kingussie, Inverness-shire   **Map Ref: 4B11**

★★★★

GUEST HOUSE

Avondale Guest House
Newtonmore Road, Kingussie, Inverness-shire, PH21 1HF
Tel/Fax: 01540 661731
E-mail: walsh.lorraine@talk21.com

1 Single	5 En Suite fac	B&B per person	Open Jan-Dec
2 Twin	1 Pub Bath/Show	£19.00-£22.00 Single	B&B + Eve.Meal
4 Double		£19.00-£22.00 Dbl/Twn	£29.00-£32.00

A splendid example of an Edwardian Home nr. centre of village, this family run Guest House is attractively furnished and equipped with all we hope you could need for a comfortable, relaxing stay. Excellent home cooking. A beautiful part of Scotland with plenty to see & do. Lots of info to help you plan your days.

Columba House Hotel & Garden Restaurant
Manse Road, Kingussie, Inverness-shire PH21 1JF
Telephone: 01540 661402 Fax: 01540 661652
e.mail: reservations@columba-hotel.co.uk
web: www.columba-hotel.co.uk

W

★★★
HOTEL

Nestling in large grounds. Candlelit Garden Restaurant, with patio onto landscaped walled garden, ideal for summertime dining, offers superb traditional Scottish cuisine. Cosy bar. Open fire in comfortable and homely lounge. Beautiful ensuite bedrooms, views, romantic four-poster rooms. Friendly atmosphere, your comfort and enjoyment is our priority. Ample parking. AA ◆◆◆◆

★★★

HOTEL

Columba House Hotel & Garden Restaurant
Manse Road, Kingussie, Inverness-shire, PH21 1JF
Tel: 01540 661402 Fax: 01540 661652
E-mail: reservations@columba-hotel.co.uk
Web: www.columba-hotel.co.uk

1 Single	All En Suite	B&B per person	Open Jan-Dec
2 Twin		from £35.00 Single	B&B + Eve.Meal
3 Double		from £30.00 Dbl/Twn	from £48.00
2 Family		Room only per person	
		from £30.00	

Nestling in large grounds. Excellent cuisine in Garden Restaurant in the landscaped, walled garden. Warm, cosy bar, open fire in lounge. Friendly atmosphere. Romantic Four-Poster rooms. Ample parking.

The Hermitage

Spey Street, Kingussie, Inverness-shire PH21 1HN
Tel: 01540 662137 Fax: 01540 662177
e.mail: thehermitage@clara.net
Enjoy the splendour of The Highlands and make Kingussie your base.
Let us help plan your daily itinerary. Wonderful walking, mountain bike trails
in easy reach of skiing, bird-watching, heritage centres and the whisky trail.
Good food and comfortable en-suite rooms enjoy a warm welcome at
The Hermitage.

★★★★

GUEST HOUSE

The Hermitage				
Spey Street, Kingussie, PH21 1HN	2 Twin	All En Suite	B&B per person	Open Jan-Dec excl Xmas
Tel: 01540 662137 Fax: 01540 662177	2 Double		from £21.00 Single	B&B + Eve.Meal
E-mail: thehermitage@clara.net	1 Family		from £21.00 Dbl/Twn	from £32.00
Web: www.thehermitage-scotland.com				

Enjoy the splendour of the Highlands and make Kingussie your base. Let us help you plan your daily itinerary. Wonderful walking and mountain bike trails. In easy reach of skiing, fishing, birdwatching, heritage centres and whisky trail. A warm welcome awaits you at the Hermitage.

🖵 🛏 P 🐕 🖠 ✗ ☕ 🍴 🍷 ⊞

C £ V

★★★

HOTEL

The Osprey Hotel				
Ruthven Road, Kingussie, Inverness-shire, PH21 1EN	1 Single	All En Suite	B&B per person	Open Jan-Dec
Tel/Fax: 01540 661510	3 Twin		from £25.00 Single	
	4 Double		from £25.00 Dbl/Twn	

Personally run hotel in centre of village, imaginative cuisine including vegetarian meals using fresh produce. Taste of Scotland member.

🖵 🛏 🐕 🖠 ✗ 🍴 🍷

C 🐾 £ V

Scot House Hotel

Kingussie, Inverness-shire PH21 1HE
Tel: 01540 661351 Fax: 01540 661111
e.mail: shh@sirocco.globalnet.co.uk   Web: www.scothouse.com
Award-winning small hotel set amid the magnificent scenery of
The Cairngorms. Relaxing, friendly atmosphere, personal service. Superb
restaurant and cosy bar (bar meals). Close to golf, fishing, skiing, sailing,
R.S.P.B., distilleries, castles, historic sites, forests, gliding, pony-trekking and
more! Central location makes ideal base for touring The Highlands.

★★★

HOTEL

Scot House Hotel				
Newtonmore Road, Kingussie, Inverness-shire, PH21 1HE	5 Twin	All En Suite	B&B per person	Open Feb-Dec
Tel: 01540 661351 Fax: 01540 661111	3 Double		from £35.00 Single	
E-mail: shh@sirocco.globalnet.co.uk	1 Family		from £30.00 Dbl/Twn	
Web: www.scothouse.com				

Award-winning family-run small hotel, situated in centre of Kingussie. Restaurant and bar meals. Ample car parking.

📞 🛏 P 🐕 🖠 ✗ 🍴 ⓕ 🎲 🍷

C 🐾 £ W V

Important: Prices stated are estimates and may be subject to amendments

Kingussie, Inverness-shire — Map Ref: 4B11

★★★ GUEST HOUSE

Sonnhalde
East Terrace, Kingussie, Inverness-shire, PH21 1JS
Tel/Fax: 01540 661266

3 Twin	4 Ensuite fac
2 Double	2 Pub Bath/Show
2 Family	

B&B per person
from £16.00 Single
from £16.00 Dbl/Twn

Open Jan-Dec
B&B + Eve.Meal
from £25.00

Your holiday is very important to us and we feel privileged to be able to look after you whether your stay is overnight or your main holiday one phone call will answer all your questions about this wonderful area and our home. Let us share it with you.

Kinlochbervie, Sutherland — Map Ref: 3H3

★★★ HOTEL

Old School Hotel
Inshegra, Kinlochbervie, Sutherland, IV27 4RH
Tel/Fax: 01971 521383

1 Single	4 En Suite fac
3 Twin	1 Pub Bath/Show
1 Double	2 Priv.NOT ensuite
1 Family	

B&B per person
from £29.00 Single
from £24.00 Dbl/Twn

Open Jan-Dec excl
Xmas/New Year

Restaurant with comfortable rooms in converted bungalow and bothy. Superb views of sea and surrounding countryside. All annexe accommodation.

Kinlochleven, Argyll — Map Ref: 3H12

★★★ HOTEL

MacDonald Hotel
Fort William Road, Kinlochleven, Argyll, PH50 4QL
Tel: 01855 831539 Fax: 01855 831416
Web: www.macdonaldhotel.co.uk

5 Twin	All En Suite
4 Double	
1 Family	

B&B per person
from £38.00 Single
from £26.00 Dbl/Twn

Open Jan-Dec

A modern, yet traditional, hotel set beside a tidal creek at the head of Loch Leven. Mid-way between Glen Nevis and Glencoe at the foot of the Mamores, the Macdonald Hotel is the perfect base to enjoy the best of West Highland walking or touring. Personally managed by the proprietors who pride themselves on providing a relaxed, informal, environment and the very best of Highland foods from fresh local produce.

★★ INN

Tailrace Inn
Riverside Road, Kinlochleven, Inverness-shire, PH50 4QH
Tel: 01855 831777 Fax: 01855 831291
E-mail: tailrace@btconnect.com
Web: www.tailraceinn.co.uk

3 Twn/Trpl	All En Suite
2 Double	
1 Family	

B&B per person
from £27.00 Single
from £20.00 Dbl/Twn

Open Jan-Dec

The Tail Race Inn is situated in the centre of the scenic village of Kinlochleven. Surrounded by the Mamore Mountains midway between Glencoe and Ben-Nevis. An ideal stopover for walkers, climbers or those who enjoy the outdoors. Excellent drying room facilities. Lively, atmospheric bar with wide-screen satellite TV. All rooms comfortably furnished with TV's and tea trays.

Kishorn, Ross-shire — Map Ref: 3F9

★★★★★ GUEST HOUSE

Shore House
Ardarroch, Kishorn, Strathcarron, IV54 8XA
Tel/Fax: 01520 733333
Web: www.shorehouse.co.uk

2 Twin	All En Suite
1 Double	

B&B per person
from £45.00 Single
from £35.00 Dbl/Twn

Open Apr-Oct
B&B + Eve.Meal
from £52.50

Very comfortable and spacious modern home with traditional warmth and character. Situated on the lochside with magnificent view across the bay and over the sea to Skye. Maureen and Douglas, formerly award winning restaurateurs, take particular pride in providing fine food, using the very best of local ingredients.

VAT is shown at 17.5%: changes in this rate may affect prices.

Key to symbols is on back flap.

Kyle of Lochalsh, Ross-shire   Map Ref: 3F9

HOTEL
★★★

Kyle Hotel
Main Street, Kyle of Lochalsh, Ross-shire, IV40 8AB
Tel: 01599 534204 Fax: 01599 534932
Web: www.btinternet.com/~thekylehotel

9 Single	All En Suite
14 Twin	
8 Double	

B&B per person
from £35.00 Single
from £32.00 Dbl/Twn

Open Jan-Dec
B&B + Eve.Meal
from £47.00

Recently modernised hotel, 5 minutes walk from the railway station, in the centre of the village. 8 bedrooms on the ground floor. Close to Skye Bridge.

TV ⌕ ☏ 🖴 P 🍴 ⚲ ✂ ⧖ 🍽 🏆 ♀

C ✈ ⬥ W V

🅿

Kylesku, Sutherland   Map Ref: 3H4

KYLESKU HOTEL
KYLESKU, BY LAIRG, SUTHERLAND IV27 4HW
Tel: 01971 502231   Fax: 01971 502313
e.mail: kylesku.hotel@excite.co.uk
Comfortable friendly hotel with wonderful lochside views. Cosy bedrooms ensuite. Good Food Guide restaurant and bar snacks. Log fires, relaxation, fishing, bird life, boating, hill walking, seals, wildlife, Great Britain's highest waterfall, boat trips to Handa Island, sandy beaches and lots more exciting interests to discover.

**SMALL
HOTEL**
★★★

Kylesku Hotel
Kylesku, by Lairg, Sutherland, IV27 4HW
Tel: 01971 502231 Fax: 01971 502313
E.mail: kylesku.hotel@excite.co.uk

2 Twin	6 En Suite fac
6 Double	2 Priv.NOT ensuite
1 Family	

B&B per person
£30.00-£35.00 Single
£27.50-£32.50 Dbl/Twn

Open Mar-7 Nov

Converted former ferry house at water's edge, spectacular views over Loch Glendhu to mountains beyond. Fresh produce, seafood a speciality. Annexed room available and some rooms without television.

TV 🎮 P 🍴 ✂ 🍽 🏆

C ✈ ⬥ V

**SMALL
HOTEL**
★★★★

Newton Lodge
Newton, Kylesku, Sutherland
Tel/Fax: 01971 502070
E-mail: newtonlge@aol.com

3 Twin	All En Suite
4 Double	

B&B per person
from £28.00 Dbl/Twn

Open Apr-Sep
B&B + Eve.Meal
from £43.00

A large modern comfortable private hotel, surrounded by an inspiring panorama of mountains and lochs. Ample car parking available. on-smoking establishment, seal colony can be seen from lounge and conservatory. Four poster room available. Ideal base for Britains highest waterfull und Handa Island bird sanctuary.

TV 🖴 P 🍴 ⚲ 🍴 🍽 🏆

⬥

Lairg, Sutherland   Map Ref: 4A6

HOTEL
★★★

The Nip Inn
Main Street, Lairg, Sutherland, IV27 4DB
tel: 01549 402243 Fax: 01549 402593
Web: www.nipinn.co.uk

2 Single	All En Suite
1 Twin	
1 Double	
2 Family	

B&B per person
from £22.00 Single
from £22.00 Dbl/Twn

Open Jan-Dec excl
Xmas/New Year

Allow us to look after you while you explore the far Northern Highlands and all they have to offer. Golf, fishing, hillwalking, cycling, birdwatching, touring rugged and untamed countryside with panoramic views and scenery. Base yourself at The Nip Inn, a small family run inn, relax in warm welcoming accommodation and enjoy our homing cooking, all fresh produce where possible. At The Nip Inn our priority is your comfort.

TV ⌕ 🖴 🍴 🍽 🏆

C ✈ ⬥ W V

Important: Prices stated are estimates and may be subject to amendments

| Lochinver, Sutherland | Map Ref: 3G5 |

The Albannach
Baddidarroch, Lochinver, Sutherland, IV27 4LP
Tel: 01571 844407 Fax: 01571 844285
Web: www.Inverlodge.com

SMALL HOTEL

19c house of great character. Spectacular views across Lochinver Bay to
Suilven. Original style cooking, emphasis on fresh produce.

2 Twin   All En Suite
3 Double

Open mid Mar-mid Nov
B&B + Eve.Meal
£85.00-£105.00 Sgl
£75.00-£87.00 Dbl

INVER LODGE HOTEL
Lochinver, Sutherland IV27 4LU
Tel: 01571 844496 Fax: 01571 844395
e.mail: stay@inverlodge.com
Web: www.inverlodge.com

*Loch Inver and the western sea is its
foreground, its backdrop the great peaks of
Sutherland – Suilven and Canisp. Inver Lodge
offers high standards of accommodation and
cuisine making the most of locally caught and
landed fish. The restaurant and all bedrooms
have superb sea views. We offer fishing on
three salmon rivers.*

**For further details
please contact Nicholas Gorton.**

Inver Lodge Hotel
Lochinver, Sutherland, IV27 4LU
Tel: 01571 844496 Fax: 01571 844395
E-mail: stay@inverlodge.com

HOTEL

Modern hotel with accent on comfort and friendliness. Restaurant and all
bedrooms can enjoy sea-scape and setting sun over Lochinver harbour.

11 Twin   All En Suite
9 Double

B&B per person
from £80.00 Single
from £65.00 Dbl/Twn

Open Mar-Dec excl
Xmas/New Year

Mrs J MacLeod
Polcraig, Lochinver, Sutherland, IV27 4LD
Tel/Fax: 01571 844429 Guests' Phone 844696
E-mail: cathelmac@aol.com

GUEST HOUSE

A warm, friendly welcome awaits you here at Polcraig. Ideally situated in
a quiet location with views across Lochinver Harbour. A short walk takes
you to a choice of places for eating out. Your hosts Jean and Cathel will
provide you with a hearty breakfast before you set out for your day.
Explore the Highlands, taking in the spectacular views and an abundance
of wildlife.

3 Twin   All En Suite
2 Double

B&B per person
£20.00-£25.00 Dbl/Twn

Open Jan-Dec

VAT is shown at 17.5%: changes in this rate may affect prices. | Key to symbols is on back flap.

Loch Ness (South), Inverness-shire — Map Ref: 4A10

★★★★

SMALL HOTEL

Craigdarroch House Hotel
South Loch Ness Side, Foyers, Inverness-shire, IV1 2XU
Tel: 01456 486400 Fax: 01456 486444

3 Twin	All En Suite	B&B per person	Open Feb-Dec
6 Double		£45.00-£65.00 Single	B&B + Eve.Meal
1 Family		£45.00-£65.00 Dbl/Twn	£69.50-£89.50

Traditional Highland country house with panoramic views over Loch Ness.

Lybster, Caithness — Map Ref: 4D4

★★★

HOTEL

The Portland Arms Hotel
Lybster, Caithness, KW3 6BS
Tel: 01593 721721 Fax: 01593 721722
E-mail: portland.arms@btconnect.com
Web: www.portlandarms.co.uk

5 Single	All En Suite	B&B per person	Open Jan-Dec
4 Twin		from £45.00 Single	
8 Double		from £58.00 Dbl/Twn	
1 Family			
4 Exec.Dbl			

Enjoy a warm welcome, very comfortable rooms and extremely good food in this very special hotel. The perfect base from which to explore the history and surrounding countryside of Caithness. Visit the Orkney Islands or just relax, unwind and enjoy life.

Mallaig, Inverness-shire — Map Ref: 3F11

Marine Hotel
MALLAIG INVERNESS-SHIRE PH41 4PY
Tel: 01687 462217
Fax: 01687 462821

At the end of the Road to the Isles. A warm welcome awaits you at our family run hotel which is conveniently situated for rail and Skye ferry terminals. Ideal base for day trips to neighbouring lochs and islands. All rooms ensuite. Enjoy fresh, local seafood and our Highland cuisine.
B&B from £28-£36 pppn
e.mail: marinehotel@btinternet.com
Web: www.road-to-the-isles.org.uk
For brochure and tariff contact: Tanya Ironside.
Taste of Scotland Member
AA ★★ RAC ★★   ★★★ Hotel

★★★

HOTEL

Marine Hotel
Mallaig, Inverness-shire, PH41 4PY
Tel: 01687 462217 Fax: 01687 462821
E-mail: marinehotel@btinternet.com
Web: www.road-to-the-isles.org.uk

3 Single	18 En Suite fac	B&B per person	Open Jan-Dec excl
10 Twin	1 Priv.NOT ensuite	£30.00-£38.00 Single	Xmas/New Year
5 Double		£28.00-£35.00 Dbl/Twn	B&B + Eve.Meal
1 Family			£40.00-£48.00

Family run hotel situated in the centre of a fishing village close to the railway station and ferry terminal. Taste of Scotland scheme member. Mallaig is still an important West Coast fishing port which enables us to source and serve an abundance of fresh seafood. Visitor attractions include heritage centre, marine world, swimming pool, 9 hole golf course (5 miles).

★

GUEST HOUSE

Springbank Guest House
East Bay, Mallaig, Inverness-shire, PH41 4QF
Tel/Fax: 01687 462459

1 Single	2 Pub Bath/Show	B&B per person	Open Jan-Dec excl Xmas
1 Twin		from £16.00 Single	B&B + Eve.Meal
1 Double		from £16.00 Dbl/Twn	from £24.50
1 Family			

Situated overlooking the busy little harbour with unobstructed views of Skye and just a few minutes walk from the village. Warm, frienldy atmosphere. Evening meals by arrangement. All bedrooms comfortably furnished with wash-hand basins and tea/coffee facilities. Large visitors lounge with TV.

Important: Prices stated are estimates and may be subject to amendments

Mallaig, Inverness-shire   Map Ref: 3F11

AA &
RAC
★★

West Highland Hotel

Mallaig, Inverness-shire PH41 4QZ
Tel: 01687 462210   Fax: 01687 462130
e.mail: westhighland.hotel@virgin.net
Web: www.road-to-the-isles.org.uk/west-highland-hotel.html

Family run hotel on the famous Road to the Isles. Ideal for visiting the Isle of Skye and Western Isles by ferry, also steam train trips to Fort William. Locally caught fish on our menu daily, all rooms ensuite, colour TV and tea-making. Fully licensed. Own large car park.

★★★

HOTEL

West Highland Hotel
Mallaig, Inverness-shire, PH41 4QZ
Tel: 01687 462210 Fax: 01687 462130
E-mail: westhighland.hotel@virgin.net
Web: www.road-to-the-isles.org.uk/west-highland-hotel.html

Hotel with recent conservatory extension. Stands above the village of Mallaig with views over the harbour to the Isle of Skye beyond. All Public Areas recently upgraded to high standard. Bar meals served and non-residents welcome. 4 annexe bedrooms.

6 Single	All En Suite	B&B per person	Open Apr-Oct
17 Twin		from £25.00 Single	B&B + Eve.Meal
11 Double		from £25.00 Dbl/Twn	from £40.00
5 Family			

Mey, Caithness   Map Ref: 4D2

★★

HOTEL

The Castle Arms Hotel
Mey, Thurso, Caithness, KW14 8XH
Tel/Fax: 01847 851244
Web: www.caithness-mm.co.uk/hotels/castlearms

Privately owned, original stone built coaching inn on Thurso to John O'Groats road, in village of Mey, 1 mile (2kms) from Castle of Mey. Loch fishing available. Ground floor bedrooms. Daily trips to Orkney from John O' Groats available in the summer months.

3 Twin	All En Suite	B&B per person	Open Jan-Dec excl
4 Double		from £30.00 Single	Xmas/New Year
1 Family		from £20.00 Dbl/Twn	B&B + Eve.Meal
		Room only per person	from £35.00
		from £15.00	

Morar, Inverness-shire   Map Ref: 3F11

★★

GUEST
HOUSE

Garramore House
South Morar, Inverness-shire, PH40 4PD
Tel/Fax: 01687 450268

Victorian lodge in 6 acres of mature woodland garden, 5 miles from Mallaig on the road to The Isles. A few minutes walk to the superb Morar beaches. Comfortable rooms - open all year. Large guests sitting room with open log fire. Perfect area for walkers, cyclists and bird spotters. Full drying facilities. Near Mallaig and Arisaig ferries to the small isles. Drinks licence. All major credit cards accepted. Informal warm family welcome.

1 Twin	2 Ensuite fac	B&B per person	Open Jan-Dec
1 Double	2 Pub Bath/Show	from £30.00 Single	
5 Family	1 Priv.NOT ensuite	from £20.00 Dbl/Twn	

VAT is shown at 17.5%: changes in this rate may affect prices. | Key to symbols is on back flap. |

Morar, Inverness-shire   Map Ref: 3F11

Morar Hotel
Morar, Mallaig PH40 4PA
Tel: 01687 462346 Fax: 01687 462212
e.mail: agmacleod@morarhotel.freeserve.co.uk
Web: www.road-to-the-isles.org.uk/morar-hotel

Family run hotel on the romantic Road to the Isles 3 miles from Mallaig, the southern gateway to Skye and the Inner Hebrides. The Hotel overlooks the silver sands of Morar. Venison, salmon/sea trout. 50% reduction for children. Hotel offers salmon/sea trout fishing on Loch Morar.

★★

HOTEL

Morar Hotel			
Morar, by Mallaig, Inverness-shire, PH40 4PA	4 Single	All En Suite	B&B per person	Open Apr-Oct
Tel: 01687 462346 Fax: 01687 462212	10 Twin		from £28.00 Single	B&B + Eve.Meal
E-mail: agmacleod@morarhotel.freeserve.co.uk	10 Double		from £28.00 Dbl/Twn	from £45.00
Web: www.road-to-the-isles.org.uk/morar-hotel	4 Family			

Family run hotel on 'Road to the Isles' with magnificent views over Silver Sands of Morar and islands of Rhum and Eigg. Some ground floor annexe accommodation. Only 3 miles from Mallaig and car ferry to Isle of Skye.

📺 🍴 P 🍵 🍽 ⛷

C 🐕 ♿ W V

Muir of Ord, Ross-shire   Map Ref: 4A8

★★★★

HOTEL

The Dower House			
Highfield, Muir of Ord, Ross-shire, IV6 7XN	2 Double	All En Suite	B&B per person	Open Jan-Dec excl
Tel: 01463 870090	2 Twin		from £65.00 Single	Xmas
E-mail: info@thedowerhouse.co.uk	1 Suite		from £55.00 Dbl/Twn	
Web: www.thedowerhouse.co.uk				

More a private house than a hotel, this highly individual conversion from a former dowagers house has created a warm and comfortable ambience. The food is excellent and memorable. The house is situated in 5 acres of mature grounds in the countryside between the Rivers Beauly and Conon, some 14 miles West of Inverness

📺 📞 🍴 P 🥢 🍽 🎿 ⛷

C 🐕 ♿ V

★★

HOTEL

Ord House Hotel			
Muir of Ord, Ross-shire, Highlands, IV6 7UH	1 Single	All En Suite	B&B per person	Open May-Oct
Tel/Fax: 01463 870492	6 Twin		from £37.00 Single	B&B + Eve.Meal
Web: www.ord-house.com	3 Double		from £42.00 Dbl/Twn	from £59.00
	1 Family			

Country house dating from 1637, set in extensive grounds of both formal garden and park and woodland. Taste of Scotland with emphasis on fresh food. Friendly and informal service in comfortable surroundings – a relaxing environment.

📞 🍴 P 🍽 🎿 🍽 ⛷ 🪑

C 🐕 ♿ V

Nairn   Map Ref: 4C8

★★

HOTEL

Alton Burn Hotel			
Alton Burn Road, Nairn, IV12 5ND	6 Single	All En Suite	B&B per person	Open Apr-Dec excl
Tel: 01667 452051 Fax: 01667 456697	14 Twin		from £35.00 Single	Xmas/New Year
E-mail: altonburn@tesco.net	3 Family		from £27.50 Twin	B&B + Eve.Meal
			Room only per person	from £45.00
			from £30.00	

Family run hotel in extensive grounds: putting green, swimming pool, tennis court, games room, table tennis. Close to beach, overlooking golf course.

📺 🍴 P 🍵 🍽 🏊 🎾 🎱 ⛷

C 🐕 ♿ V

Important: Prices stated are estimates and may be subject to amendments

Nairn

Map Ref: 4C8

Claymore House Hotel
Seabank Road, Nairn, IV12 4EY
Tel: 01667 453731 Fax: 01667 455290
E-mail: ClaymoreNairnScotland@compuserve.com
Web: www.claymorehousehotel.com

Family run hotel with the emphasis on friendliness, traditional food and
flexibility and customer care.

1 Single	All En Suite	B&B per person	Open Jan-Dec
11 Twn/Dbl		£42.00-£50.00 Single	B&B + Eve.Meal
2 Family		from £42.50 Dbl/Twn	from £47.50
		from £99.00 Family	

Golf View Hotel & Leisure Club
Seabank Road, Nairn, IV12 4HD
Tel: 01667 452301 Fax: 01667 455267
E-mail: rooms@morton-hotels.com

Victorian hotel with modern leisure centre overlooking the sea and the
hills of the Black Isle. Championship golf course nearby. Headquarters
hotel for 1999 Walker Cup. Function suite (up to 120 persons) for private
functions, weddings and conferences.

4 Single	All En Suite	B&B per person	Open Jan-Dec
25 Twin	Suite avail	£77.00-£93.00 Single	
15 Double		£51.00-£83.00 Dbl/Twn	
3 Family			

Greenlawns
13 Seafield Street, Nairn, IV12 4HG
Tel/Fax: 01667 452738
E-mail: greenlawns@cali.co.uk

Greenlawns is a large Victorian villa set in its own grounds in a central, yet
quiet corner of Nairn. Its seven en-suite bedrooms range from the ground
floor annexe, suitable for families or golfers alike, to large elegantly
appointed, antique furnished rooms with extra large bathtubs and a
complimentary dram.

3 Twin	All En Suite	B&B per person	Open Jan-Dec
3 Double		from £20.00 Single	excl 1-20 Mar
1 Single		from £20.00 Dbl/Twn	B&B + Eve.Meal
			from £32.00

Invernairne Hotel
Thurlow Road, Nairn, IV12 4EZ
Tel: 01667 452039 Fax: 01667 456760
Web: www.golf-vacations.co.uk

Former mansion house now a family run hotel in wooded garden; private
path to safe beach. Swimming pool and golf within walking distance.

2 Single	All En Suite	B&B per person	Open Jan-Dec excl
1 Twin		from £35.00 Single	Xmas/New Year
3 Double		from £30.00 Dbl/Twn	B&B + Eve.Meal
3 Family			from £40.00

Lothian House Hotel
10 Crescent Road, Nairn, Nairnshire, IV12 4NB
Tel: 01667 453555 Fax: 01667 455454
Web: www.users.globalnet.co.uk/~lothot/

Stone built house, c1850 in quiet residential area of town. Personally run
by proprietors and within easy reach of town centre, beach and 2
championship golf courses. Sea views.

1 Single	All En Suite	B&B per person	Open Jan-Dec excl
2 Twin		from £25.00 Single	Xmas/New Year
2 Double		from £20.00 Dbl/Twn	B&B + Eve.Meal
1 Family		Room only per person	from £33.00
		from £16.00	

VAT is shown at 17.5%: changes in this rate may affect prices.

Key to symbols is on back flap.

Nairn   Map Ref: 4C8

HOTEL

The Newton Hotel
Inverness Road, Nairn, IV6 2SY
Tel: 01667 453144 Fax: 01667 454026
E-mail: rooms@morton-hotels.com
Web: www.morton-hotels.com

The Newton Hotel is an elegant Georgian building set in over 20 acres of secluded grounds & overlooks the Nairn Championship Course. Its newly completed Highland Conference Centre which caters for Conferences of 400+ & banqueting for 350 also offers ISDN, Video Conferencing & 8 ground floor syndicate rooms.Sharing its amenities with The Golf View Hotel located 500yds away, together they offer 105 bedrooms with 5 suites & 30 new master bedrooms.

6 Single	All En Suite	B&B per person	B&B + Eve.Meal
31 Twin		from £85.00 Single	from £99.00
18 Double		from £51.00 Dbl/Twn	
2 Family			

GUEST HOUSE

Rhyden House
Cumming Street, Nairn, IV12 4NQ
Tel: 01667 453736 Fax: 01667 451373
E-mail: rhyden.house@which.net

Victorian sandstone house of character. 2 minutes level walk to beach. Secluded garden. Lunches and evening meals available in our resturarnt, always using local produce.

1 Single	B&B per person	Open Mar-Oct
1 Twin	from £24.00 Single	B&B + Eve.Meal
2 Double	from £22.00 Dbl/Twn	from £33.00
2 Family		

SMALL HOTEL

Sunny Brae Hotel
Marine Road, Nairn, IV12 4EA
Tel: 01667 452309 Fax: 01667 454860
E-mail: so1@sunnybraehotel.com
Web: www.sunnybraehotel.com

Small friendly family run hotel, offering personal attention to guests. Dinners emphasising fresh local produce. Located close to the town centre and all it's amenities, yet with uninterrupted sea views towards the Moray Firth. Plenty of advice available on what to do - golf, trips to Speyside, the Moray Coast or over to the West and the Far North.

1 Single	All En Suite	B&B per person	Open Mar-Nov
4 Twin		from £39.00 Single	B&B + Eve.Meal
3 Double		from £35.00 Dbl/Twn	from £52.50
1 Family			

HOTEL

The Windsor Hotel
Albert Street, Nairn, IV12 4HP
Tel: 01667 453108 Fax: 01667 456108
E-mail: windsornairnscotland@btinternet.com
Web: www.windsor-hotel.co.uk

Set within residential area of Nairn and within 3 mins walk of town centre, close to the beach, many sporting activities, including the town's two championship golf courses. It has retained much of its character, whilst being sympathetically refurbished in line with the owners commitment to a continual upgrade. Ideal base for touring the Inverness Highlands. Fort George, Culloden Battlefield, Cawdor and Brodie Castles and Loch Ness.

8 Single	All En Suite	B&B per person	Open Jan-Dec
20 Twin		from £45.00 Single	
18 Double		from £40.00 Dbl/Twn	
6 Family			

Important: Prices stated are estimates and may be subject to amendments

Nethy Bridge, Inverness-shire — Map Ref: 4C10

★ HOTEL

Nethybridge Hotel
Nethy Bridge, Inverness-shire, PH25 3DP
Tel: 01479 821203 Fax: 01479 821686
Web: www.nethybridge.com/nethybridgehotel.htm

9 Single	All En Suite	B&B per person	Open Jan-Dec
35 Twin		from £39.00 Single	B&B + Eve.Meal
19 Double		from £39.00 Dbl/Twn	from £49.00
4 Family		Room only per person	
		from £30.00	

Victorian building of character recently upgraded, situated in Highland village and ideally situated for the amenities of Strathspey.

Newtonmore, Inverness-shire — Map Ref: 4B11

★★★ HOTEL

The Alvey House Hotel
Golf Course Road, Newtonmore, Inverness-shire, PH20 1AT
Tel: 01540 673260 Fax: 01540 673003
Web: www.alveyhouse.co.uk

1 Single	All En Suite	B&B per person	Open Jan-Dec
1 Twin		from £22.00 Single	B&B + Eve.Meal
3 Double		from £22.00 Dbl/Twn	from £36.00
2 Family			

Stone built Victorian villa overlooking Strathspey. Adjacent to golf course and village centre. Alpine ski packages available in season.

★★★ HOTEL

Balavil Sport Hotel
Main Street, Newtonmore, Inverness-shire, PH20 1DL
Tel: 01540 673220 Fax: 01540 673773
E-mail: BalavilHotel@btinternet.com

6 Single	All En Suite	B&B per person	Open Feb-Dec
8 Double		from £35.00 Single	B&B + Eve.Meal
28 Twin		from £25.00 Dbl/Twn	from £35.00
4 Family			

Family hotel in centre of village with many sporting facilities including indoor swimming pool and regular entertainment. All rooms ensuite.

★★★ GUEST HOUSE

Glenquoich House
Glen Road, Newtonmore, Inverness-shire, PH20 1DZ
Tel/Fax: 01540 673461
Web: www.host.co.uk

1 Single	1 En Suite fac	B&B per person	Open Jan-Dec
2 Twin	2 Pub Bath/Show	from £17.00 Single	
1 Double		from £18.00 Dbl/Twn	
1 Family			

Lovely Victorian house near village centre. Excellent base for exploring the Highlands.

Onich, by Fort William, Inverness-shire   Map Ref: 3G12

Allt-nan-Ros Hotel
Onich, by Fort William, Inverness-shire PH33 6RY
Tel: 01855 821210 Fax: 01855 821462
e.mail: allt-nan-ros@zetnet.co.uk
web: www.allt-nan-ros.co.uk

AA ★★★ ◉◉, RAC ★★★ (3 diningroom awards), Minotel "Classic Gold" hotel, Ashley Courtenay and Taste of Scotland are all testimonies to the quality and atmosphere of this acclaimed, friendly and family run West Highland hotel. All bedrooms, lounge and restaurant, with its panoramic windows, look south down Loch Linnhe towards the hills of Appin and Morvern.

★★★★

HOTEL

Allt-Nan-Ros Hotel
Onich, by Fort William, Inverness-shire, PH33 6RY
Tel: 01855 821210 Fax: 01855 821462
E-mail: alt-nan-ros@zetnet.co.uk
Web: www.allt-nan-ros.co.uk

One of the most highly acclaimed family run hotels in the West Highlands. The 'burn of the roses' aptly describes the hotel which faces south down Loch Linnhe to the hills of Ardgour and Appin. All rooms share the same superb view and the 2 AA rosette cuisine is enjoyed by all. James and Fiona MacLeod and their staff ensure that the ambience is always relaxing and friendly and the facilites exquisite.

2 Single	All En Suite	B&B per person	Open Jan-Dec excl Xmas
7 Twin		from £45.00 Single	B&B + Eve.Meal
10 Double		from £45.00 Dbl/Twn	from £67.50
1 Family			

Camus House Lochside Lodge
ONICH, BY FORT WILLIAM, INVERNESS-SHIRE PH33 6RY
Telephone/Fax: 01855 821200
e.mail: Young@CamusHouse.Freeserve.co.uk

In extensive lochside gardens, midway between Ben Nevis and Glencoe. Ideal base for touring, walking, mountain biking, climbing and ski-ing. Most rooms are ensuite with central heating, TV and teasmaid. We provide excellent cooking, friendly service and are fully licensed.

Dinner, Bed & Breakfast – £36-£45. Weekly – £200-£280

Open from February to November. Brochure available.

★★★

GUEST HOUSE

Camus House
Lochside Lodge, Onich, Inverness-shire, PH33 6RY
Tel/Fax: 01855 821200
E-mail: Young@CamusHouse.Freeserve.co.uk
Website: www.SmoothHound.co.uk/hotels/camushouse.html

Large Victorian house in spectacular lochside location with unsurpassed views over Onich Bay to the mountains – midway between Ben Nevis and Glencoe – an ideal base for touring, walking, biking, climbing and skiing. Comfortable, tastefully furnished bedrooms with TV and hospitality tray. Excellent cuisine – restricted licence – and a warm welcome awaits you.

2 Twin	6 En Suite fac	B&B per person	Open Feb-Nov
3 Double	1 Priv.NOT ensuite	from £25.50 Single	B&B + Eve.Meal
2 Family	1 Pub Bath/Show	from £23.50 Double	from £36.00

★★

SMALL HOTEL

Creag Mhor Hotel
Onich, Inverness-shire, PH33 6RY
Tel: 01855 821379 Fax: 01855 821579

Halfway between Ben Nevis and Glencoe. Magnificent Victorian lochside family hotel. Providing the ideal base for all West Highland attractions and activities. All rooms with ensuite. Friendly, knowledgeable, local staff. Tasty home cooking, cosy lounge bar with log fire and panoramic views over loch and hill.

1 Single	All En Suite	B&B per person	Open 20 Jan-Oct,
4 Twin		from £27.50 Single	Dec and New Year
6 Double		from £27.00 Dbl/Twn	B&B + Eve.Meal
3 Family			from £35.00

Important: Prices stated are estimates and may be subject to amendments

Onich, by Fort William, Inverness-shire   Map Ref: 3G12

CUILCHEANNA HOUSE

Onich, Fort William, Inverness-shire PH33 6SD

Tel: 01855 821226

e.mail: relax@cuilcheanna.freeserve.co.uk

Surrounded by beautiful loch and mountain scenery, Cuilcheanna is the perfect base for exploring the best of the Western Highlands. Ideal for walking, sightseeing or just some serious relaxation! Our welcome is warm and genuine, our service truly personal and our food exceptional. So come and enjoy yourself!

★★★★

SMALL HOTEL

Cuilcheanna House

Onich, Inverness-shire, PH33 6SD

Tel: 01855 821226

E-mail: relax@cuilcheanna.freeserve.co.uk

Russell and Linda Scott invite you to stay at their small country hotel, peacefully situated some 300m from the main road overlooking Loch Linnhe, amidst breathtaking scenery. We pride ourselves on the standard of food we serve - freshly prepared from the best locally sourced ingredients. Set 4 course meal but alternatives include vegetarian and special diets. Fully licensed with personally selected wine and malt whisky lists. Taste of Scotland

2 Twin	All En Suite	B&B per person
5 Double		from £44.00 Single
		from £29.00 Dbl/Twn

Open Easter-Oct

B&B + Eve.Meal

from £45.00

★★★★

HOTEL

The Lodge On The Loch Hotel

Onich, nr Fort William, Inverness-shire, PH33 6RY

Tel: 01855 821582 Fax: 01855 821463

E-mail: reservations@freedomglen.co.uk

Web: www.freedomglen.co.uk

Discover seclusion and serenity — enjoy one of the West Coast's finest panoramas. 'The Lodge' is a perfect Highland retreat. Relax in peaceful lounges. Savour memorable evenings in the charming lochview Taste of Scotland restaurant — renowned for the freshest produce. Choice of many individual luxury rooms available with many personal touches.

2 Single	17 En Suite fac	D.B&B only
4 Twin		£69.50-£100.00
11 Double		

Open Easter-Nov,

Xmas/New Year

THE ONICH HOTEL

★★★
AA/RAC

★★★★
SMALL HOTEL AA

ONICH, Nr FORT WILLIAM, INVERNESS-SHIRE PH33 6RY

Tel: 01855 821214   Fax: 01855 821484

e.mail: reservations@onich-fortwilliam.co.uk

Web: www.onich-fortwilliam.co.uk

Located in glorious gardens on the shores of Loch Linnhe, all public rooms enjoy the marvellous view over to Glencoe. You can choose from our award winning restaurant which serves local cuisine and our Deerstalker lounge bar serves tasty meals throughout the day. Children and families welcome.

★★★★

SMALL HOTEL

Onich Hotel

Onich, nr Fort William, Inverness-shire, PH33 6RY

Tel: 01855 821214 Fax: 01855 821484

E-mail: reservations@onich-fortwilliam.co.uk

Web: www.onich-fortwilliam.co.uk

Personally run hotel with gardens extending to lochside. Superb all season views across Loch Linnhe to mountains. Interesting menu, local produce.

4 Single	All En Suite	B&B per person
5 Twin		from £38.00 Single
10 Double		from £33.00 Dbl/Twn
6 Family		

Open Jan-Dec excl Xmas

B&B + Eve.Meal

from £54.00

VAT is shown at 17.5%: changes in this rate may affect prices.   *Key to symbols is on back flap.*

Discover seclusion and serenity at

THE LODGE ON THE LOCH HOTEL

Take in the panoramic mountain views **and lochside garden setting** where the vista extends across the sea south to Argyll and west to the lovely hills of Morvern. Then wrap yourself up in the quiet luxury of this – your **welcoming Highland retreat.**

The Lodge on the Loch is an unrivalled **haven of comfort** with just a handful of bedrooms. You'll want to linger in our **peaceful lounges** as the day unfolds. Here long days pass peacefully into breathtaking sunsets, after which you can warm yourself by the crackling fire. As a house guest you will enjoy complimentary tea, coffee and home baking throughout your stay.

As evening falls you are invited to join us for drinks before making your way to dinner in the **acclaimed lochview restaurant.** Five courses of the freshest local produce carefully handcooked to order, make every night an evening to remember in these charming surroundings.

Choose a bedroom that suits your needs from our deluxe viewladen Chieftian Rooms with whirlpool bath, full in-room entertainment system or an economy Clansman Room. Whichever you choose you will receive 4 star comfort and **friendly, genuine service.**

The Lodge is ideally positioned as a base for roaming the Western Highlands with a lifetime of varied touring, walking and attractions on your doorstep. You are also welcome to use our nearby **Leisure Club** free of charge. Only minutes drive away you will find the temptation of an indoor heated pool, sauna, steam room, sunbed and exercise room.

Write or telephone now to make a reservation or request your colour brochure.

The Young Family, The Lodge On The Loch Hotel,
Onich, Nr Fort William,
The Scottish Highlands PH33 6RY
Telephone: 01855 821237 Facsimile: 01855 821238.
e-mail: reservations@freedomglen.co.uk
Web: www.freedomglen.co.uk

Recommended by all leading guides.

AA ★★★

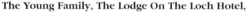

Plockton, Ross-shire — Map Ref: 3F9

The Plockton Hotel
Harbour Street, Plockton, Wester Ross, IV52 8TN
Tel: 01599 544274 Fax: 01599 544475
E-mail: sales@plocktonhotel.co.uk

SMALL HOTEL

1 Single · 2 Twin · 10 Double · 1 Family
13 Ensuite fac · 1 Priv.NOT ensuite · 1 Pub Show/Bath
B&B per person from £35.00 Single, from £30.00 Dbl/Twn
Open Jan-Dec excl New Year

Family run small hotel recently extended with spectacular views. Specialising in local seafood, Highland deer and game. Four annex bedrooms in nearby cottage.

Plockton Inn
Innes Street, Plockton
Tel: 01599 544222 Fax: 01599 544487
E-mail: plocktoninn@plocktoninn.freeserve.co.uk

INN

1 Single · 2 Twin · 2 Double · 1 Family
5 En Suite fac · 1 Priv.NOT ensuite
B&B per person £25.00-£32.00 Single, £24.00-£28.00 Dbl/Twn
Open Jan-Dec

Family run Inn 50 yards from lochside. Situated in picturesque village on Loch Carron. Bar meals and restaurant specialising in fresh local seafood dishes.

Poolewe, Ross-shire — Map Ref: 3F7

Poolewe Hotel
Poolewe, Achnasheen, IV22 2JX
Tel; 01445 781241 Fax: 01445 781786
Web: www.poolewehotel.com

HOTEL

2 Single · 3 Twin · 4 Double · 1 Family
All En Suite
B&B per person from £25.00 Single, from £25.00 Dbl/Twn
B&B + Eve.Meal from £40.00
Open Jan-Dec

Former inn dating in part from 18c. Now a family run hotel recently refurbished. Situated in village and close to Inverewe Gardens. Good food at reasonable proces.

Portmahomack, Ross-shire — Map Ref: 4C7

The Caledonian Hotel
Main Street, Portmahomack, Ross-shire IV20 1YS
Tel: 01862 871345 Fax: 01862 871757

Friendly, family run hotel on an exceptional beach-front location in a truly picturesque village. Enjoy spectacular sunsets across the Dornoch Firth from the comfort of the restaurant or sun lounge. Ideal touring or golfing base. Children welcome. Regular live music in the bar. 3 nights D,B&B for the price of 2.

Caledonian Hotel
Main Street, Portmahomack, Ross-shire, IV20 1YS
Tel: 01862 871345 Fax: 01862 871757

HOTEL

9 Twin · 1 Double · 5 Family
All En Suite
B&B per person £23.00-£33.00 Single, £40.00-£57.00 Dbl/Twn
B&B + Eve.Meal £33.00-£42.00
Open Jan-Dec

Friendly, family-run hotel on an exceptional beach-front location in a truly picturesque village. Enjoy spectacular sunsets across the Dornoch Firth. Our comfortable twin, double and family rooms are all en-suite with TV and tea/coffee facilities. Ideal touring or golfing base. Children and dogs welcome. Regular live music in the bar.

VAT is shown at 17.5%: changes in this rate may affect prices.

Key to symbols is on back flap.

Raasay, Isle of, Ross-shire · Map Ref: 3E9

★★

HOTEL

Isle of Raasay Hotel
Raasay,by Kyle, Ross-shire, IV40 8PB
Tel/Fax: 01478 660222

1 Single	All En Suite	B&B per person	Open Jan-Dec
8 Twin		from £25.00 Single	B&B + Eve.Meal
1 Double		from £25.00 Dbl/Twn	from £40.00
2 Family			

Family run hotel, overlooking Sound of Raasay towards Cuillin Hills. Hill and forest walks, trout fishing, interesting local geology/archeology. Ideal base for artists and nature watchers. Groups catered for.

Rhiconich, Sutherland · Map Ref: 3H3

★★★

HOTEL

The Rhiconich Hotel
Rhiconich, Sutherland, IV27 4RN
Tel: 01971 521224 Fax: 01971 521732
E-mail: rhiconichhotel@compuserve.com
Web: www.vacations-scotland.co.uk/rhiconich.html

3 Single	11 En Suite fac	B&B per person	Open Jan-Dec
3 Twin	1 Priv.NOT ensuite	from £29.50 Single	B&B + Eve.Meal
5 Double		from £31.00 Dbl/Twn	from £39.50
1 Family			

Imagine a place where beauty, peace & tranquility are the order of the day, where your every need is looked after by the friendliest staff, where you can Salmon & Trout fish, walk, climb, birdwatch, beachcomb or just amaze at the finest mountain & Loch scenery in the highlands, a place specializing in fresh seafood, vension, beef, lamb, halibut & sole and proud of its malt whisky selection and open log fire. No need to imagine it any longer.

Roy Bridge, Inverness-shire · Map Ref: 3H12

ROY BRIDGE, INVERNESS-SHIRE PH31 4AG
TEL: 01397 712253 FAX: 01397 712641
WEB: *www.stronlossit.co.uk*

Stronlossit Hotel is situated in an enviable position within the Fort William area with outstanding views of the Nevis range of mountains. Family owned and run, this inn style hotel offers traditional Scottish hospitality with a warm welcome, fine food and accommodation. Central location for touring the West Highlands.

★★★

INN

Stronlossit Hotel
Roy Bridge, Inverness-shire, PH31 4AG
Tel: 01397 712253 Fax: 01397 712641
Web: www.stronlossit.co.uk

1 Single	All En Suite	B&B per person	Open Jan-Dec
1 Twin		from £30.00 Single	B&B + Eve.Meal
6 Double		from £29.00 Dbl/Twn	from £44.00
1 Family			

Family run, in a small village amidst beautiful Highland scenery. Centrally situated for touring the Scottish Highlands. 12 miles (19km) to Fort William. Bar meals and recently refurbished a la carte restaurant.

Important: Prices stated are estimates and may be subject to amendments

Scourie, Sutherland   Map Ref: 3H4

HOTEL

Eddrachilles Hotel
Badcall Bay, Scourie, Sutherland, IV27 4TH
Tel: 01971 502080 Fax: 01971 502477
E-mail: enq@eddrachilles.com

7 Twin	All En Suite	B&B per person	Open Mar-Oct
3 Double		from £48.00 Single	B&B + Eve.Meal
1 Family		from £38.00 Dbl/Twn	from £51.00

Personally run with superb views over Eddrachilles Bay and standing in
320 acres of private moorland. Near to Handa Island Bird Sanctuary.

SMALL HOTEL

Scourie Hotel
Scourie, Sutherland, IV27 4SX
Tel: 01971 502396 Fax: 01971 502423
E-mail: patrick@scourie-hotel.co.uk
Web: www.scourie-hotel.co.uk

6 Single	All En Suite	B&B per person	Open end Mar-mid
6 Twin		from £35.00 Single	Oct
6 Double		from £30.00 Double	
2 Family			

Personally run, ideally situated for touring this rugged area of North West
Scotland. Hotel specialises in fishing for brown trout and salmon. Some
boats available. Four course dinner with local produce.

Shieldaig, Ross-shire   Map Ref: 3F8

SMALL HOTEL

Tigh an Eilean Hotel
Shieldaig, by Strathcarron, Ross-shire, IV54 8XN
Tel: 01520 755251 Fax: 01520 755321
E-mail: Tighaneileanhotel@shieldaig.fsnet.co.uk

3 Single	All En Suite	B&B per person	Open early Apr-
4 Twin		£48.55 Single	end Oct
3 Double		£53.80 Dbl/Twn	B&B + Eve.Meal
1 Family			£68.55-£74.80 single
			£74.00-£80.00 Dbl/Twin

Personally run, small loch front hotel in charming fishing village. All rooms
with private facilities, most with sea views. Fresh produce, local seafood.

Ardvasar, Sleat, Isle of Skye, Inverness-shire   **Map Ref: 3E11**

★★★

HOTEL

Ardvasar Hotel
Sleat, Isle of Skye, Inverness-shire, IV45 8RS
Tel: 01471 844223 Fax: 01471 844495

5 Twin	All En Suite	B&B per person	Open Jan-Dec
5 Double		from £45.00 Single	B&B + Eve.Meal
2 Family		from £40.00 Dbl/Twn	from £62.50

Under new ownership this historic 19th Century Inn has fine views across the sea to Mallaig. Established reputation for good food, member of Taste of Scotland.

---

by Broadford, Isle of Skye, Inverness-shire   **Map Ref: 3E10**

★★★

**GUEST
HOUSE**

The Skye Picture House
Ard Dorch, Broadford, Isle of Skye, Inverness-shire, IV49 9AJ
Tel: 01471 822531 Fax: 01471 822305
E-mail: gill@skyepicturehouse.co.uk
Web: www.skyepicturehouse.co.uk

2 Single	4 En Suite fac	B&B per person	Open Jan-Dec
1 Twin	1 Pub Bath/Show	£18.00-£26.00 Single	B&B + Eve.Meal
2 Double	1 Priv.NOT ensuite	£18.00-£26.00 Dbl/Twn	£29.00-£37.00
1 Family			

Spacious modern home in stunning waterside location looking over to Scalpay. Very friendly welcome. Home cooking. Professionally run photographic courses and holidays available. Proprietors both RPS distinction holders.

Carbost, Isle of Skye, Inverness-shire   **Map Ref: 3D9**

THE OLD INN
Carbost, Isle of Skye IV47 8SR
Tel: 01478 640205   Fax: 01478 640450
e.mail: oldinn@carbost.f9.co.uk

This friendly informal village inn is an ideal base for climbers and hill-walkers. The separate serviced accommodation all have sea views. Hearty meals are served daily in the bar and dining areas and drinks may be taken on the patio overlooking Loch Harpart and the Cuillin Hills.

★

INN

The Old Inn
Carbost, Isle of Skye, Inverness-shire, IV47 8SR
Tel: 01478 640205 Fax: 01478 640450
E-mail: oldinn@carbost.f9.co.uk

1 Single	5 En Suite fac	B&B per person	Open Jan-Dec
2 Twin	1 Limited ensuite	£22.50-£25.00 Single	
2 Double	1 Pub Bath/Show	£22.50-£25.00 Dbl/Twn	
1 Family		Room only per person	
		£16.00-£18.50	

An historic Inn with modern accommodation annexe on the shores of Loch Harpart near the Talisker distillery. An ideal base for hillwalkers, climbers or anyone wishing to enjoy the scenic beauty of Skye.

Important: Prices stated are estimates and may be subject to amendments

Duntulm, Isle of Skye, Inverness-shire   Map Ref: 3D7

Duntulm Castle Hotel
Duntulm, Isle of Skye IV51 9UF
Tel: 01470 552213   Fax: 01470 552292
Web: www.duntulmcastle.co.uk

Unrivalled coastal setting at the Northernmost tip of Skye with views across the Minch. Homely and comfortable inn. Ensuite bedrooms, colour TV, hot drink facilities. Excellent Scottish cuisine. Ideal for outer isles ferry at Uig. Peaceful and secluded with wonderful coast and hill walks. Beautiful self-catering cottages adjacent.

★

HOTEL

Duntulm Castle Hotel
Duntulm, Isle of Skye, IV51 9UF
Tel: 01470 552213 Fax: 01470 552292
Web: www.duntulmcastle.co.uk

3 Single	22 Ensuite fac	B&B per person	Open Apr-Oct
13 Twin	6 Priv.NOT ensuite	from £25.00 Single	B&B + Eve.Meal
6 Double		from £20.00 Dbl/Twn	from £38.00
1 Family			

Friendly hotel enjoying outstanding location with unsurpassed views over the Minch to the outer Isles. Cosy and informal atmosphere on the secluded northern most point of Skye.

Dunvegan, Isle of Skye, Inverness-shire   Map Ref: 3D9

★★★

HOTEL

Atholl House Hotel
Dunvegan, Isle of Skye, Inverness-shire, IV55 8WA
Tel: 01470 521219 Fax: 01470 521481
E-mail: reservations@athollhotel.demon.co.uk

2 Twin	All En Suite	B&B per person	Open Jan-Dec
6 Double		from £35.00 Single	B&B + Eve.Meal
1 Family		from £28.00 Dbl/Twn	from £44.00

A country house hotel to be found nestling at the head of Loch Dunvegan, overlooking the famous flat topped Macleods Tables. Enjoy award winning Scottish fare, sink into sumptuous settees, or just relax by the roaring log fire and savour the moment.

★★★★

SMALL
HOTEL

Dunorin House Hotel
Herebost, Dunvegan, Isle of Skye, IV55 8GZ
Tel/Fax: 01470 521488
Web: www.dunorin.com

1 Single	All En Suite	B&B per person	Open Apr-Oct
3 Twin		from £40.00 Single	B&B + Eve.Meal
6 Double		from £38.00 Dbl/Twn	from £58.00

Very comfortable modern family run hotel at head of Loch Roag. 2 miles (3 kms) south of Dunvegan. Excellent open views towards Cullins and Macleods Tables. Ideal for walking, birdwatching and many other outdoor pursuits.

★★★★

GUEST
HOUSE

Roskhill House
Roskhill, Dunvegan, Isle of Skye, Inverness-shire, IV55 8ZD
Tel: 01470 521317 Fax: 01470 521761
E-mail: stay@roskhill.demon.co.uk
Web: www.roskhill.demon.co.uk

1 Twin	3 En Suite fac	B&B per person	Open Jan-Dec excl
3 Double	1 Priv.NOT ensuite	from £32.00 Single	Xmas/New Year
		from £27.00 Dbl/Twn	B&B + Eve.Meal
			from £41.50

This cosy crofthouse is beautifully situated 3 miles south of Dunvegan Castle, ideal for touring this historic & romantic island, walking, climbing, bird watching, etc. Delicious old fashioned home cooking prepared fresh each day and served in the stone walled dining room with log fire & resident's bar. High standards, peaceful surroundings and personal attention assured. Your 'home away from home', stay a while.

VAT is shown at 17.5%: changes in this rate may affect prices.

Key to symbols is on back flap.

Dunvegan, Isle of Skye, Inverness-shire — Map Ref: 3D9

★★

SMALL HOTEL

The Tables Hotel

Dunvegan, Isle of Skye, Inverness-shire, IV55 8WA
Tel/Fax: 01470 521404
E-mail: bookings@tables-hotel.co.uk
Web: www.tables-hotel.co.uk

100 year old house in village, 0.75 mile (1km) from castle. Fine views over MacLeods Tables. Accent on relaxation, informality. Vegetarians welcomed.

1 Single	4 En Suite fac
1 Twin	1 Priv.NOT ensuite
2 Double	
1 Family	

B&B per person
from £27.00 Single
from £27.00 Dbl/Twn

Open Mar-Dec

SILVER

Elgol, Isle of Skye, Inverness-shire — Map Ref: 3E10

★

GUEST HOUSE

Strathaird House

Elgol Road, Strathaird, Isle of Skye,
Inverness-shire, IV49 9AX
Tel: 01471 866269/01444 452990 (off season)
E-mail: strathairdhouse@skye.co.uk
Web: www.strathairdhouse.skye.co.uk

Family run guesthouse above Kilmarie Bay on the Elgol road. Ideal for walks to Camasunary Bay, Blaven, the Cuillins, seashore exploring and boat trips to Loch Coruisk. Rambling house with glorious views, licensed 'Hayloft Restaurant', fireside library, drying room and garden.

2 Single	1 En Suite fac
1 Double	1 Priv.NOT ensuite
4 Family	5 Pub Bath/Show

B&B per person
from £25.00 Single
from £25.00 Double

Open Easter-Sep

Kyleakin, Isle of Skye, Inverness-shire — Map Ref: 3F10

★★★

HOTEL

Dunringell Hotel

Kyleakin, Isle of Skye, Inverness-shire, IV41 8PQ
Tel: 01599 534180 Fax: 01599 534460
E-mail: holiday@dunringell-hotel.co.uk
Web: www.dunringell-hotel.co.uk

Country house hotel outside this attractive island village. Tranquil setting, fine mature garden. Close to bridge. Some annexe accommodation. Unlicensed.

4 Single	11 En Suite fac
1 Twin	7 Pub Bath/Show
6 Double	
7 Family	

B&B per person
£18.00-£30.00 Single
£18.00-£30.00 Dbl/Twn

Opne Mar-Nov
B&B + Eve.Meal
£32.00-£44.00

★★★

SMALL HOTEL

White Heather Hotel

Kyleakin, Isle of Skye, IV41 8PL
Tel: 015995 34577 Fax: 015995 34427
Web: www2.prestel.co.uk/whiteheather

Our recently refurbished family run hotel is situated on the harbourside in the small fishing village of Kyleakin, with views across to Castle Moil. Ideally situated for all road, rail and sea travellers.

1 Single	All En Suite
3 Twin	
3 Double	
1 Family	

B&B per person
from £30.00 Single
from £20.00 Dbl/Twn

Open Mar-Oct

Portnalong, Isle of Skye, Inverness-shire — Map Ref: 3D9

★★

SMALL HOTEL

Taigh Ailean Hotel

11 Portnalong, Portnalong, Isle of Skye,
Inverness-shire, IV47 8SL
Tel: 01478 640271 Fax: 01478 640466
Web: www.taighailenhotel.demon.co.uk

Small family hotel with lots of local flavour, situated at the north end of the scenically beautiful, unspoilt Minginish Peninsula.

3 Double	All En Suite
2 Family	

B&B per person
£28.00-£40.00 Single
£20.00-£25.00 Double
Family Room Rate
£50.00-£60.00

Open Jan-Dec

Important: Prices stated are estimates and may be subject to amendments

THE HIGHLANDS AND SKYE

Portree, Isle of Skye, Inverness-shire | Map Ref: 3E9

HOTEL ★★★★

The Bosville Hotel
Bosville Terrace, Portree, Isle of Skye, IV51 9DG
Tel: 01478 612846
Web: www.macleodhotels.co.uk

Traditional quality and hospitality in our family run hotel off the main square of town. In elevated position overlooking the harbour. All day meals service. All rooms ensuite. Award winning seafood restaurant.

6 Twin	All En Suite	B&B per person	Open Jan-Dec
7 Twin		from £35.00 Single	B&B + Eve.Meal
2 Family		from £25.00 Dbl/Twn	from £40.00

Cuillin Hills Hotel
PORTREE, ISLE OF SKYE IV51 9QU
Tel: 01478 612003   Fax: 01478 613092
e.mail: office@cuillinhills.demon.co.uk
Web: www.cuillinhills.demon.co.uk

Superbly situated with breathtaking views over Portree Bay towards the grandiose Cuillin Mountain range. A very fine hotel open all-year-round enjoying an excellent location for exploring the island. Our chef uses the best of local produce wherever possible to create imaginative menus combining traditional favourites with Highland specialities in our award-winning restaurant and bar. Relax after dinner in front of a roaring log fire. Enjoy high standards of comfort, cuisine and service in a warm, friendly atmosphere with the very best of Highland hospitality.

From £40 per person per night.   AA ★★★

Contact: Mr Murray Mcphee

HOTEL ★★★★

Cuillin Hills Hotel
Portree, Isle of Skye, Inverness-shire, IV51 9QU
Tel: 01478 612003 Fax: 01478 613092
E.mail: office@cuillinhills.demon.co.uk
Web: www.cuillinhills.demon.co.uk

19c hunting lodge in own grounds. Outstanding views over Portree Bay to the Cuillin Mountains.

4 Single	All En Suite	B&B per person	Open Jan-Dec
10 Twin		from £40.00 Single	B&B + Eve.Meal
15 Double		from £40.00 Dbl/Twn	from £45.00
1 Family			

GUEST HOUSE ★★★

Givendale Guest House
Heron Place, Portree, Isle of Skye,
Inverness-shire, IV51 9GU
Tel: 01478 612183
E-mail: trevor@givendale7.freeserve.co.uk

Quiet area with outstanding views. 10 minutes walk from centre of Portree. Quality food and accommodation. Printed walks and maps available. Guided walks by arrangement. Please phone or write for details.

2 Twin	3 En Suite fac	B&B per person	Open Mar-Oct
2 Double	1 Priv.NOT ensuite	from £20.00 Single	
		from £20.00 Dbl/Twn	
		Room only per person	
		from £18.00	

VAT is shown at 17.5%: changes in this rate may affect prices.

Key to symbols is on back flap.

Portree, Isle of Skye, Inverness-shire | Map Ref: 3E9

★★★

GUEST
HOUSE

Pink Guest House
1 Marine Buildings, Quay Street, Portree,
Isle of Skye, Inverness-shire, IV51 9BT
Tel: 01478 612263 Fax: 01478 612181

1 Single	All En Suite	B&B per person	Open Jan-Dec
2 Twin		£20.00-£30.00 Single	
4 Double		£18.00-£30.00 Dbl/Twn	
3 Family			

Distinctive old terraced property in unique position right on the quayside overlooking Portree Bay. Comfortable rooms. Ideal central base for all Skye attractions.

★★

HOTEL

Portree Hotel
Somerled Square, Portree, Isle of Skye,
Inverness-shire, IV51 9EH
Tel: 01478 612511 Fax: 01478 613093
Web: www.hendersonhotels.com

8 Single	All En Suite	B&B per person	Open Jan-Dec
8 Twin		from £35.00 Single	
4 Double		from £30.00 Dbl/Twn	
4 Family			

Town centre hotel overlooking the Square with all amenities within short walking distance. Good centre for touring. Traditional Scottish cooking a speciality.

★★★

GUEST
HOUSE

Rosebank Guest House
Springfield Road, Portree, Isle of Skye,
Inverness-shire, IV51 9LX
Tel: 01478 612282

2 Single	2 En Suite fac	B&B per person	Open Apr-Oct
1 Twin		from £20.00 Single	
3 Double		from £20.00 Dbl/Twn	

Large modern house in quiet residential area on outskirts of village, very comfortable rooms. 5 minutes walk from village square, shops, restaurants and other local amenities. Hairdressing/Beauty salon attached.

Rosedale Hotel
Portree, Isle of Skye IV51 9DB
Tel: 01478 613131   Fax: 01478 612531

Established family-run hotel. Unrivalled waterfront location with magnificent views. 23 ensuite bedrooms, cocktail bar, coffee bar and comfortable lounge. Harbour front restaurant featuring modern innovative cuisine using quality fresh ingredients served in a fine dining ambience of crisp linen, silver and crystal. Accolades include AA Rosette, RAC merit awards for hospitality.

★★★★

HOTEL

Rosedale Hotel
Beaumont Crescent, Portree, Isle of Skye,
Inverness-shire, IV51 9DB
Tel: 01478 613131 Fax: 01478 612531
E-mail: rosedale@achnacraig.freeserve.co.uk
Web: www.rosedalehotelskye.co.uk

5 Single	All En Suite	B&B per person	Open Apr-Oct
10 Twin		from £42.00 Single	B&B + Eve.Meal
7 Double		from £36.00 Dbl/Twn	from £57.00
1 Family			Bedrms/Restaurant
			Non-smoking.

Very comfortable and unusual harbourside hotel imaginatively created from former fishermens houses dating back to the reign of William IV. Award winning cuisine in an outstanding waterside location.

Important: Prices stated are estimates and may be subject to amendments

Portree, Isle of Skye, Inverness-shire | Map Ref: 3E9

HOTEL
★★★

Royal Hotel
Bank Street, Portree, Isle of Skye, IV51 9BU
Tel: 01478 612525 Fax: 01478 613198
E-mail: info@royal-hotel.demon.co.uk

8 Twin   All En Suite
13 Double

B&B per person
from £50.00 Single
from £37.50 Dbl/Twn

Open Jan-Dec

Family run hotel in central position, looking out over Portree Bay. All rooms ensuite, open all year, leisure and fitness centre. Regular live traditional entertainment.

GUEST HOUSE
★★

The Shielings Guest House
7 Torvaig, Portree, Isle of Skye, Inverness-shire,
IV51 9HU
Tel: 01478 613024

1 Twin   All En Suite
3 Double

B&B per person
£18.00-£23.00 Dbl/Twn

Open Jan-Dec excl
Xmas/New Year
B&B + Eve.Meal
£28.00-£33.00

Converted croft cottage with superb views. Situated just 2 miles (3kms) outside Portree. Home cooking and a warm homely atmosphere.

SMALL HOTEL
★★★
&

Viewfield House Hotel
Portree, Isle of Skye, Inverness-shire, IV51 9EU
Tel: 01478 612217 Fax: 01478 613517
Web: www.skye.co.uk/viewfield

2 Single   9 En Suite fac
3 Twin   1 Pub Bath/Show
4 Double
2 Family

B&B per person
£35.00-£45.00 Single
£35.00-£45.00 Dbl/Twn

Open mid Apr-mid Oct
B&B + Eve.Meal
£55.00-£65.00

A magnificent georgian listed building set in spacious policies. Still under original family ownership and kept in as authentic a manner as possible, the house contains mostly antique furnishings and an outstanding collection of trophies and memorabilia.

---

by Portree, Isle of Skye, Inverness-shire | Map Ref: 3E9

HOTEL
★★★

Greshornish House Hotel
Greshornish, by Portree, Isle of Skye, IV51 9PN
Tel: 01470 582266 Fax: 01470 582345
Web: www.greshornishhotel.co.uk

4 Twin   All En Suite
3 Double
1 Family

B&B per person
from £35.00 Single
from £25.00 Dbl/Twn

Open Jan-Dec
B&B + Eve.Meal
from £38.00

Georgian mansion in superb lochside location. Drawing room with hand-carved oak fireplace and log fire. Rabbits on the croquet lawn, hedgehogs by the tennis court.

Skeabost, Isle of Skye, Inverness-shire | Map Ref: 3D8

HOTEL
★★★

Skeabost House Hotel
Skeabost Bridge, by Portree, Isle of Skye,
Inverness-shire, IV51 9NP
Tel: 01470 532202 Fax: 01470 532454
Web: www.sol.co.uk/s/skeabost

3 Single   All En Suite
10 Twin   1 Pub Bath/Show
9 Double
4 Family

B&B per person
from £45.00 Single
£38.00-£59.00 Dbl/Twn
Room only
£35.00-£65.00

Open Mar-Oct
B&B + Eve.Meal
£50.00-£70.00

Personally run country house with 9 hole golf course (par 31) and 8 miles (13 kms) of salmon fishing on River Snizort. Some annexe accommodation.

VAT is shown at 17.5%: changes in this rate may affect prices.

Key to symbols is on back flap.

Sleat, Isle of Skye, Inverness-shire   Map Ref: 3F10

★★★

HOTEL

Hotel Eilean Iarmain
Isle Ornsay, Sleat, Isle of Skye, Inverness-shire, IV43 8QR
Tel: 01471 833332 Fax: 01471 833275
E-mail: hotel@eilean-iarmain.co.uk
Web: www.eileaniarmain.co.uk

4 Twin	All Ensuite	B&B per person	Open Jan-Dec
6 Double		from £90.00 Single	B&B + Eve.Meal
2 Family		from £60.00 Dbl/Twn	from £91.00
4 Suites		from £180.00 p.suite	

Over 100 years old with many original antiques Hotel Eilean Iarmain is idyllically located overlooking the picturesque Isle Ornsay harbour, having a unique character, being traditional, hospitable and homely. Award winning AA rosette restaurant with menus featuring the very best of local seafood and game. All 12 bedrooms, plus 4 new superior suites alongside the hotel, all with mini bars and are furnished with every contemporary comfort.

★★★★

HOTEL

Kinloch Lodge
Sleat, Isle of Skye, Inverness-shire, IV43 8QY
Tel: 01471 833214 Fax: 01471 833277
E-mail: kinloch@dial.pipex.com

1 Single	All En Suite	B&B per person	Open Jan-Dec
14		from £50.00 Single	B&B + Eve.Meal
Twn/Dbl		from £45.00 Dbl/Twn	from £50.00
		Room only per person	
		from £40.00	

Ancestral home of Lord and Lady MacDonald in secluded lochside setting with panoramic views. Unique demonstration cooking residential breaks presented by Lady MacDonald in the Spring and Autumn months.

Staffin, Isle of Skye, Inverness-shire   Map Ref: 3E8

FLODIGARRY COUNTRY HOUSE HOTEL
Staffin, Isle of Skye IV51 9HZ   Tel: 01470 552203 Fax: 01470 552301
Web: www.flodigarry.co.uk

Taste of Scotland, Macallan Country House Hotel of the Year. Stunning sea and mountain views. Fine historic mansion in secluded wooded grounds. Superb ensuite bedrooms, central heating, log fires and old-world atmosphere. Award-winning restaurant, bar and conservatory meals. Open all year. Children welcome. Special low-season breaks.
Contact: Andrew or Pam Butler.   ★★★★

★★★★

HOTEL

Flodigarry Country House Hotel
Flodigarry, Staffin, Isle of Skye, Inverness-shire, IV51 9HZ
Tel: 01470 552203 Fax: 01470 552301
Web: www.flodigarry.co.uk

1 Single	All En Suite	B&B per person	Open Jan-Dec
5 Twin	Suite avail	£49.00-£79.00 Single	B&B + Eve.Meal
8 Double		£49.00-£79.00 Dbl/Twn	£75.00-£105.00
5 Family			

Family-run Victorian house and historic Flora MacDonald's cottage. Superb sea and mountain views, private grounds, Taste of Scotland.

★★

SMALL
HOTEL

Glenview Inn & Restaurant
Culnacnoc, Staffin, Isle of Skye, Inverness-shire, IV51 9JH
Tel: 01470 562248 Fax: 01470 562211
E-mail: valtos@lineone.net
Web: www.SmoothHound.co.uk

1 Twin	4 En Suite fac	B&B per person	Open Easter-Oct
3 Double	1 Priv.NOT ensuite	from £20.00 Dbl/Twn	B&B + Eve.Meal
1 Family			from £37.50

Tastefully converted traditional island house, ideally situated for exploring Northern Skye. Friendly atmosphere, good food. Taste of Scotland. Adequate parking available. The restaurant specialises in local fish and seafood and a choice of traditional vegetarian and ethnic delicacies are offered.

Important: Prices stated are estimates and may be subject to amendments

Struan, by Dunvegan, Isle of Skye, Inverness-shire | Map Ref: 3D9

★★★

SMALL HOTEL

Ullinish Lodge Hotel & Restaurant
Struan, Isle of Skye, Inverness-shire, IV56 8FD
Tel: 01470 572214 Fax: 01470 572341
E-mail: ullinish@theisleofskye.co.uk
Web: www.theisleofskye.co.uk

18c house visited by Johnson and Boswell during their Scottish tour in 1773. In superb situation, with fine views across Loch Harport to the Cuillins. Walking, climbing, ornithology. Own fishing and shooting rights. E-Mail - Ullinish@theisleofskye.co.uk

2 Twin	7 En Suite fac	B&B per person	Open mid Mar-Oct
4 Double	1 Priv.NOT ensuite	from £40.00 Single	B&B + Eve.Meal
2 Family		from £30.00 Dbl/Twn	from £50.00

Waternish, Isle of Skye, Inverness-shire | Map Ref: 3D8

★★

INN

Stein Inn
MacLeods Terrace, Stein, Waternish, Isle of Skye, IV55 8GA
Tel: 01470 592362 Fax: 08700 542869
Web: www.steininn.co.uk

Set in a beautiful lochside position, this historic village inn c1648 offers traditional hospitality. Comfortable rooms, good food and a warm welcome.

1 Single	5 Ensuite fac	B&B per person	Open Jan-Dec excl
2 Twin	1 Pub Bath/Show	from £23.00 Single	Xmas/New Year
4 Double		from £23.00 Dbl/Twn	
2 Family			

Spean Bridge, Inverness-shire | Map Ref: 3H12

★★★

GUEST HOUSE

The Braes Guest House
Tirindrish, Spean Bridge, Inverness-shire, PH34 4EU
Tel: 01397 71243 Fax: 01397 712108

Family run guest house in elevated position with outstanding views of Ben Nevis Mountain Range. Set in own grounds with small terraced garden. Relax in our comfortable lounge and enjoy the magnificent view. Friendly welcome, tasty home-cooking, personal attention. Ample parking. Ideal base for touring and walking. Drying facilities available.

1 Single	6 En Suite fac	B&B per person	Open Jan-Dec
1 Twin	1 Priv.NOT ensuite	from £22.00 Single	B&B + Eve.Meal
5 Double		from £20.00 Dbl/Twn	from £34.00

★★★★

GUEST HOUSE

Corriechoille Lodge
Spean Bridge, Inverness-shire, PH34 4EY
Tel: 01397 712002
E-mail: enquiry@corriechoille.com
Web: www.corriechoille.com

A recently renovated historic building of great character in a secluded situation with breathtaking mountain views. This family run guest house is ideal for walking, fishing or simply relaxing. Ground floor bedroom wtih disabled facilities available. Evening meals available by prior arrangement.

1 Twin	All En Suite	B&B per person	Open Mar-Oct
2 Double		£29.00-£34.00 Single	B&B + Eve.Meal
2 Family		£22.00-£27.00 Double	£38.00-£43.00

Spean Bridge, Inverness-shire | Map Ref: 3H12

GUEST HOUSE

★★★★

Distant Hills Guest House
Roy Bridge Road, Spean Bridge, Inverness-shire PA34 4EY
Tel/Fax: 01397 712452
Web: www.distanthills.com

4 Twin	All En Suite	B&B per person	Open Jan-Dec
3 Double		from £27.00 Single	B&B + Eve.Meal
		from £19.50 Dbl/Twn	from £32.00

Comfortable modern bungalow set in large garden at edge of Spean Bridge. Friendly and personal attention. Excellent views of Aonach Mor, ideally situated for touring, skiing, walking and cycling. Evening meals by prior arrangement. Children and pets welcome.

HOTEL

★★

Letterfinlay Lodge Hotel
Loch Lochy, Spean Bridge, Inverness-shire,
PH34 4DZ
Tel: 01397 712622

1 Single	9 Ensuite fac	B&B per person	Open Mar-Jan excl
4 Twin	3 Priv.NOT ensuite	from £28.50 Single	Xmas/New Year
5 Double		from £28.50 Dbl/Twn	B&B + Eve.Meal
2 Family			from £45.00

Originally a Victorian shooting lodge this hotel stands on an enchanting site overlooking beautiful Loch Lochy in romantic Lochaber. Family run and owned by the Forsyth family for over 30 years. Popular for bar lunches and suppers. Ideal centre for touring the Highlands. Fishing and shooting by arrangement.

GUEST HOUSE

★★★

Smiddy House
Spean Bridge, Inverness-shire, PH34 4EU
Tel: 01397 712335 Fax: 01397 712043

1 Twin	All En Suite	B&B per person	Open Jan-Dec
2 Double		£35.00-£45.00 Single	
1 Family		£22.50-£25.00 Dbl/Twn	

Completely refurbished family run guest house and licensed Bistro at the centre of this small Highland village, ideal for all local activities including touring, walking, climbing, fishing, horse riding, golf and winter skiing.

Strathpeffer, Ross-shire | Map Ref: 4A8

GUEST HOUSE

★★★

The Garden House Guest House
Garden House Brae, Strathpeffer, Ross-shire, IV14 9BJ
Tel/Fax: 01997 421242
E-mail: garden.house@virgin.net

1 Twin	All En Suite	B&B per person	Open Mar-Nov
3 Double		from £20.00 Dbl/Twn	B&B + Eve.Meal
1 Family			from £30.00

Friendly welcome at family run guest house in Spa village. Good walking country and touring base. 21 miles (32kms) from Inverness. Open March - October. Telephone/Fax bookings all year. Non smoking establishment.

Strontian, Argyll | Map Ref: 1E1

SMALL HOTEL

★★★★

Kilcamb Lodge Hotel
Strontian, Argyll, PH36 4HY
Tel: 01967 402257 Fax: 01967 402041
E-mail: kilcamblodge@aol.com
Web: www.kilcamblodge.co.uk

1 Single		Rates per room	Open Mar-Dec plus
5 Twin		from £48.00 Single	New Year
5 Double		£64.00-£130.00 Dbl	

The Good Hotel Guide 'Scottish Hotel of the Year' Kilcamb Lodge is a stone built Georgian house situated in 20 acres of own grounds facing south across Loch Sunart with half a mile of private shoreline. Our daily changing menu uses the best local produce. AA 2 rosettes for fine cuisine. Each ensuite bedroom is furnished to a high standard each with their own individual style and character.

Important: Prices stated are estimates and may be subject to amendments

Tain, Ross-shire — Map Ref: 4B7

GUEST HOUSE
★★★★

Golf View Guesthouse
13 Knockbreck Road, Tain, Ross-shire
Tel: 01862 892856 Fax: 01862 892172
E-mail: golfview@btinternet.com
Web: www.golf-view.co.uk

3 Twin	3 En Suite fac	B&B per person	Open Feb-Nov
1 Double	2 Pub Bath/Show	from £25.00 Single	
1 Family		from £20.00 Dbl/Twn	

Secluded Victorian house with panoramic views over golf course and across the Dornoch Firth. Centrally situated in Scotland's oldest Royal Burgh.

HOTEL
★★★★

Mansfield House Hotel
Scotsburn Road, Tain, Ross-shire, IV19 1PR
Tel: 01862 892052 Fax: 01862 892260

1 Single	All En Suite	B&B per person	Open Jan-Dec
9 Twin	Suite avail	£50.00-£80.00 Single	B&B + Eve.Meal
6 Double		£45.00-£70.00 Dbl/Twn	£70.00-£105.00
2 Family			

Victorian mansion house of character only 40 minutes from Inverness. Ideally situated for highland touring and golf. Award winning hospitality. Spacious bedrooms, some with jacuzzis. Two rosette award winning restaurant.

MORANGIE HOUSE HOTEL
★★★★
HOTEL
Morangie Road, Tain, Ross-shire IV19 1PY
Tel: 01862 892281 Fax: 01862 892872
★★★ **AA RAC**
e.mail: wynne@morangiehotel.com

Former Victorian mansion house tastefully modernised and with a superb reputation for outstanding food and friendly but efficient service. Under the personal supervision of the resident proprietors at all times.

HOTEL
★★★★

Morangie House Hotel
Morangie Road, Tain, Ross-shire, IV19 1PY
Tel: 01862 892281 Fax: 01862 892872
E-mail: wynne@morangiehotel.com

4 Single	All En Suite	B&B per person	Open Jan-Dec
10 Twin		from £60.00 Single	B&B + Eve.Meal
11 Double		from £42.50 Dbl/Twn	from £65.00
1 Family			

Family run, recently extended former Victorian mansion, in own grounds on northern edge of Tain. A la carte restaurant, extensive bar meal menu. Taste of Scotland. Golfing can be arranged on several courses in the area.

Thurso, Caithness — Map Ref: 4D3

SMALL HOTEL
★★★★

Forss Country House Hotel
by Thurso, Caithness, KW14 7XY
Tel: 01847 861201 Fax: 01847861 301
E-mail: jamie@forsshouse.freeserve.co.uk
Web: www.forsscountryhouse.co.uk

8 Twin	All En Suite	B&B per person	Open Jan-Dec excl
2 Double		from £57.50 Single	Xmas/New Year
		from £45.00 Dbl/Twn	

Country house hotel set in 25 acres of woodland and gardens, with the River Forss and its picturesque water mill close by. Spacious bedrooms are available in the main house, or further fully serviced accommodation is provided in the Lodges. Fishing can be arranged locally. Alternatively use the hotel as a relaxing base for exploring the far North. Taste of Scotland award. Over 200 malt whiskies.

VAT is shown at 17.5%: changes in this rate may affect prices.

Key to symbols is on back flap.

Thurso, Caithness | Map Ref: 4D3

HOTEL
★★★

The New Weighinn Hotel & Lodges
Burnside, Thurso, Caithness, KW14 7UG
Tel: 01847 893722 Fax: 01847 892112
E-mail: caithness@weighinn.co.uk

36 Twin	All En Suite	B&B per person	Open Jan-Dec excl
16 Double		from £25.00 Single	Xmas/New Year
6 Family		from £17.50 Dbl/Twn	B&B + Eve.Meal
		Lodge only per person	from £35.00
		from £12.50	

Newly built sixteen bedroom hotel, situated a short distance from the harbour, and ideal for travellers catching the Orkney ferry. The hotel also makes an excellent base for the business traveller or for the winter visitor wanting to explore the county of Caithness, and the north Sutherland coastline.

TV 📞 🛎 📠 P 🍺 🥂 🍷

C 🐕 🚲 W V

BRONZE 🍃

HOTEL
★★★

Park Hotel
Thurso, Caithness, KW14 8RE
Tel/Fax: 01847 893251/2
Web: www.parkhotelthurso.co.uk

1 Single	All En Suite	B&B per person	Open 3Jan-Dec excl
2 Double		from £30.00 Single	New Year
8 Family		from £25.00 Double	
		Room only	
		from £50.00	

Comfortable and friendly family run hotel fully licenced with 11 well appointed ensuite bedrooms all with TV, hairdryer, tea and coffee etc. All meals served. New conservatory lounge and dining room. Large private car park.

TV 📞 🛎 P 🍺 🥂 🍴 🎱 🥂

C 🐕 🚲 W V

SILVER 🍃🍃

Tongue, Sutherland | Map Ref: 4A3

The Ben Loyal Hotel

TONGUE, SUTHERLAND IV27 4XE
Tel: 01847 611216 Fax: 01847 611212
e.mail: Thebenloyalhotel@btinternet.com Web: www.benloyal.co.uk
"A Sanctuary from the Stress of Urban Living" ★★★ HOTEL AA ⚜

Open all year, discover the clear sea and golden sands of this Highland oasis. Overlooking the Kyle and Ben Loyal we are renowned for our warm welcome, friendly staff and Taste of Scotland cooking. Trout and salmon fishing can be arranged. Ashley Courtenay recommended hotel. **£58.50-£64 for D,B&B or £287-£385 per week D,B&B.**

HOTEL
★★★

Ben Loyal Hotel
Tongue, Sutherland, IV27 4XE
Tel: 01847 611216 Fax: 01847 611212
E-mail: Thebenloyal@btinternet.com
Web: www.benloyal.co.uk

2 Single	All En Suite	B&B per person	Open Jan-Dec excl
5 Twin		£38.00-£40.00 Single	Xmas/New Year
4 Double		£38.00-£40.00 Dbl/Twn	B&B + Eve.Meal
			from £58.50

Stone built hotel with fine views of Ben Loyal and Kyle of Tongue. Friendly atmosphere. Fishing and real ale available. One AA rosette.

TV 📞 🛎 P 🍺 ✂ 🍴 🥂 🥂

C 🐕 🚲 V

Important: Prices stated are estimates and may be subject to amendments

Tongue, Sutherland   Map Ref: 4A3

Borgie Lodge Hotel

Skerray, Tongue, Sutherland KW14 7TH
Tel: 01641 521332 Fax: 01641 521332
e.mail: info@borgielodgehotel.co.uk Web: www.borgielodgehotel.co.uk

THE TREES OF SCOTLAND

Relax in the traditional comfort of a Highland lodge. Tales of massive salmon and red deer stags mingle with the peaty malt whisky, while perusing Jacquis award winning menus featuring Sutherland venison and lamb, locally caught Skerray lobster is a speciality! Enjoy her own garden vegetables – they are superb.

★★★★
SMALL HOTEL

Borgie Lodge Hotel
Skerray, Tongue, Sutherland, KW14 7TH
Tel/Fax: 01641 521332
E-mail: info@borgielodgehotel.co.uk
Web: www.borgielodgehotel.co.uk

Converted former hunting lodge quietly located within its own grounds. Daily changing Scottish menus feature game, seafood and fresh local produce.

3 Twin	All En Suite
3 Double	
1 Family	

B&B per person from £40.00 Single
from £35.00 Dbl/Twn
Room only per person from £30.00

Opne Feb-Nov
B&B + Eve.Meal from £59.50

★★★
B&B

Rhian Guest House
Rhian Cottage, Tongue, Sutherland, IV27 4XJ
Tel: 01847 611257
E-mail: jenny.anderson@tesco.net

Charming modernised gamekeeper's cottage, 0.5 miles (1km) outside village. Dramatic views of Ben Loyal. Ideal base for fishing, bird watching, walking and touring. Annexe outwith scheme.

1 Twin	2 En Suite fac
1 Double	1 Priv.NOT ensuite
1 Family	

B&B per person £27.00-£30.00 Single
£20.00-£22.00 Dbl/Twn

Open Jan-Dec excl Xmas/New Year
B&B + Eve.Meal from £35.00

★★★★
SMALL HOTEL

Tongue Hotel
Tongue, Sutherland, IV27 4XD
Tel: 01847 611206 Fax: 01847 611345

A traditional Victorian Highland hotel retaining original style and charm. Panoramic views over Kyle of Tongue, ideal base for nature enthusiasts.

4 Twin
10 Double
2 Family

B&B per person from £25.00 Single
from £25.00 Dbl/Twn

Open Mar-Oct

BRONZE

Ullapool, Ross-shire   Map Ref: 3G6

Ardvreck Guest House
Morefield Brae, Ullapool, Ross-shire, IV26 2TH
Tel: 01854 612028 Fax: 01854 613000
Web: www.smoothhound.co.uk/hotels/ardvreck.html

Guest house set amidst some of the best hillwalking country and breathtaking scenery in Scotland. Elevated country position overlooking Ullapool and Lochbroom. Spacious, well appointed rooms most with spectacular sea view, all with ensuite shower room, T.V and tea/coffee facility. Residents lounge available at all times. Local facilities include a leisure centre, swimming pool, sauna, golf course, fishing and museum.

GUEST HOUSE
★★★★

2 Single	All En Suite	B&B per person	Open Mar-Oct
2 Twin		from £23.00 Single	
4 Double		from £23.00 Dbl/Twn	
2 Family		Room only per person	
		from £20.00	

Brae Guest House
Shore Street, Ullapool, IV26 2UJ
Tel: 01854 612421

Ullapool's longest established Guest House built in 1800's. Family run and on Ullapool's seafront with views over Loch Broom. Restaurant attached to Guest House where the emphasis is on traditional Scottish cooking. Close to shops and all amenities.

GUEST HOUSE
★★★

1 Single	9 En Suite fac	B&B per person	Open May-Oct
3 Twin	2 Pub Bath/Show	from £20.00 Single	
4 Double		from £20.00 Dbl/Twn	
2 Family			

Dromnan Guest House
Garve Road, Ullapool, Ross-shire, IV26 2SX
Tel: 01854 612333 Fax: 01854 613364
E-mail: dromnan@msn.com

Family run guest house on outskirts of the west coast fishing village of Ullapool, overlooking Loch Broom. 5 minutes from ferry to the Outer Isles.

GUEST HOUSE
★★★★

2 Twin	All En Suite	B&B per person	Open Jan-Dec
3 Double		£30.00-£36.00 Single	
2 Family		£23.00-£26.00 Dbl/Twn	

Point Cottage Guest House
22 West Shore Street, Ullapool, Ross-shire
Tel: 01854 612494 Fax: 01854 613464
E-mail: stay@pointcottage.co.uk
Web: www.pointcottage.co.uk

Tastefully converted 18c fisherman's cottage where a warm welcome and a high level of local knowledge are assured. Marvellous lochside views to mountains beyond. Very quiet location but only 2 minutes walk to village centre. Vegetarian cooked breakfast available.

GUEST HOUSE
★★★★

1 Twin	All En Suite	B&B per person	Open Feb-Oct
2 Double		£25.00-£45.00 Single	
		£20.00-£26.00 Dbl/Twn	

Strathmore House
Morefield, Ullapool, Ross-shire, IV26 2TH
Tel: 01854 612423 Fax: 01854 613485
E-mail: murdo@strathmore.fsnet.co.uk

Guest house enjoying panoramic views over Loch Broom and Ullapool. Some bedrooms have separate front entrance. Ideal touring base for north west coast. Comfortable TV lounge and reading room.

GUEST HOUSE
★★★

6 Double	All En Suite	B&B per person	Open Easter-Sep
		from £25.00 Single	
		from £20.00 Double	

Important: Prices stated are estimates and may be subject to amendments

Wick, Caithness   Map Ref: 4E3

HOTEL
★★★

MacKays Hotel
Union Street, Wick, Caithness, KW1 5ED
Tel: 01955 602323 Fax: 01955 605930
E-mail: mackays.hotel@caithness.mm.co.uk
Web: www.mackayshotel.co.uk

9 Single
6 Twin
10 Double
2 Family

All En Suite

Rates on
application

Open Jan-Dec excl
Xmas/New Year

Victorian purpose built hotel, now modernised to provide comfortable
accommodation for the business or leisure traveller. Choice of bars, a
restaurant and function facilities. Centrally situated on the riverside and
near to the railway station. Free golf for residents on four courses within
the County.

GUEST HOUSE
★★★

Wellington Guest House
43 High Street, Wick, Caithness, KW1 4BS
Tel: 01955 603287 Fax: 01955 602237

6 Twin

All En Suite

B&B per person
from £24.00 Single
from £19.00 Twin

Open Mar-Oct

Conveniently situated in the town centre next to the Tourist Office. Private
off street parking. Plenty to do in the area - fishing, walking,
birdwatching, exploring the varied coastline of Caithness and much more.

THE OUTER ISLES ARE FOR VISITORS SEEKING ADVENTURE, A SENSE OF BEING OUTSIDE BRITAIN – YET STILL A PART OF IT – AND SEEING A DIFFERENT CULTURE. ALL THREE ISLAND GROUPINGS – THE WESTERN ISLES, ORKNEY AND SHETLAND – CONTRAST WITH EACH OTHER. ORKNEY AND SHETLAND SHARE A NORSE HERITAGE, WHILE THE WESTERN ISLES ARE THE STRONGHOLD OF THE GAEL. EXCELLENT FERRY AND AIR LINKS MEAN GETTING TO ANY OF THESE GROUPS OF ISLANDS IS STRAIGHT FORWARD.

Old Man of Hoy, Isle of Hoy, Orkney

THE WESTERN ISLES offer some of Scotland's finest seascapes and beaches, as well as the springtime flowers of the machair – the shell-sand coastal pasture. Ancient monuments such as the spectacular Callanais Standing Stones are a reminder of the heritage of prehistory on the islands. The preserved Black House at Arnol is a reminder of the more recent life of the crofters on these islands, and is one of many heritage museums on the islands.

ORKNEY'S GREEN ISLANDS, like the Western Isles, have a strong sense of continuity stretching back to ancient times. The past is all around at places like Skara Brae, a magnificently preserved Stone Age village, and Maes Howe, a unique burial chamber already more than a millennium old when pillaged by Vikings. Kirkwall is the setting for

St Magnus Cathedral, the most magnificent Norman work in Scotland. Another theme to explore is the seagoing tradition, including the recent history of Scapa Flow as a naval anchorage, portrayed at the fascinating museum at Lyness on Hoy. Orkney's wildlife includes spectacular seabird colonies along its dramatic coastline.

Voe, Shetland Mainland

Traditional crofters' cottages, Western Isles

SHETLAND HAS THE STRONGEST SENSE of somewhere different. Here the Scandinavian influence is apparent – in dialect, music, even architecture and traditions. The sea pervades the way of life, with nowhere more than three miles from salt water. Like Orkney, there is an abundance of wildlife – seals, otters and seabirds – from Sumburgh Head in the south of the islands past the national nature reserve at Herrmaness on Unst to Muckle Flugga at the most northerly point of Britain. Shetland is for adventurers, with long summe daylight hours in 'the land of the simmer dim' leaving even more time to enjoy the unique island ambience.

HOTELS & GUEST HOUSES

EVENTS
OUTER ISLANDS:
WESTERN ISLES, ORKNEY
&SHETLAND

1 JANUARY
Men & Boy's "Ba"
Kirkwall Town Centre,
Orkney
Traditional street football game
where there can be up to 400
players in teams of "Uppies" and
"Doonies". Also played on
Christmas day.
Contact: J.D.M Robertson
TEL: **01856 872961**

30 JANUARY
Up Helly Aa
Lerwick Town Centre, Shetland
Traditional Viking fire festival
culminating in the burning of a
replica galley.
Contact: Shetland Islands
Tourism
TEL: **01595 693434**

***3-6 MAY**
Shetland Folk Festival
Various venues, Shetland
Traditional Scottish music
festival.
Contact: Festival Office
TEL: **01595 694757**

24-27 MAY
Orkney Folk Festival
Various venues, Orkney
Four day folk festival,
featuring a wide range of
traditional music in and
around Stromness.
Contact: Johnny Mowat,
Folk Festival Office
TEL: **01856 851331**

22-27 JUNE
St Magnus Festival
Various venues, Orkney
Annual festival of music, drama,
dance and visual art.
Contact: Glynis Hughes
TEL: **01856 871445**

31 AUG-3 SEPTEMBER
Walk Shetland 2001
Various venues, Shetland
A 5 day celebration of the
Islands on foot.
Contact: Shetland Islands
Tourism
TEL: **01595 693434**

12—19 OCTOBER
Royal National Mod
Various venues, Stornoway
Scotland's premier festival of
Gaelic music, song, drama,
dance and literature.
Contact: Donald John McSween
TEL: **01851 703487**

*provisional dates

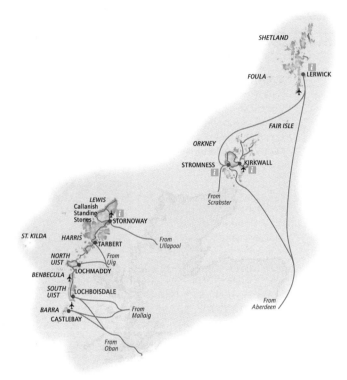

WESTERN ISLES

TOURIST BOARD

26 Cromwell Street

Stornoway

Isle of Lewis

HS1 2DD

TEL: **01851 703088**

FAX: **01851 705244**

www.witb.co.uk

ORKNEY TOURIST BOARD

6 Broad Street

Kirkwall

Orkney

KW15 1NX

TEL: **01856 872856**

FAX: **01856 875056**

www.visitorkney.com

SHETLAND SCANDS

TOURISM

Market Cross

Lerwick

Shetland

ZE1 0LU

TEL: **01595 693434**

FAX: **01595 695807**

www.shetland-tourism.co.uk

WESTERN ISLES TOURIST BOARD

CASTLEBAY
Main Street
Isle of Barra
TEL: **(01871) 810336**
Easter-Oct

LOCHBOISDALE
Pier Road
Isle of South Uist
TEL: **(01878) 700286**
Easter-Oct

LOCHMADDY
Isle of North Uist
TEL: **(01876) 500321**
Easter-Oct

STORNOWAY
26 Cromwell Street
Isle of Lewis
TEL: **(01851) 703088**
Jan-Dec

TARBERT
Pier Road
Isle of Harris
TEL: **(01859) 502011**
Easter-Oct

ORKNEY TOURIST BOARD

KIRKWALL
6 Broad Street
Orkney
TEL: **(01856) 872856**
Jan-Dec

STROMNESS
Ferry Terminal Building
The Pier Head
Orkney
TEL: **(01856) 850716**
Jan-Dec

SHETLAND TOURIST BOARD

LERWICK
The Market Cross
Shetland
TEL: **(01595) 693434**
Jan-Dec

Castlebay, Isle of Barra, Western Isles   Map Ref: 3A11

Craigard Hotel
Castlebay, Barra, Western Isles, HS9 5XD
Tel: 01871 810200 Fax: 01871 810726

★★★

SMALL
HOTEL

Small family hotel delightfully situated overlooking Kisimul Castle in Castlebay. Fresh seafood a speciality. 5 minutes walk from the ferry terminal.

1 Single	All En Suite
2 Twin	
2 Double	
2 Family	

B&B per person
£33.00-£35.00 Single
£30.00-£32.00 Dbl/Twn
Room only per person
£27.00-£30.00

Open Jan-Dec

Tangasdale, Isle of Barra, Western Isles   Map Ref: 3A11

Isle of Barra Hotel
Tangasdale Beach, Isle of Barra, Western Isles, HS9 5XW
Tel: 01871 810383 Fax: 01871 810385
Web: www.isleofbarra.com/iob.html

★★★

HOTEL

Family run hotel, with friendly local staff, specialising in fresh local seafood, Aberdeen Angus beef and fine wines. Superbly situated overlooking beautiful white sandy bay washed by the Atlantic Ocean.

26 Twin	All En Suite
4 Double	

B&B per person
from £37.00 Single
from £32.00 Dbl/Twn
Room only per person
from £25.00

Open end Mar-
begin Oct
B&B + Eve.Meal
from £47.00

Creagorry, Isle of Benbecula, Western Isles   Map Ref: 3B9

Creagorry Hotel
Creagorry, Isles of Benbecula, Western Isles, HS7 5PG
Tel: 01870 602024 Fax: 01870 603108
E-mail: darkislandhotel@msn.uk

★

HOTEL

Long established hotel (over 100 years) with popular local bar and regular entertainment. Bar lunches and suppers available, non-residents very welcome. Hotel has fishing rights over 16 Lochs and some sea-pools.

8 Single	7 En Suite fac
7 Twin	9 Limited ensuite
1 Double	2 Pub Bath/Show

B&B per person
from £26.00 Single
from £20.00 Dbl/Twn
Room only per person
from £22.00

Open Jan-Dec excl
Xmas/New Year
B&B + Eve.Meal
from £33.00

Liniclate, Isle of Benbecula, Western Isles   Map Ref: 3B8

Dark Island Hotel
Liniclate, Benbecula, Western Isles, HS7 5PJ
Tel: 01870 603030 Fax: 01870 602347
E-mail: darkislandhotel@msn.uk

★★

HOTEL

Modern hotel in centre of Benbecula, near sandy beaches, about 4 miles (7kms) from airport. Free golf and trout fishing available.

9 Single	All En Suite
13 Twin	
20 Double	

B&B per person
from £35.00 Single
from £30.00 Dbl/Twn
Room only per person
from £29.00

Open Jan-Dec excl
Xmas/New Year
B&B + Eve.Meal
from £42.00

Tarbert, Isle of Harris, Western Isles   Map Ref: 3C6

Harris Hotel
Isle of Harris, Western Isles, HS3 3DL
Tel: 01859 502154 Fax: 01859 502281

★★

HOTEL

Ideal centre for touring Lewis and Harris. Old established family hotel where you will find friendliness, peace and tranquility. 5 minutes to ferry terminal. A la carte menu available serving fresh local seafood, bar menu also available.

4 Single	15 En Suite fac
10 Twin	4 Pub Bath/Show
7 Double	
3 Family	

B&B per person
£30.00-£43.50 Single

Open Jan-Dec
B&B + Eve.Meal
£45.00-£60.00

Important: Prices stated are estimates and may be subject to amendments

Achmore, Isle of Lewis, Western Isles — Map Ref: 3D5

GUEST HOUSE

Cleascro Guest House
Achmore, Lochs, Lewis, Western Isles, HS2 9DU
Tel/Fax: 01851 860302
E-mail: donnamurray@compuserve.com
Web: www.with.co.uk/links/cleascro.htm

2 Twin   All En Suite
1 Double

B&B per person
from £25.00 Single
from £25.00 Dbl/Twn

Open Jan-Dec excl
Xmas/New Year
B&B + Eve.Meal
from £45.00

Modern family house, with attractive garden, in rural setting. Centrally located for visits to all parts of the island. Home-cooked evening meal available with fresh local produce.

Breasclete, Isle of Lewis, Western Isles — Map Ref: 3D4

GUEST HOUSE

Loch Roag Guest House
22a Breasclete, Isle of Lewis, HS2 9EF
Tel/Fax: 01851 621357
Web: www.lochroag.com

2 Single   All En Suite
1 Twin
1 Family

B&B per person
£23.50-£29.50 Single
£23.50-£29.50 Twin

Open Jan-Dec
B&B + Eve.Meal
£41.50-£47.50

Lochroag Guest House offers a perfect blend of comfort, the best of local cuisine, spectacular scenery and easy access to all attractions.

Callanish, Isle of Lewis, Western Isles — Map Ref: 3D4

GUEST HOUSE

Eshcol Guest House
21 Breasclete, Callanish, Lewis, Western Isles, HS2 9ED
Tel/Fax: 01851 621357

2 Twin   2 En Suite fac
1 Double   1 Priv.NOT ensuite

B&B per person
from £29.00 Single
from £29.00 Dbl/Twn

Open Jan-Dec excl
Xmas/New Year
B&B + Eve.Meal
from £47.00

Modern detached house quietly situated in the crofting village of Breasclete, with an open outlook over Loch Roag towards the Uig hills. Good base to explore Lewis, or just to relax. Only 2 miles to the Callanish standing stones. All bedrooms non-smoking. Local produce used where possible in our highly recommended evening meals. B.Y.O.B.

South Galson, Isle of Lewis, Western Isles — Map Ref: 3D3

GUEST HOUSE

Galson Farm Guest House
South Galson, Isle of Lewis, HS2 0SH
Tel/Fax: 01851 850492
Web: www.galsonfarm.freeserve.co.uk

2 Twin   All En Suite
1 Dbl/Fam 1 Pub Bath/Show

B&B per person
from £29.00 Single
from £29.00 Dbl/Twn

Open Jan-Dec
B&B + Eve.Meal
from £45.00

18c restored working croft, close to shore with views to Butt of Lewis. Home cooking and licensed. Non-smoking. Modern bedrooms are cosily situated under the eaves, flush with facilities. Sun circles the many windowed library.

CABARFEIDH HOTEL

Manor Park, Stornoway, Isle of Lewis HS1 2EV
Tel: 01851 702604 Fax: 01851 705572
Web: www.calahotels.com

The Cabarfeidh, known as Stornoway's finest hotel, set in its own attractive gardens overlooking the Lews Castle grounds. The ambience here is of quiet sophistication where comfort and hospitality go hand in hand from the first warm welcome to the final farewell. Our friendly staff are dedicated to making your stay enjoyable.

★★★

HOTEL

Cabarfeidh Hotel
Manor Park, Stornoway, Isle of Lewis, HS1 2EV
Tel: 01851 702604 Fax: 01851 705572
E-mail: caberfeidh@calahotels.com
Web: www.calahotels.com

10 Single	All En Suite	B&B per person	Open Jan-Dec
26 Twin		from £72.00 Single	B&B + Eve.Meal
8 Double		from £46.00 Dbl/Twn	from £67.00
2 Family			

Recently refurbished hotel with a la carte restaurant offering interesting choice of dishes with emphasis on local produce. Lift to all floors.

ROYAL HOTEL

Cromwell Street, Stornoway, Isle of Lewis HS1 2DG
Tel: 01851 702109 Fax: 01851 702142 Web: www.calahotels.com

The Royal Hotel nestles in the heart of Stornoway and enjoys a delightful view over the colourful bustling harbur and marina to the splendour of the Lews Castle and its grounds. Traditional hospitality has been part of our service since the 1850's and is still very much in evidence today.

★★

HOTEL

The Royal Hotel
Cromwell Street, Stornoway, Isle of Lewis, HS1 2DG
Tel: 01851 702109 Fax: 01851 702142
Web: www.calahotels.com

8 Single	All En Suite	B&B per person	Open Jan-Dec
11 Twin	2 Pub Bath/Show	from £38.00 Single	B&B + Eve.Meal
6 Double		from £36.00 Dbl/Twn	from £55.00
1 Family			

This friendly and comfortable hotel has fine views of Stornoway's fishing harbour and castle. Our Boatshed Restaurant offers fine cuisine using fresh local produce.

Important: Prices stated are estimates and may be subject to amendments

Stornoway, Isle of Lewis, Western Isles   Map Ref: 3D4

SEAFORTH HOTEL

11 JAMES STREET, STORNOWAY, ISLE OF LEWIS HS1 2QN
TEL: 01851 702740 FAX: 01851 703900
WEB: www.calahotels.com

Situated close to the centre of town and the closest of hotel's to both the ferry terminal and Stornoway airport, but it's not just it's prime location that makes the Seaforth special. We offer real value for money and pride ourselves in our traditional Hebridean cuisine and hospitality.

★★

HOTEL

The Seaforth Hotel
11 James Street, Stornoway, Isle of Lewis, HS1 2QN
Tel: 01851 702740 Fax: 01851 703900
Web: www.calahotels.com

22 Single	All En Suite	B&B per person	Open Mar-Oct
27 Twin		from £29.00 Single	from £50.00
19 Double		from £34.50 Dbl/Twn	
1 Family			

Modern hotel, the largest on the island, situated in the centre of Stornoway, within walking distance of the ferry terminal. Local leisure and fitness centre is just across the road. The hotel makes an excellent base for exploring Lewis and Harris.

Carinish, Isle of North Uist, Western Isles   Map Ref: 3B8

★★★

INN

Carinish Hotel
Carinish, Isle of North Uist, Western Isles, HS6 5EJ
Tel: 01876 580673 Fax: 01876 580665

2 Twin	All En Suite	B&B per person	Open Jan-Dec
4 Double		from £35.00 Single	B&B + Eve.Meal
2 Family		from £30.00 Dbl/Twn	from £45.00
		Room only	
		from £25.00	

Recently completely refurbished to comfortable contemporary standards. Central location suitable for exploring the length of Uist, easily reached from ferry terminal and airport, only 10 miles to Balranald nature reserve.

Locheport, Isle of North Uist, Western Isles   Map Ref: 3B8

Langass Lodge

NORTH UIST, THE WESTERN ISLES HS6 5HA
Telephone: 01876 580285 Fax: 01876 580385
e.mail: langass@btinternet.com
Commanding scenic views over a sea loch and situated beside a stone circle and neolithic burial chamber. This comfortable small hotel is the ideal base for exploring the Western Isles. All the well-appointed rooms have ensuite facilities and the excellent restaurant specialises in seafood and game.
Prices from £36 B&B.

★★★

**SMALL
HOTEL**

Langass Lodge Hotel
Locheport, North Uist, Western Isles, HS6 5HA
Tel: 01876 580285 Fax: 01876 580385
E-mail: langass@btinternet.com

1 Single	All En Suite	B&B per person	Open Jan-Dec
4 Twin		from £36.00 Single	
2 Double		from £30.00 Dbl/Twn	

Traditional Inn, set in splendid isolation, overlooking Loch Eport and about 8 miles (13kms) from Lochmaddy ferry terminal. Popular retreat for anglers, ornithologists and lovers of the outdoors. Fishing available on all of the North Uists renowned lochs.

VAT is shown at 17.5%: changes in this rate may affect prices. | *Key to symbols is on back flap.*

Lochmaddy, Isle of North Uist, Western Isles — Map Ref: 3B8

HOTEL ★★

Lochmaddy Hotel
Lochmaddy, North Uist, Western Isles, HS6 5AA
Tel: 01876 500331/500332 Fax: 01876 500210

8 Single | All En Suite
3 Twin
3 Double
1 Family

B&B per person
£32.50-£40.00 Single
£30.00-£37.50 Dbl/Twn

Open Jan-Dec
B&B + Eve.Meal
£45.00-£55.00

Providing Hebridean hospitality and good food situated 200 yards from ferry terminal. Free trout fishing for guests. Salmon and sea trout fishing also available to guests on reduced rate, priority permits.

Dounby, Orkney — Map Ref: 5B11

INN ★★

Smithfield Hotel
Dounby, Orkney, KW17 2HT
Tel: 01856 771215 Fax: 01856 771494
Web: www.orkney-hotels.co.uk

1 Single | All En Suite
2 Twin
2 Double

B&B per person
from £30.00 Single
from £30.00 Dbl/Twn

Open Apr-Oct
B&B + Eve.Meal
from £46.00

Charming village Inn recently refurbished, but retaining true Orcadian character. Friendly comfortable atmosphere and good food. Well situated as a base for exploring the many historic sites of Orkney's mainland or for birdwatching or fishing.

Kirkwall, Orkney — Map Ref: 5B12

HOTEL ★★★★

Ayre Hotel
Ayre Road, Kirkwall, Orkney, KW15 1QX
Tel: 01856 873001 Fax: 01856 876289
Web: www.ayrehotel.co.uk

18 Single | All En Suite
6 Twin
9 Double

B&B per person
from £66.00 Single
from £45.00 Dbl/Twn

Open Jan-Dec excl Xmas/New Year
B&B + Eve.Meal
from £65.00

Family owned hotel on harbour front. Refurbished to a high standard. Some rooms with sea views. Close to town centre and all amenities. Proprietors Roy and Moira Dennison guarantee their guests a comfortable and peaceful stay in their hotel.

GUEST HOUSE ★★

Sanderlay Guest House
2 Viewfield Drive, Kirkwall, Orkney, KW15 1RB
Tel: 01856 875587 Fax: 01856 876350
E-mail: enquiries@sanderlay.co.uk
Web: www.sanderlay.co.uk

1 Single | 4 En Suite fac
1 Twin | 1 Pub Bath/Show
2 Double
2 Family

B&B per person
£18.00-£22.00 Single
£14.00-£20.00 Dbl/Twn
Room only per person
£11.00-£19.00

Open Jan-Dec

Comfortable modern house in quiet residential area on outskirts of town. Some ensuite and 3 self-contained family units. Private parking available. Credit cards accepted. Ideal base for exploring the Orkney mainland or for visiting the North Isles.

HOTEL ★★★

West End Hotel
Main Street, Kirkwall, Orkney, KW15 1BU
Tel: 01856 872368 Fax: 01856 876181
Web: www.orkneyisles.co.uk/westendhotel

8 Single | All En Suite
4 Twin
4 Double

B&B per person
from £40.00 Single
from £29.00 Dbl/Twn

Open Jan-Dec excl Xmas/New Year

Friendly family run hotel, built in 1824, within easy reach of Kirkwall's historic sites, such as St Magnus Cathedral and the Earl's Palace. Also well situated for the business traveller. Private car parking, all rooms en-suite. Some annex accommodation.

Important: Prices stated are estimates and may be subject to amendments

North Ronaldsay, Orkney — Map Ref: 5D10

GUEST HOUSE ★★

The Observatory Guest House
North Ronaldsay Bird Observatory, North Ronaldsay,
Orkney, KW17 2BE
Tel: 01857 633200/633200 Fax: 01857 633207
E-mail: alison@nrbo.prestel.co.uk

Unique eco-friendly activity centre offering comfortable accommodation in
a crofting environment. Resident specialists in ornithology.

2 Twin	All En Suite	B&B per person	Open Jan-Dec excl
2 Double		from £23.00 Single	Xmas/New Year
		from £18.00 Dbl/Twn	B&B + Eve.Meal
			from £27.00

Sanday, Orkney — Map Ref: 5D10

GUEST HOUSE ★★

The Belsair Retreat Centre
Kettletoft, Sanday, Orkney, KW17 2BJ
Tel: 01857 600206
E-mail: Joy.retreat@quista.net

Relax in this peaceful and comfortable island retreat centre. Warm
welcome and home cooking. Beautiful beaches and ideal for walking.
Make time for yourself with a break away from busy lifestyles. Send for
our brochure for more detailed information.

2 Single	3 En Suite fac	B&B per person	Open Jan-Dec excl
1 Twin	1 Pub Bath/Show	from £17.50 Single	Xmas/New Year
1 Double	1 Priv.NOT ensuite	from £17.50 Dbl/Twn	B&B + Eve.Meal
			from £26.00

Stenness, Orkney — Map Ref: 5B12

HOTEL ★★★

Standing Stones Hotel
Stenness, Orkney, KW16 3JX
Tel: 01856 850449 Fax: 01856 851262
E-mail: standingstones@sol.co.uk

Situated on the shores of the Loch of Stenness, just off the main Kirkwall
to Stromness road. This is an excellent central base for exploring Orkney's
many historical and archaeological attractions, or for fishing or
birdwatching.

4 Single	All En Suite	B&B per person	Open Jan-Dec excl
6 Twin		from £30.00 Single	Xmas/New Year
4 Double		from £30.00 Dbl/Twn	B&B + Eve.Meal
3 Family		Room only per person	from £45.00
		from £25.00	

Stromness, Orkney — Map Ref: 5B12

HOTEL ★★★

Stromness Hotel
The Pier Head, Stromness, Orkney, KW16 3AA
Tel: 01856 850298 Fax: 01856 850610
E-mail: info@stromnesshotel.com
Web: www.stromnesshotel.com

Recently refurbished hotel, situated in the heart of the fishing port of
Stromness. Overlooking the harbour, with views out towards Scapa Flow.
Much to see and do locally, plus all of Orkney's famous archaeological
sites. Fishing, golf, birdwatching are all available.

6 Single	40 En Suite fac	B&B per person	Open Jan-Dec
21 Twin		£30.00-£40.00 Single	B&B + Eve.Meal
9 Double		£30.00-£40.00 Dbl/Twn	£42.00-£52.00
6 Family		Room only per person	
		£24.00-£34.00	

Lerwick, Shetland — Map Ref: 5G6

GUEST HOUSE ★★★

Breiview Guest House
43 Kanterstead Road, Lerwick, Shetland, ZE1 0RJ
Tel/Fax: 01595 695956

Modern house on outskirts of town with fine views. Owner formerly chef
on cross channel ferry speaks French and German. All rooms en-suite and
most on the ground floor.

3 Twin	All En Suite	B&B per person	Open Jan-Dec
2 Double		£30.00-£35.00 Single	B&B + Eve.Meal
1 Family		£25.00-£30.00 Dbl/Twn	£35.00-£45.00

VAT is shown at 17.5%: changes in this rate may affect prices.

Key to symbols is on back flap.

Lerwick, Shetland				Map Ref: 5G6

The Lerwick Hotel
15 South Road, Lerwick, Shetland, ZE1 0RB
Tel: 01595 692166 Fax: 01595 694419
E-mail: reception@Lerwickhotel.co.uk

7 Single   All En Suite   B&B per person   Open Jan-Dec excl
19 Twin   £69.00 Single   Xmas/New Year
8 Double   £44.75 Dbl/Twn   B&B + Eve.Meal
1 Family   £52.50

Modern hotel in Lerwick, on sea shore overlooking Breiwick Bay and
Bressay Island. Catering for holiday and business travel. Tours organised.

Queen's Hotel
Commercial Street, Lerwick, Shetland Islands,
ZE1 0AB
Tel: 01595 692826 Fax: 01595 694048

8 Single   All En Suite   B&B per person   Open Jan-Dec excl
13 Twin   from £65.00 Single   Xmas/New Year
5 Double   from £45.00 Dbl/Twn
1 Triple

Traditional stone building on the very edge of the sea. Magnificent views
over to the Island of Bressay. Sympathetically refurbished yet retaining
many of the unique qualities of the Lodberry architecture.

The Shetland Hotel
Holmsgarth Road, Lerwick, Shetland, ZE1 0PW
Tel: 01595 695515 Fax: 01595 695828
E-mail: reception@shetlandhotel.co.uk

45 Twin   All En Suite   B&B per person   Open Jan-Dec excl
15 Double   £73.00 Single   Xmas/New Year
4 Family   £46.00 Dbl/Twn   B&B + Eve.Meal
£54.00

Modern hotel with spacious bedrooms. Views to busy harbour and Isle of
Bressay.

Whiteness, Shetland				Map Ref: 5F5

The Westings, The Inn on the Hill,
Whiteness, Shetland, ZE2 9LJ
Tel: 01595 840242 Fax: 01595 840500
E-mail: westingsinn@aol.com
Web: www.westings.shetland.co.uk

3 Single   All En Suite   B&B per person   Open Jan-Dec
2 Twin   from £37.50 Single
1 Double   from £35.00 Dbl/Twn
2 Family   Room only per person
from £27.50

Built on land acquired from the Earl of Zetland in 1943, the view
overlooks Whiteness Voe and its islands beyond. On a clear day the peaks
of Foula can be seen. Privately owned. Tastey bar meals and lounge.
Family bedroom option available, with outdoor childrens play area.

Daliburgh, Isle of South Uist, Western Isles				Map Ref: 3B10

Borrodale Hotel
Daliburgh, South Uist, Western Isles, HS8 5SS
Tel: 01878 700444 Fax: 01878 700446

2 Single   All En Suite   B&B per person   Open Jan-Dec
6 Twin   1 Pub Bath/Show   from £30.00 Single   B&B + Eve.Meal
5 Double   from £27.50 Dbl/Twn   from £46.00
1 Family

Family run hotel with all bedrooms recently refurbished in village of
Daliburgh. Only 3 miles (5kms) from Lochboisdale ferry terminal. Bar
lunches and suppers available, non-residents very welcome.

Important: Prices stated are estimates and may be subject to amendments

isdale, Isle of South Uist, Western Isles | Map Ref: 3B10

GUEST HOUSE

Patricia Murray
Brae Lea House, Lochboisdale, South Uist,
Western Isles, HS8 5TH
Tel/Fax: 01878 700497

Modern bungalow with full ensuite facilities. Quietly situated at edge of village. Well situated for ferry. Open views towards Lochboisdale and surrounding countryside. Sauna also available.

1 Single	All En Suite
1 Twin	
2 Double	
1 Family	

B&B per person
£25.00-£30.00 Single
£25.00-£30.00 Dbl/Twn
Room only per person
£20.00-£25.00

Open Jan-Dec

VAT is shown at 17.5%: changes in this rate may affect prices.

Key to symbols is on back flap.

THE SCOTTISH
TOURIST BOARD, in
conjunction with the English
Tourism Council and Wales
Tourist Board operates a
national accessible scheme
that identifies, acknowledges
and promotes those accommodation establishments that
meet the needs of visitors with
disabilities.

The three categories of accessibility, drawn up in close
consultation with specialist
organisations concerned
with the needs of people with
disabilities are:

CATEGORY 1

Unassisted wheelchair
access for residents

CATEGORY 2

Assisted wheelchair
access for residents

CATEGORY 3

Access for residents with
mobility difficulties

CATEGORY 1

ABERDEEN PATIO HOTEL
Beach Boulevard
Aberdeen
AB24 5EF
TEL: 01224 633339

ACHILTY HOTEL
Contin
by Strathpeffer
Ross-shire
IV14 9EG
TEL: 01997 421355

**AIRLIE MOUNT HOLIDAY
SERVICES**
2 Albert Street
Alyth
Perthshire
PH11 8AX
TEL: 01828 632986

AIRLIE HOUSE
Main Street
Strathyre
Stirling
FK18 8NA
TEL: 01877 384247

ARDGARTH GUEST HOUSE
1 St Mary's Place
Portobello
Edinburgh
EH15 2QF
TEL: 0131 669 3021

**BATTLEDOWN BED &
BREAKFAST**
off Station Road
Forgandenny
by Perth
Perthshire
PH2 9EL
TEL: 01738 812471

**BEARDMORE HOTEL &
CONFERENCE CENTRE**
Beardmore Street
Clydebank
Nr Glasgow
G81 4SA
TEL: 0141 951 6000

**THE BEECHES GUEST
HOUSE**
112 Victoria Street
Dyce
Aberdeen
Aberdeenshire
AB21 7AU
TEL: 01224 722249

MRS S BOARD
Fourpenny Cottage
Skelbo
Dornoch
Sutherland
IV25 3QS
TEL: 01862 810727

**BRAE LODGE GUEST
HOUSE**
30 Liberton Brae
Edinburgh
EH16 6AF
TEL: 0131 672 2876

MR J G BRISTOW
56 Dumbreck Road
Glasgow
G41 5NP
TEL: 0141 427 0129

**BURRASTOW HOUSE
HOTEL & RESTAURANT**
Walls
Shetland
ZE2 9PD
TEL: 01595 809 307

CARLOGIE HOUSE HOTEL
Carlogie Road
Carnoustie
Angus
DD7 6LD
TEL: 01241 853185

HOTELS &
GUEST HOUSES

FACILITIES
FOR VISITORS WITH DISABILITIES

343

THE OFFICIAL WHERE TO STAY G

CARLTON GEORGE HOTEL
44 West George Street
Glasgow
G2 1DH
TEL: 0141 353 6373

CLAYMORE HOUSE HOTEL
Seabank Road
Nairn
IV12 4EY
TEL: 01667 453731

COILLE-MHOR HOUSE
20 Houston Mains Holdings
Uphall
West Lothian
EH52 6PA
TEL: 01506 854044

COVENANTERS' INN
Auldearn
Nairn
IV12 5TG
TEL: 01667 452456

CREAG MHOR HOTEL
Onich
Inverness-shire
PH33 6RY
TEL: 01855 821379

CRUACHAN GUEST HOUSE
Monument Hill
Dalmally
Argyll
PA33 1AA
TEL: 01838 200496

CUIL-NA-SITHE
Lochyside
Fort William
Inverness-shire
PH33 7NX
TEL: 01397 702 267

**DALHOUSIE COURTE
HOTEL**
Cockpen Road
Bonnyrigg
EH19 3HS
TEL: 0131 660 3200

DHAILLING LODGE
155 Alexandra Parade
Dunoon
Argyll
PA23 8AW
TEL: 01369 701253

DOLLY'S B&B
33 Aignish Point
Isle of Lewis
HS2 0PB
TEL: 01851 870755

**DRUMOIG HOTEL & GOLF
COURSE**
Leuchars
by St Andrews
Fife
KY16 0BE
TEL: 01382 541800

DRYBURGH ABBEY HOTEL
St Boswells
Roxburghshire
TD6 0RQ
TEL: 01835 822261

DUNVALANREE HOUSE
Portrigh Bay
Carradale
Argyll
PA28 6SE
TEL: 01583 431226

EMPIRE TRAVEL LODGE
Union Street
Lochgilphead
Argyll
PA31 8JS
TEL: 01546 602381

EXPRESS BY HOLIDAY INN
Stoneyfield
Inverness
IV2 7PA
TEL: 01463 732700

FOREST HILLS HOTEL
Kinlochard,
by Aberfoyle
Perthshire
FK8 3TL
TEL: 01877 387277

GARDEN HOUSE HOTEL
Sarkfoot Road
Gretna
Dumfriesshire
DG16 5AJ
TEL: 01461 337621

GLASGOW HILTON
1 William Street
Glasgow
G3 8HT
TEL: 0141 204 5555

**GLASGOW MARRIOTT
HOTEL**
500 Argyle Street
Glasgow
G3 8RR
TEL: 0141 226 5577

THE GLENEAGLES HOTEL
Auchterarder
Perthshire
PH3 1NF
TEL: 01764 662231

THE GLENHOLM CENTRE
Broughton
by Biggar
Lanarkshire
ML12 6JF
TEL: 01899 830408

GREENACRE
Aberfeldy Road
by Killin
Loch Tay
Perthshire
FK21 8TY
TEL: 01567 820466

HIGHLAND COTTAGE
Breadalbane Street
Tobermory
Isle of Mull
PA75 6PD
TEL: 01688 302407

HILDASAY GUEST HOUSE
Upper Scalloway,
Scalloway
Shetland
ZE1 0UP
TEL: 01595 880822

HOLIDAY INN EXPRESS LIVINGSTONE
Starlaw Road
Bathgate
West Lothian
EH48 1LQ
TEL: 01506 650650

HOLIDAY INN EXPRESS - STIRLING
Springkerse Business Park
Stirling
FK7 7XH
TEL: 01786 449922

HOLIDAY INN GLASGOW
161 West Nile Street
Glasgow
G1 2RL
TEL: 0141 352 0110

HOWARD JOHNSON HOTEL
Cartsburn
Greenock
PA15 4RT
TEL: 01475 786666

HUNTERS LODGE HOTEL
Annan Road
Gretna
Dumfriesshire
DG16 5DL
TEL: 01461 338214

INCHYRA GRANGE HOTEL
Grange Road
Polmont
Stirlingshire
FK2 0YB
TEL: 01324 711911

THE INVERCAULD ARMS HOTEL
Invercauld Road
Braemar
Aberdeenshire
AB35 5YR
TEL: 01339 741605

INVERNESS MARRIOTT HOTEL
Culcabock Road
Inverness
IV2 3LP
TEL: 01463 237166

INVERNETTIE GUEST HOUSE
South Road
Peterhead
Aberdeenshire
AB42 0YX
TEL: 01779 473530

ISLE OF SKYE HOTEL
Queensbridge
18 Dundee Road
Perth
Tayside
PH2 7AB
TEL: 01738 624471

ISLES OF GLENCOE HOTEL & LEISURE CENTRE
Ballachulish
nr Fort William
Argyll
PA39 4HL
TEL: 01855 821582

JAMES WATT COLLEGE
Waterfront Campus
Custom House Way
Greenock
Renfrewshire
PA15 1EN
TEL: 01475 731360

JARVIS INTERNATIONAL
Almondview
Livingston
West Lothian
EH54 6QB
TEL: 01506 431222

JURYS EDINBURGH INN
43 Jeffrey Street
Edinburgh
Lothian
EH1 1DH
TEL: 0131 500 3300

LAV'ROCKHA GUEST HOUSE
Inganess Road
St Ola
Kirkwall
Orkney
KW15 1SP
TEL: 01856 876107

LOCH TORRIDON HOTEL
Torridon
Achnasheen
Ross-shire
IV22 2EY
TEL: 01445 791242

MRS MACKENZIE DAWSON
Gattaway Farm
Abernethy
Perthshire
PH2 9LQ
TEL: 01738 850746

HOTELS &
GUEST HOUSES

FACILITIES
FOR VISITORS WITH DISABILITIES

345

THE OFFICIAL WHERE TO STAY G

THE MARCLIFFE AT PITFODELS
North Deeside Road
Pitfodels
Aberdeen
AB15 9YA
TEL: 01224 861000

MELVILLE GUEST HOUSE
2 Duddingston Crescent
Edinburgh
Lothian
EH15 3AS
TEL: 0131 669 7856

MONCREIF
133 Alexandra Parade
Dunoon
Argyll
PA23 8AW
TEL: 01369 707945

NORTHBAY HOUSE
Balnabodach
Castlebay
Isle of Barra
HS9 5UT
TEL: (01871) 890 255

NORTH LODGE GUEST HOUSE
Canonbie
Dumfriesshire
DG14 0TF
TEL: 01387 371409

THE OLD STATION
Stravithie Bridge
St Andrews
Fife
KY16 8LR
TEL: 01334 880585

PANMURE HOTEL
Tay Street
Monifieth
Angus
DD5 4AX
TEL: 01382 532911

POSTHOUSE GLASGOW CITY
Bothwell Street
Glasgow
G2 7EN
TEL: 0870 400 9032

RATHCLUAN
Carslogie Road
Cupar
Fife,
KY15 4HY
TEL: 01334 650000

ROSSLEA HALL HOTEL
Ferry Road
Rhu
by Helensburgh
Dunbartonshire
G84 8NF
TEL: 01436 439955

ROWANTREE GUEST HOUSE
38 Main Street
Glenluce
Wigtownshire
DG8 0PS
TEL: 01581 300244

MRS E RYRIE
24 Lindsay Drive
Wick
Caithness,
KW1 4PG
TEL: 01955 603001

SHERATON GRAND HOTEL EDINBURGH
1 Festival Square
Edinburgh
EH3 9SR
TEL: 0131 229 9131

THE SHETLAND HOTEL
Holmsgarth Road
Lerwick
Shetland
ZE1 0PW
TEL: 01595 695515

SHOREFIELD
Edinbane
Isle of Skye
IV51 9PW
Tel: 01470 582444

SIMPSONS
79 Lauriston Place
Edinburgh
EH3 9HZ
TEL: 0131 622 7979

SPEEDBIRD INN
Argyll Road
Dyce
Aberdeen
AB21 0AF
TEL: 01224 772884

STEWART HALL OF RESIDENCE
Motherwell College
Dalzell Drive
Motherwell
Lanarkshire
ML1 2PP
TEL: 01698 261890

STIRLING MANAGEMENT CENTRE
University of Stirling
Stirling
FK9 4LA
TEL: 01786 451712

STRATHPEFFER HOTEL
Strathpeffer
Ross-shire
IV14 9DF
TEL: 01997 421200

STRONSAY HOTEL
Stronsay
Orkney
KW17 2AR
TEL: 01857 616213

**THISTLE ABERDEEN
AIRPORT**
Aberdeen Airport
Argyll Road
Aberdeen
AB21 0AF
TEL: 01224 725252

**THISTLE ABERDEEN
ALTENS**
Souterhead Road,
Altens
Aberdeen
AB12 3LF
TEL: 01224 877000

THISTLE EDINBURGH
107 Leith Street
Edinburgh
EH1 3SW
TEL: 0131 556 0111

THISTLE IRVINE
46 Annick Road
Irvine
Ayrshire
KA11 4LD
TEL: 01294 274272

THORNDALE
Manse Road
Stonehouse
Lanarkshire
ML9 3PQ
TEL: 01698 791133

TIGH-NA-CHEO
Garbhein Road
Kinlochleven
Argyll
PA40 4SE
TEL: 01855 831434

**TRAVELODGE EDINBURGH
SOUTH**
46 Dreghorn Link
A720 City Bypass
Edinburgh
EH13 9QR
TEL: 07775 846074

THE TREFOIL CENTRE
Gogarbank
Edinburgh
EH12 9DA
TEL: 0131 339 3148

TURNBERRY HOTEL
Turnberry
Ayrshire
KA26 9LT
TEL: 01655 331000

UNIVERSITY OF DUNDEE
West Park Villas
West Park Road
Dundee
DD2 1NN
TEL: 01382 344039

**UNIVERSITY OF
ABERDEEN**
King's College
Aberdeen
AB24 3FX
TEL: 01224 273444

VIEWFIELD HOUSE HOTEL
Portree
Isle of Skye
Inverness-shire
IV51 9EU
TEL: 01478 612217

WELCOME LODGE
M74 Motorway Junc 13
Abington
Biggar
Lanarkshire
ML12 6RG
TEL: 01864 502782

WELCOME LODGE
Welcome Break Service Area
M74
Gretna Green
Dumfriesshire
DG16 5HQ
TEL: 01461 337566

**WESTWOOD GUEST
HOUSE**
Houndwood
by St Abbs
Berwickshire
TD14 5TP
TEL: 01361 850232

MRS WILLIAMS
Strathwhillan House
Brodick
Isle of Arran
KA27 8BQ
TEL: 01770 302331

THE WINDSOR HOTEL
18 Albert Street
Nairn
IV12 4HP
TEL: 01667 453108

CATEGORY 2

ABERDEEN MARRIOTT
Overton Circle
Dyce
Aberdeen
AB21 7AZ
TEL: 01224 770011

ARDENCAPLE HOTEL
Shore Road
Rhu
by Helensburgh
Dunbartonshire
G83 8LA
TEL: 01436 820200

ARDEN HOUSE
Newtonmore Road
Kingussie
Inverness-shire
PH21 1HE
TEL: 01540 661369

**AUCHENDINNY GUEST
HOUSE**
Treaslane
Skeabost Bridge
Isle of Skye
Inverness-shire
IV51 9NX
TEL: 01470 532470

AUCHENSKEOCH LODGE
by Dalbeattie
Kirkcudbrightshire
DG5 4PG
TEL: 01387 780277

**AUCHRANNIE COUNTRY
HOUSE HOTEL**
Brodick
Isle of Arran
KA27 8BZ
TEL: 01770 302234

BALBIRNIE HOUSE HOTEL
Balbirnie Park
Markinch
by Glenrothes
Fife
KY7 6NE
TEL: 01592 610066

**THE BALLACHULISH
HOTEL**
Ballachulish
nr Fort William
Argyll
PH49 4JY
TEL: 01855 811606

THE BALTASOUND HOTEL
Baltasound
Unst
Shetland
ZE2 9DS
TEL: 01957 711334

BARNTON HOTEL
Queensferry Road
Edinburgh
EH4 6AS
TEL: 0131 339 1144

BARONY HOTEL
Birsay
Orkney
KW17 2LS
TEL: 01856 721327

THE CALEDONIAN
Princes Street
Edinburgh
EH1 2AB
TEL: 0131 459 9988

CLAN MACDUFF HOTEL
Achintore
Fort William
Inverness-shire
PH33 6RW
TEL: 01397 702341

CLONYARD HOUSE HOTEL
Colvend
Dalbeattie
Kirkcudbrightshire
DG5 4QW
TEL: 01556 630372

COMELY BANK
32 Burrell Street
Crieff
Perthshire
PH7 4DT
TEL: 01764 653409

**DALL LODGE COUNTRY
HOUSE HOTEL**
Main Street
Killin
Perthshire
FK21 8TN
TEL: 01567 820217

DRYFESDALE HOTEL
Lockerbie
Dumfriesshire
DG11 2SF
TEL: 01576 202427

DYCE SKEAN DHU
Farburn Terrace
Dyce
Aberdeen
AB21 7DW
TEL: 01224 723101

EWOOD HOUSE
12 Kings Gate
Aberdeenshire
AB15 4EJ
TEL: 01224 648408

ALISTAIR FORTUNE
Glenaveron
Golf Road
Brora
Sutherland
KW9 6QS
TEL: 01408 621601

GARVOCK HOUSE HOTEL
St John's Drive
Transy
Dunfermline
KY12 7TU
TEL: 01383 621067

GLASGOW MOAT HOUSE
Congress Road
Glasgow
G3 8QT
TEL: 0141 306 9988

HILCROFT HOTEL
East Main Street
Whitburn
West Lothian
EH47 0JU
TEL: 01501 740818

**HILTON EDINBURGH
AIRPORT**
Edinburgh International
Airport
Edinburgh
EH28 8LL
TEL: 0131 519 4400

**HILTON EDINBURGH
GROSVENOR HOTEL**
7-21 Grosvenor Street
Edinburgh
EH12 5EF
TEL: 0131 226 6001

**HOLIDAY INN GARDEN
COURT**
Queensferry Road
Edinburgh
EH4 3HL
TEL: 0131 332 2442

HUNTINGTOWER HOTEL
Crieff Road
Perth
PH1 3JT
TEL: 01738 583771

IVORY HOUSE
14 Vogrie Road
Gorebridge
Midlothian
EH23 4HH
TEL: 01875 820755

**JARVIS CALEDONIAN
HOTEL**
Church Street
Inverness
IV1 1DX
TEL: 01463 235181

KEAVIL HOUSE HOTEL
Crossford
Dunfermline
Fife
KY12 8QW
TEL: 01383 736258

KINLOCH HOUSE HOTEL
Kinloch
by Blairgowrie
Perthshire
PH10 6SG
TEL: 01250 884237

LOCH FYNE HOTEL
Newtown
Inveraray
Argyll
PA32 8XT
TEL: 01499 302148

LOG CABIN HOTEL
Glen Derby
Kirkmichael
Blairgowrie
Perthshire
PH10 7NB
TEL: 01250 881288

**MRS F MEREDITH
CLUNEBEG LODGE**
Clunebeg Estate
Drumnadrochit
Inverness-shire
IV3 6UU
TEL: 01456 450387

**KYANACHAN LOCH
TUMMEL HOTEL**
Tummel Bridge
Perthshire
PH16 5SB
TEL: 01389 713713

THE MILL
Grahamshill
Kirkpatrick Fleming
by Lockerbie
Dumfriesshire
DG11 3BQ
TEL: 01461 800344

MOORINGS HOTEL
114 Hamilton Road
Motherwell
ML1 3DG
TEL: 01698 258131

CLOISTERS
Church Holme
Talmine
Sutherland
IV27 4YP
TEL: 01847 601286

**MUCKRACH LODGE
HOTEL**
Dulnain Bridge
Inverness-shire
PH26 3LY
TEL: 01479 851257

MURRAYPARK HOTEL
Connaught Terrace
Crieff
Perthshire
PH7 3DJ
TEL: 01764 653731

THE OFFICIAL WHERE TO STAY G

NAVIDALE HOUSE HOTEL
Navidale
Helmsdale
Sutherland
KW8 6JS
TEL: 01431 821258

NETHYBRIDGE HOTEL
Nethy Bridge
Inverness-shire
PH25 3DP
TEL: 01479 821203

**NEW LANARK MILL
HOTEL**
New Lanark
Lanarkshire
ML11 9DB
TEL: 01555 667200

**THE NEW WEIGH INN
HOTEL**
Burnside
Thurso
Caithness
KW14 7UG
TEL: 01847 893722

**THE OBSERVATORY GUEST
HOUSE**
North Ronaldsay
Orkney
KW17 2BE
TEL: 01857 633200

**OLD PINES RESTAURANT
WITH ROOMS**
by Spean Bridge
Inverness-shire
PH34 4EG
TEL: 01397 712324

ORASAY INN
Lochcarnan
South Uist
Outer Hebrides
HS8 5PD
TEL: 01870 610298

PATIO HOTEL
1 South Avenue
Clydebank Business Park
Clydebank
Glasgow
Dunbartonshire
G81 2RW
TEL: 0141 951 1133

POSTHOUSE EDINBURGH
Corstorphine Road
Edinburgh
EH12 6UA
TEL: 0870 400 9026

TOR-NA-COILLE HOTEL
Inchmarlo Road
Banchory
Kincardineshire
AB31 4AB
TEL: 01330 822242

**TRAVELODGE
DUMBARTON**
A82, Milton
Dumbarton
Strathclyde
G82 2TY
TEL: 01389 765202

**KINGS HALL UNIVERSITY
OF ABERDEEN**
Aberdeen
AB24 3FX
TEL: 01224 273444

**WHITCHESTER
GUEST HOUSE**
Hawick
Roxburghshire
TD9 7LN
TEL: 01450 377477

CATEGORY 3

AARON GLEN GUEST HOUSE
7 Nivensknowe Road
Loanhead
Midlothian
EH20 9AU
TEL: 0131 440 1293

ABBEY LODGE HOTEL
137 Drum Street
Gilmerton
Edinburgh
EH17 8RJ
TEL: 0131 664 9548

ABERDOUR HOTEL
38 High Street
Aberdour
Fife
KY3 0SW
TEL: 01383 860325

ABERFELDY LODGE GUEST HOUSE
11 Southside Road
Inverness
IV2 3BG
TEL: 01463 231120

ALCORN GUEST HOUSE
5 Hyndford Street
Dundee
Angus
DD2 3DY
TEL: 01382 668433

ANCHORAGE GUEST HOUSE
31 Balloch Road
Balloch
Dumbartonshire
G83 8SS
TEL: 01389 753336

THE ANCHORAGE HOTEL
Shore Road
Ardnadan
Dunoon
Argyll
PA23 8QD
TEL: 01369 705108

APPLEACRE
Birgham Main Street
by Coldstream
Berwickshire
TD12 4NF
TEL: 01890 830306

ARDBEG COTTAGE
19 Castle Street
Lochmaben
Dumfriesshire
DG11 1NY
TEL: 01387 811855

ARNABHAL
5 Gearraidh Bhailteas
Bornish
South Uist
HS8 5RY
TEL: 0178 710371

ASHBANK
105 Main Street
Redding
Falkirk
Stirlingshire
FK2 9UQ
TEL: 01324 716649

ATHOLL VILLA
29 Atholl Road
Pitlochry
Perthshire
PH16 5BX
TEL: 01796 473820

AVALON GUEST HOUSE
79 Glenurquhart Road
Inverness
Inverness-shire
IV3 5PB
TEL: 01463 239075

THE KNOWES
32 Riddrie Knowes
Glasgow
G33 2QH
TEL: 0141 770 5213

BALAVIL SPORT HOTEL
Main Street
Newtonmore
Inverness-shire
PH20 1DL
TEL: 01540 673220

BALLATHIE HOUSE HOTEL
Kinclaven
by Stanley
Perthshire
PH1 4QN
TEL: 01250 883268

BEEHIVE COTTAGE
12 Kingston
North Berwick
East Lothian
EH39 5JE
TEL: 01620 894785

BIRCHBANK ACTIVITY LODGE
Knockan
Elphin
by Lairg
Sutherland
IV27 4HH
TEL: 01854 666203

BRAEFIELD GUEST HOUSE
Braefield Road
Portpatrick
Wigtownshire
DG9 8TA
TEL: 01776 810255

BRIAR COTTAGE
Well Brae
Pitlochry
Perthshire
PH16 5HH
TEL: 01796 473678

HOTELS &
GUEST HOUSES

FACILITIES
FOR VISITORS WITH DISABILITIES

351

THE OFFICIAL WHERE TO STAY G

BRITANNIA HOTEL
Malcolm Road
Aberdeen
AB21 9LN
TEL: 01224 409988

BROOMFIELD HOUSE
Thorn Street
Earlston
Berwickshire
TD4 6DR
TEL: 01896 848084

THE BUNGALOW
81 High Street
Buckie
Banffshire
AB56 1BB
TEL: 01542 832367

CHERRYBANK INN
210 Glasgow Road
Perth
PH2 ONA
TEL: 01738 624349

CHESTERTON HOUSE
Formaston Park
Aboyne
Aberdeenshire
AB34 5HF
TEL: 013398 86740

**CLARKE COTTAGE GUEST
HOUSE**
139 Halbeath Road
Dunfermline
Fife
KY11 4LA
TEL: 01383 735935

CORMISTON COTTAGE
Cormiston Road
Biggar
Lanarkshire
ML12 6NS
TEL: 01899 220200

**CORSEWALL LIGHTHOUSE
HOTEL**
Kirkcolm
by Stranraer
Wigtownshire
DG9 0QG
TEL: 01776 853220

COUL HOUSE HOTEL
Contin
by Strathpeffer
Ross-shire
IV14 9EY
TEL: 01997 421487

CRAIGATIN HOUSE
165 Atholl Road
Pitlochry
Perthshire
PH16 5QL
TEL: 01796 472478

CRAIGLYNNE HOTEL
Woodlands Terrace
Grantown-on-Spey
Moray
PH26 3SX
TEL: 01479 872597

CRAIGNETHAN HOUSE
Jedburgh Road
Kelso
Roxburghshire
TD5 8BZ
TEL: 01573 224818

CRAIGVRACK HOTEL
38 West Moulin Road
Pitlochry
Perthshire
PH16 5EQ
TEL: 01796 472399

CRANSHAWS SMIDDY
Cranshaws
Duns
Berwickshire
TD11 3SL
TEL: 01361 890277

CRIEFF HYDRO
Crieff
Perthshire
PH7 3LQ
TEL: 01764 655555

BARN LODGE
Croftside
Pirnhill
Stirling
Stirlingshire
FK7 8EX
TEL: 01786 813591

CROIT ANNA HOTEL
Achintore Road
Fort William
Inverness-shire
PH33 6RR
TEL: 01397 702268

CROMASAIG
Torridon Road
Kinlochewe
Ross-shire
IV22 2PE
TEL: 01445 760234

CROSS KEYS HOTEL
36-37 The Square
Kelso
Roxburghshire
TD5 7HL
TEL: 01573 223303

DARROCH LEARG HOTEL
Braemar Road
Ballater
Aberdeenshire
AB35 5UX
TEL: 013397 55443

**DINWOODIE LODGE
HOTEL**
Johnstone Bridge
by Lockerbie
Dumfiesshire
DG11 2SL
TEL: 01576 470289

DREAMWEAVERS
Mucomir
by Spean Bridge
Inverness-shire
PH34 4EQ
TEL: 01397 712548

DROMNAN GUEST HOUSE
Garve Road
Ullapool
Ross-shire
IV26 2SX
TEL: 01854 612333

DRUMFORK FARM
Helensburgh
Dumbartonshire
G84 7JY
TEL: 01436 672 329

DRUMNADROCHIT HOTEL
Drumnadrochit
Inverness-shire
IV63 6TU
TEL: 01456 450218

**DRUMOSSIE PARK
COTTAGE**
Drumossie Brae
Inverness
Inverness-shire
IV2 5BB
TEL: 01463 224127

DUNALLAN HOUSE
Woodside Avenue
Grantown-on-Spey
PH26 3JN
TEL: 01479 872140

DUNEDIN
42 Strath
Gairloch
Ross-shire
IV21 2DB
TEL: 01445 712050

DUNMORE
19 Newton Street
Blairgowrie
Perthshire
PH10 6HT
TEL: 01250 874451

DUNROAMIN
South Keiss
Wick
Caithness
KW1 4XG
TEL: 01955 631283

**EAST HAUGH HOUSE
COUNTRY HOTEL &
RESTAURANT**
East Haugh
by Pitlochry
Perthshire
PH16 5JS
TEL: 01796 47 3121

EDINBURGH FIRST
University of Edinburgh
Pollock Halls
Edinburgh
Lothian
EH16 5AY
TEL: 0131 667 0662

ETTRICKVALE
33 Abbotsford Road
Galashiels
Selkirkshire
TD1 3HW
TEL: 01896 755224

FAIRFIELD HOUSE HOTEL
12 Fairfield Road
Ayr
Ayrshire
KA7 2AR
TEL: 01292 267461

FALLS OF LORA HOTEL
Connel Ferry
by Oban
Argyll
PA37 1PB
TEL: 01631 710483

FENDOCH GUEST HOUSE
Sma' Glen
Crieff
Perthshire
PH7 3LW
TEL: 01764 653446

FENWICK HOTEL
Fenwick
by Kilmarnock
Ayrshire
KA3 6AU
TEL: 01560 600478

FERNHILL HOTEL
Heugh Road
Portpatrick
Wigtownshire
DG9 8TD
TEL: 01776 810220

**FINDLAY, ROSS (IONA)
LTD**
Martyr's Bay
Isle of Iona
Argyll
PA76 6SP
TEL: 01681 700357

**THE FISHERMANS TAVERN
HOTEL**
10-16 Fort Street
Broughty Ferry
Dundee
Angus
DD5 2AD
TEL: 01382 775941

FISHERS HOTEL
75-79 Atholl Road,
Pitlochry
Perthshire
PH16 5BN
TEL: 01796 472000

FORBES ARMS HOTEL
Milltown of Rothiemay
Huntly
Aberdeenshire
AB54 7LT
TEL: 01466 711248

FORSS HOUSE HOTEL
Forss
by Thurso
Caithness
KW14 7XY
TEL: 01847 861201

ERSKINE BRIDGE HOTEL
Erskine
Renfrewshire
PA8 6AN
TEL: 0141 812 0123

WAVERLEY
35 Strathspey Avenue
Aviemore
Inverness-shire
PH22 1SN
TEL: 01479 811226

FREEDOM INN
Aviemore Centre
Aviemore
Inverness-shire
PH22 1PF
TEL: 01479 810781

GAIRLOCH VIEW
3 Digg
Staffin
Isle of Skye
IV51 9LA
TEL: 01470 562718

THE GALLEY OF LORNE INN
Ardfern
by Lochgilphead
Argyll
PA31 8QN
TEL: 01852 500284

GLEN ORCHY HOUSE
20 Knab Road
Lerwick
Shetland
ZE1 OAX
TEL: 01595 692031

GLEN MHOR HOTEL
9-12 Ness Bank
Inverness
IV2 4SG
TEL: 01463 234308

ROADCHEF LODGE
Hamilton Roadchef Service
Area (M74N)
Hamilton
Lanarkshire
ML3 6JW
TEL: 01698 891904

THE GOLDENSTONES HOTEL
Queens Road
Dunbar
East Lothian
EH42 1LG
TEL: 01368 862356

GORDON HOTEL
Wellington Road
Nigg
Aberdeen
AB12 3GH
TEL: 01224 873012

EDENMOUTH FARM
Kelso
Roxburghshire
TD5 7QB
TEL: 01890 830391

GREENLAWNS
13 Seafield Street
Nairn
Inverness-shire
IV12 4HG
TEL: 01667 452738

GREEN PARK HOTEL
Clunie Bridge Road
Pitlochry
Perthshire
PH16 5JY
TEL: 01796 473248

HAZELDEAN HOUSE
4 Moffat Road
Dumfries
DG1 1NJ
TEL: 01387 266178

HEATHPETE
24 Balloch Road
Balloch
Dunbartonshire
G83 8LE
TEL: 01389 752195

HETLAND HALL HOTEL
Carrutherstown
Dumfriesshire
DG1 4JX
TEL: 01387 840201

HILTON EDINBURGH BELFORD
69 Belford Road
Edinburgh
EH4 3DG
TEL: 0131 332 2545

HILTON STRATHCLYDE
Phoenix Crescent
Bellshill
N. Lanarkshire
ML4 3JQ
TEL: 01698 395500

HILTON DUNDEE HOTEL
Earl Grey Place
Dundee, Angus
DD1 4DE
TEL: 01382 229271

HOLLAND HOUSE
18 Holyrood Park Road
Edinburgh
EH16 5AY
TEL: 0800 028 7118

HOLLY TREE HOTEL
Kentallen
Appin
Argyll
PA38 4BY
TEL: 01631 740292

HORIZON HOTEL
Esplanade
Ayr
Ayrshire
KA7 1DT
TEL: 01292 264384

INNISCHONAIN HOUSE
Tarbet
Arrochar
Argyll
G83 7DD
TEL: 01301 702 726

KELLY'S GUEST HOUSE
3 Hillhouse Road
Edinburgh
EH4 3QP
TEL: 0131 332 3894

KILDONAN HOTEL
27 Queens Terrace,
Ayr
Ayrshire
KA7 1DX
TEL: 01292 285122

**KILSPINDIE HOUSE
HOTEL**
Aberlady
Longiddry
EH32 0RE
TEL: 01875 870682

THE KIMBERLEY HOTEL
Dalriach Road
Oban, Argyll
PA34 5EQ
TEL: 01631 571115

KINGSPARK LLAMA FARM
Berriedale
Caithness
KW7 6HA
TEL: 01593 751202

KINKELL HOUSE
Easter Kinkell
by Conon Bridge
Ross-shire
IV7 8HY
TEL: 01349 861270

**KIRKLAND COUNTRY
HOUSE HOTEL**
Ruthwell
Dumfriesshire
DG1 4NP
TEL: 01387 870284

THE KIRKTON INN
1 Main Street
Dalrymple
Ayrshire
KA6 6DF
TEL: 01292 560241

THE KNOWE
Ancaster Road
Callande
Perthshire
FK17 8EL
TEL: 01877 330076

LILYBANK GUEST HOUSE
Shore Road
Lamlash
Isle of Arran,
KA27 8LS
TEL: 01770 600230

LINDSAY GUEST HOUSE
108 Polwarth Terrace
Edinburgh
EH11 1NN
TEL: 0131 337 1580

LINKS HOTEL
Mid Links
Montrose
Angus
DD10 8RL
TEL: 01674 671000

LOCH TUMMEL INN
Strathtummel
Pitlochry
Perthshire
PH16 5RP
TEL: 01882 634272

**LOCHAN COTTAGE GUEST
HOUSE**
Lochyside
Fort William
Inverness-shire
PH33 7NX
TEL: 01397 702695

CROFTERS WAYSIDE INN
Lochton of Durris
by Banchory
Aberdeenshire
AB31 6DB
TEL: 01330 844543

LOMOND COUNTRY INN
Main Street
Kinnesswood
Kinross
KY13 9HN
TEL: 01592 840253

LYNDALE
Station Road
Beauly
Inverness-shire
IV4 7EH
TEL: 01463 782252

LYNEDOCH
7 Mayne Avenue
Bridge of Allan
Stirlinghsire
FK9 4QU
TEL: 01786 832178

HOTELS &
GUEST HOUSES

FACILITIES
FOR VISITORS WITH DISABILITIES

355

THE OFFICIAL WHERE TO STAY GU

**MARDON
BED & BREAKFAST**
37 Kenneth Street
Inverness
IV3 5DH
TEL: 01463 231005

2 MULINDRY COTTAGES
Bridgend
Isle of Islay
Argyll
PA44 7PZ
TEL: 01496 810397

MILLSEAT
Inverugie Road
Hopeman
Morayshire
IV30 5SX
TEL: 01343 830097

MILTON LEA
by Balmullo
St Andrews
Fife
KY16 0AB
TEL: 01334 839144

**DUMFRIES & GALLOWAY
COLLEGE**
Heathhall
Dumfries
DG1 3QZ
TEL: 01387 243840

MORAYDALE
276 High Street
Elgin
Morayshire
IV30 1AG
TEL: 01343 546381

AVALON
12 Westside
Tarbert
Harris
Western Isles
HS3 3BG
TEL: 01859 502334

MOYNESS HOUSE
6 Bruce Gardens
Inverness
IV3 5EN
TEL: 01463 233836

NEWBYRES COTTAGE
8 Hunterfield Road
Gorebridge
Midlothian
EH23 4TR
TEL: 01875 821268

THE NORTHERN HOTEL
1 Great Northern Road
Aberdeen
AB24 3PS
TEL: 01224 483342
FAX: 01224 276103

**THE OLD MILL AND
RESTAURANT**
Mill Lane
Pitlochry
Perthshire
PH16 5BH
TEL: 01796 474020

**PIERSLAND HOUSE
HOTEL**
15 Craigend Road
Troon
Ayrshire
KA10 6HD
TEL: 01292 314747

**PITBAUCHLIE HOUSE
HOTEL**
Aberdour Road
Dunfermline
Fife
KY11 4PB
TEL: 01383 722282

THE PRIORY
Bracklinn Road
Callander
Perthshire
FK17 8EH
TEL: 01877 330001

PRIORY LODGE
8 The Loan
South Queensferry
West Lothian
EH30 9NS
TEL: 0131 331 4345

**QUALITY HOTEL STATION
PERTH**
Leonard Street
Perth
PH2 8HE
TEL: 01738 624141

**QUALITY HOTEL STATION
AYR**
Burns Statue Square
Ayr
Ayrshire
KA7 3AT
TEL: 01292 263268

RED HOUSE HOTEL
Station Road
Coupar Angus
Perthshire
PH13 9AL
TEL: 01828 628500

THE REIVERS REST
81 High Street
Langholm
Dumfriesshire
DG13 0DJ
TEL: 013873 81343

RHUGARBH CROFT
Appin
Argyll
PA38 4BA
TEL: 01631 730309

RICHMOND PARK HOTEL
26 Linlithgow Road
Bo'ness
West Lothian
EH51 0DN
TEL: 01506 823213

ROB ROY MOTEL
Aberfoyle
Stirlingshire
FK8 3UX
TEL: 01877 382245

ROCKMOUNT COTTAGE
Dura Den Road
Pitscottie
Cupar
KY15 5TG
TEL: 01334 828164

ROMAN CAMP HOTEL
off Main Street
Callander
Perthshire
FK17 8BG
TEL: 01877 330003

**ROSE COTTAGE GUEST
HOUSE**
Gelson
Castle Douglas
Kirkcudbrightshire
DG7 1SH
TEL: 01556 502513

RSR BRAEHOLM
31 East Montrose Street
Helensburgh
Argyll & Bute
G84 7HR
TEL: 01436 671880

**RUFFLETS COUNTRY
HOUSE HOTEL**
Strathkinness Low Road
St Andrews
Fife
KY16 9TX
TEL: 01334 472594

SCOTTIES B&B
213 Nicol Street
Kirkcaldy
Fife
KY1 1PF
TEL: 01592 268596

SHAWLANDS HOTEL
Ayr Road
Canderside Toll
by Larkhall
Lanarkshire
ML9 2TZ
TEL: 01698 791111

**SOLUIS MU THUATH
GUEST HOUSE**
Braeintra
by Achmore
Strome Ferry
Ross-shire
IV53 8UP
TEL: 01599 577219

SPINNAKER HOTEL
12 Albert Road
Gourock
Renfrewshire
PA19 1BU
TEL: 01475 633107

SPRINGVALE HOTEL
18 Lethame Road
Strathaven
Lanarkshire
ML10 6AD
TEL: 01357 521131

STAKIS EAST KILBRIDE
Stewartfield Way
East Kilbride
Lanarkshire
G74 5LA
TEL: 01355 236300

STRATHBURN HOTEL
Burghmuir Drive
Inverurie
Aberdeenshire
AB51 4GY
TEL: 01467 624422

SUNBANK HOUSE HOTEL
50 Dundee Road
Perth
PH2 7BA
TEL: 01738 624882
FAX: 01738 442515

SWALLOW HOTEL
Kingsway West
Invergowrie
Dundee
Angus
DD2 5JT
TEL: (01382) 641122

TOBERMORY HOTEL
53 Main Street
Tobermory
Isle of Mull
PA75 6NT
TEL: 01688 302091

THE TONTINE HOTEL
6 Ardgowan Square
Greenock
Renfrewshire
PA16 8NG
TEL: 01475 723316

TORBAY LODGE
31 Lovers Walk
Dumfries
DG1 1LR
TEL: 01387 253922

**TRAVELODGE GLASGOW
CENTRAL**
5 Hill Street
Glasgow
G3 6RP
TEL: 0141 333 1515

THEATRE HOTEL LTD
25/27 Elmbank Street
Glasgow
G2 4PB
TEL: 0141 227 2772

WHINRIG
12 Burgh Road
Lerwick
Shetland
ZE1 0LB
TEL: 01595 693554

WOLSELEY PARK HOTEL
Stirling Road
Callander
Perthshire
FK17 8DA
TEL: 01877 330261

WOODLAND HOUSE
Torlundy
Fort William
Inverness-shire
PH33 6SN
TEL: 01397 701698

HOTELS &
GUEST HOUSES

AREA CODES

A SOUTH OF SCOTLAND: AYRSHIRE 2
AND ARRAN, DUMFRIES AND
GALLOWAY, SCOTTISH BORDERS

B EDINBURGH AND LOTHIANS 47

C GREATER GLASGOW 99
AND CLYDE VALLEY

D WEST HIGHLANDS & ISLANDS, 118
LOCH LOMOND, STIRLING AND
TROSSACHS

E PERTHSHIRE, ANGUS AND 167
DUNDEE AND THE KINGDOM
OF FIFE

F SCOTLAND'S CASTLE AND 214
WHISKY COUNTRY — ROYAL
DEESIDE TO SPEYSIDE

G THE HIGHLANDS AND SKYE 244

H OUTER ISLANDS: WESTERN ISLES, 328
ORKNEY, SHETLAND

THE SCOTTISH TOURIST BOARD

produces a series of four accommodation guides to help you choose your holiday accommodation. The most comprehensive guides on the market, they give details of facilities, price, location and every establishment in them carries a quality assurance award from the Scottish Tourist Board.

SCOTLAND: HOTELS & GUEST HOUSES 2001
£9.50 (INCL. P&P)

Over 1,400 entries, listing a variety of hotels and guest houses throughout Scotland. Also includes inns, lodges, restaurant with rooms, bed and breakfasts, campus accommodation, serviced apartments and international resort hotels. Comprehensive location maps. Completely revised each year. Full colour throughout.

SCOTLAND: BED & BREAKFAST 2001
£6.50 (INCL. P&P)

Over 1,700 entries, listing a variety of bed and breakfast establishments throughout Scotland. Also includes hotels, guest houses, inns, lodges, restaurant with rooms and campus accommodation. Comprehensive location maps. Completely revised each year.

SCOTLAND: CARAVAN & CAMPING 2001
£4.50 (INCL. P&P)

Over 200 entries, listing caravan parks and individual caravan holiday homes for hire. Includes self-catering properties. Comprehensive location maps. Completely revised each year.

SCOTLAND: SELF CATERING 2001
£7.00 (INCL. P&P)

Over 1,100 entries, listing cottages, flats, chalets, log cabins and serviced apartments to let. Many in scenic areas or bustling towns and cities. Caravan holiday homes included. Comprehensive location maps. Completely revised each year. Full colour throughout.

TOURING GUIDE TO SCOTLAND
£6.00 (INCL. P&P)

A new, fully revised edition of this popular guide which now lists over 1,500 things to do and places to visit in Scotland. Easy to use index and locater maps. Details of opening hours, admission charges, a general description and information on disabled access.

TOURING MAP OF SCOTLAND
£4.00 (INCL. P&P)

A new and up-to-date touring map of Scotland. Full colour with comprehensive motorway and road information, the map details over 20 categories of tourist information and names over 1,500 things to do and places to visit in Scotland

YOU CAN ORDER ANY OF THE ABOVE BY FILLING IN THE COUPON ON THE NEXT PAGE OR BY TELEPHONE.

MAIL ORDER

Please tick the publications you would like, cut out this section and send it with your cheque, postal order (made payable to Scottish Tourist Board) or credit card details to:

SCOTTISH TOURIST BOARD, FREEPOST, DUNOON, ARGYLL PA23 8PQ

SCOTLAND: **HOTELS & GUEST HOUSES 2001**	£9.50 (INCL. P&P)	☐
SCOTLAND: **BED & BREAKFAST 2001**	£6.50 (INCL. P&P)	☐
SCOTLAND: **CARAVAN & CAMPING 2001**	£4.50 (INCL. P&P)	☐
SCOTLAND: **SELF CATERING 2001**	£7.00 (INCL. P&P)	☐
TOURING GUIDE TO SCOTLAND	£6.00 (INCL. P&P)	☐
TOURING MAP OF SCOTLAND	£4.00 (INCL. P&P)	☐

BLOCK CAPITALS PLEASE:

name (Mr/Mrs/Ms)

address

post code telephone No.

total remittance enclosed £

please charge my *visa/access account (*delete as appropriate)

card no. ☐☐☐☐☐☐☐☐☐☐☐☐☐☐☐☐   expiry date ☐☐☐☐

Signature

Date

TELEPHONE ORDERS

To order BY PHONE: simply call free 08705 511511 (national call rate) quoting the books you would like and give your credit card details.